STONECHATS

A Guide to the Genus *Saxicola*

STONECHATS

A Guide to the Genus *Saxicola*

EWAN URQUHART

ILLUSTRATED BY ADAM BOWLEY

CHRISTOPHER HELM
LONDON

Published 2002 by Christopher Helm, an imprint of A & C Black Publishers Ltd.,
37 Soho Square, London W1D 3QZ

ISBN 0-7136-6024-4

A CIP catalogue record for this book is available from the British Library

Production and design by Fluke Art, Cornwall

A & C Black uses paper produced with elemental chlorine-free pulp, harvested
from managed sustainable forests.

www.acblack.com

Printed in Hong Kong through Phoenix Offset Ltd

10 9 8 7 6 5 4 3 2 1

CONTENTS

To Guen and Polly – all the love in the world

ACKNOWLEDGEMENTS

To write a book of this kind requires a great deal of help and assistance from many different people, virtually all of whom on being contacted have unhesitatingly and patiently responded to my many questions, with much information and kindness. If I have missed anyone and they find they are not mentioned here I apologise; it does not mean that they or their contribution, no matter how small, is thought of any the less.

In particular, I must extend my very great thanks to Linda Birch, Head Librarian and also her staff at the Alexander Library, Edward Grey Institute of Field Ornithology, Oxford University, for being unfailingly helpful and patient whilst allowing me access to a huge collection of books, papers and periodicals, or, if they did not have them, always making every effort to obtain copies for me. My thanks go to Mike Wilson, also of the Alexander Library, who translated texts from both German and Russian and assisted me in obtaining valuable information from his Russian contacts. I must also thank Robert Prys-Jones, Curator of Birds, and his staff of the Bird Group, The Natural History Museum, Tring, who gave me unrestricted access to their large collection of *Saxicola* specimens, with special acknowledgement to Mark Adams. Thanks also to James Dean, Collections Manager, Division of Birds, National Museum of Natural History, Washington DC, and Paul Sweet, Collection Manager, Dept. of Ornithology, American Museum of Natural History, New York, for loaning skins and supplying digital photographs of White-bellied Bushchat, and supplying digital photographs of Hodgson's Bushchat.

I would like to record my personal thanks to Nigel Collar for his help, understanding and patience in dealing with my questions and appeals for advice, and also Martin Collinson for guidance on taxonomic matters at very short notice.

I must also give a special mention to John Callion, another *Saxicola* fanatic and a fellow amateur who, despite a busy working life, has allowed me access to much unpublished information from his breeding studies of European Stonechat and Whinchat in Cumbria, England, as well as sparing a great deal of his time and hospitality to discuss various aspects of their breeding biology. A special thank you also to Barbara Helm of the Max Planck Research Centre for Ornithology in Andechs, Germany, who read and made many helpful and constructive observations on the draft text for the Common Stonechat complex, assisted with German contacts and references, and gave me most welcome and enthusiastic encouragement. Various staff at the British Trust for Ornithology have also assisted me, and in particular I would like to thank Humphrey Crick for loaning me Nest Record Cards, Chris Wernham and Mike Toms for sending me advance drafts of the Whinchat and European Stonechat chapters from the BTO Migration Atlas, David Glue and Caroline Dudley. I would also like to express my thanks to Richard Ranft, Curator of the Wildlife Section, British Library National Sound Archive, for supplying tapes and sonograms of *Saxicola* species.

I would also like to record my special thanks to Adam Bowley whose artwork graces this book, and to Michael Wink and his colleagues for contributing an important chapter on the genetic relationships of stonechats.

Others who assisted me and to whom I am most grateful are as follows: David Allen; Des Allen, for reading and commenting on the draft text of *S. jerdoni*; Prasad Anand; V. Ananian; Hem Sagar Baral, who read and commented on the draft text for *S. leucura* and sent photos of *S. insignis*; Peter H. Barthel; Janis Baumanis; Hans-Martin Berg; Arnoud B. van den Berg; K. David Bishop, who read and made many useful comments on the draft texts for *S. caprata*, *S. insignis*, *S. gutturalis*, *S. ferrea* and *S. jerdoni*; Ulli Brucher; Ian Buxton; Geoff Carey; Anthony Cheke, for help and translations of texts for *S. tectes*; Gargi Choudhary; Josef Chytil; the late Philip Clancey; Andrew W. Clarke; Victor Ciochia; Tom Conzemius; Jacqueline Crozier; Nikhil Devasar, for photos of *S. macrorhyncha*; P. Dubois; Will Duckworth, who read and made helpful comments on the draft text for *S. jerdoni*; Robert Edgar; Clem Fisher; Heiner Flinks; Sharifin Gardiner; I. Gorban; Marco Gustin; G.I. Handrinos; John Harrison; Bill Harvey; Christopher Helm; E. Hirschfeld; Sue Hitchins; Paul Holt; Jon Hornbuckle; Rune Jabekk; E. de Juana; Mikhail Kalyakin; Shannon Kenney; Nils Kjellen; Vilju Lilleleht; Tom Lindroos; V.M. Loskot; Gabor Magyar; Sarah Mackenzie; Mike Mildren; Richard Millington; Paul Milne; Muchai Muchane, for allowing me to see his unpublished information on *S. bifasciata*; Richard Noske, for reading and commenting on the draft text of *S. gutturalis*; E.N. Panov; T. Pettay; Gunnlaugur Petursson; Andrew Pierce; Gerhard Pfeifer; Jean-Michel Probst; Asad Rahmani; S.M.A. Rashid; Brian Rasmussen; Visa Rauste; Colin Richardson; Don Roberson; Mike Rogers; Phil Round, for reading and commenting on the draft text for *S. jerdoni* and supplying tapes of *S. jerdoni* song and calls; A.E. Sadler; Jevgeni Shergalin; Thejaswi Shivanand; Brian Small; Gunter de Smet; James Smith; Soren Sorensen; Tadeusz Stawarczyk; the late L.S. Stepanyan; Ray Symonds; Warwick Tarboton, for photos and information on *S. bifasciata*; Joe Sultana; Tom Tarrant; Joe Tobias; Hans Uhl; Bernard Volet; David Walker; Raz Walloper; M.J. Walters; J. Walton; Jacqueline Weicker; Reuven Yosef.

My thanks also to Nigel Redman, Mike Unwin and especially Marianne Taylor at Christopher Helm for much patience, help and guidance and similarly Julie and Marc Dando at Fluke Art.

I would also like to thank all the following persons who responded to my appeal for photos for inclusion in the book: Des Allen; Hem Sagar Baral; Hans-Heiner Bergmann; Nigel Blake; Roger Charlwood; Nikhil Devasar; Lieuwe Dijksen; Will Duckworth; Juan José Ramos Encalado; Heiner Flinks; Stephen Gwilliam; Martin Hale; Alan Hands; Bill Harvey; John Hewitt; Jon Hornbuckle; Jan Kåre Ness; Nils Kjellén; Gordon Langsbury; Olaf Lessow; Otto Pfister; Tim Loseby; Karno Mikkola; Muchai Muchane; Tomi Muukonen; Richard Noske; E.N. Panov; Jean-Michel Probst; Asad Rahmani: George Reszeter; Don Roberson; Thomas Sacher; Brian Small; Per Smitterberg; Albert Steen-Hansen; Werner Suter; Thomas Tams; Warwick Tarboton; Alan Tate; Ray Tipper; Magnus Ullman; Arnoud B. van den Berg; Marten van Dijl; Chris van Rijswijk; William Velmala; James Walford; David Walker; S.G. William; Mark Yates.

FOREWORD

My earliest encounters and memories, which undoubtedly stimulated my lifelong fascination with the species in this genus, are of European Stonechats and Whinchats in the far north of Scotland, on seemingly endless summer holidays with my grandparents. As with many of his generation, my father had to seek work away from his native land and settled in the south of England, but as a family we would go back to Scotland every summer for the holidays. Consequently, it was my grandfather, noticing my awakening interest in natural history and birds in particular, who encouraged me, by taking me on the crossbar of his bicycle up country roads where motorcars were thankfully virtually non-existent. We would cycle for miles, stopping to look at anything that took his or my interest, and I can to this day recall our delight at seeing European Stonechats and Whinchats sitting on telephone wires or on the tops of gorse bushes. To a small boy only used to suburban Surrey with its House Sparrows and Starlings, they were a fascinating, almost exotic, combination of colours, and always present in a romantic and beautiful environment. These first encounters made an indelible impression on me. Eventually, as I became older and more independent, I found that a pair of European Stonechats bred on Epsom Common only three miles from my home in Surrey. Many boys of my generation indulged in the pastime of bird's-nesting, taking one egg of a species for a small collection. Although by today's standards such behaviour is thoroughly reprehensible, this pastime both stimulated and advanced a general knowledge not only of bird identification but also of their ecology. Many older ornithologists can point to such a beginning as the foundation on which their interest and sometimes career was based. Thankfully boys of today no longer go bird's-nesting, as the world of technology and leisure now provide more sophisticated pleasures. Sadly, though, many younger birders now only concentrate on identification and seeing as many different species as possible, without taking time to study the all-round ecology of the species they see.

I never did find a European Stonechat's nest on those early forays to Epsom Common, but soon I obtained a book which told me that they were placed on the ground and very hard to find. Armed with this information and the optimism of youth, I set about deciphering the breeding secrets of European Stonechats. Eventually, after days of frustration, I managed to find my first European Stonechat nest. This was something very special and I could not, nor did I want to, remove an egg, as it was a far greater prize to know the location of an active nest and keep the secret close to my heart. Instead, I made daily visits, keeping records in a little red notebook. Unwittingly I had graduated from the reckless abandon of youthful nest-hunting and casual observation to a crude form of systematic observation and recording. Over the ensuing years I came to live in rural East Sussex and from 1987 to 1991 I undertook a four-year study, in association with the Beachy Head Ringing Group, of the population of European Stonechats at Beachy Head. Apart from an intensive study of the nests and ringing the young, I also made notes based on many hours of observation of the adults' behaviour, habitat preferences and plumage. In fact, anything I considered of interest and relevance was noted down until, after four years, I had a mass of notes, and it is this which has served as the impetus to write a book on the genus *Saxicola*. I have not seen all the species that I have written about here, but eventually I will. In writing this book I have learned a lot more about both the species I have seen and those I have not, which has served to strengthen my desire to further my knowledge of this fascinating genus. I hope some of the enthusiasm and enjoyment I feel for my subjects will communicate itself and stimulate others to do the same.

Kingham, Oxfordshire 2001

SEQUENCE AND TAXONOMY

This book follows the current accepted taxonomic classification of Ripley (1964) with the major exception that I have accepted that there is now a sufficient weight of evidence that points to the fact that the Ripley classification of the single species of Common Stonechat can now be split into three species. Currently, a considerable amount of time and effort is being devoted to the taxonomic classification of birds, and there are a growing number of changes that have either been accepted or are proposed for consideration, mainly at genera, species and subspecies level. It is not within the scope of this book to give a detailed commentary on the merits of traditional taxonomy, the Biological Species Concept (BSC) versus the new taxonomic classifications proposed using the Phylogenetic Species Concept (PSC). They both address the question of how we define and recognise a species.

Both have their merits and disadvantages with the consequence that there is to date no definitive method to recognise what is a species, and possibly never will be, as the evolution of avian diversity does not stop but is dynamic and requires our views on classification to change as new methodology and data arise. Consequently, taxonomy will always remain relatively inexact and therefore a controversial subject. A review of recent correspondence since the mid 1990s such as in the UK magazines *Birding World* and *British Birds* demonstrates how controversial this subject is and how passionate the proponents of each concept can become.

Both Collinson (2001) and Elphick *et al.* (2001) give a comprehensive and readable review of both the BSC and the PSC and other refinements to taxonomic classification, as well as the use of mitochondrial DMA (mtDNA) techniques, an assessment of their relative merits and their limitations, and a view on the changes taking place within avian taxonomy. Although the BSC is still the established method for defining a species, its concepts are now being challenged and/or complemented by the PSC and the progress made since the DNA-DNA hybridisation studies and techniques of Sibley & Ahlquist (1990) and Sibley & Monroe (1990) were first published. DNA-DNA classification differs from the traditional classification in its added complexity with additional categorical levels, sequence of groups, and to a certain extent the composition of groups. This is undoubtedly an advance in the science of taxonomy, but this system is still in its infancy and even Sibley & Monroe, while believing that "it probably represents a closer approach to the true phylogeny than any other system proposed", accepted that it is imperfect.

The overall picture is further complicated by the rapid progress since the 1990s that has been made in comparing mtDNA sequences of perceived related taxa. It is possible, using this method, to evaluate the most likely phylogenetic relationship between the taxa analysed and then draw up an evolutionary tree.

There has been an increasing use of these mtDNA techniques to measure the degrees of genetic similarities or disparities at lower taxonomic levels between different genera, species or subspecies in an attempt to clarify their relationships. Such studies are increasing and producing some surprising results. It is important to stress that the evidence of mtDNA sequence research used in this book with regard to reclassifying Common Stonechat has not been taken in isolation to indicate species status but as a very strong indication, which is combined with other traditional criteria used under the BSC to come to a more satisfactory answer than exists at the moment. Unfortunately, it appears to be a misconception amongst some birding circles that with regard to DNA data where there is a large percentage divergence this alone provides conclusive evidence of species status.

It is surely sensible and to be hoped that the positive aspects of both the BSC and PSC can and will be combined when assessing taxonomic changes to produce a more satisfactory whole rather than entrench opinion into two separate camps with an ever widening gulf of mistrust and misconception.

To date, only one species in the genus *Saxicola*, Common Stonechat, has received detailed attention from mtDNA techniques (Wittman *et al.* 1995, Wink *et al.* 2001, 2002). Their research did not attempt to analyse every subspecies and the genetic relationship between them, but took a series of closely related sub-species in one geographical area and compared them to a similar grouping in another geographical area. The same techniques were also used to view the relationship of Common Stonechat to three other closely related species within the genus *Saxicola* and the relationship of that genus to other supposedly related genera (Wink *et al.* 2001, 2002). Their research provides, in my opinion, very strong evidence that the Common Stonechat can actually be split into three species. In my proposals for changes to the taxonomic classification of the species Common Stonechat and its many subspecies, I have incorporated both the traditional BSC criteria and the mtDNA results of Wittman *et al.* (1995) and Wink *et al.* (2001, 2002) to justify this.

At the lower taxonomic level, the last major work to classify the sequence of species and, where applicable, subspecies pre-DNA was that of Ripley (1964) and Voous (1977). At a higher taxonomic level the classification of Sibley, Monroe and Ahlquist (1988), Sibley & Ahlquist (1990) and Sibley & Monroe (1990,

1993) placed thrushes, muscicapine flycatchers and chats in the family Muscicapidae as traditionally they had been before, but then differed in that they split this family into two subfamilies: Turdinae (typical thrushes) and Muscicapinae, this latter comprising two tribes: Muscicapini (Old World flycatchers) and Saxicolini (chats). It had previously been considered that chats were most closely related to the larger turdine thrushes, as ecologically they appeared and behaved like them, but DNA analysis demonstrated that they were more closely related to muscicapine flycatchers than to any other group.

TAXONOMIC CLASSIFICATION PRE- & POST-DNA

Ripley 1964

Order Passeriformes
Suborder Oscines
Family Muscicapidae
Subfamily Turdinae (Thrushes), consisting of
    49 genera including *Saxicola*

Sibley & Monroe 1990

Parvorder Passerida
Superfamily Muscicapoidea
Family Muscicapidae
Subfamily Turdinae (True Thrushes)
Subfamily Muscicapinae (Flycatchers)
Tribe Muscicapini (Old World Flycatchers)
Tribe Saxicolini (Chats), consisting of 30 genera
    including *Saxicola*

The 30 genera of chat incorporate 155 species in Sibley & Monroe's revised 1993 classification of the tribe Saxicolini, and within this grouping the genus *Saxicola* contains 12 species:

Whinchat *Saxicola rubetra*

Stoliczka's Bushchat *Saxicola macrorhyncha*

Hodgson's Bushchat *Saxicola insignis*

Canary Island Stonechat *Saxicola dacotiae*

Common Stonechat *Saxicola torquata*

Réunion Stonechat *Saxicola tectes*

White-tailed Stonechat *Saxicola leucura*

Pied Bushchat *Saxicola caprata*

Jerdon's Bushchat *Saxicola jerdoni*

Grey Bushchat *Saxicola ferrea*

White-bellied Bushchat *Saxicola gutturalis*

Buff-streaked Bushchat *Saxicola bifasciata*

Sibley & Monroe (1990, 1993) based their classifications on DNA (mainly at the higher level), but where no such research had been done they had to rely on informed opinion rather than scientific fact, and this was and still is the case concerning most of the genus *Saxicola*. To date (2002), as mentioned above, the only work that has been conducted using mtDNA techniques on the genus *Saxicola* is that of Wittman *et al.* (1995) and Wink *et al.* (2001). Prof. M. Wink's chapter in this book is, in addition, the first published research based on mtDNA techniques concerning relationships between species of the genus *Saxicola*, as well as their relationship to other closely similar genera.

Another polytypic species in the genus which would undoubtedly benefit from similar mtDNA analysis is Pied Bushchat, where a number of subspecies are weakly supported using BSC criteria but to date no such analysis has been contemplated. The current taxonomic status of Buff-streaked Bushchat *S. bifasciata* and White-bellied Bushchat *S. gutturalis* are undoubtedly worthy of further investigation as there is evidence that they may not belong in this genus and even Jerdon's Bushchat *S. jerdoni* and Grey Bushchat *S. ferrea* may possibly be worth examining. I do not suggest that mtDNA results on their own would conclusively decide where these species taxonomically belong, but it would surely create a greater understanding of their precise relationship to other taxa in the genus *Saxicola* and allow a more educated assessment of their taxonomic position.

Based on the research by Wittmann *et al.* (1995) and Wink *et al.* (2001, 2002) and other more traditional taxonomic criteria, I have accepted that Common Stonechat can be split into at least three species. However, I have still incorporated the pre-DNA classifications of subspecies within these three species as no specific mtDNA research has been done on all 25 accepted subspecies, and there may well be other species to be identified in this complex. It is also surely important to be able to recognise these subspecific groups even though some or all may be found to be synonymous with one of the three species proposed. It does not seem sensible to discard at this time a large number of subspecies which is necessary if one follows the PSC to the letter. Subspecies in many cases are quite distinct and some may yet prove to be separate species, such as the subspecies of African Stonechat *S. torquata albofasciata* and Siberian Stonechat *S. maura variegata*.

One of the main reasons for this book is to give a detailed guide to identification. Many birders, both professional and amateur, now possess sophisticated optical aids which allow very detailed study of plumage in the field. Many birders take much pleasure and satisfaction in identifying differences in plumage and applying these to subspecies just as much as they do identifying true species. This kind of study and attention to detail can only add to our knowledge of a species and it hardly seems logical to jeopardise all this wealth of information collected by older generations and still being collected today to follow rigidly one particular taxonomic dogma. Avian diversity does not stand still. I have therefore endeavoured to accommodate the needs of those interested in identification with as reasoned an approach as possible to taxonomy, based on up-to-date biological and genetic information. This approach concerning subspecies has been followed for all polytypic species in this book. Therefore, I have included a description of all subspecies as listed by Ripley (1964).

Three changes to the classification of either Ripley or Voous have been accepted, based on subsequent published information. The first involves the Réunion Stonechat, which Ripley (1964) classified as a subspecies of Common Stonechat but in Sibley & Monroe (1990) was treated as a full species, and this is now generally accepted by most ornithologists. The second refers to Buff-streaked Bushchat, which was previously included in the genus *Oenanthe* but, based on traditional taxonomic criteria, was placed in the genus *Saxicola* by Tye (1989). This has generally been accepted as such although I query whether it really should be included in *Saxicola* (see chapter on Buff-streaked Bushchat). The third is a new subspecies of Common Stonechat, *Saxicola torquata altivaga*, proposed by Clancey (1988) and accepted in the second updating report to the South African Ornithological Society (SAOS) Checklist (1991).

ENGLISH NAMES OF BIRDS

The English names used for each species mainly follow those which appeared, whilst researching and writing this book, to be currently the most widely used and universally acceptable, both in literature and in everyday communication amongst English-speaking birders and ornithologists.

The current contentious issues of taxonomy and controversies over producing an agreed taxonomic order for all bird species appear to have stimulated a similar desire to create a standard list of English names for all bird species in the world. *A World Checklist of Birds* by Monroe & Sibley (1993), based on the revolutionary treatise on avian molecular evolution, *Distribution and Taxonomy of Birds of the World* (Sibley & Monroe 1990), is currently being used as the baseline for producing a world standardisation of English names for all bird species by a working group, set up under the auspices of the International Ornithological Congress.

The names of species in this book differ from Sibley & Monroe 1990 & 1993 and some other standard references as follows:

Stoliczka's Bushchat *S. macrorhyncha*
The existing name is unique and honours the ornithologist who first discovered it and there seems little justification in renaming it White-browed Bushchat.

Canary Island Stonechat *S. dacotiae*
Beaman (1994) remarked that it is "unhelpful to coin new names for *Saxicola* species that simplify 'stonechat' to 'chat' as the latter is not specific to the genus". Canary Islands Chat used by Sibley & Monroe (1993) is thus unsatisfactory. In the light of Wink *et al.* (2001, 2002) suggesting that it is closely related to the European Stonechat it is surely more appropriate to call it Stonechat rather than Chat. It may also be more appropriate to call it 'Canary Island' rather than 'Canary Islands' Stonechat, as it now only occurs on one of the islands, Fuerteventura.

Hodgson's Bushchat *S. insignis*
The existing name is unique and honours the ornithologist who first discovered it and there seems no real justification in renaming it White-throated Bushchat. There are also other species in the genus which have a white throat all year round.

Common Stonechat *S. torquata*
Common Stonechat as used by Sibley & Monroe (1990 & 1993) was a marked improvement on the still widely used name Stonechat, as it at least differentiated the species from other stonechats such as Réunion Stonechat *S. tectes* and White-tailed Stonechat *S. leucura*. However, Common Stonechat *Saxicola torquata* should be split into three species. Therefore, the three species will need a modifier to distinguish them from the current all encompassing name Common Stonechat used by Sibley & Monroe in 1990 & 1993 and which I now propose should be dropped.

European Stonechat *S. rubicola*

Siberian Stonechat *S. maura*

African Stonechat *S. torquata*
Siberian Stonechat has for a number of years been widely used to describe individuals of the six eastern Palearctic subspecies. European Stonechat therefore seems a more suitable name to cover the two western Palearctic subspecies than to retain Common Stonechat. The use of 'modifiers' in front of the proposed new species of stonechat also makes it easier if the need should arise to name further new species of stonechat, such as possibly Caucasian Stonechat for the current subspecies of Siberian Stonechat, *S. m. armenica* and *S. m. variegata,* as well as Ethiopian Stonechat for the subspecies of African Stonechat *S. t. albofasciata.*

It is worth mentioning that only the subspecies *S. m. maura* and *S. m. stejnegeri* are truly Siberian in that they breed in that area, whereas *S. m. armenica, variegata, indica* and *przewalskii* do not. If either *indica* and/or *przewalskii* are also deemed in future to be species then they will also require naming, and a similar situation may arise with certain subspecies of African Stonechat.

Buff-streaked Bushchat *S. bifasciata*
Although only recently renamed Buff-streaked Chat from Buff-streaked Wheatear by Tye (1988), it would be more appropriate to call it Buff-streaked Bushchat or Buff-streaked Stonechat, as 'Chat' is not specific to the genus. It is also perhaps pertinent to mention that in South Africa, where this species is an endemic, any extensive area of uncultivated natural habitat is frequently referred to as 'bush'.

The wisdom of such an exercise as standardising English names of bird species and the likelihood of it succeeding are open to considerable doubt. Many attempts have been made and are still being made to produce a standardised list of English names. This is a highly contentious matter and can arouse much passion amongst various nationalities who consider their vernacular name entirely acceptable and not to be changed arbitrarily at the dictate of a committee, no matter how illustrious. It is highly unlikely that there will ever be a consensus on a standard worldwide list of English names. Names evolve over a period of time and generally have to be used and accepted by the majority of birders to become standard. It is highly unlikely that for example 'skua' or 'diver' will be replaced by the American 'jaeger' or 'loon' in the United Kingdom and vice versa. Nor with the sophistication of mtDNA techniques and the consequent ever-growing number of 'splits' of species is it wise to believe that any English name is the definitive one for that species.

English names of other species referred to in the book follow those published in the *The British List* by the British Ornithologists' Union (BOU) in 1999.

SPECIES ACCOUNTS

All species have their own binomial scientific name. The first part denotes the generic (genus), and the second the specific (species); thus European Stonechat is *Saxicola rubicola*. A third trinomial name is added to denote a race or subspecies where relevant; thus the European Stonechat inhabiting the United Kingdom is *Saxicola rubicola hibernans*. Each of the 14 species in the genus *Saxicola* is described in detail under the headings listed below. It is intended to give as much detail as possible, not only on the identification but also on the complete biology and ecology of each species so that as comprehensive and readable an account as possible is given. For some species, such as the Common Stonechat complex and Whinchat, there is a large amount of information based on numerous studies conducted in many countries. For others, such as Hodgson's Bushchat and Jerdon's Bushchat, there is little information on their ecology, and for others, notably Stoliczka's Bushchat and White-bellied Bushchat, virtually nothing is known of their ecology. As is to be expected, those species such as European Stonechat and Whinchat that occur in the western Palearctic (where there is a strong tradition of ornithological research), are relatively comprehensively covered. However, for the remainder of the species in this genus, stretching east across the Palearctic and the Oriental regions and south through the Afrotropical and Malagasy regions, there are many aspects of their ecology which remain unknown and unstudied or for which there is only a small amount of information. Much more research needs to be done on these species and especially those which have now declined to such an extent that they are now included under the International Union for Conservation of Nature and Natural Resources (IUCN) criteria as under threat.

How To Use This Book

SPECIES ACCOUNTS

In this book, each recognised species is given its own chapter. It should be noted that the three 'new' species of Common Stonechat (European, Siberian and African) are given individual chapters, dealing mainly with Identification, Distribution, Status and Movements. They are proceeded by a chapter entitled 'The Common Stonechat Complex' which deals with taxonomic and identification matters of the group as a whole, as well as biological and ecological aspects of all three species. Thus, the sections for Breeding, Habitat, Voice, Food, Behaviour, Moult and Conservation for European, Siberian and African Stonechats appear only in the Common Stonechat Complex chapter.

The English name of each species is given at the head of the chapter together with its current scientific (generic and specific) name. The next line gives the type citation, i.e. the orginal scientific name, the person(s) who first described it, the bibliographical reference and the date of first description together with the location (i.e. the type locality) at which it was collected.

Etymology A brief explanation of the translation, meaning or significance of the species' scientific name is given.

Alternative names English names that have been used in the past, and which are in some cases still being used for the species, are listed.

TAXONOMY

Classification in this book broadly follows 'traditional' taxonomic authorities such as Ripley (1964) and Voous (1977). The taxonomic status of each species is reviewed, together with that of its subspecies, if any. Polytypic species have all their currently recognised subspecies listed here, but further details such as distribution of each subspecies are given later. See Introduction (p.11) for a discussion of general taxonomic issues.

IDENTIFICATION

Size is given in both centimetres and inches. The basic overall appearance, shape and main plumage identification features are given for each species so that its identity can be correctly established.

Confusion species The main differences in plumage and shape between it and other species in the genus with which it could be confused in any of its plumage forms are listed, cross-referenced and compared, to allow the reader to identify with confidence the species in the field.

DESCRIPTION

This provides a more detailed and comprehensive description of the complete range of plumages for breeding and non-breeding adults, juveniles and, where applicable, first-year individuals. The sequence of feather detail commences with the head and upperparts, including forehead, crown, lores, malar region, ear-coverts, nape, neck, mantle, scapulars, back, rump and uppertail-coverts; then the underparts, including chin, throat, breast, flanks, belly, ventral area and undertail-coverts. The flight feathers are then described beginning with the rectrices followed by the remiges plus the upperwing-coverts, alula, underwing-coverts and axillaries. Finally, the bill, legs, feet and irides are described.

It is extremely difficult to be precise about colours; they are notoriously prone to different perception by individual observers with a consequent proliferation of differing colour descriptions all referring to one plumage colour. For instance, the breast-patch colour of the male European Stonechat (UK subspecies *S. rubicola hibernans*), has been described by various authors as orange, chestnut, rufous or russet. I have endeavoured to be consistent in the use of colour descriptions of plumage for all species, aiming for reasonable accuracy without using unfamiliar names of colours which will fail to convey to the reader the true appearance of the feathers in question. In many cases, the colour of the feathers is a compound description in which the basic colour word is placed last. Thus 'reddish-brown' is browner than 'brownish-red'. Many basic colours in the species descriptions have been modified in this way with qualifiers such as buffish, tawny, olive, greyish or rufous to attempt to create a more accurate and easy-to-understand description of a feather tract. For a straightforward explanation of colour descriptions with reference to birds, the *Identification Guide to European Passerines* (fourth edition, 1992) by Lars Svensson is highly recommended.

For those species which are polytypic the nominate subspecies is described in detail. The other subspecies have only the main plumage differences between them and the nominate subspecies described. However, more detailed descriptions have been given for all European and Siberian Stonechat subspecies. The subspecies of African Stonechat *S. t. albofasciata* is also described in greater detail, as it may be a species in its own right.

Reference should also be made to the plates to determine the subtle differences in plumage where subspecies are not well demarcated. However, as Svensson (1992) has noted, individual variation can be problematic and should never be underestimated. No age or sex category is ever precise or easily defined and there will always be individuals which do not quite fit the category.

Where applicable, aberrant plumages such as leucism or albinism are described. Records of such plumages are very scarce in the literature, and perhaps equally so in reality, although it is possible that such occurrences may often go unrecorded. Examples of melanism in the genus *Saxicola* appear to be non-existent in the literature and it must therefore be assumed that they are non-existent or extremely rare in life.

Measurements Wing, tail and bill measurements are given in millimetres at the end of this section for both male and female. In many cases these measurements have been taken by the author from specimens in various collections in the AMNH, BMNH, MCML, USNM, ZMUC or, in the case of some races of Pied Bushchat and some specimens of White-bellied Bushchat, from historical sources. In the case of 'Common Stonechat' and Whinchat they are based on *The Birds of the Western Palearctic*, volume 5, by Cramp *et al.* (1988). All sources other than those of the author are acknowledged. Wing lengths were taken by using the maximum length method where the folded wing is measured from the carpal joint (bend of wing) to the tip of the longest primary, by being flattened and straightened against the ruler as much as possible. Many historical wing measurements were probably made using the flattened wing method, where the primaries are flattened against the ruler but not straightened, and therefore may be shorter than mine. However, measurements by Stresemann (1920) were made by using the maximum length method. Bill measurements are the length of the culmen from the skull to the tip of the upper mandible. Tail length is measured from the base of the central tail feathers to the tip of the longest tail feather.

DISTRIBUTION

This section gives as detailed a description as possible of the geographical breeding distribution of each species, including altitudes, together with occurrences of breeding outside the known regular distributional range. Where a species is polytypic the breeding distribution of each subspecies is described. The status of each species in its breeding range is also examined and for some species, such as European and Siberian Stonechat and Whinchat, detailed population figures are given, but for other species such as Hodgson's, Stoliczka's and White-bellied Bushchat, where there is comparatively little information, a list of both historical and contemporary records is provided to give an indication of range and status.

This is supported by maps which show each species' distributional range and also occurrences outside the known distributional range. The maps also show the geographical breeding range of each of the subspecies of a polytypic species. It is extremely difficult to be precise in showing the distributional limits of a species and its subspecies, both in its breeding and wintering range, as the accuracy is very much dependent on the availability or lack of availability of up-to-date information. Areas on the edge of a species' breeding range may not be occupied every year and populations may be more abundant in some years than others with consequent expansion and contraction of ranges. When using the maps for reference, the chapter on Movements should also be consulted.

Many location names and, to a lesser extent, national names change over a period of years, often for political reasons (e.g. Burma). Old place names, if they have not changed completely, have often changed in the way they are spelt. Every effort has been made to find the contemporary name or spelling for historical records if they differ, and such records where quoted have the original name or spelling first and the current name or spelling in parentheses. For expediency, Lao Peoples Democratic Republic (PDR) is referred to as Laos, Burma is referred to as Myanmar and the former Soviet Union as the Russian Federation.

Some countries, notably Mongolia and China, have a bewildering variation of spellings for a particular location or area, all of which appear to be in current use depending on which reference is used. The majority of spellings and names have been checked using *The Times comprehensive atlas of the world* (tenth edition, 2001), but if the site in question is not mapped there, the most detailed available map of the country concerned has been consulted. This is especially relevant to Mongolia, and all Mongolian spellings are based on the *International Travel Map of Mongolia* (second edition, Vancouver, 1998).

BREEDING

The complete breeding cycle, or as much as is currently known for each species, is outlined, including nest-site selection, nest building, description of the nest and measurements, egg-laying, description and measurements of the eggs, incubation period, nestling period from birth to fledging, and post-fledging care of the young. Behavioural aspects of the adults throughout the breeding cycle are also treated under this heading. The breeding biology aspect of a species is now somewhat neglected; the emphasis in modern birding, with a few notable exceptions, seems to be on taxonomy and identification. However, there is much still to be learned, and the breeding ecology of species in this particular genus remains relatively unknown. Some species have been studied very intensively, such as European, Siberian and African Stonechats and Whinchat, with notable studies being carried out in both the UK and Germany by E.D.H. Johnson and P.W. Greig-Smith on European Stonechat and H.-V. Bastian and A. Bastian on Whinchat. The rest of the genus is comparatively unstudied, with only little and somewhat dated information available, and none whatsoever for Stoliczka's Bushchat (whose nest has never to date been found) and White-bellied Bushchat.

HABITAT

The regular habitat in which each species is found and for which it shows a preference is described in detail, together with variations found within both the breeding and wintering range of each species. The majority of species in the genus *Saxicola* prefer open areas with scattered low vegetation and short to medium-height perches from which to hunt for food and maintain territorial vigilance. Others, such as Réunion Stonechat and White-bellied Bushchat, will also use forested areas, although such utilisation has been little studied. On current knowledge, Jerdon's Bushchat appears to be mainly restricted to a habitat closely associated with water, although historically it has been found in other habitats apparently far from water.

VOICE

Vocalisations of birds can basically be ascribed to two categories: song and other miscellaneous vocalisations (calls) associated with particular situations and behavioural circumstances. All species in this genus have a song together with a range of calls. Both the song and other vocalisations, where known, are described in detail, and where relevant, associated behaviour from the species is described, such as song periods, song flights and display. The song of all species in this genus is only given by the male in the breeding season apart from the taxonomically controversial Buff-streaked Bushchat in which both male and female sing, and song is produced in both the breeding and non-breeding season. The species in this genus are similarly undemonstrative outside the breeding season apart from Buff-streaked Bushchat and those individuals of European Stonechat when they are establishing winter territories. Occasionally, birds if surprised outside of the breeding season will give a subdued alarm call but are generally silent and slip into cover.

Little apart from the basic description is known of the song and calls of most of the species in this genus. However, song and calls of two species in the genus, European Stonechat and Whinchat have been studied fairly comprehensively but no research appears to have been conducted in the past into such aspects of *Saxicola* song as geographical, regional or even individual differences. In the case of European, Siberian and African Stonechat such differences would assist in confirming species status. The sonograms of these three species indicate some difference in song between European, Siberian and African Stonechat and that there is also an apparent difference between at least two subspecies of Siberian Stonechat *S. m. przewalskii* and *S. m. maura*. The songs of these three species when heard do demonstrate some noticeable differences. Research on this subject is now being undertaken both at species and subspecies level. Particular emphasis is now being placed on the Siberian Stonechat subspecies *armenica variegata* and *przewalskii* (Urquhart in press). Indeed, the British Library National Sound Archive has only one very short recording of Siberian Stonechat song. This has been used in this book as a sonogram to demonstrate that there are differences in the songs of European and Siberian Stonechats.

Calls are difficult to describe in human words and in this book they have been described using descriptions in the literature and from the author's interpretation of recordings. However, this is far from satisfactory as one observer's interpretation may be difficult for another observer to interpret. Sonograms have, unjustly in my opinion, often been left out of books as they are perceived as difficult to interpret. Although it is difficult to judge what a song or call sounds like from a sonogram, there is much other information that can be gained from sonograms such as the length of a song or call, its structure, frequency and timing.

FOOD

Species in this genus apparently feed virtually exclusively on small invertebrates. Small amounts of vegetative matter have been found in some samples but not enough to indicate that the species concerned is omnivorous. It is thought that such vegetable matter found in a sample is the result of involuntary ingestion when an invertebrate item is snatched from vegetation.

A detailed list is provided of the food items that comprise the regular diet of each species where known. Unusual prey taken as food and abnormal behavioural occurrences relating to feeding are also listed. Apart from European Stonechat and Whinchat there are few detailed dietary records of species in the genus. Studies concerning these two species, and especially on European Stonechat, that have been undertaken in respect of feeding behaviour, changes of food during the year and food brought to the young are incorporated into the section in the relevant species chapter.

MOVEMENTS

This section describes the regular migratory movements of a species where applicable, together with its normal wintering range. It contains detailed information on migratory routes for both autumn and spring migration, and timings for occurrences in both transitional countries and those where breeding and wintering occur. Vagrant records and unusual occurrences outside the normal range are also listed. The distributional maps should also be consulted as these show the wintering range for those species which are migratory as well as records of vagrancy.

BEHAVIOUR

Rather than list a series of behavioural traits under a separate section, where possible it seems logical and easier for the reader if behavioural traits of a species associated with a particular activity, such as breeding or feeding, are described under such headings rather than separately. Where no such heading appears to be relevant to a form of behaviour it is incorporated under this heading.

MOULT

In the genus *Saxicola*, moult usually takes place on the breeding areas and before any movement, either local or long-distance, is commenced. The sequence of moult in both adult and juvenile birds is given for each species for which there is information. The majority of adult *Saxicola* have one main moult occurring after breeding (post-breeding) and probably have similar plumage moult sequences to that of European Stonechat. Juveniles have a partial post-juvenile moult into first-year or first-adult plumage a few months after birth. This usually involves a partial replacement of the body feathers and the lesser, median and usually the inner greater coverts on the upperwing. The number of post-juvenile moulted coverts can vary within and between species. The remiges and rectrices are usually not moulted and consequently can appear considerably more worn and brown than adult individuals in the following year, particularly towards the end of the breeding season and before the full post-breeding moult is commenced. The post-juvenile moult may be synchronised with or start earlier than the adult post-breeding moult, depending on when the individual fledged.

First-year and older adults both undergo a full post-breeding moult. In the case of first-year birds, their first post-breeding moult will be in their second calendar year. The only species in the genus known to have a different moult is Whinchat. This species has similar moults to European Stonechat in the autumn but also undergoes a partial pre-breeding moult early in the year, usually before it leaves its wintering area, and in which all returning individuals of any age participate.

All species in the genus *Saxicola* have ten primaries. The numbering of primaries is done either ascendently (from the outside to the inside) or descendently (from the inside to the outside). The descendent system is used in this book as that is the most widely accepted system in literature on moult, and the numbering also corresponds with the usual sequence of primary moult in passerines which is descendent. This means that the outermost (and in this genus proportionately much the shortest) primary is number P10 and the innermost is number P01. The innermost primary is often the same length as the outermost secondary (S01) and it is very hard to distinguish these in the field. Other publications such as Vaurie (1959) and Svensson (1992) number the primaries ascendently, so the innermost is P10 and the outermost P01. Primaries are moulted descendently, i.e. commencing from the innermost outwards, whilst the secondaries commence ascendently, i.e. outermost inwards. Only one or two are replaced at a time and symmetrically (i.e. simultaneously on both wings).

The secondaries, of which there are usually nine, are numbered ascendently, so the outermost is number S01 (next to primary P01) and the innermost number 09. Note that the innermost three (07–09) are usually referred to as the tertials, with tertial 07 being the largest and tertial 09 the smallest (approximately half the length of the longest 07). The longest tertial is usually the same length or slightly longer than the innermost secondary (S06).

In most passerines, including the genus *Saxicola*, there are usually 12 rectrices (tail feathers), and these are numbered in pairs from the centre of the tail. Thus the central pair is 01 and the outermost tail feathers on each side of the tail form pair 06. The detailed descriptions in the text of some species refer to primaries and secondaries as well as tail feathers by their specific number.

Birds that have recently completed their moult are described as being in 'fresh plumage', while those whose feathering shows signs of progressive wear are in 'worn plumage'. The majority of species in the genus *Saxicola* attain their breeding plumage by wear to the feathers acquired in the post-breeding moult. These feathers when new have extensive fringes which obscure the breeding colours and create the so-called winter plumage of the species. As the fringes wear away through abrasion they reveal more and more of the breeding colours of the species. The only known exception to this in *Saxicola* is the Whinchat, which acquires a large proportion of its breeding plumage by a pre-breeding moult. This may also possibly be the case for Stoliczka's Bushchat although the evidence so far is inconclusive.

CONSERVATION

Current and potential threats to a species are discussed, and recommendations and actions to counter the various threats are listed under those species where there is detailed knowledge of conservation issues and threats. In 1994, development of the World Bird Database (WBDB) was commenced by BirdLife International and in 1998 the database was expanded to cover both sites and species. From the information gathered under the WBDB it is known that under the IUCN Red List criteria, of the 1186 globally threatened species, 1175 (99%) are threatened by human activities such as agriculture, logging, hunting and trapping (Stattersfield & Capper 2000). Much work is being done by BirdLife International to conserve birds, their habitats and global biodiversity by a combination of governmental pressure, both national and local, as well as education in schools and dialogue with commercial interests, whilst at the same time building up a database of information on which to base their conservation strategies. The majority of species in the genus *Saxicola* have suffered due to loss of, degradation and/or conversion of habitat to man's uses. Even the large populations of European Stonechat and Whinchat are in decline in the western Palearctic due to such pressures. The only species that apparently benefits from man's adaptation and clearing of habitat is Pied Bushchat *Saxicola caprata*, whilst the populations of Réunion Stonechat *Saxicola tectes*, Buff-streaked Bushchat *Saxicola bifasciata*, African Stonechat *Saxicola torquata* and Siberian Stonechat *Saxicola maura* appear to be stable.

Under IUCN Red List criteria, two species in the genus are considered globally threatened: Stoliczka's Bushchat *Saxicola macrorhyncha* and Hodgson's Bushchat *Saxicola insignis*, whilst two others are listed as Lower Risk/Near Threatened: Canary Island Stonechat *Saxicola dacotiae* and White-bellied Bushchat *Saxicola gutturalis*. It is surely vital that the currently unknown breeding areas of Stoliczka's Bushchat are found soon in order to protect them and currently only one or two regular wintering areas are known for Hodgson's Bushchat. Again, urgent action needs to be taken to find other wintering areas if they exist as it is the loss of habitat in its wintering area that is the main threat to this species.

REFERENCES

Sources of information are given within each species chapter by use of author(s) surname and date of publication of the article or book from which the information came. A complete alphabetical list of all references will be found at the end of the book in which greater detail of the reference is given. The author recommends further reading of these sources as an adjunct to information contained in this book.

TOPOGRAPHY

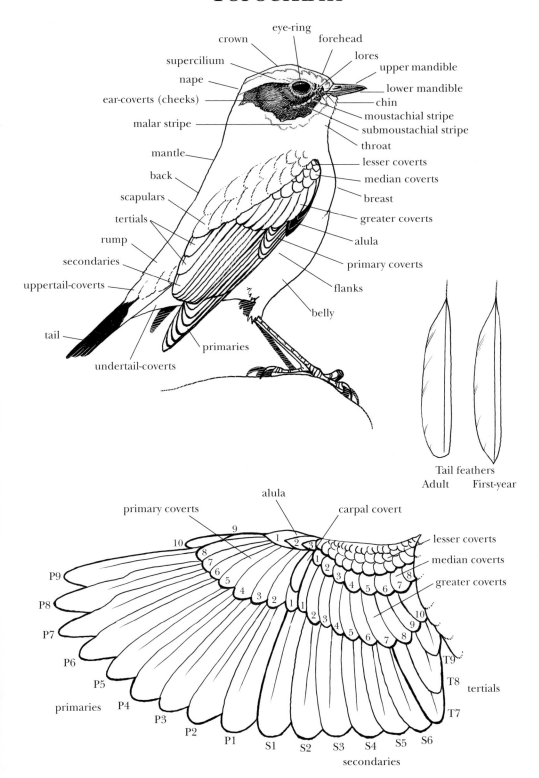

eye-ring
crown
forehead
supercilium
lores
nape
upper mandible
ear-coverts (cheeks)
lower mandible
malar stripe
chin
moustachial stripe
submoustachial stripe
mantle
throat
back
lesser coverts
scapulars
median coverts
tertials
breast
rump
greater coverts
secondaries
alula
uppertail-coverts
primary coverts
flanks
belly
tail
primaries
undertail-coverts

Tail feathers
Adult   First-year

primary coverts
alula
carpal covert
lesser coverts
median coverts
greater coverts
P9
P8
P7
P6
P5
P4
primaries
P3
P2
P1   S1   S2   S3   S4   S5   S6
secondaries
T9
T8   tertials
T7

A MOLECULAR PHYLOGENY OF STONECHATS AND RELATED TURDIDS

by

Michael Wink, Heidi Sauer-Gurth, Petra Heidrich, Hans-Heinrich Witt and Eberhard Gwinner*

Institut für Pharmazeutische Biologie, Universität Heidelberg, Im Neuenheimer Feld 364, 69120 Heidelberg, Germany
*Max-Planck-Research Centre for Ornithology, Von der Tannstr. 7, 82346 Andechs, Germany

INTRODUCTION

Systematic relationships are usually based on similarity, and taxa showing the least difference are considered to be closely related. Since morphological similarity in two lineages of organisms can be due to adaptation to similar ecological constraints, adaptive characters can lead to incorrect taxonomic classifications.

The analysis of nuclear or mitochondrial marker genes has become a widely applied tool in all fields of zoology, including ornithology, to reconstruct phylogenies and phylogeographic relationships (see overviews in Avise 1994 and Mindell 1999). Molecular data have the great advantage that convergence does not impair an analysis to the same degree as morphological data. If taxa belong to the same species, their marker genes are identical and do not show genetic distances that are typical for established species. Molecular data also give evidence for the timescale in which a particular evolutionary step has taken place ('molecular clock') and therefore allow both a phylogenetic and phylogeographic analysis of the unknown past of a group of organisms. Sequence data have therefore become an important tool for taxonomy and evolutionary studies. In our laboratory we have used sequences of mitochondrial DNA (mtDNA) to infer the phylogeny of diurnal and nocturnal raptors, shearwaters, gulls, bustards and warblers (Gaucher *et al.* 1996; Heidrich & Wink 1998; Heidrich *et al.* 1995, 1996, 1998; Helbig *et al.* 1995, 1996; Leisler *et al.* 1997; Seibold *et al.* 1996; Wink 1995, 1998; Wink & Heidrich 1999; Wink *et al.* 1996, 1998).

Few molecular studies have addressed phylogenetic relationships in stonechats and other turdids. Based on the analysis of a partial sequence (300 base pairs) of the mitochondrial cytochrome-*b* gene, preliminary data have suggested that the European Stonechat *Saxicola torquata*, Siberian Stonechat *Saxicola maura* and African Stonechat *Saxicola axillaris* have already diverged to a high degree (Wittman 1994; Wittman *et al.* 1995) [1].

In the analysis presented here we have sequenced most of the cytochrome-*b* gene of 23 turdid taxa (seven genera) and have also enlarged the dataset by including more stonechat taxa than in our previous study (Wittmann *et al.* 1995).

MATERIALS AND METHODS

Blood and tissues were either preserved in an EDTA buffer (0.1 M Tris, pH 7.4, 10% EDTA, 1% NaF, 0.1% thymol) or in ethanol (Wink 1998) and stored at −20°C until processing. Total DNA was extracted from the blood samples by an overnight incubation at 37°C in lysis buffer (10 mM Tris [pH 7.5], 25 mM EDTA, 75 mM NaCl, 1% SDS) including 1 mg of Proteinase K (Boehringer Mannheim), followed by a standard phenol/chloroform protein extraction. DNA was precipitated from the supernatant with 0.8 volume of cold isopropanol, centrifuged, washed, dried and resuspended in TE buffer. The mitochondrial cytochrome-*b* gene was amplified by PCR using primers MT-A3 GCC CCA TCC AAC ATC TCA GCA TGA TGA AAC TTC G, MT-F2 CTA AGA AGG GTG GAG TCT TCA GTT TTT GGT TTA CAA GAC CAA TG OR MT-FS TAG TTG GCC AAT GAT GAT GAA TGG GTG TTC TAC TGG GTT. PCR products were sequenced directly using the dideoxy chain termination method with the cycle sequencing Kit (Amersham Life Science, RPN 2438/RPN 2538) in combination with internal CY-5 labelled primers. For cycle sequencing a two-stage programme containing an initial denaturing step at 94°C for 4 min and 25 cycles at 60°C (40sec), and 94° (30sec) was used. The primers employed were MT-C2-CY XGA GGA CAA ATA TCA TTC TGA GG, MT-U2-CY XGG GGT GAA GTT TTC TGG GTC, MT-C4-CY XAG TGT TGG GTT GTC TAC TGA, MT-V-cy TGG AGG GGR AAR AAT CGG T, MT-b2-cy GCC CAG AAK CAT ATT TGT CCT CA, MT-le-cy TCA AAC CCG AAT GAT AYT TCC TAT T, and MT-c5-cy TCA GTA GAY AAC CCM ACA CT. CY-5 labelled fragments

---

[1] Wink *et al.* (2002) use of binominals for European Stonechat (*S. torquata*) and African Stonechat (*S. axillaris*) differ from those used throughtout this book. In the Common Stonechat Complex account and European, Siberian and African Stonechat accounts, European Stonechat is *S. rubicola* and African Stonechat *S. torquata* the reasoning for this is given on pages 133–134.

were analysed on an automated DNA sequencer (Amersham Pharmacia Biotech, ALF-Express II). Sequences of >1000 nt were obtained directly from ALF-Express and aligned. The phylogenetically informative characters of turdids are illustrated in Table 1.

Sequences of ca. 900 nt length were used to reconstruct phylogenetic trees, employing PAUP*4.0b8a (Swofford 1998) with maximum parsimony (MP). More details on the methodology can be found in Wink (1998) and Heidrich *et al.* (1998).

RESULTS AND DISCUSSION

The analysis was restricted mainly to species of the western Palaearctic and comprised the following genera: stonechats and bushchats *Saxicola*, rock thrushes *Monticola*, redstarts *Phoenicurus*, wheatears *Oenanthe*, robins *Erithacus*, nightingales and Bluethroat *Luscinia*, and thrushes *Turdus*. The dippers *Cinclus* were included as a possibly related ingroup and the wrens *Troglodytes* as a distantly related outgroup. Although we sequenced several individuals of each taxon (between 6 and 20 in the case of stonechat subspecies), within any given subspecies all individuals clustered as a single genealogically related group derived from a single common ancestor (a monophyletic clade). One or two representatives of each taxon were chosen for an analysis which aimed to outline the patterns of phylogeny and speciation within stone-chats and related Turdidae. A more complete analysis will be published elsewhere (see Wink *et al.* 2002).

In Figures 1a and 1b the results of maximum parsimony of mtDNA are given. Members of the genus *Saxicola* form a monophyletic clade (supported by a bootstrap value of 92%), which derives from a common ancestor that is shared with Rock Thrush *Monticola saxatilis*. Within the *Saxicola* clade either the Whinchat *Saxicola rubetra* or the Pied Bushchat *Saxicola caprata* take a basal position. The Canary Island Stonechat *Saxicola dacotiae*, the European Stonechat *Saxicola torquata*, the Siberian Stonechat *Saxicola maura*, the Réunion Stonechat *Saxicola tectes* and the African Stonechat *Saxicola axillaris* follow as a well-supported monophyletic clade (bootstrap 88%). The latter forms have often been treated as subspecies of a single species, Common Stonechat *S. torquata* (Sibley & Monroe 1993), but because of diagnostic differences in morphology, breeding biology and distribution these taxa have also been recognised as distinct species in recent literature.

If the members of the *S. torquata* complex were closely related subspecies, we should expect a cluster showing little or no genetic differences between each of the taxa. Instead, the cytochrome-*b* sequence data exhibit a well-developed phylogenetic pattern with relatively long branch lengths separating them (Figures 1a and 1b; Table 2). Genetic distances between the taxa of the *S. torquata* complex range between 4.3% and 6.8%, whereas distances within a given subspecies do not exceed 1% (data, based on larger samples of 10 to 20 individuals, will be documented elsewhere).

The Canary Island Stonechat *S. dacotiae* is closely related to the European Stonechat *S. torquata*; the genetic distance of 4.7% implies that both taxa have diverged about 2.3 million years ago (if the '2% per million years' rule [*Wilson et al. 1987*] is used for calibration of mtDNA. Most likely, the Canary Island Stonechat derived from a migratory population of European Stonechats which became resident on the Canary Islands. Both taxa share common ancestry with the Siberian Stonechat *S. maura*, from which they differ by 4.3% and 5.3% nucleotide substitutions respectively.

The African Stonechat *S. axillaris* differs from the European Stonechat *S. torquata* by 5.7% nucleotide substitutions. It clusters as a sister taxon to the Réunion Stonechat *S. tectes* which has recently been recognised as a distinct species. Pairwise distances amount to 5.3%. The *axillaris* group and the *rubicola* group form a sister group in all reconstructions, deriving from a common ancestor. These differences imply divergence times of 2–3 million years.

Genetic distances in our dataset for other closely related but distinct species such as Common Nightingale *Luscinia megarhynchos* and Thrush Nightingale *Luscinia luscinia*, Northern Wheatear *Oenanthe oenanthe* and Isabelline Wheatear *Oenanthe isabellina*, and Fieldfare *Turdus pilaris* and Song Thrush *Turdus philomelos* (Table 2) are similar in range to members of the *S. torquata* complex.

It is, therefore, highly likely that the taxa within the 'Common Stonechat' complex represent distinct genetic lineages which deserve species status. Not only do they differ in genetic terms, they also differ by their distinct allopatric distribution, ecology, physiology (Gwinner & Scheuerlein 1999; Helm & Gwinner 1999) and morphology. Using genomic fingerprinting with ISSR-PCR, we could confirm that the *S. t. rubicola*, *S. axillaris* and *S. maura* complex forms three distinct genetic entities (complete data will be published elsewhere), indicating that the results obtained from mitochondrial cytochrome-*b* sequences correctly reflect the phylogeny of this group of birds.

The *Monticola-Saxicola* clade is phylogenetically related to the genera *Luscinia*, *Oenanthe*, *Phoenicurus* and *Erithacus*. These genera form a well-supported monophyletic clade with a bootstrap value of 96%. Members of the genus *Turdus*, which also form a monophyletic clade (88% bootstrap support), always cluster as a sister group to the stonechat-wheatear assemblage. The White-throated Dipper *Cinclus cinclus*, which superficially resembles a blackbird, shows no close affinity to members of the genus *Turdus*, (pairwise genetic distances of 12-15%), or to wrens, with which they have also been associated. We need a more complete dataset of all Passeriformes before considering the real affinities of dippers and wrens.

CONCLUSIONS

Sequence data of the mitochondrial cytochrome-*b* gene and genomic fingerprinting provide good evidence that the geographically separated taxa of the stonechats in this study represent distinct genetic lineages which have become separated more than one million years ago. The distinct genetic pattern implies that hybridisation and gene flow between these lineages no longer takes place to a significant degree, otherwise the differences would not be so clear-cut. Since these lineages also differ in morphology, breeding behaviour, vocalisations and annual rhythmicity, we believe that it is justified to treat them as good species (as many field guides already do).

ACKNOWLEDGEMENTS

We thank U. Wittmann for preliminary studies and D. Ristow, P. Heidrich, W. Bednarek and Heidrun Albrecht for providing samples for this study.

REFERENCES

Avise, J.C. (1994) *Molecular markers, natural history and evolution.* Chapman and Hall, London

Gaucher, P., Paillat, P., Chappuis, C., Saint Jalme, M., Lotfikhah, F., & Wink, M. (1996) Taxonomy of the Houbara Bustard *Chlamydotis undulata* subspecies considered on the basis of sexual display and genetic divergence. *Ibis* 138: 273-282.

Gwinner, E. & Scheuerlein, A. (1999) Photoperiodic responsiveness of equatorial and temperate-zone stonechats. *Condor* 101: 347-359.

Heidrich, P. & Wink, M. (1998) Phylogenetic relationships in holarctic owls (order Strigiformes): Evidence from nucleotide sequences of the mitochondrial cytochrome-*b* gene. Pp 73-87 in *Holarctic Birds of Prey.* (eds. R.D. Chancellor, B.-U. Meyburg, J.J. Ferrero). Adenex & WWGBP.

Heidrich, P., Amengual, J. & Wink, M. (1998) Phylogenetic relationships in Mediterranean and North Atlantic *Puffinus* Shearwaters (Aves: Procellariidae) based on nucleotide sequences of mtDNA. *Biochemical Systematics and Ecology* 26: 145-170.

Heidrich, P., Ristow, D. & Wink, M. (1996) Molekulare Differenzierung von Gelb- und Schwarzschnabelsturmtauchern (*Calonectris diomedea, Puffinus puffinus, P. yelkouan*) und Großmöwen des Silbermöwenkomplexes (*Larus argentatus, L. fuscus, L. cachinnans*). *Journal für Ornithologie* 137: 281-294.

Heidrich, P., König, C. & Wink, M. (1995) Bioakustik, Taxonomie und molekulare Systematik amerikanischer Sperlingskäuze (Strigidae: *Glaucidium* spp.). *Stuttgarter Beiträge zur Naturkunde* A. 534: 1-47.

Helbig, A. J., Seibold, I., Martens, J. & Wink, M. (1995) Genetic differentiation and phylogenetic relationships of Bonelli's Warbler *Phylloscopus bonelli* and Green Warbler *P. nitidus. Journal of Avian Biology* 26: 139-153.

Helbig, A.J., Martens, J., Henning, F., Schottler, B., Seibold, I. & Wink, M. (1996) Phylogeny and species limits in the Palaearctic chiffchaff (*Phylloscopus collybita*) complex: mitochondrial genetic differentiation and bioacoustic evidence. *Ibis* 138: 650-666.

Helm, B., & Gwinner, E. (1999) Timing of postjuvenal molt in African (*Saxicola torquata axillaris*) and European (*S. t. rubicola*) stonechats: Effects of genetic and environmental factors. *Auk* 116: 589-603.

Leisler, B., Heidrich, P., Schulze-Hagen, K. & Wink, M. (1997) Taxonomy and phylogeny of reed warblers (genus *Acrocephalus*) based on mtDNA sequences and morphology. *Jounal für Ornithologie* 138: 469-496.

Mindell, D.P. (1999) *Avian molecular evolution and systematics.* Academic Press, San Diego.

Seibold, I., Helbig, A. J., Meyburg, B.-U., Negro, J. &, Wink, M. (1996) Genetic differentiation and molecular phylogeny of European *Aquila* eagles according to cytochrome-*b* nucleotide sequences. Pp. 1-15 in *Eagle Studies* (eds. B.-U. Meyburg & R. Chancellor). WWGBP, Berlin, London & Paris.

Sibley, C.G. & Monroe, B.L. (1993) *A Supplement to the Distribution and Taxonomy of Birds of the World.* Yale University Press, New Haven.

Swofford, D.L. (1998) PAUP-Phylogenetic analysis using parsimony. Version PAUP*4.0b4a.

Wilson, A.C., Ochman, H. & Prager, E.M. (1987) Molecular time scale for evolution. *Trends Genetics* 3: 241-247.

Wink, M. & Heidrich, P. In press. Molecular systematics of owls (Strigiformes) based on DNA sequences of the mitochondrial cytochrome-*b* gene.

Wink, M. In press. Advances in DNA studies of diurnal and nocturnal raptors.

Wink, M. (1998) Application of DNA-Markers to Study the Ecology and Evolution of Raptors. Pp 49-71 in *Holarctic Birds of Prey.* (eds. R.D. Chancellor, B.-U.Meyburg & J.J. Ferrero), Adenex & WWGBP.

Wink, M., & Heidrich, P. (1999) Molecular evolution and systematics of the owls (Strigiformes). Pp 39-57 in *Owls: A Guide to the Owls of the World* by C. König, F. Weick & J.H. Becking. Pica Press, Sussex.

Wink, M., Heidrich, P. & Fentzloff, C. (1996) A mtDNA phylogeny of sea eagles (genus *Haliaeetus*) based on nucleotide sequences of the cytochrome-*b* gene. *Biochemical Systematics and Ecology* 24: 783-791.

Wink, M., Seibold, I., Lotfikhah, F. & Bednarek, W. (1998) Molecular systematics of holarctic raptors (Order Falconiformes). Pp 29-48 in *Holarctic Birds of Prey* (eds. R. D. Chancellor, B.-U. Meyburg & J. J. Ferrero). Adenex & WWGBP.

Wink, M. (1995) Phylogeny of Old and New World vultures (Aves: Accipitridae and Cathartidae) inferred from nucleotide sequences of the mitochondrial cytochrome-*b* gene. *Z. Naturforsch.* 50C: 868-882.

Wittmann, U. (1994) Zur molekularen Phylogenie der Drosseln (Aves: Familie Turdidae). Diploma Thesis, University of Heidelberg.

Wittmann, U., Heidrich, P., Wink, M. & Gwinner, E. Poster, IOC Vienna.

Wittmann, U., Heidrich, P., Wink, M. & Gwinner, E. (1995) Speciation in the stonechat (*Saxicola torquata*) inferred from nucleotide sequences of the cytochrome-*b* gene. *J. Zoo. Syst. Evol. Research* 33: 116-122.

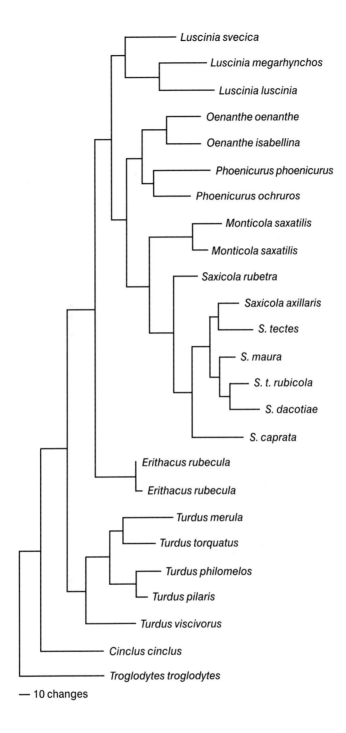

Figure 1a A molecular phylogeny of stonechats and related turdids based on sequence data of the mitochondrial cytochrome-*b* gene.

Maximum parsimony analysis (unweighted analysis); representation as a phylogram (branch lengths correspond to the number of character changes) of one of three equally parsimonious trees.

Tree length: 1197 steps; HI= 0.499; CI= 0.501; RI= 0.542; of 904 analysed characters, 425 characters are variable and 271 parsimony informative.

Bootstrap

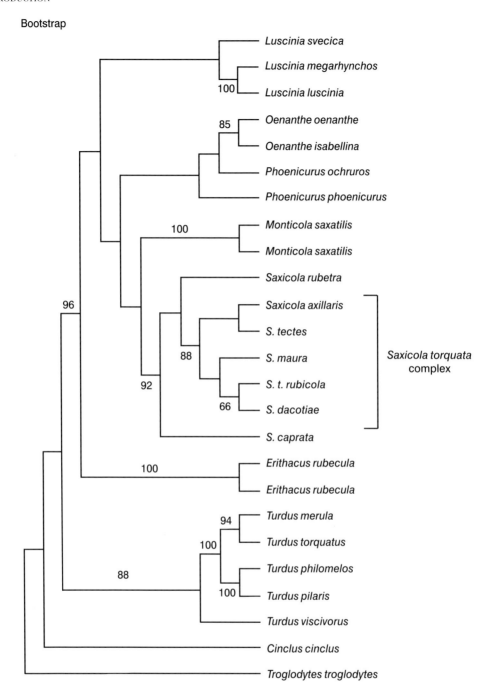

Figure 1b A molecular phylogeny of stonechats and related turdids based on sequence data of the mitochondrial cytochrome-*b* gene.

Maximum parsimony analysis; representation as a bootstrap cladogram (bootstrap values above 60% are given at the corresponding bifurcations).

Tree length: 1197 steps; HI= 0.499; CI= 0.501; RI= 0.542; of 904 analysed characters, 425 characters are variable and 271 parsimony informative.

Table 1 Parsimony informative characters in the analysed data set of turdids. Numbering refer to the complete cytochrome-*b* gene covering 1140 bp.

```
                      11111111111111111111111111111111111112222222222222222222222222222333333333333
                      0001111222233334444555556666888889990000112223334444566677889900001222334444
Taxon/Node            5891248046923894780146925801349248147909258157036924780659170698157066568
```

Taxon/Node	Sequence
Luscinia svecica	ATCATAACCCCACCGCTCGTCACCCCATCCCCAACCCTACAACCCATACCTCATCCTCCCCACTCCACACAC
Luscinia megarhynchos	ACTACAACCACACCACTCGTCCCCCCATCCTCAAATCCACAGCTCACACCCCATCCCTCCCACCCCACACGA
Luscinia luscinia	ACCACAACCATACCACTCGCCCCCCCCAACCTCAAACCCACAGCCCACACCTCATCCCTCCCACATCACGCGA
Oenanthe oenanthe	GATACGATCAAACTACTCGTCACCCCCTTCTCCCCCTTACAACCCACACCCTATCTTCACCCCCTCATACGA
Oenanthe isabellina	??ATATTCCAACATTCTCGTCACCCCCTCCCCCCCCCCTACAACCCACACTCTATCCCCACCACCCCACATGA
Ph. phoenicurus	AACCCAACCATACTGCTTACCATGCTCTCCCCCACCCTATAGCTTACCCCCCATCCCCGCAACCCCACGTAC
Ph. ochruros	AGCATAACCCCACTGCTCGTCACACCCTCTCTCAGCCTATAACCCACCCCTCATCCCCATAATCCCGCACGC
Erithacus rubecula	ACCACAACCCCCCACTCCCCACCCCCTCCCCAACCCTACAACCCTCATCTCATCCCCCCCACCCTACACAC
Monticola saxatilis	AACACAATCCCGCCACCCCCCACACCCGCCCCAACCCTACAGTCCATACCTCATCCCCACCTCACCACACGC
Turdus merula	GACACAATTATACTAACTACCACGTCCTCCCCAACCCTATCATCCACCCCTCAAACTCTTCGTCGCACACAC
Turdus philomelos	GACATAACTACACTGTCCACTACACCCTACTCAATCTTGCCATCCCCCCCCCATCCCCCCTCCCACTTACAT
Turdus torquatus	GACTCAATTATACCGACTACCACGTCCTTCCCAGTCCTACCACYTACCCCCCAAGTCCCTCACCCCTCACAC
Turdus viscivorus	GACACGATCGCACCATCTACCACGCCTTCCCCAACCCTACGATTCACACCTCATCCCCTCCGCCACCCATAC
Turdus pilaris	GACACAATTACACTAACTACCACGTCCTCCCCAACTCTACCACCTACCCCCCACATCCCTCACCACCCACAC
Cinclus cinclus	AACCCAACCACCCCACACTCCTCACCTTTCCCAAATCTACCACCCACACACTATCCCCTCCCCCACGCACGT
T. troglodytes	GACCCAGCCGCCCCACCCACCACACCATCCCCATACCTGTCATTTACCCGCACCCCCCCTCACCCCTCATGT
Saxicola rubetra	GACATAGCTACACCATCCGCCACCCCCACCTCAACCTTACAATCCACACCCCTCCCCCCCACCTCACATGC
S. axillaris	GACTCAATTACTCCGCCCGCCATACTCGCCCCAACCCTACAACCCATACCCTCTTCCCTCCATCCCATGTGC
S. maura	GACACAATTACCCCGCCCGCCATACTCGCTCTAACCTTATAACCCATACCCCCTCTCCTCCACCTCATGTGC
S. t. rubicola	GACCTAATTACTCCGCCCGCCATACTCGCTCTAACCTTACAACCCATACCCCCTTTCCTCCACCTCATGTGC
S. caprata	GACACAATTATACCGCCCGCCATATCCATCTTAACCTTACAATCCACACTCTTTCCCCTCCACCCCACGCGC
S. dacotiae	???CCAATTAMCACGCGCGCCATCTTCCCTCTAACCTTACAACCAATACCCCCTTTCCTCCACCTTATGTGC
S. tectes	GACCGGATTAATACGCCCGTTATACTCGCCCCAACCCCCGCAACCCATACCTCTCCCCTCCACCCCATGTGT

```
                      333333333333333333334444444444444444444444445555555555555555555555555556
                      555566666667788899900111223444555667788899000122223344445556667777889990
Taxon/Node            1457034678902147369251470921470392514019251476256814016935815702693B1473
```

Taxon/Node	Sequence
Luscinia svecica	AAGTCCCAGTACACTCCTCACAAAACTTCCACACCTTACAACCCCCCACCGCACGACCAAACCCTCCCTCCAG
Luscinia megarhynchos	GCACCCCAATACATCCCCTGCAAAACTCMCATCCA?C?CAACAACCAACAAATGACCACAGCCCCTTTCTAA
Luscinia luscinia	ACACCCCAATACATCCCCCATAAAATTCCCATACACCAGAA?AACCAACVCATGACCGCACCCCCCCCCCAA
Oenanthe oenanthe	ATACCCCGGTCCTTCCCTCTCCGACATCCCATACCCCCTAACAACCAACACACGACCATACCCTGTCCCCAC
Oenanthe isabellina	ACACCCCAGTCCCCCCCTCCCCAACGTCCCACACCCCCCCAACAATCAACACACGTCCATACCCTCTTCCCAC
Ph. phoenicurus	GCACTCTACTCCATCTCCACAAAACACCCCACACATCACAATAACCAAHACACGCCCACACCTTCCCCCAAA
Ph. ochruros	ACATCCCACTCTACCCCTACAAAACACCCCATACATCACAACAATCAACGCACGCCCACACCTTCCCTCCAG
Erithacus rubecula	ACACCCCAACCCACCCCCCCCAGAAGTCCCACACCTCACAACAGTTCTCCCACACCCTATCCTTACCCCCCC
Monticola saxatilis	AAATCTCAATCCATCCCCCTCAAAAGTCTCGCACACCACAACGACCCATACCTGTCCCAACCTTTCCATCAA
Turdus merula	ATATACCAACCCATCCCCATCAAGAGTCCCACACCC?ACAACGACCCANDGACGCCCCCAGCTCGCCATCCG
Turdus philomelos	ATACGCCAACCTATCCCCACCAAAAGTCTCACACCTCACAGTAACCCACAAGCGCCCCCAGTCCACCGCCCA
Turdus torquatus	ATACATCAACCCGTCCCCACCAAAAGTCTTACATATCACAACCACCCACAAACGCCCCCCGCCCGCCATCCA
Turdus viscivorus	ATACACCAGCCCACCCCTACCAAGAGTCTTACACCTCACAACGACCAACAAACGTCCCCAGCCCCCCCCCTCC
Turdus pilaris	ATGTGTCAACCTATCCCCACCAAAAGTCTCACACCTCACAGTAACCCACAAGCGCCCCCAGTCCACCGCCCA
Cinclus cinclus	GAACACTAGCCCACCCTCAGCAAAAGTCCCACACACCACAACAACCTACACATGACCAGAGACTTCTCCACA
T. troglodytes	ACCCTTTAGCCCCCCTTTAACCAAAGTCACACATCCCCCGAAAACCACCACCTGCCCAGCCTTCAACACCCC
Saxicola rubetra	ATGCCCCAATCCACCCCTCCCAAAAGATCCGCCCATCACAGCGCCCCATACACGCTCATAGCCTCTTTCTAA
S. axillaris	ACGCCTTACTCCATTCCCCCCAAGACATCCGTCCATTACAACGCCCCATACACGCTCACAGCCTCTTCTCAA
S. maura	ACACCCCGMTCCATTCCCCCCAAAACATTCGCCCATTACGACRCCCCATACACGYTCATAGCCTCTTCCCAA
S. t. rubicola	ACACTCCACTCTATTCACCCCAAAACATCCACTCATTACAACGCCCCACATACGCTCATAGCCTCCTTCCAA
S. caprata	ACACCTCTCTCCATCCCCCCCCCAACCATCCACCCATCATAGCACCTCACATACGTCCACAGCTTCCCSCCTA
S. dacotiae	ACACTCCACTCTATTCACCCCAAAACATCCACCCATTACAACGCCCCATACACGCTTATAGCCTCTTTCCAA
S. tectes	ACACTCTACTCCATTCCCCCTAAGACATCCACTCATTACAACGCCCCACATACGCTTATAGCCTCCTTCCAA

```
                6666666666666666666666677777777777777777777777777777777777888888888888
                0011123334455667779999000111122222233344444555566778888889990011123333444
Taxon/Node      692587039081709258016925814670123462814789013658140236792581703596147036
```

Taxon/Node	Sequence
Luscinia svecica	CGAAGAACCGCCTAACCCCCCTACACCTATGTCTCCCCCCCTACAAACCATACACAAACCTACAGTTATCTA
Luscinia megarhynchos	CAACAAACCGCTCAACTCCCACACAACTAAGTCTCCCACCCTACAAACCACACACTCAACTATAACTCCCCA
Luscinia luscinia	CAACAAACTGCCCAACCCCCATACAATTAAGTCTCCYACCCTKSARACTACACACACAACTATGGCTCACTA
Oenanthe oenanthe	CAACAAACCGCCCAACCCCCACACACCCTCATCGCCCCCCCTACATACCGTACACACACCCACAACTACCCG
Oenanthe isabellina	TAACAAACCTTCCAACCCCCGCACACCCCCATCGCCCCCCCTACACATCGCACACATATCCACGACTACCCA
Ph. phoenicurus	TAACAAACCGCCCAACCCTCCCAAGCCCATGTCGCTCCCCCTATACACCACACATACCCTTATAACCACCCA
Ph. ochruros	TAACAAACCTTCCAATTTCCGCACACC?CTGTCGCCCCCCCTACACATCGCACACACATCCACAACCACCCA
Erithacus rubecula	TAACAAACCGCCCACTCCCCCCACGCTTACATCTCTTCCCCTACACATTACACTCATACCTACAACCACCCA
Monticola saxatilis	CGACAGACCGTCCAACCTTCCCACATCCCCATTGTCTCTCCTGTAAACCACACACGCAATCACAATCACCTC
Turdus merula	CAAGTAAACGCTCCTCCCCCATAAACCTAAGTCTCCTCCTGCACCGACCGCACACACACTCGTAACCACCCT
Turdus philomelos	CAAAAAGACGCCCCCTCCTCACAAGTCTGTGTCTCCCCTTGCACCAACTACACACACACACAACCACCCT
Turdus torquatus	CAAAGAAACGCCCTCCCCCATAAATCTATGTCTCCTCATGCACCAACCACATACCCACATGCAGCCACCCT
Turdus viscivorus	CACAAAAATGTCCCCCCCCCACAAACCTACACTTCCCCCCATACTAGCCCCACACACACATATAACCATCTC
Turdus pilaris	CAAAAAGACGCCCCCTCCTCACAAGTCTGTGTCTCCCCTTGCACCAACTACACACACACAGAACCACCCT
Cinclus cinclus	CAAAAAAAAGTCCAACCCCCACCAATCTCCGCCTCCCCACATACACGCCACATCTACTCTCATAACCATTCC
T. troglodytes	CAACACAAATCCTAACCACCACCAAACTATGCTATCCACCCTACAAATCACACCCACACACAAAACTTCCCA
Saxicola rubetra	CAACAGACTGCTCAACCCTTCCACGCCTCTGTCGTCCCCCCTGCAAATCCCACCCATATCCACAACCACTCA
S. axillaris	CAACAAACTGCTCAACCCCCCCACGCCTCTGTCGTCCCCCCTGCAAATCTCACCCATACTCACAACCACTCA
S. maura	CAACAAACTGCTCAACCCCCCCATRCCTCTATCGTCCCCCCTGCAAATCACATCCATACTCATAACCACTCG
S. t. rubicola	CAGCAAACTGCTCAACCCTTCCACGCCTCTGTCGCCCCCCCTGCAAATCACGBCCATCTTCATAACTACTCG
S. caprata	CAACAAACTGCTTAACCCCCATACGCCTCCGTCGCCCCCCCTACAAATTASACCCACATTCACAACCACTTA
S. dacotiae	CAACAAACTGCTCAACCCTC?CACGCCTTTGTCGCCTCCCCTGCAAATCTSDKCCATAC?CACAACCACTCG
S. tectes	CAGCAAACTGCTCAACCCCCCCACGCCCCCATCGCCCCCCCTGCAAATCTCGKCCATACTCAGAACCACTCA

```
                                                       111
                88888888888888899999999999999999999999999999999999999999000
                4556677788899990001111112222333344445566666777788999000
Taxon/Node      92557036238145734902348914790389256817013690235250790 25
```

Taxon/Node	Sequence
Luscinia svecica	CCTCAAAACCTCCACCCCCAACACAATCGTAACACGTCTACAAGCCAGCCCATTC
Luscinia megarhynchos	ACTCARTACCAMAGCCCCTAGCACATCCAAAACACATACACBAATCAGCBDMTCC
Luscinia luscinia	ACCCARSACTCTAGCCCCCAGCACGTMAAAAACACATACACCAGCCAGCCCACCC
Oenanthe oenanthe	CTCTACACACTACGACCCCAACACAACCGCTACACATATATAAGCCCGCCCATCT
Oenanthe isabellina	CCCCACRCCCTACGACCCCAACACGATCACTASNTA?GTATAAGCCAGCACATCT
Ph. phoenicurus	CCCCAGCACCTACGACCCCAACACACCCACAACATACATATAAACCAGTCCATCC
Ph. ochruros	CCCCACACCCTACGACCCCAACTCGATCACTACACACAKATAAGCCAGCACATCT
Erithacus rubecula	CCCCAACACCCACCCTCCCAACCCACCCAAAACACACACACCAACTAACACATTT
Monticola saxatilis	CCTCAACACCTATGACCCCAACACACCCACAACCCAAATACAAGCCAGCCCATCC
Turdus merula	ACCCAAAAACACCGCCCCTACCTCTA??AGAATAAACACCGAAACCAGCACCCAC
Turdus philomelos	ATTCAAAAACACCGCCCTCCACACCTCAAAAGAAAACACCAAGACCAGCGCCCAC
Turdus torquatus	ACCCAAAGACACCGCCCTCCACCCTACAAAAACAAACACCAAAACCAGCACCCAC
Turdus viscivorus	AACCGSAAACTCCGCCCCCCATCCATCAAAAASAAATRCCAAAACCAACACCCAC
Turdus pilaris	ATTCAAAAACACCGCCCTCCACACCTCAAAAGAAAACACCAAGACCAGCGCCCAC
Cinclus cinclus	ACCCGAAAATACAGCATCCCCTCCCACCAAAAAAAGCAACAAAACCAACCACCCT
T. troglodytes	ACCCAATACCTCCACCCCTAGTTCACCCACAACAAACACATCAGCCCACTCTCCT
Saxicola rubetra	CCCTAAAACCTCCGACCCTAGCATACCCACTACACACACACAAGCCAGCCCCTCC
S. axillaris	CTCCAGACCCTACGACCCCAGTCCATCCACTACACACACACGAGCTAGCCCTTCC
S. maura	CTCCAAACCCTACGATCCCAGCTCATCCATTACACACGCACSAGCCAGCTCTTCC
S. t. rubicola	CTCTAAACCCTACGATCCTAACCTATCCATTACACACATACGAGTCAGTCCTTCC
S. caprata	CCCCAARCCCTACGATTCCGATCTATCCACTACACGTGCATAAGCCAGCCCTTCC
S. dacotiae	CTCCAAACCCTACGACCCCAACTTATCCCCTASACACACACCAGTCAGCCCTTCC
S. tectes	CCCCAAATCCTACGACCCCAACCCGTCCACTACACACATACGAGCCAGCCCTCCC

Table 2 Genetic distances based on pairwise nucleotide substitutions (uncorrected p distance) in the cytochrome-*b* gene.

	2	4	7	14	18	21	25
2 *Luscinia svecica*	-						
4 *Luscinia megarhynchos*	0 12456	-					
7 *Luscinia luscinia*	0 13300	0 10060	-				
14 *Oenanthe oenanthe*	0 11202	0 12570	0 14199	-			
18 *Oenanthe isabellina*	0 11946	0 13742	0 14866	0 07010	-		
21 *Ph. phoenicurus*	0 12545	0 12709	0 14215	0 11338	0 11071	-	
25 *Ph. ochruros*	0 10761	0 13582	0 15098	0 09779	0 07793	0 09003	-
33 *Erithacus rubecula*	0 10527	0 12671	0 13088	0 11645	0 10677	0 10450	0 10214
34 *Erithacus rubecula*	0 10964	0 13109	0 13426	0 12091	0 11134	0 10999	0 10659
35 *Monticola saxatilis*	0 13145	0 15352	0 15794	0 12826	0 13583	0 11731	0 13071
36 *Monticola saxatilis*	0 11197	0 13350	0 13774	0 11435	0 12061	0 11107	0 11323
37 *Turdus merula*	0 14721	0 15563	0 16547	0 14279	0 16118	0 13616	0 13844
39 *Turdus philomelos*	0 15056	0 14886	0 16648	0 14073	0 16318	0 13425	0 14301
41 *Turdus torquatus*	0 14522	0 15231	0 16562	0 14758	0 16242	0 13337	0 14885
43 *Turdus viscivorus*	0 13660	0 14845	0 16185	0 13448	0 14453	0 13364	0 14692
44 *Turdus pilaris*	0 14759	0 14700	0 16687	0 14439	0 16356	0 12899	0 14333
46 *Cinclus cinclus*	0 15827	0 14453	0 16862	0 14845	0 15294	0 14421	0 15521
49 *T. troglodytes*	0 16836	0 16612	0 18779	0 16520	0 15969	0 15655	0 16186
63 *Saxicola rubetra*	0 11294	0 12005	0 14414	0 10865	0 10921	0 11539	0 11085
96 *S. axillaris*	0 12631	0 13586	0 15424	0 11872	0 12056	0 10994	0 11656
111 *S. maura*	0 12650	0 13626	0 15354	0 11221	0 11976	0 11367	0 11690
131 *S. t. rubicola*	0 12634	0 14039	0 16215	0 11988	0 12857	0 11105	0 11772
138 *S. caprata*	0 13298	0 14581	0 15108	0 11327	0 12186	0 12102	0 11885
141 *S. dacotiae*	0 13807	0 14904	0 16888	0 12359	0 13152	0 12489	0 12809
151 *S. tectes*	0 13002	0 14401	0 15805	0 11905	0 11178	0 11243	0 12133

	33	34	35	36	37	39	41
33 *Erithacus rubecula*	-						
34 *Erithacus rubecula*	0 00553	-					
35 *Monticola saxatilis*	0 12927	0 13484	-				
36 *Monticola saxatilis*	0 10650	0 11200	0 04172	-			
37 *Turdus merula*	0 13371	0 13931	0 15185	0 13728	-		
39 *Turdus philomelos*	0 12736	0 13287	0 15082	0 14071	0 10669	-	
41 *Turdus torquatus*	0 13089	0 13640	0 14974	0 14089	0 07985	0 08536	-
43 *Turdus viscivorus*	0 12326	0 12880	0 15774	0 13569	0 10929	0 10901	0 10473
44 *Turdus pilaris*	0 12536	0 13088	0 14783	0 13547	0 08903	0 03772	0 06885
46 *Cinclus cinclus*	0 14063	0 14615	0 16517	0 14732	0 14598	0 13275	0 13744
49 *T. troglodytes*	0 15404	0 15846	0 17730	0 16405	0 17093	0 16494	0 16190
63 *Saxicola rubetra*	0 10967	0 11515	0 11564	0 10192	0 13922	0 12611	0 14407
96 *S. axillaris*	0 11969	0 12417	0 11231	0 10976	0 14724	0 15057	0 14639
111 *S. maura*	0 11576	0 12121	0 10505	0 10902	0 14769	0 14330	0 14681
131 *S. t. rubicola*	0 12760	0 13302	0 11799	0 12201	0 15607	0 14506	0 15310
138 *S. caprata*	0 12316	0 12861	0 12242	0 12194	0 15281	0 14403	0 14539
141 *S. dacotiae*	0 12930	0 13487	0 12518	0 13262	0 16372	0 15816	0 15731
151 *S. tectes*	0 12676	0 13227	0 11712	0 12009	0 15545	0 14878	0 15354

	43	44	46	49	63	96	111
43 *Turdus viscivorus*	-						
44 *Turdus pilaris*	0 10256	-					
46 *Cinclus cinclus*	0 12089	0 13529	-				
49 *T. troglodytes*	0 15779	0 16090	0 15829	-			
63 *Saxicola rubetra*	0 13334	0 13086	0 15044	0 15385	-		
96 *S. axillaris*	0 14569	0 14543	0 15387	0 16506	0 06754	-	
111 *S. maura*	0 14393	0 14257	0 15302	0 16324	0 06781	0 04455	-
131 *S. t. rubicola*	0 15457	0 14542	0 15722	0 17726	0 06868	0 05655	0 04337
138 *S. caprata*	0 14693	0 14446	0 15285	0 17615	0 09081	0 08425	0 08449
141 *S. dacotiae*	0 16773	0 15290	0 17165	0 18633	0 08081	0 06397	0 05302
151 *S. tectes*	0 14827	0 15464	0 15211	0 17331	0 08663	0 05338	0 06248

	131	138	141	151
131 *S. t. rubicola*	-			
138 *S. caprata*	0 08869	-		
141 *S. dacotiae*	0 04716	0 10213	-	
151 *S. tectes*	0 05105	0 09448	0 06860	-

FOOTNOTE

At the time of going to press, further published research has refined and improved the dataset of genetic distances given in the above chapter for Canary Island Stonechat *Saxicola dacotiae*, European Stonechat *Saxicola torquata*, Siberian Stonechat *Saxicola maura*, African Stonechat *Saxicola axillaris* and Réunion Stonechat *Saxicola tectes*. The new data give slightly different genetic distances from those quoted in the above chapter, but reconfirm that these taxa are all valid species.

The genetic distances for these five taxa are now as follows:

Canary Island Stonechat and Siberian Stonechat	4.2-5.1%
European Stonechat and Siberian Stonechat	2.7-4.9%
Canary Island Stonechat and European Stonechat	2.7-3.7%
African Stonechat and European Stonechat	4.6-5.7%
Réunion Stonechat and African Stonechat	4.4-5.1%

Wink *et al.* (2002)

COLOUR PLATES
1–14

PLATE 1: WHINCHAT

Whinchat *Saxicola rubetra*   **Text and map p. 61, photos p. 289**

Western Palearctic from UK and Scandinavia east across Russian Federation to central Siberia, and south through Europe to Mediterranean. Trans-Saharan migrant, wintering in subtropical and tropical southern Africa.

1   **Adult male breeding** Prominent white supercilium and white line running below the cheeks encompassing black face-mask. Orange-buff throat and breast. White triangles at base of tail. White patches on inner and outer wing. Rump/uppertail-coverts rufous-brown with black spots.

2   **Adult male non-breeding** Prominent head and upperpart patterning obscured by extensive buff fringes to feathers. Supercilium and tail-patches still prominent but buff-white, mantle and scapulars spotted with white tips and white inner wing-patch much reduced. Underparts buff not orange, with dark brown spotting on breast.

3   **First-year male** Resembles non-breeding adult but duller. Prominent buff supercilium. Triangular tail patches buff-white rather than pure white. Underparts buff with dark brown spotting.

4   **Adult female breeding** Buff-white supercilium and brown head. No face-mask. Paler, buffier throat and breast and less distinct buff-white wing- and tail-patches than male.

5   **Adult female non-breeding** Head, upperparts and underparts similar to adult male non-breeding, marginally less bright. White tail-patches suffused with buff. Buff-white patch on inner wing is small, occasionally absent. First-year female similar.

6   **Juvenile** Brown on head and upperparts with prominent pale buff fringes and shaft-streaks. Indistinct buff supercilium. No white wing-patches. Buff-white tail base. Underparts creamy buff, mottled brown on throat and breast.

7   **Adult male breeding** In flight from above. Prominent white patches on inner and outer wing, and tail base. White areas on tail base sharply demarcated from black. Spotted rump, uppertail-coverts.

8   **Adult male breeding** In flight from below. Orange-buff throat, breast and flanks, rest buff-white, undertail-coverts pinkish-buff. Underwing-coverts and axillaries creamy-white.

9   **Adult female breeding** In flight from above. Similar pattern to male but more subdued. Little white on outer wing and much reduced white inner wing-patch. Tail-patch white but not as sharply demarcated from black as in male.

10   **Adult male** Upperwing pattern after complete post-breeding moult. Note still prominent white on inner greater and median wing-coverts and on primary coverts.

11   **First-year male** Upperwing pattern after partial post-juvenile moult. Note extensive white on inner greater and median coverts, but only marginal buff bases visible on outer primary coverts. Also buff outer webs are just visible on primaries 02–04.

12   **Adult female** Upperwing pattern after complete post-breeding moult. Note complete absence of white on inner wing-coverts and small amount of white (c50%) on outer primary coverts.

13   **First-year female** Upperwing pattern after partial post-juvenile moult. Note complete absence of white on inner wing-coverts and primary coverts. Slightly more extensive and paler sandy-buff fringes and tips to lesser, median and greater wing-coverts. Note buff outer webs of outer primary coverts and extensive pale buff tips. Also just visible buff outer webs to primaries 02–05.

[Wing illustrations after Jenni & Winkler 1994.]

PLATE 2: WHITE-TAILED STONECHAT AND STOLICZKA'S BUSHCHAT

White-tailed Stonechat *Saxicola leucura*   Text and map p. 217, photos p. 290

Southern Asia from northern Pakistan east through northern India, Bangladesh (not reported since 1990), Nepal and Myanmar.

1 **Adult male breeding** Similar to Siberian Stonechat in pattern and colour apart from tail. Outer webs of all rectrices except central pair are white, evident even when tail is closed. Central pair black but with pale fringes. Central breast rufous, rest of underparts white.

2 **Adult male non-breeding** Most of black upperparts obscured by pale grey-brown fringes. Tail pattern as breeding but obscured by buff fringes. Rufous breast-patch ill-defined due to buff-orange fringes to underparts.

3 **Adult female non-breeding** Upperparts pale grey-brown with indistinct streaking. Buff supercilium. Rump tawny-buff, faint streaking only on uppertail-coverts. Underparts tawny-buff, paler than Siberian Stonechat. Tail is medium brown with pale grey-buff inner webs.

4 **Juvenile male** Tail is similar in pattern to adult, otherwise plumage identical to juveniles of Siberian Stonechat. Juvenile female does not show white upperwing-patch until after post-juvenile moult. Some show no white even after moult.

5 **Adult male breeding** In flight from above. Large amount of white in tail and on rump/uppertail-coverts. Prominent white inner wing-patch.

6 **Adult female breeding** In flight from above. Pale greyish-brown upperparts. Dull buff-orange rump. Tail paler overall than Siberian Stonechat, especially pale grey-buff inner webs. Very restricted amount of white on inner wing.

7 **Adult male non-breeding** Upperside of tail. Large amount of white on inner webs and base of outer webs of all rectrices, apart from central pair. Extensive grey-brown fringes and tips to rectrices slightly reduce contrast between white and black. White rump/uppertail-coverts with buff-orange fringes.

8 **Adult female non-breeding** Upperside of tail. Far less contrast between webs of rectrices than in male. However, tail paler overall than Siberian Stonechat. Inner webs of rectrices pale grey-buff, outer webs slightly darker brown. Pale tips and fringes wear away in breeding plumage, as do faint streaks on uppertail-coverts.

Stoliczka's Bushchat *Saxicola macrorhyncha*   Text and map p. 90, photos p. 291

Formerly distributed from Afghanistan/Pakistan border east through India but now apparently occurs only in arid areas of north-west India (although breeding areas are still not precisely known).

9 **Adult male breeding** Black-brown on crown and sides of head with prominent white supercilium. Rest of upperparts black-brown apart from white lower rump and uppertail-coverts. Wing-coverts blackish-brown with prominent white patch on inner wing and all-white primary coverts. Underparts dull white with yellowish-buff breast patch. Rectrices mainly white on inner webs and black-brown on outer webs.

10 **Adult male non-breeding** Pale sandy-buff on head and upperparts with darker black-brown streaking. Supercilium less distinct and buff, not white. Appearance similar to female but can be told by prominent white inner webs of rectrices and white wing-patches. Prominent buff fringes to flight feathers, tertials and upperwing-coverts. Rump/uppertail-coverts chestnut-buff.

11 **First-year male** Similar to adult male non-breeding but white in tail much less extensive. White inner wing-patch also less prominent, and no white on primary coverts.

12 **Adult female breeding** Head and upperparts sandy-buff with darker brown streaking. Prominent buff supercilium. Rump and uppertail-coverts pale buff. Tail pattern similar to male but less extensive and inner webs pale buff, not white. White inner wing-patch small or absent and no white on primary coverts. Underparts uniform buffish-white with slightly stronger buff on breast.

13 **Juvenile** Brown head and upperparts profusely streaked and spotted buff. Sex can be told by distinctive tail pattern which reflects adult patterning. No white wing-patches. Underparts buffish-white with darker brown mottling on throat and breast.

14 **Adult male breeding** In flight from above. Black-brown head and upperparts contrasting with prominent white supercilium. Large amount of white in dark tail. Prominent white patches on wings and white lower rump/uppertail-coverts.

15 **Adult female breeding** In flight from above. Pale buff head and upperparts. Distinctive tail pattern, pale areas less extensive than male. Rectrices have buff not white inner webs. No white on rump/uppertail-coverts or wings. Supercilium buff not white.

PLATE 3: HODGSON'S BUSHCHAT

Hodgson's Bushchat *Saxicola insignis*   Text and map p. 104, photos p. 292

Central Asia, in extreme eastern Russian Federation, possibly Kazakhstan, north-west and central Mongolia. Migrates through Tibet and central China to winter in Nepal and extreme northern foothills of India.

1   **Adult male breeding** Superficially similar to male Siberian Stonechat but has all-white chin and throat. Much white in wings, extending over all inner upperwing-coverts and bases of all primaries, secondaries and tertials to create large white wing-patch. All-white upperwing primary coverts. Extensive white neck-patch, often meeting on hind-neck and extending onto upper mantle and scapulars. Underparts predominantly white with rufous on breast only.

2   **Adult female breeding** Superficially similar to female Siberian Stonechat but differs in having large amount of white on wing-coverts and bases of primaries, secondaries and tertials. Wing similar in pattern to male but white slightly less extensive. Also shows small white neck-patch. Head and upperparts greyish-brown with darker streaking and buff supercilium. Chin, throat and rest of underparts buffish-white with stronger buff-orange on breast and flanks.

3   **Adult male non-breeding** Extensive white area on wings still visible. Black on crown, mantle and wings much obscured by greyish-buff fringes creating streaked appearance. Chin and throat remain predominantly white with buff-orange tips. Neck-patch partially obscured by mixture of buff and grey fringes. Rump and uppertail-coverts white with orange-buff tips but white never totally obscured. Tail feathers with prominent greyish-white fringes. Underparts extensively chestnut-buff. Black spotting across upper breast.

4   **Adult female non-breeding** Subdued version of breeding female. Head and upperparts greyish-brown with dark brown streaking. Underparts buff-orange. Wing pattern same as breeding but white is suffused with buff.

5   **Adult male breeding** In flight from below. Chin, throat and rest of underparts all-white except rufous breast-patch. Underwing-coverts and axillaries black although latter can retain whitish tips.

6   **Adult female breeding** In flight from above. Extensive white patches on wing in distinctive pattern. Greyish-brown head and upperparts with faint streaking.

7   **Adult male breeding** In flight from above. Extensive white patches on wing in distinctive pattern. Also large areas of white around neck extending onto upper mantle and on rump extending onto lower back.

8   **First-year male** Similar to adult male non-breeding but duller and less strongly patterned. White on wings more diffused with buff. Black spots form necklace across the upper breast.

Juvenile male feathers (after Panov 1976)

9   **Primary feather 2**
10   **Primary feather 9**
11   **Outer secondary**
12   **Central secondary**
13   **Inner secondary**
14   **Primary covert**
15   **Outer greater covert**
16   **Inner greater covert**
17   **Contour feather/mantle**
18   **Contour feather/breast**

PLATE 4: CANARY ISLAND AND RÉUNION STONECHATS

Canary Island Stonechat *Saxicola dacotiae*   **Text and map p. 121, photos p. 302**

Endemic resident on Fuerteventura, Canary Islands. Formerly occurred on Santa Clara and Alegranza, Canary Islands.

1   **Adult male breeding** Black head with thin white supercilium of variable length. White chin and throat, white extending onto sides of neck. Small orange-buff patch on upper breast contrasts with rest of dull buff-white underparts.

2   **Adult male non-breeding** Head and upperparts show less strong pattern, being uniform greyish-brown due to extensive fringes to feathers. Supercilium more extensive but buffier and less clearly defined than in breeding male. Rump pale greyish-brown, not prominently streaked, uppertail-coverts white with rufous tips. White neck-patch and inner upperwing-patch much obscured. Chin and throat remain white but rest of underparts more uniform pinkish-buff.

3   **Adult female breeding** Duller, browner and paler than male; head brown. Supercilium buff-white and indistinct. Small, sometimes absent, white inner wing-patch. Upper breast indistinct dull yellowish-buff, rest of underparts buff-white.

4   **Adult female non-breeding** Head and upperparts uniform greyish-brown with darker brown streaking. White inner wing-patch very small, sometimes absent. Rump and uppertail-coverts brighter yellowish-brown streaked dark brown. Buff supercilium. Chin and throat dull white. Breast variably pinkish-buff, rest of underparts paler buff.

5   **Juvenile** Similar to female. Head and upperparts dull greyish-brown with numerous small white spots on feathers. Supercilium buffish-white. Rump and uppertail-coverts buff-brown, faintly streaked darker brown. Breast yellowish-buff and rest of underparts slightly paler buff. Some brown spotting on breast.

6   **Adult male breeding** In flight from above. Dark head contrasts with rest of upperparts. Prominent white inner wing-patch. Lack of contrast between streaked rump and mantle. Small white patch on uppertail-coverts. Blackish tail.

7   **Adult female non-breeding** In flight from above. Uniform grey-brown head and upperparts. Small white inner wing-patch. Mantle and rump concolorous. No white on uppertail-coverts. Dark brown tail.

     First-year male (not illustrated) Same as adult male but black on head has many brown fringes and underparts are less buff.

     First-year female (not illustrated) Virtually identical to adult female, variably paler on underparts.

Réunion Stonechat *Saxicola tectes*   **Text and map p. 210, photos p. 293**

Endemic resident on Réunion Island, Western Mascarene Islands.

There are two types of extreme variation in males. One is the predominant colour of the head and upperparts, which varies from grey-brown (female-like) to black. The other is the amount of white around the eye and on the neck, wing and rump. There are many intermediate variations.

8   **Adult male breeding (variation 1)** Male is similar in pattern to African Stonechat, showing much black on the head and upperparts with prominent white patches on the neck, inner upperwing and rump/uppertail-coverts. It differs in having a white chin and throat and variable amounts of orange-buff on the breast and flanks. This male shows a prominent white supercilium.

9   **Adult male breeding (variation 2)** Similar to variation 1 but with very restricted orange-buff on upper breast and no supercilium.

10   **Adult male non-breeding (variation 1)** Black on head and upperparts obscured by extensive rufous-brown fringes with minimal streaking. Supercilium buff. Chin, throat and centre of breast pure white, rest of underparts orange-buff, more rufous on breast. White patches, especially on neck and lower rump/uppertail-coverts, obscured by chestnut-buff fringes. Upper rump grey-brown, paler than lower mantle.

11   **Adult male (variation 1)** In flight from above. Black head and upperparts, uppertail-coverts white tipped buff. Prominent white wing-patch.

12   **Adult female** In flight from above. Dark brown head and upperparts with faint streaking. Prominent buff supercilium. White patch on inner upperwing small, sometimes absent. No white neck-collar.

13   **Adult female non-breeding** Pale brown head and upperparts. Prominent buff supercilium. Breast and flanks orange-buff. Rump/uppertail-coverts only slightly paler brown than mantle and faintly streaked. Differs from female-type male form in that chin and throat are buff, not white, there is no white neck-patch, and white patch on inner upperwing is smaller and sometimes absent.

14   **Adult female breeding** Head and upperparts become a more uniform, darker brown. Grey-black feather bases visible on centre of chin and throat. White throat-sides extending slightly onto sides of neck. Breast orange-buff and rest of underparts white, with black streaking (due to feather wear) on flanks.

15   **Juvenile** Dark brown head and upperparts. Head with fine pale buff streaks, mantle and scapulars with larger buff tips. Indistinct buff supercilium. Rump slightly paler brown than rest of upperparts. Chin and throat dull grey-white, breast and flanks chestnut-buff with dark brown spotting. Rest of underparts buff-white. No white on inner upperwing.

European Stonechat *Saxicola rubicola* Text and map p. 169, photos pp. 294–295

Two subspecies; UK, Scandinavia east to Ukraine and Transcaucasia south to Mediterranean countries and coastal north Africa. Northern populations migratory or partially migratory, resident southern populations are augmented by northern immigrants in winter.

Saxicola rubicola hibernans

1 **Adult male breeding** All-black head, mantle and tail. Compared to *S. r. rubicola* has smaller white neck- and inner wing-patches and most extensive amount of orange-buff on underparts.

2 **Adult male non-breeding** Black on head and upperparts obscured by dark rufous-brown fringes creating streaked appearance. Entire underparts dark rufous-buff. Buff fringes to flight feathers slightly darker than in *rubicola*. White collar-patch virtually obscured.

3 **Adult female breeding** Head and upperparts dark olive-brown. Variable faint buff supercilium. Rump/uppertail-coverts tawny-brown streaked darker brown. Chin and throat greyish-black. No white neck-patch but small white inner wing-patch. Underparts brownish-orange, brightest on breast.

4 **Adult female non-breeding** Similar to breeding female but not so bright. Head and upperparts with extensive pale brown fringes creating streaked appearance. Chin and throat buff, with variable grey tinge. Underparts uniform brownish-orange with no brighter colouring on breast. Wing-patch often obscured by buff fringes.

Saxicola rubicola rubicola

Very similar to *hibernans* but marginally paler. Racial differentiation where the two subspecies meet is virtually impossible in the field.

5 **Adult male breeding** Similar pattern to *hibernans* male but rufous on underparts is often less extensive with white extending up flanks and sides of breast, and onto lower breast. White on neck and on rump/uppertail-coverts can also be more extensive but still variably streaked or spotted black on latter.

6 **First-year male non-breeding** Flight feathers appear browner as not moulted in autumn. With wear during winter/spring this becomes more obvious. Buff fringes to feathers in fresh plumage are more extensive but less demarcated than adult.

7 **First-year female** Virtually identical to adult female but flight feathers retained and can appear marginally browner than adult's due to wear in winter/spring. White inner wing-patch often entirely absent but some adult females also lack this.

8 **Juvenile** Head and upperparts dark brown with buff streaks on head and buff triangular marks on mantle and scapulars. Faint buff supercilium. Rump/uppertail-coverts rufous, liberally spotted/streaked black (unstreaked in *S. maura* and *S. torquata*). Chin and throat buff, breast to flanks and belly brighter yellowish-brown, all with grey or black speckling. Males show white inner wing-patch from feathered nestling stage; females do not until partial post-juvenile moult in autumn.

9 **Adult male non-breeding** Very similar to *hibernans* but can appear slightly paler due to lighter rufous fringes to upperparts (although this may not be discernible in field). Lower rump/uppertail-coverts often show pure white even just after autumn moult. Neck-patches less obscured by buff fringes. Underparts variably less uniform and marginally paler than *hibernans*, with buff-white extending into centre of breast.

10 **Adult female breeding** Very similar to *hibernans* but can appear slightly paler and greyer on head and upperparts and lighter orange-buff on underparts. Supercilium buff, variably more prominent.

11 **Adult female non-breeding** Virtually identical to *hibernans* but marginally paler on both head, upperparts and underparts.

12 **Adult male breeding** In flight from above. Solid black head including chin and throat. Prominent white areas on neck and inner wing. Variable white area on rump/uppertail-coverts streaked and spotted black/brown.

13 **Adult female breeding** In flight from above. Dark brown upperparts with tawny-brown streaked rump/uppertail-coverts. White on inner upperwing restricted.

14 **Adult male breeding** In flight from below. Underwing-coverts and axillaries grey or grey-black, never solid black as in *S. maura*. More extensive white on neck than *hibernans*, and underparts with white extending into centre of lower breast.

15 **Adult male breeding** Upperside of tail. All-black with no buff fringes and tips. White rump/uppertail-covert patch smaller than in *S. maura*, with black streaks.

16 **Adult female breeding** Upperside of tail. Brown rather than black with indistinct paler brown fringes. Rump dark rufous-brown prominently streaked black.

17 **Adult male non-breeding** Upperside of tail. Rectrices show prominent pale buff fringes and tips. White on rump/uppertail-coverts variably obscured by rufous tips and fringes, and prominently streaked black.

Siberian Stonechat *Saxicola maura* Text and map p. 181, photos pp. 296–298

Six subspecies spread over central and eastern Eurasia from north-west and central Russian Federation and eastern Transcaucasus east through Siberia to China and Japan south to northern India, Pakistan and northern Indochina. Various subspecies winter in north-east Africa, southern India, Pakistan and southern Indochina.

Saxicola maura maura

1   **Adult male breeding** Similar pattern to *S. rubicola*. Differs in large area of unstreaked white on rump/ uppertail-coverts and rufous restricted to centre of breast. Also white neck-patches usually more extensive, variably extending onto hind-neck and white inner upperwing-patch larger.

2   **Adult male non-breeding** Much paler than *S. rubicola*. Black of upperparts obscured by long pale buff fringes with only indistinct darker streaking. Some black on forehead, around eye, chin and throat but never as extensive or intense as in *S. rubicola*. White on rump/uppertail-coverts variably obscured by long orange-buff tips and fringes but always unstreaked. Prominent pale panel on inner wing caused by pale fringes to tertials and inner secondaries. Solid black centres to tertials and prominent white fringes to primary coverts. Tail almost black with prominent whitish fringes and tips. Breast very pale orange-buff, rest of underparts pale buff.

3   **Adult female non-breeding** Unstreaked tawny-orange rump occasionally showing some white with extreme wear. Head and upperparts pale buff, streaked darker. Prominent buff supercilium. Chin and throat buff-white. Underparts pale buff with stronger buff-orange on breast. White on inner upperwing more extensive than *S. rubicola*, thus more obvious.

4   **First-year male (autumn)** Some individuals appear very similar to adult female non-breeding with no greyish/black markings on the head, chin and throat. However, often some grey or black marking is evident although restricted. Recent study suggests that the black on head is acquired by pre-breeding moult. Extensive and prominent buff supercilium and inner wing panel.

Saxicola maura indica

5   **Adult male breeding** Virtually identical to *maura* and *stejnegeri*. Marginally smaller. The white on the rump/ uppertail-coverts is less extensive (but more extensive than on *S. rubicola*). Rufous on underparts restricted to breast and fore-flanks with rest of underparts totally white. Rufous on flanks fades towards end of breeding season.

6   **Adult male non-breeding** Darker than *maura* and marginally darker than *stejnegeri* from eastern part of range, due to upperpart fringes being rufous rather than sandy-buff. Underparts marginally darker in shade with stronger colouring on breast.

Saxicola maura stejnegeri

7   **Adult male breeding** Virtually identical to *maura* but variably shows less white on rump/uppertail-coverts, closer to *indica*. Rufous on the breast slightly more extensive than *maura*.

8   **Adult male non-breeding** Fringes to upperpart and underpart feathers darker rufous than *maura* but not quite as dark as *indica*. This becomes more apparent on individuals from further east in their range. Females of *indica* and *stejnegeri* not illustrated but virtually identical to *maura*.

Saxicola maura przewalskii

9   **Adult male breeding** Largest of six subspecies. Black on head and upperparts shows slight gloss. Black on throat extends onto central upper breast. Breast and flanks are deep chestnut even in very worn plumage, accentuating contrast with white on rest of underparts. Very extensive white on neck, inner upperwing and rump/uppertail-coverts.

10 **Adult male non-breeding** Black of head and upperparts obscured by dark olive-brown fringes – darkest of all six subspecies and even darker than *S. rubicola hibernans*. Underparts from breast to vent deep chestnut-brown. Rump, uppertail- and undertail-coverts white with large orange-buff tips.

11 **Adult female breeding** Darker than other six subspecies. No white on neck but noticeable white upperwing-patch. Rump/uppertail-coverts orange-buff. Chin and throat dark grey, almost black. Breast and flanks slightly paler rufous-buff than non-breeding, rest of underparts slightly paler, but overall still darker than other subspecies.

12 **Adult female non-breeding** Head and upperparts dark brown with indistinct streaking. Chin and throat show darker grey feather bases through buff fringes. Faint buff supercilium. Entire underparts from breast to undertail-coverts rufous-buff, slightly richer on breast. Rump/uppertail-coverts orange-buff.

Siberian Stonechat *Saxicola maura* Text and map p. 181, photos pp. 296–298

Saxicola maura variegata

This subspecies is unique in that both sexes show a large amount (greater than 50%) of visible white or buff-white in the tail.

1 **Adult male breeding** Largest amount of white on wings, neck and rump of any of six subspecies. Inner webs of rectrices apart from central pair mainly white with variable black tips. Rufous breast-patch is least extensive of any subspecies – confined to central upper breast. Rest of underparts white.

2 **Adult male non-breeding** Black on head and upperparts obscured by sandy-buff fringes although black on sides of head, chin and throat is purer. Large white wing-patch and neck-patch are suffused with buff but still visible. Tail pattern as in breeding male. Underparts uniform pale orange-buff, brightest on breast. White on rump/uppertail-coverts never wholly hidden under orange-buff tips and fringes.

3 **Adult female non-breeding** Similar to female *maura*. Very pale appearance overall. Extensive buff supercilium. Pale inner wing-panel. Large white upperwing-patch. Pure buff-white chin and throat. Rump/uppertail-coverts unstreaked pale orange-buff. Differs from females of all other subspecies in having visible buff-white base to tail. Pattern similar to male but pale areas less extensive.

4 **First-year male** Similar to female but shows much dark grey or black on chin, throat and sides of head. Forehead, crown and upperparts slightly darker brown in tone but still pale. Rump/uppertail-coverts orange-buff, unstreaked and with variable amount of white visible. Tail pattern as in adult male breeding but with very pale buff-white fringes and tips to feathers.

5 **Adult male breeding** In flight from above. Large amount of white on inner wing, neck and unstreaked rump/uppertail-coverts. Striking tail pattern reminiscent of Northern Wheatear – predominantly white tail with mainly black central pair of tail feathers. Small area of rufous on breast, underparts otherwise white.

6 **Adult female non-breeding** In flight from above. Tail has similar pattern to male but pale areas less extensive. Whitish-buff tips to outer tail feathers. Unstreaked pale orange-buff rump/uppertail-coverts. Pale head, upperparts and underparts.

7 **Adult male breeding** Upperside of tail. Extensive white on inner webs of rectrices decreasing towards central pair. Even on closed tail white visible on edges. Large area of unstreaked pure white on rump and uppertail-coverts.

8 **Adult female breeding** Upperside of tail. Mirrors pattern of male but pale areas less extensive and colour is pale buff, not white. Central pair of tail feathers sometimes has no pale base at all. Rump and uppertail-coverts are unstreaked pale orange-buff. Some pale tips to tail retained, only lost in very worn plumage.

Saxicola maura armenica

9 **Adult male breeding** Larger than all other six subspecies apart from *przewalskii*. Same head and body pattern as *variegata*, with similar amount of white on neck, inner upperwing and rump/uppertail-coverts. Rufous on underparts marginally more extensive than *variegata*. Tail has much smaller amount of white at base variably just visible under uppertail-coverts.

10 **Adult male non-breeding** Similar to male *variegata* although slightly darker on both upperparts and underparts. Lacks *variegata*'s extensive white base to tail. Variably small amount of white is visible beyond the long outer uppertail-coverts.

11 **Adult male breeding** In flight from above. Similar in pattern to *variegata* but tail appears all-black with variably small amount of white at base just visible beyond uppertail-coverts.

12 **Adult male non-breeding** Upperside of tail. Very small amount of white at base of outer tail feathers creating Whinchat-like pattern but white less extensive. Pale greyish-white fringes and tips to outer tail feathers. Rump/uppertail-coverts mainly orange-buff, unstreaked with some white feather bases showing through.

Saxicola maura maura

13 **Adult male breeding** In flight from below. Solid black underwing-coverts and axillaries. Orange only on breast, rest of underparts white.

14 **Adult female breeding** In flight from below. White chin and throat. Very pale underparts with only pale orange-buff on breast.

15 **Adult male breeding** Upperside of tail. White base to the tail, although present, is too small to be visible beyond the tail coverts. Tail thus appears wholly black, contrasting with extensive unstreaked white rump/uppertail-covert patch.

African Stonechat *Saxicola torquata*   **Text and map p. 198, photos p. 299**

Resident in west, central, north-east and southern Africa, separate subspecies occur in Madagascar, Yemen and on Grand Comoro Island.

Saxicola torquata torquata (South Africa)

1   **Adult male breeding** Head and entire upperparts black with slight gloss. Pure white, unstreaked rump and uppertail-coverts. Breast and flanks deep reddish-chestnut contrasting with extensive pure white neck-patches, breast sides and remainder of underparts. Extensive white patch on inner upperwing sometimes extending onto inner secondaries. Tail black with small white base hidden by uppertail-coverts. Underwing-coverts and axillaries black.

2   **Adult male non-breeding** Head and upperparts olive brown with black streaks. Upper mantle purer black. Underparts from breast to vent buff-orange, stronger chestnut on breast and flanks. Undertail-coverts pure white with black and buff tips. Rump and uppertail-coverts predominantly white but with orange and grey tips mainly on uppertail-coverts.

3   **Adult female breeding** Head and upperparts dark brown. Buff supercilium. No white neck-patches but extensive white inner upperwing-patch. Chin and throat dark grey, almost black. Breast and flanks chestnut-buff contrasting with dull white of rest of underparts. Lower rump and uppertail-coverts mainly white with some dark streaks on outer uppertail-coverts.

4   **Adult female non-breeding** Head and upperparts buff-brown with slight darker streaking. Chin and throat buff with grey feather bases visible. Extensive white inner upperwing-patch. Lower rump and uppertail-coverts mainly white with variable orange-buff tips; also black streaks on outer uppertail-coverts.

Saxicola torquata albofasciata (Ethiopia)

5   **Adult male breeding** Head and upperparts completely black apart from pure white neck-patch, upperwing-patch and rump/uppertail-coverts. Tail all-black. Chin, throat and breast black, rest of underparts pure white. Black of breast uneven where meets white of belly. No rufous on underparts.

6   **First-year male** Similar to adult male but black feathers of breast are tipped with highly variable amount of rufous, sometimes creating narrow rufous band across breast. Some rufous tips occasionally on head, flanks and belly. Flanks mottled black and white and demarcation of black breast uneven where it meets white belly.

7   **Adult female breeding** Head and upperparts dark brown. Indistinct buff supercilium. Lower rump and uppertail-coverts variably white with black/brown streaks and chestnut fringes to outer coverts. White upperwing-patch. Chin buff but throat almost black extending onto upper breast. Breast chestnut-buff, rest of underparts paler.

8   **Juvenile** Head and upperparts black with chestnut-buff tips and thin black fringes. Uppertail-coverts white with long buff tips. Breast and flanks buff, all with large black fringes. Rest of underparts buff. Large white upperwing-patch extending onto innermost tertial.

PLATE 9: AFRICAN STONECHAT II

African Stonechat *Saxicola torquata*   **Text and map p. 198, photos p. 299**

Saxicola torquata torquata (South Africa)

1   **Adult male breeding** In flight from above. Huge white wing-patch extending over all inner wing-coverts, innermost tertial and base of inner secondaries. White of neck-patches nearly meeting on hindneck and extending irregularly onto upper mantle.

Saxicola torquata albofasciata (Ethiopia)

2   **Adult male breeding** In flight from above. Glossy black with contrasting white neck-patch, upperwing-patch and rump/uppertail-coverts. Occasionally shows white tips to outer tail feathers.

3   **Adult male breeding** In flight from below. Black underwing-coverts and axillaries with variable small grey-white tips. Ragged edge to black breast where it joins white of belly.

4   **Adult female breeding** In flight from above. Dark brown above. Mainly white rump and uppertail-coverts with small buff tips and black/brown streaks to uppertail-coverts. Contrast between dark brown upperparts and tail, and pale rump patch.

The following figures illustrate the varying amounts of chestnut on the breast of males of various subspecies of African Stonechat, which is one of the main distinguishing criteria. For further differences please see the text concerning the various subspecies on page 198.

5   *Saxicola torquata clanceyi* Rufous on breast only reaching about level with tips of primary coverts. White of neck-patch extends down onto sides of breast.

6   *Saxicola torquata stonei* Upper breast and flanks paler chestnut with more yellowish tone than in *S. t. torquata*, and rest of underparts are not white but pale pinkish-buff forming less contrast with chestnut breast-patch. Also has more extensive white on sides of breast.

7   *Saxicola torquata oreobates* Breast and flanks darker rufous with belly and ventral area pale buff not white.

8   *Saxicola torquata promiscua* Black on throat extends markedly onto the breast, and rufous patch on upper central breast is the most restricted of all subspecies, sometimes virtually absent. The lower breast, sides of breast, flanks and belly are pure white.

9   *Saxicola torquata altivaga* Similar to *promiscua* and *stonei*. Clancey (1988) split it from *promiscua* on the basis that the rufous on the breast extends down onto the flanks. It differs from *stonei* in having the belly, ventral area and undertail-coverts white not buff.

10   *Saxicola torquata axillaris* Very similar to *promiscua* with black of throat extending onto breast. The black feathering sometimes extends onto lower breast beyond the rufous, suggesting a link with *albofasciata*. It usually shows slightly more rufous on the upper breast than *promiscua* although all the above features are highly variable.

11   *Saxicola torquata salax* Very similar to *clanceyi*. Underwing-coverts and axillaries differ in being grey-brown not black; chestnut on the breast is paler and restricted to the upper breast in a thin band. Breast-patch is slightly more extensive than *axillaris* and does not extend onto sides of breast and fore-flanks as in *clanceyi* and *torquata*.

     Saxicola torquata pallidigula (not illustrated) Slightly narrower chestnut band on upper breast but is considerably larger and is the largest subspecies in the species' range.

     Saxicola torquata adamauae (not illustrated) Similar in plumage to *pallidigula* but similar in size to *salax*.

12   *Saxicola torquata moptana* Underwing-coverts and axillaries are mainly white. The chestnut breast-patch is very small, confined to central upper breast and pale (paler than *salax*).

13   *Saxicola torquata nebularum* Breast-patch is very dark chestnut and this colouring extends over the entire breast and flanks, contrasting with the pure white breast sides and belly.

14   *Saxicola torquata jebelmarrae* Paler chestnut on the breast than *torquata* but still darker than any *S. rubicola* or *S. maura* with ginger tone rather than red. Chestnut extends over the entire breast and flanks.

15   *Saxicola torquata felix* Chestnut area is confined to the breast but is paler and more orange in tone than *torquata*. Sides of breast and belly pure white.

16   *Saxicola torquata sibilla* Black on the throat extends onto the upper breast. Chestnut on lower central breast confined to very small crescent-shaped patch under black. Underwing-coverts and axillaries pure white.

17   *Saxicola torquata voeltzkowi* Almost identical to *torquata*, but chestnut on breast and flanks slightly more extensive.

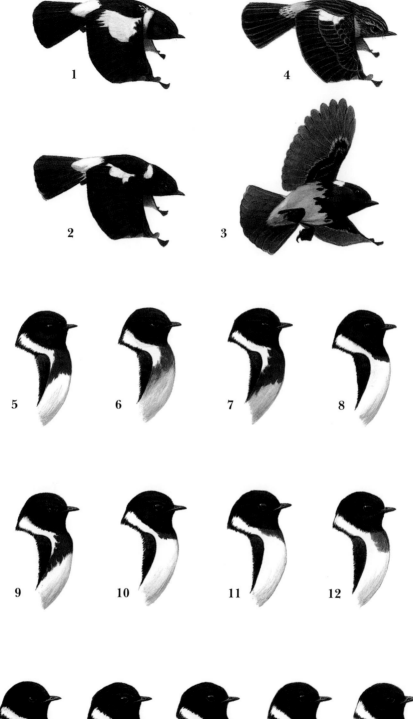

Pied Bushchat *Saxicola caprata*   Text and map p. 224, photos pp. 300–301

Southern Eurasia from eastern Iran and south-east Turkmenistan east through Afghanistan, Pakistan, India, Sri Lanka, Indochina, Indonesia, Philippines to New Guinea and New Britain. Northern populations in west of range (Kazakhstan, Afghanistan, India and Pakistan) move south to join resident populations in those countries.

MALES

All subspecies have black upperparts apart from a white upperwing-patch and rump/uppertail-coverts. Differences are in amount of white on underparts and upperwing as well as size. Males of some subspecies are identical.

Saxicola caprata caprata

1   **Adult male breeding** Glossy black on head, upperparts, wings and tail. Extensive white upperwing-patch extending from all inner wing-coverts onto inner secondaries. Underparts only white on undertail-coverts.

2   **Adult male non-breeding** White rump, upper- and undertail-coverts are tipped with rufous-buff. Narrow buff-brown fringes on head and upperparts, fringes broader on underparts. Pale buff fringes to wings and tail, fringes broader to tertials.

3   **First-year male** Black is dull with no gloss, tinged brown. Broad greyish-brown fringes to upper- and underparts. White undertail-coverts less demarcated from black than in breeding adult. White upperwing-patch smaller.

4   **Juvenile male** Head and upperparts blackish-brown with pale buff spots increasing in size from head to mantle. No supercilium. Chin, breast and flanks rufous buff with narrow dark fringes. Male in juvenile plumage usually shows indistinct white upperwing-patch; female does not. Rump and uppertail-coverts are unstreaked pale rufous, contrasting with black/brown tail.

5   **Adult male breeding** In flight from above. Extensive white on inner wing and rump/uppertail-coverts.

6   **Adult male** Underwing pattern. All-black underwing-coverts and axillaries – compare to *randi* (15).

Saxicola caprata bicolor

7   **Adult male breeding** Larger than *caprata*. White on underparts more extensive, extends variably from lower belly to undertail-coverts. Black plumage not so glossy.

Saxicola caprata rossorum

8   **Adult male breeding** Has most extensive amount of white on underparts of all subspecies. On typical western individuals, white extends from lower breast across belly, ventral area and undertail-coverts. Black plumage shows no gloss.

Saxicola caprata nilgiriensis

9   **Adult male breeding** Upperwing-patch much smaller than *caprata* only white on innermost greater and median coverts. Underparts all-black apart from white ventral area and undertail-coverts.

Saxicola caprata burmanica

10   **Adult male breeding** Virtually identical to *caprata*. White on undertail-coverts occasionally extends onto rear flank feathers.

Saxicola caprata albonotata

11   **Adult male breeding** Identical to *caprata* except that males show narrow black fringes and tips to white upperwing-coverts.

Saxicola caprata atrata

12   **Adult male breeding** Larger and with longer bill than *caprata*, smaller than *wahgiensis* and *belensis*. Differs from *caprata* in that black plumage is not glossy, and in presence of white on ventral area as well as undertail-coverts.

Saxicola caprata wahgiensis

13   **Adult male breeding** Largest subspecies apart from *belensis*. Black very glossy. White inner upperwing-coverts, rump, uppertail-coverts, ventral area and undertail-coverts.

14   **First-year male** Deep glossy black as in adult, with no pale fringes to head and body apart from variable white tips to lower mantle feathers. *Belensis* and *aethiops* subspecies (not illustrated) are similar but *belensis* is larger and *aethiops* smaller.

Saxicola caprata randi

15   **Adult male** Underwing. Identical in plumage to *caprata* apart from white tips to the black axillaries. Males of *S. c. anderseni* (not illustrated) are identical. Males of *S. c. cognata*, *francki*, *fruticola* and *pyrrhonota* (not illustrated) are very similar to *anderseni* and *randi* but do not show white tips to axillaries and vary slightly in size.

Pied Bushchat *Saxicola caprata* Text and map p. 224, photos pp. 300–301

FEMALES I

Saxicola caprata caprata

The subspecies *atrata* and *nilgiriensis* are indistinguishable in plumage from *caprata*. *Atrata* is, however, much larger.

1 **Adult female breeding** In flight from above. Plain greyish-brown head and upperparts with 'open-faced' appearance. Dark brown wings and tail contrasting with unstreaked rufous rump/uppertail-coverts. No white upperwing patch.

2 **Adult female** Underwing. Underwing-coverts and axillaries pale buff, contrasting with grey-brown undersides of remiges.

3 **Adult female non-breeding** Plain grey-brown head and upperparts with variable faint streaking. No supercilium. Wing-coverts and tertials show prominent pale buff fringes. Chin and throat grey-buff. Breast to vent grey-brown, slightly rufous. Rufous strongest on lower breast, flanks and belly, which also show some variable dark streaking. Rump/uppertail-coverts unstreaked rufous. No white on upperwing.

4 **Adult female breeding** Similar to non-breeding female but appears darker brown due to abrasion of pale grey-brown fringes on upperparts, wing-coverts and tertials. Rufous on underparts less pronounced and streaking more pronounced.

5 **Juvenile female** Dark brown (not blackish-brown as in male) upperparts. Otherwise like juvenile male but with no white on the upperwing.

Saxicola caprata bicolor

6 **Adult female** Overall darker brown than neighbouring subspecies *rossorum* with darker rufous uppertail-coverts. Large area of apparent intergrading between the two subspecies creates much variation and only safe to identify individuals on the extreme west and east of their respective ranges.

Saxicola caprata rossorum

7 **Adult female** Overall, much lighter grey-brown than *bicolor* (breeding immediately to the east), sometimes sandy, with no rufous tone to underparts. Rufous rump/uppertail-coverts can show some white towards end of breeding season. Belly and undertail-coverts white. No dark streaking on the underparts. Same intergrading warning as for *bicolor*.

Saxicola caprata randi

8 **Adult female** Upperwing. White on inner upperwing-coverts and inner tertials. Only visible on spread wing. A few individuals show no white.

9 **Adult female** Much darker on upperparts than *caprata*. Chin and throat white not grey-buff. Heavy and distinct dark streaking on underparts and dark spotting on feathers of tibia. Undertail-coverts paler buff, showing more contrast with rufous on belly.

Saxicola caprata burmanica

10 **Adult female** Closely similar to *caprata* but with darker grey-brown head and upperparts. Chin, throat and extreme upper breast grey-buff. Rest of underparts slightly darker, increasingly suffused with rufous towards tail. Undertail-coverts rufous-buff not buff. Variably the lower breast and flanks are streaked darker brown.

Saxicola caprata anderseni

11 **Adult female** Upperwing. Very small white patch on innermost greater coverts. Invisible until the bird flies.

12 **Adult female** Distinctly paler than *caprata*, particularly on underparts which are greyish-tawny with very faint streaking. Head and upperparts lack brown tone of *caprata*. Chin and throat paler greyish-white.

Saxicola caprata cognata

13 **Adult female** Dark brown overall with no grey tone to plumage. Prominent dark streaking to the upperparts. Rump and uppertail-coverts are pure white contrasting with dark brown tail and mantle.

Saxicola caprata albonotata

14 **Adult female** Dark ashy grey on upperparts, and whitish-grey on underparts with dark streaking. No rufous wash to underparts. The rump, upper and undertail-coverts are pure white.

15 **Adult female** Upperwing. Shows large white patch on inner upperwing, largest of all subspecies, white extends partially onto median coverts as well as greater coverts. White still partially visible on closed wing.

16 **Adult female** Underwing. The underwing-coverts and axillaries are white, not buff as in other subspecies (see 2).

Pied Bushchat *Saxicola caprata*   Text and map p. 224, photos pp. 300–301

FEMALES II

Saxicola caprata belensis

1   **Adult female** Largest subspecies in species range. Dark grey-brown on head and upperparts, slightly paler on underparts which show indistinct streaking. Rump, uppertail-coverts and undertail-coverts white. Unlike *albonotata* to west and *aethiops* to east of its range, does not have white on inner upperwing.

Saxicola caprata aethiops

2   **Adult female** Upperwing. Similar to *albonotata*. Small white or pale buff patch on innermost upperwing-coverts, smaller than *albonotata*.

3   **Adult female** Larger than *albonotata*. Whitish-grey on underparts shows browner tone. White on rump, upper- and undertail-coverts. White on inner upperwing occasionally visible on closed wing.

Saxicola caprata wahgiensis

4   **Adult female** Very similar to neighbouring subspecies *belensis* in both plumage and size. Slightly smaller and shows stronger streaking on underparts, and richer buff on flanks and belly.

Saxicola caprata fruticola

Similar to *pyrrhonota* but overall the plumage is colder and greyer in tone, the underparts are noticeably streaked and the undertail-coverts white. Much subtle plumage variation between individuals inhabiting different islands. The following are examples:

5   **Adult female, Sumbawa variation** Very grey in tone with no trace of rufous on plumage apart from rump/uppertail-coverts.

6   **Adult female, Bali variation** Greater rufous tone to the plumage especially on the underparts. Rump/uppertail-coverts rufous.

7   **Adult female, Flores variation** Darkest in tone of all variants, with cold, grey caste to the overall plumage except rufous rump/uppertail-coverts.

8   **Adult female, Java variation** Rump and uppertail-coverts mainly white with faint rufous wash.

Saxicola caprata pyrrhonota

Rufous-brown in tone overall, especially on the underparts which are unstreaked. Rump and uppertail-coverts rufous. Can vary in size on the various islands in their range.

9   **Adult female, Savu variation** White bases to greater coverts of the inner upperwing and pale rufous-brown rump/uppertail-coverts. Undertail-coverts white. Rump can show white patches after wear.

10   **Adult female, Timor variation** No white on inner upperwing. Rump, upper- and undertail-coverts uniform deep rufous.

11   **Adult female, Kisar variation** No white on inner upperwing but has white undertail-coverts. Rump and uppertail-coverts deep rufous.

Saxicola caprata francki

12   **Adult female** Overall plumage tone differs from *pyrrhonota* in being a more uniform and lighter grey-brown. The underparts are unstreaked. Rump, upper- and undertail-coverts white.

Jerdon's Bushchat *Saxicola jerdoni* Text and map p. 248, photos p. 303

Southern Asia from northern Pakistan east through northern India, Nepal, southern Tibet, northern/central Myanmar, northern Thailand, north-west Laos, northern Vietnam and south-west China. Possibly localised resident or local movements within country of residence.

1   **Adult male breeding** Long rounded tail and rounded wing. Head, entire upperparts, wings and tail uniform glossy bluish-black. Pure white on underparts with sharp demarcation between white of chin and throat and black on sides of head. Males in fresh plumage post-moult are often creamy buff on underparts, but chin and throat always silky white.

2   **Adult female breeding** Head and upperparts unstreaked rufous-brown. No supercilium. Rump/uppertail-coverts chestnut-brown. Wings and tail entirely dark brown. Silky white chin and throat contrasting with buff breast and belly. Chestnut suffusion to rear flanks.

3   **First-year male** Similar to adult male but much duller bluish-black on head and upperparts and with extensive brown fringes. Wings dark brown fading with wear to progressively show more contrast with blue-black mantle. Tail slightly darker brown often with white tips to outer three feathers. Chin and throat pale buff-white and consequently show less contrast with darker buff breast.

4   **Juvenile** Head and upperparts brown with fine buff streaks on forehead and crown and buff tips to mantle and scapular feathers. No supercilium. Chestnut rump/uppertail-coverts. Wings and tail dark brown. Chin and throat buff. Breast and flanks buff with narrow brown fringes. Rest of underparts plain buff-white.

5   **Adult male breeding** In flight from above. Long graduated and rounded tail. Uniform blue-black above and white below.

6   **Adult female breeding** In flight from above. Long graduated and rounded tail with no chestnut fringes. Uniform brown above apart from chestnut rump/uppertail-coverts.

Grey Bushchat *Saxicola ferrea* Text and map p. 258, photos p. 303

Southern Asia from north-west Pakistan border, through northern India east to Nepal, Bhutan, southern Tibet, south-east China, northern Myanmar, north-west Thailand, northern Laos, Cambodia and north/central Vietnam. Winters to southern parts of breeding range in Pakistan, India and Indochina.

Saxicola ferrea ferrea

7   **Adult male breeding** Head mainly black with broad, long, white supercilium. Chin and throat white. Mantle and scapulars mainly black but with varying amount of grey fringes. Small white patch on inner upperwing. Rump pure grey, uppertail-coverts and long tail black with outer edge of tail white. Underparts mainly dull white with grey wash on breast.

8   **Adult male non-breeding** Head and upperparts ash-grey with faint black streaking. Prominent white supercilium and black face-mask. Underparts, including chin and throat, mainly grey. Wings and tail black with grey fringes. Small white patch to inner upperwing and white edges to tail.

9   **First-year male** Hardly any white visible on head or body. Supercilium and entire underparts grey, wing-coverts, tertials, remiges and rectrices with broad grey fringes. Chin and throat buff with grey fringes. Outer edges of tail white suffused with grey.

10 **Adult female** Head and upperparts rufous-brown (slightly paler than Jerdon's Bushchat) with faint dark streaks. Dark rufous-brown ear-covert patch contrasts strongly with broad buff supercilium and pale buff-white chin and throat. Rump/uppertail-coverts unstreaked chestnut merging into chestnut on tail. Breast to undertail-coverts buff, with grey wash on breast. Rear flanks suffused chestnut but not as strongly as Jerdon's Bushchat.

11 **Adult male** In flight from above. Long tail. Huge white supercilium contrasting with black face mask. White edges to tail and white patch on upperwing. Pure grey unstreaked rump.

12 **Adult female** In flight from above. Long tail. Huge buff supercilium contrasting with dark brown face mask. Rufous rump joining mainly rufous tail.

13 **Juvenile** Head and upperparts black/brown with extensive buff streaks and spots. Indistinct buff supercilium. Ear-coverts black/brown contrasting with paler colouring on rest of head. Rump/uppertail-coverts chestnut. Tail long, dark brown but with prominent chestnut fringes and pale tips. Buff tips to greater coverts form wing-bar. Chin and throat pale buff, breast and flanks grey-buff all mottled with dark streaks/fringes. Males can possibly be distinguished by very small buff-white patch on extreme inner upperwing. Females have no pale patch on upperwing.

Saxicola ferrea harringtoni

14 **Adult male breeding** Almost identical to male *ferrea* but underparts whiter in breeding plumage, especially on breast and belly.

PLATE 14: BUFF-STREAKED AND WHITE-BELLIED BUSHCHATS

Buff-streaked Bushchat *Saxicola bifasciata*   Text and map p. 277, photos p. 304

Endemic resident in eastern South Africa, Lesotho and Swaziland.

1   **Adult male breeding** Striking black, white and buff pattern. Head, upper breast, wings and tail glossy black with broad buff-white supercilium extending from bill to nape and merging with buff-white neck-patches. Scapulars buff-white forming distinct 'V' shape extending from neck to rump, on either side of mottled black-brown mantle. Unstreaked rump and entire underparts orange-buff, uppertail-coverts pale buff contrasting with glossy all-black tail.

2   **Adult female breeding** Head and upperparts brown. Grey-buff supercilium. Unstreaked rump/uppertail-coverts orange-buff. Wings and tail blackish-brown. Chin and throat buff-white, rest of underparts orange-buff with fine streaking on chin, throat, breast and flanks.

3   **First-year male** Subdued version of adult male, but black feathers have extensive ginger-brown fringes. Buff areas of plumage are much darker. Wings and tail are brown not black.

4   **Adult male** In flight from above. Note continuous buff-white line from bill along sides of mantle to rump forming distinctive 'V' pattern. All-black tail and wings.

5   **Adult female** In flight from above. No distinctive pattern of buff and black on upperparts. Uniform dark brown head and upperparts apart from greyish-buff supercilium and orange-buff rump/uppertail-coverts.

6   **Juvenile** Head and upperparts dark brown spotted and streaked buff. Unstreaked rump/uppertail-coverts buff-orange. Wings and tail dark brown. Mantle and scapulars buff with small black fringes. Entire underparts yellowish-buff. Chin, throat, breast and flanks with brown mottling and some streaks on flanks.

White-bellied Bushchat *Saxicola gutturalis*   Text and map p. 267, photos p. 304

Endemic resident on Timor, Roti and Semau, Lesser Sunda Islands, Indonesia.

Saxicola gutturalis gutturalis

7   **Adult male** Head to uppertail-coverts glossy black. Entire underparts silky white, variable amount of buff on underparts from breast downwards in fresh plumage. Wings and tail glossy black with extensive areas of white. Elongated white patch on wing, over all the inner wing-coverts, base of tertials and inner secondaries. Smaller white patch on primary coverts. White in tail extending from base c65% of length, visible on closed tail.

8   **Adult male variation** Individual with indistinct white supercilium. Majority of males appear to not have a supercilium. Those that do show much variation.

9   **Adult female** Head and upperparts dull rufous with faint dark streaks. Extensive buff supercilium. Rump same colour as upperparts but uppertail-coverts and tail are bright chestnut. Chin and throat white, breast and flanks creamy buff and rest of underparts white. No white in tail. Wings dark brown.

10   **Juvenile male** Head and upperparts similar to female but have more grey tone. Buff supercilium. Chin and throat dull white, breast and flanks buff with faint brown streaks. Uppertail-coverts glossy black with chestnut tips. Tail feathers are black with the same pattern of white extending from the base as in adult male but slightly less white in proportion to tail length.

11   **Adult male** In flight from above. Black and white pattern. Two prominent white patches on wing and extensive white in tail.

12   **Adult female** In flight from above. Head and upperparts brown. Buff supercilium. Chestnut lower rump and uppertail-coverts merging with chestnut tail. Central pair of rectrices dark brown. Small buff inner upperwing-patch.

13   **Juvenile male** In flight from above. Similar to female but head and upperparts colder grey-brown. Supercilium buff but less distinct and greyish. Lower rump and uppertail-coverts black merging with black tail. White in tail mirrors adult male pattern but not so extensive.

Saxicola gutteralis luctuosa

14   **Adult male** Identical to *gutturalis* but white in tail is either virtually absent or much reduced. Primary coverts and inner upperwing-patch also show less white than *gutturalis*.

Motacilla Rubetra Linnaeus, 1758, *Syst. Nat.*, ed. 10,1, p.186—Europa [= Sweden]

Etymology *rubetra* from Latin for a small bird

Alternative name European Whinchat

TAXONOMY

Monotypic. In contrast to European Stonechat *Saxicola rubicola* the geographical variation in plumage is not great, although individual and seasonal plumage differences are marked. There are no recognised subspecies (Ripley *et al.* 1964), although a number of attempts have been made over the last 100 years to categorise certain populations into races/subspecies based on perceived differences in plumage and size. The current view is that all plumage differences are clinal, with colouring becoming lighter towards the east and south-east of the range. No fewer than six subspecies have been proposed but only one has been proposed since Ripley *et al.* (1964).

Pratincola rubetra spatzi Erlanger 1900 – Gafsa Oasis, Tunisia
Pratincola rubetra noskae Tschusi 1902 – Labathal, northern Caucasus
Pratincola rubetra margarethae Johansen 1903 – Tomsk, western Siberia
Saxicola rubetra incerta Trischitta 1939 – Sardinia & Sicily
Saxicola rubetra hesperophila Clancey 1949 – Newton Mearns, East Renfrewshire, south-west Scotland
Saxicola rubetra sengüni Kumerloeve 1969 – Van Golu, south-east Turkey

Vaurie (1959), who judged this species monotypic, remarked that "The geographical variation in this species is very slight and not constant. The following trends can be discerned. Approximately half of the birds from Great Britain (*hesperophila*) are a little darker than typical *rubetra* from Scandinavia and northern Europe. Specimens from Dalmatia (Yugoslavia) and some from northern Africa (*spatzi*) are usually slightly paler and greyer whilst those from the eastern part of their range (*noskae*) average slightly paler and larger."

Johansen (1954) was unrelated to Johansen (1903) although both had a Christian name beginning with the initial H. Johansen 1954 was Hans, Johansen 1903 was Hermann. Johansen (1954) examined Johansen's (1903) evidence for the race *magarethae* and found it insupportable. The claim was based on the fact that the overall plumage of *magarethae* was marginally paler in tone than specimens of *rubetra* from western Europe but was based on only one specimen! Johansen (1954) examined a large number of specimens from the West Siberian Plain and the Altai with a series from European Russia, the Baltic and western Europe.

He noted individual variation was quite noticeable but also stated that as feather wear progressed rapidly through the breeding season the bird's individual appearance was constantly changing. Consequently, it is easy to discern differences if the specimens from each area are examined in differing plumage states or if only a few specimens are examined (only one in the case of Johansen 1903). Johansen (1954) was unable to find any difference in a uniform series between Siberian (including Altai) birds and Scandinavian and east European birds, thus confirming Hartert & Steinbacher's (1932–1938) opinion that West Siberian birds could not be separated into a valid race.

Johansen (1954) did find that Whinchats from western Europe appeared to have slightly stronger plumage tones than those from Eastern Europe and there was possible evidence that birds increased in size from east to west (male wing Siberia 75.0–78.0mm; male wing Europe 75.0–81.0).

Birds proposed by Erlanger as *spatzi*, breeding in south-west and southern Jugoslavia had the dark feather centres on the upperparts supposedly slightly narrower and the feather fringes a slightly paler yellowish-brown, but these also were often no different from specimens obtained from further north in their range. Their size was also similar to birds from western and central Europe.

Populations (*noskae*) from the eastern end of the plumage cline in the northern Caucasus and western Siberia showed pale feather fringes similar to *spatzi* but the dark feather centres were supposed to be broader and the general size of individuals larger, with wing measurements 80.0–82.0mm. However, further examination of a small sample from Siberia did not confirm this, with five males having wing lengths of 76.0–79.0mm.

Male birds (*hesperophila*) from Great Britain and Ireland, at the darker western end of the plumage cline, were identified as showing stronger colouring than *rubetra* from mainland Europe and West Siberia, with purer, more extensive black feather centres on the crown, mantle and ear-coverts as well as more rufous feather fringes on the upperparts. Juveniles were considered darker brown. However, Vaurie (see above) pointed out that c.50% were inseparable from Scandinavian birds.

Vaurie (1959) lumped all populations in the eastern part of the range under *rubetra* including *noskae* (Tschusi 1902) but stated that populations "in the eastern parts of the range average slightly paler and larger". Kumerloeve (1969) disagreed and, based on two specimens from south-east Turkey (Van-Yuksekova), proposed the race *sengüni* which he described as "clearly darker above (broad brown-black longitudinal streaks on a sandy-brown background or to some extent rather a brownish streaking on a dark background) and contrasting strongly with birds from Central Europe such as Bulgaria". He also added that the race he proposed *sengüni* was smaller in wing measurements 75.0 and 77.0mm than *noskae* wing 80.0–82.0mm. Although he admitted that the sample was so small that it would require further confirmation, he felt encouraged to propose the east Anatolian populations as another race *S. r. sengüni*. Cramp *et al.* (1988) do not recognise this race as the sample was so small.

IDENTIFICATION

Size 12.5cm/4.9 inches. Similar in size to the European Stonechat but appears slightly less compact and rounded with a more angular and attenuated appearance caused by a less rounded, flatter head and back. It often perches with a less upright posture than European Stonechat and appears less nervous and excitable although it flicks its wings and flirts its tail regularly when anxious. The wings are longer than the European Stonechat but equal to Siberian Stonechat, with the primary projection c.75% that of the overlying tertials. Male birds in spring have a prominent long white supercilium reaching to the nape contrasting with the black or dark brown crown and ear-coverts. There is also a white lower border to the cheeks which terminates in an upturned patch at the rear. The dark face-mask is highly variable, with strongly coloured individuals showing the crown and especially lores, malar region and ear-coverts almost black. Duller-plumaged males, apart from the white supercilium and sides of neck, can sometimes appear hardly different from the adult female. Between these extremes there is much variation between individual males. The back is dark brown and the rump is paler with dark spots and streaks. The tail is slightly shorter than European Stonechat and is square, black or very dark brown with prominent white triangular patches at the base of the tail. The wings are dark brown with prominent white patches on the inner wing-coverts and primary coverts. The underparts of strongly coloured males are a uniform cinnamon-brown from the central throat to the rear flanks, with colouring particularly strong on the breast (appearing bright rufous-brown at times).

Females are duller than males with the supercilium smaller but still prominent and less pure white. The crown and ear-coverts are a paler brown, showing less contrast with the supercilium. The upperparts are paler brown. The underparts are paler cinnamon-brown with little stronger colouring on the breast, and the white triangles at the base of the tail are duller, less defined and smaller. The white on the inner wing-coverts and primary coverts is also less distinct. In autumn, adult males resemble both females and first-winter birds, with the plumage showing less contrast and appearing paler and more uniform owing to the feathers being extensively tipped buff. Most of the white areas are also duller or buff.

Juveniles are a dull dark brown on the upperparts with prominent pale buff or reddish-brown tips to the mantle and scapulars. The uppertail-coverts are also reddish-brown and contrast with the darker brown tail. The supercilium is never as well developed or as long as in the adult, often only being apparent behind the eye, and is usually dull buff, showing far less contrast with the pale cheeks. There is no white on the wing-coverts. The underparts are uniform buff speckled with dark brown on the throat and upper breast.

Whinchats of all ages and both sexes are somewhat similar in autumn, when they all resemble females. In spring, the amount of white on the upperwing greater and median coverts varies considerably irrespective of age. Only adult males have one or more upperwing median coverts completely white. Second-year males have only a very small amount of white on the upperwing primary coverts and only males with fewer than three primary coverts showing white can be identified with any certainty as second-year males. The amount and rate of increase in white on the primary coverts amongst males varies so much that it is impossible to tell between males two years old and older (Labhardt 1984). Although some second-year males cannot be told from females, most males can be identified in spring by the extensive white patch on the upperwing greater coverts and the black or blackish-brown (not brown) face-mask. Following the post-breeding moult, only males with an extensive white upperwing-patch can be identified with any certainty owing to the wide variation amongst individuals. Birds with single wholly white upperwing median and/or greater coverts are males. Birds with no white in the upperwing greater coverts are first-year males or females that have not moulted any upperwing greater coverts (Glutz & Bauer 1988).

Leucistic and complete or partial albino individuals are rare or at least rarely recorded in the literature. Sage (1962) recorded it as occurring in the United Kingdom without citing any specific examples. There was a creamy-white individual on the Inner Farne Islands, England, from 25 September to 7 October 1998. This bird was described as leucistic rather than albino (J. Walton *in litt.* 2001). Another leucistic individual was photographed at Maasvlakte, Rotterdam, Netherlands, on 2 September 2000. It appeared a very pale milky-brown on the entire upperparts including the wings and tail, but showed a slightly darker brown crown and a definite darker eye-stripe running from the lores to the rear of the ear-coverts (C. van Rijswijk *in litt.* 2001).

Confusion species The only species in the genus likely to cause confusion is European and Siberian Stonechat. Whinchat can be distinguished in all plumages by the white or buff-white triangular bases on the tail, the extensive and broad, cream to white supercilium and orange-buff throat fringed with white. However, care should be taken in identifying *S. rubetra* in autumn from first-year and female Siberian Stonechat, as these can look superficially similar at this time of year. *S. rubetra* has triangular white or buff-white bases to the tail visible both when perched and in flight, while *S. maura* can be told by the lack of a visible white base to the tail in all subspecies apart from *variegata* (which has extensive white on the tail but in a different pattern to that of *S. rubetra*, with the white extending far further down the tail on the outer feathers, creating a pattern more like in Northern Wheatear *Oenanthe oenanthe*); *S. rubetra* breast is cinnamon-buff usually spotted in autumn, *S. maura* is a deeper unspotted chestnut-buff; *S. rubetra* upperparts always show a greater degree of contrasting spots and streaks often with white tips, *S. maura* upperparts are duskier, more uniform and there are no white tips to the dark streaks; *S. rubetra* supercilium is always prominent, extensive and noticeable, on *S. maura* it is often relatively ill-defined, creating a more open-faced appearance; *S. rubetra* rump and uppertail-coverts never contrast with the mantle, being a similar colour and prominently streaked and/or spotted; *S. maura* rump and uppertail-coverts are unstreaked, extensive pale chestnut-brown and contrast markedly with the black tail and darker mantle.

For more detail see under European Stonechat.

DESCRIPTION

Adult male in fresh breeding plumage The upperparts are yellowish-buff to cinnamon-brown with dark centres to the feathers either in the form of streaks or spots. The forehead and crown are black with fine buff fringes, whilst the mantle and scapulars are more buff with round black spots. The fringes can be variable in colour, with individuals showing pinkish, yellowish or even greyish tones to the buff coloration. There is a broad, long and very distinct white supercilium curving from the base of the upper mandible, above and enclosing the upper part of the eye as far back as the side of the nape. The supercilium, although not joined on the nape, curves towards its opposite and sometimes a narrow buff line runs between the two across the nape. There is a thin, white eye-ring with a wide break in front of the eye and a narrower one behind. The lores and cheeks are black whilst the ear-coverts can also be black but are often mainly olive-brown with some black spots and buff mottling towards the rear. There is a short white moustachial stripe extending from the lower mandible to just below the eye, bordered above by the black of the lores and below by a thin black stripe. The chin and sides of the throat are pure white forming a white malar stripe which extends under the black of the cheeks broadening into a distinct extensive white patch on the side of the neck. The centre of the throat, upper breast, sides of lower breast and flanks are a deep cinnamon-brown, becoming paler yellowish-buff towards the rear of the flanks. The centre of the lower breast, belly, ventral area and undertail-coverts are paler cinnamon- or rufous-buff. The rump is buff with reduced dark oval streaks, formed by dark centres to the feathers. The uppertail-coverts are long and paler buff, also with reduced black streaks half-way down the shafts, and then a large subterminal, triangular black mark fringed with buff at the tip of the feather. The lower coverts, although marked the same, have paler, almost white tips which contrast more markedly with the black subterminal spot.

The tail feathers are black or very dark brown with lighter cinnamon fringes. All but the central pair show white on the basal two-thirds, which is sharply demarcated from the black on the tip of the feather. The central pair are black-brown with an olive tinge and have a tiny amount of white at their base hidden by the uppertail-coverts. The white is most extensive on the outer pair of feathers (06), becoming progressively less across the other feathers towards the central pair. The outermost three pairs of feathers usually have more than 13mm of white at their bases. The white is generally greater on the innerweb of the feather and, from a sample of 68 adult males, ended 14–22mm from the tip of feather 06 (Svensson 1992). On feathers 02 and 03 and very slightly on 04 the dark brown/black on the outerweb extends towards the centre of the feather but is virtually absent from the remaining outer two (05–06). There is a narrow white outer edge to the outermost feather (06) and a narrow white fringe on feather 05 which becomes pale cinnamon-buff on the distal third.

The remiges are black or dark brown with a greyish or olive tinge and with the fringes to the innerwebs dull white, broadest at the base apart from the tips which are brown. Primaries 09 and especially 01–05 as well as all the secondaries have cinnamon-brown fringes to the outerwebs, broadest at the base and narrowing towards the tips. The tips of the secondaries and the outer edges and tips of the inner primaries are pale buff. The basal 25% of the outerweb of inner primaries 02–04 (occasionally 05–06) vary from white to cinnamon-white or pale buff extending approximately 3–6mm beyond the tip of the inner upper primary-coverts (Svensson 1992). The upperwing greater coverts and tertials are a deep dark brown to brownish-black with cinnamon-buff outer fringes and tips. There is white on the basal half of the outerwebs of the tertials, and the innermost greater upperwing-coverts (07–10) are white. The innerweb of the central greater upperwing-coverts (05–06) can on some individuals (older?) be white. The inner and central median coverts, together with the inner lesser coverts, are often all white. The outer median and lesser coverts are black with indistinct fine buff fringes. The upperwing primary coverts are also white although this can vary between individuals, with the outer ones having black tips 3.5–6.5mm in length and the inner ones less black at the tips. Schmidt & Hantge (1954) suggest that fully mature individuals older than three years have one or a few inner upper primary coverts without or with only a minimum of black at the tips, and the proximal parts of the outerwebs of the inner primaries are almost invariably pure white so that the white of the primary coverts and 'mirrors' of the primaries merge seamlessly. The axillaries are creamy-white to white with dark grey or black bases and innerwebs to the feathers. The underwing-coverts are slightly darker with cinnamon-buff fringes.

As the plumage wears by June/July, many of the buff fringes to the upperpart feathers have worn away except for those on the inner scapulars, lower mantle and uppertail-coverts which still appear buff but with prominent black streaks. The top and sides of the head are almost completely black, accentuating the long white supercilium. The throat and upper breast fade to a paler cinnamon-buff with the lower breast and flanks fading to a pale buff. Bill black. Legs and feet black. Irides dark brown.

Adult male in non-breeding plumage The upperparts appear similar to the adult female in breeding plumage, with the colour of the feather fringes reddish-brown rather than cinnamon-buff. The feathers of the mantle, scapulars, uppertail-coverts and occasionally crown have narrow, crescent-shaped white fringes, giving a slightly spotted appearance. The supercilium and eye-ring are buff rather than white, and consequently show less contrast with the sides of the head. The central lower breast, belly, ventral area and undertail-coverts are pale buff. The upper breast and flanks are a slightly darker reddish-brown, with each feather fringed paler and usually with a small droplet-shaped subterminal black spot, although occasionally these are much reduced in size or almost absent towards the flanks, appearing as dark shaft-streaks. The remiges, rectrices, tertials and greater upper primary coverts are the same as in breeding plumage but with broad and dark cinnamon-brown fringes on the secondaries and upperwing-coverts. The tertials have partially white bases and the primary coverts are largely white. The central and inner median upperwing-coverts and the inner lesser coverts have a variable amount of white at their tips or bases. Svensson (1992) states that one or a few inner median coverts are completely white. The inner greater coverts (07–10) are also white but with variable black tips.

First-year male non-breeding Similar to both adult male and female in non-breeding plumage, but the black tips to the tail feathers contrast more than on the adult female. The proximal parts of the outerwebs to occasionally primary 05, but usually 02–04, are buff-white or white, more restricted than on the adult male and not extending beyond the tips of the overlying upperwing primary coverts. The primary coverts have a smaller proportion of white than in the non-breeding adult female and are dusky white at the base (from a third to a half) and brown to grey-brown at the tip. The upperwing greater coverts can show variable amounts of white, from predominantly white on inner greater coverts 08–10 to virtually no white at all apart from the central tips (Svensson 1992). In some cases in autumn it is possible to distinguish these individuals by the differing amount of wear between moulted and, therefore, fresher upperwing greater coverts and older and more worn juvenile greater coverts.

First-year male breeding Similar to adult male breeding but tertials, outerwebs to the inner primaries and upperwing primary coverts have less white or pale buff to their bases, although a few birds replace these feathers with adult-type ones. Some juvenile outer upperwing greater coverts are retained and appear browner than the newer moulted inner greater coverts. The breast usually lacks black spotting.

Adult female in fresh breeding plumage Similar to the non-breeding male, therefore without conspicuous face-mask. Plumage tones are more subdued overall and lack much of the pure white features found in the adult male. The supercilium is as broad and long as in the male but is not so distinct, being pale cinnamon-buff rather than white and showing less contrast with the sides of the head owing to brown replacing the black of the male on the lores, cheeks and ear-coverts. There is a thin pale buff eye-ring.

The lores and upperpart of the ear-coverts are dark brown. The lower part of the ear-coverts are buff with greyish spots and thin, pale cinnamon-buff streaks. The cheeks are also buff. The lower edge of the cheeks and rear of the ear-coverts are sometimes bordered with a thin black line. The sides of the neck behind the cheeks often have a very pale buff to white patch. However, in some adult females the sides of the neck can be distinctly white and contrast markedly with the surrounding plumage. The upper chin is pale cinnamon-buff to white, merging almost imperceptibly into a warmer cinnamon-brown on the upper breast and flanks, although never with the depth of colour found in the male. There is no contrasting white stripe along the lower cheeks. Some of the feathers at the sides of the upper breast can show greyish-black subterminal spots. The lower breast, belly, ventral area and undertail-coverts are a pale cinnamon-buff to off-white. The rump and uppertail-coverts are not so bright and the darker chestnut fringes to the feathers do not accentuate the dark spots so much as in the male.

The tail is similar to the male in pattern and colour with the base of the feathers showing dull white to pale buff bases, most prominently on the outer three pairs (04–06) of feathers. The extent of these pale bases is similar to the male, ending 14–23mm from the tip of the outermost feather (06) in 42 specimens examined (Svensson 1992). However, the pale bases are not sharply demarcated from the brown tips as in the male, with often a cinnamon-buff suffusion showing where the brown meets the white. This can create the impression that the amount of white or buff at the base is less than in the male and also accentuates the less precise demarcation in the tail pattern. This is a good identification point for females of any age. The remiges are as in the male except that the white inner borders and pale bases to the outerwebs of the inner primaries are suffused with buff, less extensive and show less contrast. The upper median and lesser wing-coverts are similar to the rest of the upperparts, with the inner ones having triangular white tips which in some individuals can be extensive (but never as in the male with the feather all or mainly white); often they are mainly brownish-grey edged or tipped with white (Svensson 1992). The upperwing greater coverts and tertials are brownish-black with wider buff fringes than in the male. The tertials have a small amount of pale buff at the base of the outerweb. The innermost upperwing greater coverts (08–10) are partially white although not invariably so and, if present, form a small white patch on the inner wing, but much smaller than in the male. The upperwing primary coverts are dull black with narrow dull white fringes and buffish-white bases, forming an indistinct pale patch. In worn plumage the upperparts become darker as the pale fringes wear away but the sides of the head do not become almost black as in the male. The underparts also lose some of their colour, fading to pale buff.

Adult female in non-breeding plumage Similar to adult male in non-breeding plumage. The sides of the head and upperparts are slightly warmer in tone and a similar reddish-brown to the non-breeding male, and also possess the same crescent-shaped white fringes. The underparts are pale buff but some females show a stronger reddish-brown tone on the breast, often with dull black spots. The tail is similar to the breeding female with the contrast between the white and black less well demarcated than in the non-breeding male. The remiges, tertials and upperwing primary coverts are virtually the same as in breeding plumage but the cinnamon-buff at the bases is less evident. The rest of the upperwing-coverts are also similar to adult female breeding but with much variation; the upperwing inner greater coverts generally show less white and there are never completely white feathers under the upperwing median and lesser coverts.

First-year female non-breeding Similar to adult female and first-year non-breeding male except for less contrast in the tail pattern than the male. Many are impossible to age by plumage but usually the inner five upperwing greater coverts have no white but show thin pale buff fringes; some have white triangular tips and also fringes (Svensson 1992).

First-year female breeding Virtually identical to adult female breeding. The inner upperwing-coverts show less white than in the adult female, but not invariably.

Juvenile The feathers of the forehead, crown, lower mantle and back have extensive dark grey or dark brown bases with arrow-shaped yellowish-buff shaft-streaks and pale ginger-buff fringes, each with a black spot at the tip. The scapulars are similar or, as in later plumage, dark brown with cinnamon-brown fringes in the area near the shaft of the feather. The shaft is tipped with contrasting light buff.

The nape, sides of neck and upper mantle are buff with darker spots, giving a mottled appearance. The rump and uppertail-coverts are pale cinnamon-brown with black spots and pale buff tips to the feathers. The supercilium is less extensive than in adult or first-year birds, being pale buff, weakly defined and only extending from above the eye back towards the nape. If present in front of the eye it is very indistinct. The lores, cheeks and ear-coverts are buffish-brown, with black spotting on the lores and upper ear-coverts and buff-white streaks on the lower ear-coverts. The underparts from chin to undertail-coverts are pale greyish-buff with slightly stronger coloration on the throat, upper breast and sides of breast. Occasionally the entire underparts apart from the chin, belly and ventral area are suffused with warm yellowish-brown, especially on the breast. These areas also show a liberal amount of narrow, dull, dark grey fringes to the feathers which can appear as ill-defined scalloping. The tail is similar to adult birds, and juveniles show the same sexual difference in the degree of contrast between white and black as in adult birds. The upperwing lesser coverts, central and outer median and greater upperwing-coverts are black or dark brownish-grey. The lesser coverts are fringed with yellowish-buff. The innermost greater and median coverts are dark brownish-grey with rufous- to cinnamon-brown fringes with buff shaft-streaks widening to pale buff spots at the tips. On the innermost upperwing greater and median coverts there may, on males, be a thin white shaft-streak extending into a noticeable white spot at the base of the outerweb and a triangular pale buff spot at the tip of each feather. The rest of the greater and median coverts are brownish-black to black with broad reddish-brown fringes on the outerweb and tip. The upperwing primary coverts have cinnamon-buff tips. The outer upperwing primary coverts have none or only a little buff or creamy-white at their base, but primary coverts 10–08 may show over 5mm of cream-white and extend as far as primary covert 06. The remiges and tertials are similar to non-breeding adult birds.

Birds that have moulted from their juvenile plumage into their first-winter plumage are very like adult females in non-breeding plumage but they partially retain their upperwing-coverts and remiges. Some individuals can be told by the contrast between the unmoulted and browner *versus* moulted and darker greater coverts, although the difference is slight. Some individuals (up to 20%) do not moult any upperwing greater coverts but may be told by the pale shaft-streaks and tips on greater coverts 09 and 10, but this is not readily apparent and is lacking in some individuals.

Measurements

	Male	Female
Wing	73.0–81.0 (mean 77.6)	74.0–79.0 (mean 75.5)
Tail	42.0–49.0 (mean 44.9)	41.0–46.0 (mean 43.1)
Bill	13.8–15.5 (mean 14.8)	14.2–15.4 (mean 14.8)

[Cramp 1988]

First-year birds (Switzerland)

	Male	Female
Wing	75.0–79.0 (mean 78.1)	75.0–77.0 (mean 76.2)
Tail	45.0–49.0 (mean 46.7)	44.5–46.5 (mean 45.5)
Bill	13.3–16.3 (mean 14.8)	same as male

Wing measurements SW Germany

Second year male	74.0–78.5 (mean 75.8)	Second year female	73.0–77.0 (mean 75.0)
Older males 2+	75.0–78.0 (mean 77.6)	Older females 2+	74.0–79.0 (mean 75.5)

[Schmidt & Hantge 1954]

Breeding birds from the Vaud, Pre-Alps, Switzerland

Male wing [n=173] 70.5 –79.5 (mean 75.8)
one year old individuals [n=61] 70.5–79.5 (mean 74.9) and
older individuals [n=112] 73.5–79.5 (mean 76.3) demonstrated
that older individuals had significantly longer (p less 0.001) wings.

Female [n=106] 68.5–77.0 (mean 73.4) significantly shorter (p less 0.001) wing than male.
Significant differences (p<0.001) from year to year were considered attributable to prevailing weather conditions during the preceding moult of flight feathers (Labhardt 1984).

DISTRIBUTION AND STATUS

The Whinchat breeds exclusively in the Palearctic, inhabiting the temperate, boreal, steppe and mountain regions of Europe and central parts of western Asia. Eastwards, its northern limit inclines south to avoid the extended spring frosts of the central landmass. It occurs only locally in the Mediterranean area.

In western and northern Europe, it is found on the western extreme of its range, in mainly central and northern parts of the United Kingdom (but not in the Shetlands and only exceptionally in the Orkneys), north-east and central Ireland, France and north of both Portugal and Spain. In Fennoscandia, it extends throughout Norway, Sweden, Finland and Denmark up to around 70°N in Finnmark and exceptionally on the Varanger Peninsula (Haftorn 1971, Risberg 1972). Eastwards, the northern limit in the Russian Federation at around 69°N falls back southwards in three large gradations: from an area around Kirkenes east of Varangerfjord it runs approximately through Kandalaksha Bay, the extreme south-east of the Kola Peninsula and the Mezen River delta. Further east, it falls to Syktyvkar (61°42´N 50°45´E) and on the Pechora River it occurs north to the Aranets River at approximately 65°N; then into the areas of Surgut on the Ob (61°13´N 73°20´E) descending to Tobolsk, Tara and Omsk on the Irtysh River (56°55´N 74°24´E). Further east, the entire range shifts more to the south. It occurs again near to Tomsk and then continues

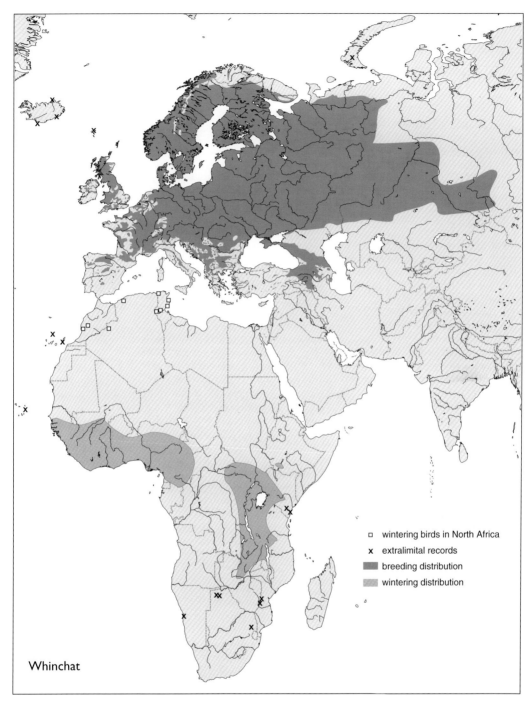

wintering birds in North Africa
x extralimital records
breeding distribution
wintering distribution

Whinchat

at that latitude to the eastern limit of its range c.60km north-east of Krasnoyarsk on the Yenisey River and the easternmost parts of the Sayans in Vyezhii Log on the middle reaches of the Mana River c.150km south-east of Krasnoyarsk (Dement'ev & Gladkov 1968, Glutz & Bauer 1988).

At the southernmost limits of its range, it inhabits virtually exclusively montane and subalpine zones up to 2,200–2,300m. In the Haute Maurienne/Savoie, nest building has been recorded at 2,370m and exceptionally perhaps it has bred as high as 2,420m (Meylan 1937, P. Isenmann in Glutz & Bauer 1988). It has also bred at similar high altitudes in Armenia (2,230m). It occurs at lower levels as far south as the edge of the Mediterranean zone, with an occasional occurrence further south e.g. three breeding pairs on the Etang de Canet/Roussillon in 1983 (Mayaud 1938 in Glutz & Bauer 1988) and there have been occasional breeding records on Majorca, the first breeding attempt being confirmed at Puerto Colom on 30 May 1971 (Parrack 1973). The range limit then skirts the Garonne basin and runs along the southern foothills of the Cantabrian Mountains and Pyrenees (with outposts in the Serra do Larouco in the Galicia–Portugal border area and also in the Sierra de Guadarrama (Coverley 1933, Bernis 1958), the Cévennes, Alpes de Provence and Alpes Maritimes, following the edge of the Alps from Liguria into north-west Slovenia.

It is scarce in Corsica with fewer than 10 records of breeding, 1927–1996, on the coast and inland up to 1,600m (Thibault 1983, Thibault & Bonaccorsi 1999), possibly as high as 2,000m (Thiollay 1967), and in parts of the Apennines. Breeding was claimed from Sicily in 1869–1974 and 1958 but not adequately verified (Iapichino & Massa 1989). It is also found irregularly in the mountains of the Balkan peninsula, distributed south to Thessaly and, since 1969, regularly in northern Greece (Mt Varnous east to Mt Tzena and in eastern Macedonia, northern parts of the Pindos range and Mt Olympos) and southern Bulgaria. There are three breeding records from low-altitude areas further south in the Aegean: two in Crete in 1968 and 1976 and one from the island of Kythnos in 1990 (Handrinos & Akriotis 1997). In Romania it is found in the lowlands east to the Danube Delta from where the southern range limit runs across Moldova and southern Ukraine.

Further east its range is defined by the southern limit of the wooded steppe (predominantly meadow steppe) or by the herb-rich feathergrass steppe. The range then crosses the Volga north of Volgograd, the Ural River at c.51°N (south of Ural'sk) and extends north of Aktyubinsk through Kokchetav and south of Omsk to the Barabinsk steppe. It then follows the eastern edge of the Kuznetzk Alatau range in the Kulunda steppe through Barnaul, heading south to Ust-Kamenogorsk and from there to the Altai Range in north-west Mongolia. Here it breeds only in the northern, north-western and western margins without penetrating deeper into the mountains. It does not breed in the Zaysan region and near Semipalatinsk or anywhere else in the Kyrgyz steppe. It is found east to about 94°E in eastern Sajan in the Russian Federation (Johansen 1954, Dement'ev & Gladkov 1968, Glutz & Bauer 1988).

An offshoot population is separated from the main range by the Manych lowland. This population includes the Caucasus, Transcaucasia (Armenia and Azerbaijan), adjoining areas of east and north-east Anatolia in Turkey – where it is relatively scarce, thinly distributed and fragmented over a large area (Kumerloeve 1969, Beaman 1974–1975, 1978) – and probably continuing to adjoining parts of Iraq (Allouse 1953) as well as the mountains of north-west Iran (possibly the Zagros and Elbur mountain ranges although proof is inconclusive) (Erard & Etchecopar 1970).

Over 75% of the breeding range lies within Europe. Between 1970 and 1990 the largest European populations in eastern Europe and Fennoscandia, which comprise 90% of the total number of pairs, remained relatively stable, but throughout the rest of Europe the species is in decline especially in the north-western and central parts. Overall c.20% of the population was in decline between 1970 and 1990 (Tucker & Heath 1994). However, Bastian & Bastian (1994) differed with some of the findings of Tucker & Heath and stated that the Scandinavian populations had showed negative trends for the last ten years. Since 1965 it has been declining steadily in Finland (J. Haapala in Hagemeijer & Blair 1997) but still remains in good numbers and is a stronghold for the species, although gaps in its distribution have occurred in some eastern woodlands and in the far north (H. Pietiainen 1983). The majority of eastern European populations appear to be stable and in some may even have increased since 1985 (see Estonia).

The total European population is estimated at 2,300,000–4,900,000 (Heath *et al.* 2000). However, Bastian & Bastian (1994) gave a considerably larger estimate of 3,500,000–7,500,000. Counts made in habitats subject only to natural changes such as meadows cut in the traditional manner, heath and bogs have shown that there is a considerable fluctuation in numbers from year to year ranging from 30 to 50% (von Willi 1985, Grotenhuis & van Os 1986).

Changing agricultural land use has influenced the population of this species for the last 120 years. Up until the first third of the twentieth century the area of potential suitable habitat increased significantly owing to the conversion of heath, wasteland and riverine woodland into damp meadowland (Glutz & Bauer 1988). The population trend from after the Second World War to the present has been one of decline in all western and central European countries, accelerating since the 1970s. In Fennoscandia local decreases have become apparent since the 1980s.

North-eastern and eastern Europe, however, maintain high breeding densities of from 20–50 breeding pairs per 10km², as much prime habitat remains. Towards southern and western Europe densities decline, with large gaps evident in the range since 1955. This is due to many meadows in the region losing much of their plant and animal diversity because of intensive agricultural practices, including the advance of the first silage harvest to late May. Populations in the Netherlands, UK, Luxembourg, Belgium and Germany have consequently fallen by 50% or more. Since the 1980s this trend, although continuing, has slowed owing to a partial reduction or complete cessation of cultivation in some areas (Bastian & Bastian 1994). In the Netherlands there has been an increase in numbers on damp nature reserves. However, numbers in Germany have continued to decline from 66,000 breeding pairs in 1985 to an estimated 33,500– 64,000 pairs in 1994 (Bastian & Bastian 1994).

Total breeding pairs for each country are given below based mainly on the following sources: Tucker & Heath (1994), Bastian & Bastian (1994, 1996), Hagemeijer & Blair (1997), Snow & Perrins (1998), Heath *et al.* (2000). Where no citation is given, the information derives from one of these references. Dates in brackets are year(s) to which population estimate refers and data was collected.

Countries with stable populations
Andorra (1998) 75–200; Belarus (1988–1998) 550,000–650,000; Bulgaria (1990–1997) 1,000–5,000; Croatia (post-1992) 10,000–20,000; Czech Republic (1985–1995) 10,000–20,000 (1); Estonia (post-1992) 50,000– 100,000 (1); Greece (1997) 50–500; Hungary (1998) 50,000–100,000; Latvia (post-1992) 300,000–500,000; Moldova (1988) 5,000–7,000; Norway (1990) 50,000–300,000; Poland (post-1992) 150,000–300,000 (2); Portugal (1989) 10–100; Republic of Ireland (1998) 1,500–2,000; Romania (post-1992) 200,000–300,000; Russia (post-1992) 100,000–1,000,000; Slovenia (post-1992) 8,000–12,000; Sweden (1990) 200,000–500,000; Ukraine (1986) 27,000–32,000.

(1) = small increase of 20–49%
(2) = possibly now decreasing (Tryjanowski 1995)

Countries with declining populations
Austria (1985–1988) 5,000–8,000 (1); Belgium (1981–1990) 350–500 (2); Denmark (1993–1994) 14,000– 20,000 (1); Finland (1990–1995) 400,000–600,000 (1); France (1997) 10,000–100,000; Germany (1993) 33,000–64,000 (2); Italy (1988–1997) 10,000–15,000 (1); Liechtenstein (1996) 31–40 (1); Lithuania (1996– 1998) 50,000–120,000 (1); Luxembourg (1996) 30–40 (1); Netherlands (1983) 700–1,100 (2), over 75% compared with 1960s; Slovakia (post-1992) 10,000–20,000 (1); Spain (post-1992) 15,000–20,000 (1); Switzerland (1993–1996) 10,000–15,000 (2); United Kingdom (1988–1991) 14,000–28,000 (1).

(1) = small decline of at least 20% but less than 50%
(2) = large decline of at least 50%

Countries for which population status is uncertain
Azerbaijan uncommon; Armenia uncommon (Adamian & Klem 1999); Kazakhstan 50,000–250,000; Iran unknown but a few pairs likely to be breeding; former Yugoslavia 100,000–200,000; Caucasus States 10,000– 50,000; Estonia 50,000–100,000, probably increasing between 1971 and 1990 and stable 1991–1997, although not based on accurate quantitative data. Currently only 20% of Estonian fields are cultivated with the remaining 80% being allowed to grow over. It is considered that in c.10–20 years when the fields get too overgrown the population of Whinchats will decline (T. Pettay *in litt.* 2000); Turkey 500–5,000, but its exact status remains unverified.

Numbers refer to pairs.

BREEDING
Whinchats form monogamous pair-bonds and breed in their first year, but partners often change during the breeding season. Of 33 replacement nests 42% involved a change of partner and during the nestling and fledging stages of the breeding cycle partners may desert their mate and pair with another individual, leaving the former mate to rear the young alone. Unpaired one-year-old males and less usually older males can also join a breeding pair and occasionally assist in feeding and defending the young, usually being tolerated by the male of the established pair. A male ringed as a nestling was unpaired in its fourth and seventh year and assisted other pairs in those years. In the years in between this male bred normally and successfully four times (Parker 1990). A possible polygynous relationship in the UK between one male and two females was observed in May 1917 when a nest with 12 eggs was found, suggestive of two females laying in it. One female was observed to return to the nest to incubate whilst the male and another female also returned to the vicinity. Although the male visited the nest the second female did not do so during 60 minutes of observation (Wilcock 1921). Pair-bonds are sometimes renewed in successive years and there is a record of siblings pairing in their first breeding year (Schmidt & Hantge 1954).

Two studies in Germany showed that of birds ringed as adults site-fidelity rates were 47% and 39% for males and 27% and 43% for females (Schmidt & Hantge 1954, Bezzel & Stiel 1977). Comparatively few nestlings appear to return to breed in their natal area. In Switzerland none of 79 ringed juveniles returned (Geroudet 1957) and only 6.5% of juveniles did so in a study in Germany. Only one such bird, a female, was breeding in its parents' territory, the others breeding over 250m away. From 54 adult breeding males 47% returned to the same area after one year, 15% for two years and 4% for three years. Almost 50% of both males and females were faithful to the territory they occupied in the previous year (Schmidt & Hantge 1954). This same study also found that 8–11% of birds ringed in the nest returned directly to their natal area at one year old or older.

In Cumbria in northern England a male ringed on 20 June 1997 as a nestling from a brood of six returned in at least three subsequent years (1998–2000) to the same territory which was 300m from its natal territory (J. Callion pers. comm. 2001) this is consistent with the German study above.

An analysis of 521 recoveries of ringed Whinchats found the following. As in the German studies above one-year-old birds were much less likely to return to their birthplace than older birds were to their breeding site. Fidelity to the previous year's breeding territory was found to be most pronounced in older males (second year +) 86%, followed by older females (second year +) 57%. Only 22% of male and 26% of female nestlings hatched in the previous year returned to their birthplace in the study area in one of the subsequent years.

Thus the territory fidelity of nestlings is significantly lower than that of adults in both males and females. Territory fidelity of adult males is slightly but significantly higher than the territory fidelity of adult females. This study also implies that juveniles return to the birthplace more frequently than is apparent from the studies in Germany mentioned above. The results of this study indicate that the Whinchat is similar to many other passerines in that adults are generally site-faithful whilst young settle further from their birthplace, and adult males are more site-faithful than adult females generally.

Conversely an extreme example of a young bird settling well away from its birthplace is the record of a nestling ringed in July 1930 near Braunschweig, northern Germany, being recovered breeding in July 1931 in Herault, southern France, some 1,051km to the south (Bastian 1992).

Individual pairs are territorial. In southern Scotland eight Whinchat territories were counted along a disused railway 0.75km long and 200m wide. Nests varied from 60m to 126m apart with a mean of 99.0m (n=7) (Gray 1973).

In another study area in southern Scotland, an area measuring 8 x 1km and consisting mainly of upland farms verging into moorland and forests maintained a steady population of 25–30 pairs in the years 1966–1968, giving one breeding pair per 32–39ha (Gray 1974). The density of breeding pairs varies considerably over its breeding range, largely owing to differences and suitability in habitat. In alpine meadows in Switzerland 80 pairs perkm^2 over 1 kha were found at 1,000m and 100 pairs per km^2 at 2000m (Oggier 1979). In contrast only 2.5 pairs per km^2 over 78.5ha were found in Alsace, France (Kempf 1982). In Uppland, Sweden, a density of only 1.2 pairs per km^2 was determined (Olsson 1947). In Scotland in young conifer forest (seven years old) up to an elevation of 330m with a field layer of heather, density was 2.2 pairs per km^2 but in similar forest at 240–270m with a field layer of grass it was 19.3 per km^2 (Phillips 1973). In Vantaa, Finland, on drained cereal fields only 2.1 pairs per km^2 were found, but in abandoned fields 94.5 pairs per km^2 were found (Tiainen & Ylimaunu 1984). In Estonia the density of populations is very variable and in many floodplain meadows the Whinchat is one of the dominant passerine species but in others, such as Kasari Delta, Laanemaa district, the population declined from only four pairs per km^2 in 1957–1960 to occasional pairs in 1977–1980. However, in the north-east of Kuresoo Bog, Viljandimaa district, the population rose from one pair in 1959 to 52 pairs in 1986 (two pairs per km^2). The breeding density in the Nigula Bog, Parnumaa district, was 0.5–2 pairs per km^2 in the 1970s but six pairs per km^2 in the 1980s (Leibak et al. 1994). In eastern Europe local breeding densities can be up to 40 breeding pairs per 10 km^2.

Bastian & Bastian 1994 state "The (statistical) breeding density across the whole range is nearly five breeding pairs per 10km^2". In the main breeding area of Finland, the Baltic States, Poland, Russia, Belarus and Ukraine the breeding density is between 9–12 breeding pairs per 10 km^2. In west and central Europe it is mainly lower – around one breeding pair per 10km^2 (Bastian & Bastian 1994).

In the UK the breeding season extends from the first week of May until the second week of July (11 weeks duration), although there are exceptions such as a nest with six eggs found on 28 April 1973 (the earliest ever recorded in the UK); breeding appears to be relatively synchronised throughout the country (Fuller & Glue 1977). In southern Scotland nest building commenced each year between 6–10 May in a study from 1966 to 1968 (Gray 1974). In central Europe the timing of egg laying has been found to vary with altitude. In the Val Ferret in south-western Switzerland the first egg was laid at c.1,500m on 21 June and at 1,800m on 6 July (Geroudet 1957). At Heidelberg, southern Germany (114m a.s.l.), almost 80% of the population had commenced laying by the 5–10 May – whilst laying did not commence until the 25–30 May in the Pre-Alps of western Switzerland (Schmidt & Hantge 1954, Kunz 1988, Labhardt 1988b).

Breeding commences in the Kharkov region of the former USSR in May with unincubated full clutches found from late May onwards until about mid-June (in Belovezh a nest with five eggs was found on 22 June). In western Siberia breeding commences from the end of May. Full clutches of eggs have been recorded in Barabinsk steppe on 27 May but at Tobol'sk not before 10–15 June (Johansen 1954). Around Kiev nests with fresh eggs are found from mid-May onwards. Further south in Moldova and the southern parts of Minsk region breeding commences earlier, around mid-April.

The distance between nests can be relatively small. In Germany it was less than 100m (Schmidt & Hantge 1954) whilst in Scotland in more or less linear habitat the mean was 99m (60–126m [n = 7]) (Gray 1973). Territory size was less than 1ha in Scotland (Gray 1973), 0.75ha in Germany (Schmidt & Hantge 1954), and averaged 0.43ha in the Netherlands (Frankevoort & Hubatsch 1966). Areas can contract as arriving birds set up territories and disputes with existing pairs take place, but later in the season territories may well expand again as pairs leave.

Once pairs are formed the male constantly guards his mate, following her closely around their territory and rarely being more than 2–3m away at the early stage in the breeding cycle (Bastian & Bastian 1996).

Nest site selection The female generally chooses the nest site on her own, with the male sometimes in attendance although rarely interfering or showing interest. Females in the process of site selection have been observed repeatedly dropping into and rising from a selected site with the male present but not inspecting the site. Occasionally the male will interfere. One such occurrence involved a male aggressively driving his mate away from the site to which she was in the early stages of bringing nest material and guiding her to a new site 12m away, to which she then brought nest material and built a nest (Eccles 1955). Bastian & Bastian considered that the male takes an active part in site selection, reasoning that as he arrives 1–2 weeks earlier than the female on the breeding territory he has a better knowledge of sites in it as he has had time to explore the territory and reconnoitre potential nest sites. Also the same adult males return to the same sites in successive years and will thus be familiar with the territory. It may be that females arrive later in central Europe than in western Europe, as they arrived only 3–8 days after the males in Scotland (Gray 1973).

	STONECHAT			WHINCHAT	
Location	Number	Percent		Number	Percent
Gorse	175	33.5		23	4.8
Other scrub/scrubs	46	8.8		23	4.8
Open grass	113	21.6		276	58.0
Open heather	109	20.8		33	6.9
Open bracken	54	10.3		68	14.3
Mixed low vegetation	23	4.4		52	10.9
Stone wall	3	0.6		1	0.2
TOTAL	523	100%		476	99.9%

Stonechat and Whinchat nest sites (After Fuller & Glue 1977)

Nests are placed in similar situations to those of the European Stonechat, on or very near to the ground, well hidden, although the actual site is far less likely to be under scrub or bushes than with the latter species. Walpole-Bond (1938) describes it as "being on the ground or sunk into a scrape therein, either under rank herbage edging up generally through the fringe of a furze bush (often isolated) or beneath a tuft of grass, heath, bracken or other vegetation growing full in the open though some such examples repose at the foot of wire fencing". Nests have also been recorded on banks, small slopes, in trenches and ditches. Bannerman & Lodge (1954) mention nests being very well concealed amongst the roots of heather and Dement'ev & Gladkov (1968) note them being found in tall grass or under large weed cover. In Corsica a favourite nest site is in thick vegetation on the sides of ditches. In the UK the commonest reported nest site (58% from 476 Nest Record Cards held by the BTO) was amongst or beneath grass in an open situation, followed by 14.3% in bracken, 10.9% in mixed low vegetation, 6.9% in open heather, 4.8% in gorse, 4.8% in other low scrub and shrubs and 0.2% in a stone wall (see figure above). As with European Stonechat many nests were located in areas with scattered bushes providing exposed perches for feeding and song. Whinchats were recorded predominantly in grasses in agricultural situations, although on moorland sites nests among bracken were as frequent as those in grass (Fuller & Glue 1977). In southern Scotland Gray (1974) studied 25–30 pairs and found that low gorse patches were the most commonly selected sites. There was much rivalry between males to establish territories in such sites and it was in this habitat that the first nests were found. The nest is built by the female alone usually a few days after the site has been selected. She is accompanied by the male who will drive her back if she appears to stray from their territory. On occasions males will select nest material for the female if she ceases building, and once a female was observed to add nest material to the nest even though it already contained one egg (Gray 1974).

Nest building and construction Nest building takes 2–5 days. It is slightly less in warmer regions, e.g. 2–3 days in Heidelberg, southern Germany (Schmidt & Hantge 1954), than in colder areas where it takes 3–5 days (Parker 1990). These differing times reflect the amount of insulating material required for the nest and its consequent thickness. An analysis of 239 BTO Nest Record Cards found that 232 (97.1%) were located on or just above ground level (0–15cm), with 212 (88.7%) on the ground. Only seven nests were in excess of 15cm above ground, with six (2.5%) being 15–30cm up and one (0.4%) 38cm up (this last was in a low Blackthorn *Prunus spinosa*) (Fuller & Glue 1977). The foundation of the nest consists of coarse dry grasses with some moss, lined with finer grasses and/or rootlets and often strands or tufts of horsehair. Walpole-Bond (1938) reports no wool, fur or feathers in the lining of the nest, but Gray (1974) found wool in the lining of several nests in Scotland, probably reflecting the local availability of materials and possible need for increased insulation. Some nests have been constructed almost exclusively of moss (Walpole-Bond 1938, Bannerman & Lodge 1954). The outside diameter of the nest is 160mm with a height of 45mm. The diameter of the cup is 80mm with a depth of 35mm (Dement'ev & Gladkov 1968).

Egg-laying Laying commences within 1–2 days of nest completion. Eggs are laid singly at 24-hour intervals, normally between 07:00hrs and 10:00hrs, until the clutch is complete. The female only visits the nest to lay the egg and both adults otherwise stay away from the vicinity and frequently leave the territory altogether for long periods. As with arrival on their breeding territory, nest building and egg laying are correlated with longish spells of fine weather (Bastian & Bastian 1996).

Incubation Incubation lasts 11–14 and sometimes as long as 15 days, and commences with the laying of the last egg. Near Balingen in southern Germany the incubation period was 12–13 days for 73% of nests, and 11–12 days for 27% (Rebstock & Maulbetsch 1988). In Lapland it is shorter at 10–12 days, this being an adaptation to the shorter summer which constrains the length of the breeding season (Lennerstedt 1964). In the Alpine foreland of Germany the incubation period for replacement clutches was found to average one day longer at 13 than for first clutches at 12 (Bezzel & Stiel 1977).

Incubation is undertaken by the female alone. The egg temperature is kept constant at 26–30 °C, even when the ambient temperature is only just above 0°C. In Lapland where the Arctic nights are very light females only incubated tightly for 3–5 hours, the maximum period being from 23:00–05:00hrs but usually from only after 24:00hrs (Lennerstedt 1973). The egg temperature can be kept high by the thermal insulating effect of the nest without the need for long unbroken incubation periods. Conversely there is a record from Nottinghamshire, England, of a nest with four eggs on the point of hatching being surrounded by a grass fire with the area around and up to the edges of the nest being burnt but the interior cup remained unharmed. The insulating effects of the nest protected the eggs from the extreme heat and they hatched and the three young eventually fledged (Hope & Pipe 1961). For several pairs observed over a total of 23 hours in Germany the incubation stints on the day before hatching lasted 1.2–54 minutes with breaks of 3.5–10 minutes around midday and up to 30 minutes in the evening (Bastian & Bastian 1996).

Individual incubating females can display a wide variety of behaviour when an intruder appears in their territory. Some will leave the nest when the intruder is 30–40m away, while others are less sensitive and only leave when the intruder is at the nest. The female sits increasingly tightly as incubation proceeds and she can even be caught by hand at the nest after day nine of the incubation period (Schmidt & Hantge 1954, Parker 1990). The male often remains perched close to the nest and the incubating female. Observations in Scotland showed that during incubation the male becomes noticeably aggressive and changes his song post from low-level posts, fences and bushes around 1–2m high to elevated vantage points such as the tops of small trees or telegraph poles 4–7m high (Gray 1974). A male has been seen on two occasions to take food to an incubating female, and another male fed a female brooding recently hatched young (Schmidt & Hantge 1954).

The female only leaves the nest briefly to feed and the male will also call her off if a potential predator is in the vicinity. When undisturbed she leaves the nest unobtrusively in a long low rapid flight. When returning after being alarmed or flushed off the nest she does so by several short flights, pausing briefly between each one before perching just above the nest and then dropping onto it. However, when returning from an undisturbed feeding period she usually makes one long flight, again perching just above the nest. A female leaving her nest is immediately escorted by her mate. In the early part of incubation the pair keep in very close contact, 10–15m apart. As incubation progresses the male is less inclined to leave the vicinity of the nest site and maintains a vigil over it while the female feeds. Periods off the nest are shorter if the weather is cold and/or wet. It is important for the male to accompany the female as he can warn her of any potential danger, allowing her to feed more rapidly before resuming incubation. His presence also prevents her from copulating with any stray male in order to assure his paternity in the event that a replacement clutch will be required.

Clutch size Clutches usually consist of 4–7 eggs although extremes of two and eight do occur. First clutches of six eggs were the most frequent in the UK (68%) followed by clutches of five (16%). In the Fichtelgebirge mountains of Germany a similar circumstance prevails, with 69% of first clutches consisting of six eggs. First clutches are on average 1.1 eggs larger than replacement clutches (first clutch mean 5.86 eggs, n=194; second clutch mean 4.77, n=35), and the commonest replacement clutch size is five eggs (40% in Germany) (Feulner 1995, Schmidt & Hantge 1954, Bezzel & Stiel 1977, Bastian and Bastian 1996). Full clutches with less than four eggs are usually replacement clutches and unfertilised eggs are more likely in replacement clutches, possibly attributable to hormonal factors (Horstkotte 1962).

Clutches of eight eggs are very rare, with only one being found in 619 nests in the UK and Germany (Bastian & Bastian 1996). Larger reported clutches, such as two of 12 eggs (Wilcock 1921, Eccles 1967) are probably the result of more than one female laying in the same nest. The proportion of fledged young can be significantly higher in 6–7 egg clutches (70% and 80% respectively) than from those of 4–5 eggs (mean 30% for both) and older females have a higher breeding success than one-year-old females (Feulner 1995). The mean clutch size for 152 clutches in UK was 5.66 ± 0.07. Larger clutches (mean 5.88 ± 0.08) were laid in April and May than in June and July (mean 5.31 ± 0.12). This is influenced by the general availability of food whilst the female is forming eggs or when the young are in the nest. There was also a suggestion that mean clutch size increases with increasing altitude up to 230m (Fuller & Glue 1977). Two surveys in southern Scotland of eight and 33 nests recorded mean clutch sizes of 6.2 and 5.8 eggs respectively (Gray 1973, 1974). In Finland from 11 clutches 4% had four eggs, 13% had five, 45% had six, 32% had seven and 6% had eight eggs, giving a mean of 6.2 (von Haartman 1969). In northern Europe clutch size is significantly larger than in the south of its range and increases from south to north by 0.08 eggs per degree of latitude (Bastian & Bastian 1996).

Description of eggs Whinchat eggs are subelliptical, with a smooth and matt gloss (Bastian & Bastian 1996) surface, deep greenish-blue with numerous very fine reddish-brown speckles. Walpole-Bond described them as bright turquoise-blue tinged with green whilst some eggs lack the greenish tinge altogether. Occasionally the speckles are almost absent or concentrated into an ill-defined zone or cap at the broader end. Dimensions of 250 eggs in Germany averaged 18.9 x 14.3mm with variables of 16.6–21.5 x 13.3–15.4 (Schönwetter 1979). The average of 100 eggs in the UK was 19.16 x 14.47mm, with maxima of 21.5 x 14.5 and 19.8 x 15.5 and minima of 17.2 x 14.1 and 18.0 x 13.5mm (Witherby *et al.* 1948).

Number of broods, and brood size In the former USSR Dement'ev & Gladkov (1968) state that the species is generally single-brooded, with replacements being laid for lost clutches. In southern Scotland all eight pairs observed breeding along a disused railway track from May–July were single-brooded and no replacements or second broods were attempted (Gray 1973). However, as far north as the southern parts of the Minsk region in Russia two broods have been recorded and two broods are not infrequently raised throughout its range in Europe, although generally they should still be regarded as exceptional.

In northern and western Europe intensive agricultural practices have generally displaced Whinchats from relatively warm lowlands into higher regions, which means that the potential breeding season has been shortened by around two weeks. These increased time constraints make it more difficult to compensate for failed first breeding attempts by replacement clutches or to improve overall breeding success with second broods. The interval between the loss of a clutch and its replacement can be as short as seven days and as long as four weeks; it is longer the earlier the loss of the first clutch or brood occurs in the breeding period. Pairs invariably change their nest site and in around 50% of such cases also their mate (Schmidt & Hantge 1954, Parker 1990). Not all pairs lay a replacement clutch or brood if the first is lost, especially if the loss occurs just before the young fledge, leaving insufficient time to commence a replacement. These failed breeders are the first to start their southward autumn migration.

Fuller & Glue (1977) found that brood sizes in the UK followed a pattern similar to that in clutch size, with brood sizes in April/May (mean 5.16 ± 0.08) larger than those in June/July (mean 4.42 ± 0.15), with an overall mean of 4.96 ± 0.08. The mean brood size for eight nests in southern Scotland was 5.6 (Gray 1973).

Hatching and feeding nestlings Towards the end of the incubation period, males increasingly remain near the nest on their favourite perch. They catch insects and perch with their prey for several minutes. This behaviour has been interpreted as the male 'expecting' the young to hatch. Males will occasionally fly to the nest with food before the young have hatched and then either give it to the female or eat it themselves. This has been interpreted as a test-run for when the young hatch (Bastian & Bastian 1996) and as behaviour which strengthens the pair-bond (Parker 1990). Nestlings are fed by both parents who take a roughly equal share in feeding duties and removing faecal sacs. The male usually starts feeding the young after he has first seen the female do so. The young mainly hatch from the end of May at a time when arthropod prey is at its peak. The young can hatch over a period of 24 hours with the last one to do so apparently suffering no reduced survival prospects. Any infertile eggs remain in the nest but the shells from hatched eggs are removed by the adults.

Only the female broods the young. Brooding is most intense on the day of hatching, when it occupies 70% of her daytime activity. She continues to brood the young for the first five days after hatching, as in this period they are incapable of thermoregulation, but she does so in steadily reducing periods, until by day five, brooding comprises only 5% of her time. As with incubation, periods of brooding vary, lasting from 1–45 minutes. To reduce heat loss between periods of brooding the young clump together, and when they are older they form a 'warmth pyramid' in which the head and neck rest on the sibling opposite. The female may resume brooding after day five but only if the weather is cold and/or wet.

The feeding rate increases as the young grow. Eight German breeding pairs showed a feeding rate of c.3 feeds per 15 minutes in the first four days, increasing to c.7 over days 5–8 and peaking at c.10 in days 9–11. Both parents fed the young equally in the first four days but from day five the male averaged higher rates with the female only increasing to equal the male's effort from day nine. A brood of five with one nestling fed per visit would mean each nestling is fed about every 30 minutes in the first four days, then every 5–10 minutes (Bastian & Bastian 1996). Other studies have found the female to take the larger share of feeding (Kierdorf-Traut 1975).

The faecal sacs from the nestlings are swallowed by the adults for the first two days but thereafter are carried away and dropped in flight or from a perch. Usually the food for the young is collected from within the territory within a radius of 100–150m from the nest. However, in Scotland Gray (1973) observed food collected from hayfields outside the territory, while conversely Phillips (1970) saw a pair gathering food as close as 25m to the nest. In Arctic areas with almost continuous summer daylight pairs of Whinchat and other species were observed to stop feeding young and 'rest' for 3–4 hours after 24:00hrs (Lennerstedt 1964). As with European Stonechat, should one of a pair disappear during the nestling stage the remaining adult seems capable of raising the brood on its own. In one case cited by Bastian & Bastian (1996), both parents were feeding their six young for the first two days (male 3.5 feeds per 15 minutes, female 2.1 feeds) but by day three the male had disappeared and the female increased her feeding rate to over six feeds per 15 minutes, thus fully compensating for the absent male. As the young also needed brooding in the early stages she spent 40% of her daytime activity at or on the nest, but all the young fledged successfully. Her only unusual behaviour was to fly several times directly to the nest from a long distance; usually females are more circumspect in their approach, first perching nearby to check for danger.

Growth of nestlings When they hatch the nestlings weigh 2.1 ± 0.2g and are roughly equal to the weight of a well-incubated egg (Bastian & Bastian 1993). In the first hour of life they weigh 1.8 g, after 6 hours 2 g, and by the end of the first day 2.5 g. Accepting a hatching weight of 1.8 g and adult weight of 17 g, a newly hatched nestling equals 11% of the adult weight, distinctly above the normal passerine average of 6–8% (Nice 1943). Whinchat nestlings in central Europe were found to reach the adult weight of 17 g by day nine, and thus gain on average 1.63 g per day with the maximum increase on day five. In the first five days the daily weight increase is 40–50% of the body weight on a particular day, this then dropping to 5–15% (Bastian & Bastian 1993). In Lapland it was more, with a mean daily increase of 2.0 g. This could possibly be an adaptation to the subarctic conditions as the birds would consequently reach thermoregulatory condition more rapidly. In northern Sweden the fastest-growing members of two broods of five and seven respectively reached 18–19 g by day 9/10 and remained constant or lost a little weight over the subsequent 2–3 days whilst the others steadily but more slowly increased weight to c.17 g over 12–13 days (Lennerstedt 1964).

The young's eyes open on the fourth or fifth day, the feather quills are visible on day 3–4 and break through on the fifth day, when the brooding activity of the female decreases markedly. By this time the young have acquired the ability to thermoregulate and day five marks a crucial point in the development of the young. The head and back are fully feathered on day eight and feather growth increases rapidly from then on; thus the length of the exposed part of the longest primary (8) averages on day eight 11.6mm, day nine 16.6mm, day ten 22.4mm, day 11 24.9mm, day 12 28.5mm, day 13 30.8mm, day 14 35.0mm, and day 15 39.00mm (A. Labhardt in Glutz & Bauer 1988).

On day nine the secondaries and belly feathers break out of their quills. By day 12, 95–100% of the body is covered (Rebstock & Maulbetsch 1993). The feet of the young at 8–9 days old are disproportionately large, which is typical of nidicolous young. At this age the size of the tarsometatarsus and the toes equals the adults. In comparison with the rest of the body the development of the legs and feet is very rapid. The wing and body length are conversely only 60–65% of their maximum size even by day 12. Nests on the ground, whilst generally well protected from aerial attack, are vulnerable to terrestrial predators and accidental trampling, mostly by livestock. It is therefore advantageous for ground-nesting species to fledge their young as rapidly as possible. The rapid development in the legs (tarsometatarsus and tibiotarsus) of the Whinchat allows the young to leave the nest 'on foot' by day nine in an emergency, such as when threatened by danger (Rebstock & Maulbetsch 1993).

Fledging Birds that have left their nest prematurely have occasionally been found to return but usually they scatter and remain concealed in the nearby vegetation. If undisturbed the young normally leave the nest on foot after 11–14 days, although in subarctic areas this happens after 10–12 days (Lennerstedt 1964). They conceal themselves in the surrounding vegetation and remain in dense cover on the ground waiting to be fed, keeping constant contact with their parents by calling (Schmidt & Hantge 1954, Rebstock & Maulbetsch 1993). When the nestlings fledge they weigh between 17.0 and 20.8 g (Bastian & Bastian 1993, Rebstock & Maulbetsch 1993) which exceeds the adult weight by up to 20%. This contrasts with fledging and adult weights of Northern Wheatear, which are almost equal, and Skylark *Alauda arvensis*, which normally leave the nest at nine days old and are consequently up to 30% lighter at this stage than adults (Verbeek 1988). The young when fledging normally leave the nest in the space of a few hours and usually do not return even to roost (Rebstock & Maulbetsch 1988). Daily the young increase their distance from the nest site, remaining very secretive and hiding in tall, dense meadow vegetation, herbaceous perennials or cereal fields. Sibling youngsters at this time can be separated by up to 150m (Horstkotte 1962).

The parents usually divide the fledged brood between them and feed them for 2–3 weeks after they have left the nest. The young are able to fly properly at c.17–19 days of age. An encounter with a family of recently fledged (3–4 days) and just able to fly young in Nottinghamshire, England, resulted in one young bird adopting a 'bittern-like' posture in response to the male parent's alarm calls: exposed in a bare, dead bramble bush *Rubus fruticosus*, it imitated the brown upward spikes of dead bramble by stretching its upper back, upper breast and neck into a thin elongated line with its bill pointed upwards at 60° from the horizontal, maintaining this position all the time there was a perceived danger and until the intruder was at least 50m away (Andrews 1981). Adult birds have also been seen to adopt this posture when a raptor flies over.

Once the young can fly the family reunites and after 14 days out of the nest the young can be seen perched on bushes with the adults (Garling 1933, Rebstock & Maulbetsch 1988). At this stage they often leave the territory, moving into areas with a rich food supply such as potato, beet and wheat fields. The male defends these new feeding areas from conspecifics as long as the family remains together (Schmidt & Hantge 1954, Horstkotte 1962). Even though juveniles can feed themselves from day 21 (Stobener 1977) the adults regularly feed them up to the age of c.30–31 days. The family unit usually splits up from around 26–28 days after leaving the nest.

Nest predation and success rate of broods Breeding success with replacement clutches is almost the same as for first clutches and occasionally higher owing to the smaller number of total failures (Sacher 1993, Feulner 1995). In central Europe nestlings were occasionally predated by Red Fox *Vulpes vulpes*, domestic or feral cats, Stoat *Mustela erminea* and Weasel *Mustela nivalis*. There are occasional losses to mice, slugs and, once, ground beetles (Carabidae) (Schmidt & Hantge 1954, Bezzel & Stiel 1977, Feulner 1995), although in these cases it may have been they were observed on birds that had previously died. Breeding pairs with nests have been seen to attack and chase away from the nest Red-backed Shrike *Lanius collurio* (Groebbels 1950) and Common Cuckoo *Cuculus canorus* (Hortskotte 1962), and very exceptionally a male once attacked a man investigating its nest (Geroudet 1957). The species is parasitised by Common Cuckoo in the European parts of the former USSR (Malchevskiy 1987). However, an analysis of 650 nests of species recorded as host to Common Cuckoo found only two related to Whinchat (Henning 1967).

During the first week after leaving the nest the mortality of young in one study in Scotland was high. The mean of young leaving 33 nests was five per nest but had reduced to two by the end of the first week after leaving. The main predators were Stoat and Weasel. Hedgehog *Erinaceus europaeus* were found to predate nests during the incubation and nestling periods. Heavy rain also caused some nests to fail by flooding and chilling eggs or drowning or chilling nestlings. The success of nests in this particular study area was also affected by activities of man. Breeding success in gorse was unaffected by human disturbance and 63% of nests were successful, but nests built on a railway embankment and in roadside verges had only a 52% and 46% success rate respectively. The late burning of vegetation on the railway embankment and cutting roadside verges in mid-June caused heavy losses. When this disturbance was curtailed nesting success rose overall by 18%. Grazing animals also had an adverse effect on breeding success. Part of a railway embankment that contained several pairs of Whinchats was abandoned completely when cattle accidentally grazed the area. Nests on grass verges were also damaged and exposed to predators by cattle grazing through fences (Gray 1974).

Breeding success in different populations can vary widely from 25% to 70% of eggs laid, with on average 3–5 young fledging per pair (Bezzel & Stiel 1977, Fuller & Glue 1977, Labhardt 1988, Rebstock & Maulbetsch 1988, Smith 1990). The majority of losses happen before the young fledge, and of eggs that hatch only c.66% of young survive into their first breeding year. In central Europe on meadows where grass is mowed, the mowing itself is the most significant cause of mortality, followed to a much lesser degree by predation by corvids (Bastian & Bastian 1996). A population in western Switzerland where lowland mowing took place lost 39 (62%) of 63 nests to mowing, and even when the young have left the nest but cannot fly mowing is still a danger to the young concealed in the vegetation. Conversely a meadow at a higher elevation under alpine meadow management where mowing only took place at the end of July maintained a constant level of breeding success. In this area only one nest was destroyed by mowing (5.3%), the heaviest losses being caused by grazing stock (63%). Near Heidelberg, southern Germany, Magpies *Pica pica* destroyed 15 (12%) from a total of 129 nests. In this same population, however, a further 40 breeding attempts failed owing to mowing and artificial flooding of meadows, but despite this it managed to remain constant (Schmidt & Hantge 1954). In the Pre-Alps of Bavaria a population located close to a rubbish tip with consequent high density of corvids including Raven *Corvus corax* suffered 54% of all losses to corvids. At the end of June in central Europe the majority of Whinchat breeding territories are deserted, and they are completely deserted by mid-July with the young and adults dispersing randomly. By late July and early August the first autumn departures south and south-west commence.

HABITAT

The Whinchat breeds predominantly to the north of European Stonechat in the boreal and temperate zones, but only marginally more north in the steppe and Mediterranean zones of middle and upper middle latitudes (Cramp 1988). The general separation of the respective ranges points to an avoidance of interspecific competition between the two species, but where it does occur the resident species predominates (see Phillips 1970).

It is mainly a meadow-frequenting species but, despite the broad spectrum of plant communities occupied, it has very specific needs for a varied vegetative habitat. For nesting it needs a herb or small shrub layer to provide cover, and for feeding it needs the vegetation to be low and open with suitable higher perches. Favoured habitats are wet meadows, pastures, bogs, upland grasslands, heath, and dry or wet open scrubland. For breeding it prefers grassland plains from Atlantic neutral grassland in a showery, airy climate to damp grassland, or gently sloping sites. Hedges reduce the population density, and areas with more than 115m of hedges per 10ha were found to be devoid of Whinchats (M. Muller in Labhardt 1988). It also tends to avoid the proximity of continuous stretches of woodland, although it will inhabit areas near narrow belts of woodland close to water (Glutz & Bauer 1988). It usually requires areas of bare ground with a highly structured soil profile on which to sight and capture prey. It utilises herbaceous perennial plants, isolated bushes and trees, overhead cables, wires and fences which provide perches above the general level of surrounding vegetation and can also serve as song posts. Uncultivated or partially cultivated wet areas are preferred to dry or intensively cultivated areas (Bastian *et al.* 1997).

Over large areas of temperate Europe the requirements listed above are met by large hay meadows divided into small blocks (and either cut once, late in the year, or not cut at all) and by extensively grazed unimproved pasture. As the majority of these meadows up to 670m a.s.l. are cut several times per season any Whinchats breeding there concentrate into the damper, less intensively cultivated areas alongside streams in broad valleys, waterlogged ground or on slopes with high groundwater emerging as springs. These areas often have herbaceous perennials such as thistle *Cirsium*, angelica *Angelica* and meadowsweet *Filipendula ulmaria*. In central Europe at lower levels the habitats are often false oat grass communities *Arrhenatherion elatioris* with perches in the form of taller species of Umbelliferae such as cow parsley *Anthriscus*, hogweed *Heracleum* or buttercups. In subalpine zones it frequents meadows of yellow oat grass (Polygono-Trisetion) which have such plants as great yellow gentian *Gentiana lutea* or false helleborines *Veratrum* providing suitable perches.

Unlike European Stonechat it is able to use areas with only a few perches, often inhabiting areas where the only perches are tall weeds, fences and posts. It is consequently less dependent on heaths and moors and favours grassy areas. In Switzerland it is also fond of nitrophilic alpine pasture flora around alpine huts and also the remaining meadows (*Streuewiesen*) used to provide bedding for domestic animals. It also spreads from these habitats to *Carex* sedge beds with sparse *Phragmites* cover, so long as the ground does not flood and suitable perches are available, and into orchard margins adjoining the landward side of sedge beds as well as into low-growing young spruce plantations. Its distribution and abundance on pastureland varies. Alpine pastures that are farmed fairly intensively for short periods are generally utilised as a last resort but it sometimes attains high densities and high breeding success in such habitat, such as in the Massif Central in France. In the Swiss alpine zone it breeds up to around 1,800m, exceptionally as high as 2,000–2,200m. It is rarely found in pure clover, potato or cereal fields but can apparently survive there if there is suitable nesting habitat in the form of small fallow areas of grassland such as can be found along ditches, canals, roadside verges, tracks, fences and embankments (Glutz & Bauer 1988).

In areas of Europe influenced by the Atlantic climate, drier areas such as bracken *Pteridium aquilinum*, heathland with gorse *Ulex europaeus*, dunes, young plantations with grass growing between the trees, or grassy clearings appear to be more readily accepted. Fuller & Glue (1977), comparing breeding habitats of European Stonechat and Whinchat in the UK, found that coastal and heath/moor habitat accounted for 80% of European Stonechat nests but only 36% of Whinchat nests. It appeared that inland agricultural sites assumed far greater importance for Whinchat than European Stonechat. Of 151 Whinchat nests in agricultural situations 67% were in grassland (including hill grazings and water meadows), while only 6% were in arable farmland. Transitional zones appear to be important to the species. In Scotland they appear to favour marginal sites where agriculture meets moorland (Phillips 1970), and Gray (1973) found that disused railways were also a favoured site. Industrial waste ground, building sites, old sewage works, rubbish tips, small airfields, colliery tips, overgrown parks and even large gardens are also habitats utilised for nesting. In the UK it was also found to breed at considerably higher altitudes than European Stonechat (91% of European Stonechat nests below 122m whereas only 40% of Whinchat) and it commonly breeds up to 305m with some nests as high as 500m. Gray (1974) found in his study area, which ranged from 120–240m, that it only exceptionally bred below the 90m contour. The highest breeding records come from Armenia (2,230m) and the Swiss Alps (2,300m) (Bastian et al. 1997). In the UK Lack (1933) showed that in young conifer plantations it increased to a maximum population when the trees were 4–5 years old and then declined, with none seen after seven years of tree growth. Phillips (1973) studied two areas of similar planted forestry in Scotland and found Whinchats were present in forestry with field layers of heather and grass respectively.

In Scandinavia open birchwoods are also used and some birds breed in raised bogs and peat extraction areas. In the subalpine zone Whinchats are found in open dwarf shrub areas containing juniper *Juniperus*, bearberry *Arctostaphylos*, bilberry *Vaccinium* and rhododenron *Rhododendron* which are mixed with grazed areas of matgrass *Nardion*. A few pairs in southern Europe breed on slopes with thorny xerophytes (Thibault 1983).

In the former USSR inhabits generally moist, plain hilly meadows with large weedy vegetation but sparse bushes. It also inhabits forest glades, areas of felled and burnt forest, even being found in clearings surrounded by large areas of dense unbroken forest, ploughed areas and gullies. In Estonia it is found generally in open habitat with generous grass cover and scattered bushes, floodplain meadows, bogs, fens, alvars and field edges. In a survey in the Nigula Bog, Parnumaa district, most breeding territories were situated in the edges of bogs (Leibak et al. 1994). In the Caucasus it breeds chiefly in the meadows in the subalpine zone and sometimes extends up to the forests in the alpine zone. In the Pambak mountains of Armenia it nests as high as 2,230m in mountain steppe and alpine meadows, preferring wet meadows, waterlogged fields with lush vegetation, mountain glades and forest edges (Dement'ev & Gladkov 1968, Adamian & Klem 1999). In Greece the breeding habitat is clearings within montane beech (*Fagus*) or coniferous forest and alpine meadows near the treeline, usually 850–1,900m.

When dispersing from breeding areas and on migration it appears in a wide variety of generally open, cultivated and uncultivated land as well as waste ground and areas of open scrub. In the UK it frequents areas where it does not breed such as racecourses, waste ground, older sewage farms, coastal pasture and scrub and set-aside areas on arable farms. It has been seen on ploughed fields and in cabbage fields (see Breeding) in Germany, also the edges of reedbeds and areas of raised bog. In Liberia on migration it occurs on airfields and along logging roads in high forest (Gatter 1997).

In south-west England in the years 1978–1992, a survey of passage Whinchats and Common Redstarts *Phoenicurus phoenicurus* at a lowland site consisting of mixed farmland with a high density of hedges, some small copses and extensive scrub revealed a marked habitat segregation with Redstarts preferring the predominantly tall mature hedges and scrub found in the western half of the site and Whinchats favouring the short dense hedges and scrub in the eastern half of the site. The fact that these species arrived in fine weather and at low density demonstrated that these were real microhabitat choices made by the respective species (Duckworth 1994).

In its wintering areas in Africa it is common to abundant especially in guinea savanna and savanna/forest mosaic but less common in the soudan belt (Keith et al. 1992). It is found from sea level to over 3,000m wherever there are vegetated areas with preferably moist open spaces and suitable perches from which to hunt, open or lightly vegetated areas, grassy marshes, scrub on rocky hillsides and forest edges. Patches free of vegetation which are visible from hunting perches are important and a preference is shown for areas with a degree of dampness in the soil (Ledant 1986, Glutz & Bauer 1988). In the savanna north of Congo it is especially fond of cultivation, whilst in Uganda it occurs up to 2,300m, favouring tall grassland (Keith et al. 1992). However, in Kenya and Tanzania it prefers short grass with scattered bushes (Moreau 1972). In West Africa in coastal areas it occurs in gardens and on farms. It is also found in open areas where crops have been cleared or bush recently cut as well as in forest clearings and up to the barest hilltops.

In Liberia the highest densities are found in burnt areas of savanna where this is available, ricefields, open farmland and gardens (Gatter 1997). In Sierra Leone it can occur in any open site, especially in grassland and on occasions in grassy areas in woodland. It has occasionally been seen amongst smaller mangroves. In Ghana it is found in forest clearings, savanna and the coastal thicket zone (Grimes 1987). In Kumasi in Ghana wintering birds lived in areas where crops or bush had been recently cleared and in southern Nigeria it is a common visitor to farms and gardens (Bannerman 1936).

VOICE

The Whinchat is generally silent outside of the breeding season, although warning calls for potential predators such as raptors or other dangers may be given at any time of year. Occasionally males about to commence or already on spring passage will be heard in song. Birds have been heard singing as early as March in Ghana and a male was heard singing several times successively from the top of a bush on 4 April 1952 near Freetown, Sierra Leone (Almond 1956). Others have been heard singing on spring passage in central Europe.

Song is only given by the male and the song period usually commences with arrival on the breeding areas from late April/May and ceases in mid- to late July, although exceptionally it continues into August (Glutz & Bauer 1988).

The song has been described as "sweet, mellow and almost fluty" and in sound and phrasing similar to the song of a Mistle Thrush *Turdus viscivorous* heard from afar (Walpole Bond 1938), whilst parts are also said to resemble Northern Wheatear *Oenanthe oenanthe* and Common Redstart *Phoenicurus phoenicurus*.

Song can be assigned to three categories: territorial, courtship and excitement (Schmidt & Hantge 1954). The territorial song, produced in lengthy bouts, is comprised of short phrases 0.6–1.6/1.8 seconds long. The frequency range is around 2.8 kHz, which is slightly wider than that of European Stonechat and includes far more lower-pitched sounds (Schwager & Guttinger 1984). The phrases consist of clicking, rattling and whistling units of variable structure given in rapid succession and the song sounds more melodious and not so shrill and harsh compared to European Stonechat. This is due to the wider frequency range, the song containing more low-pitched sounds and also the larger pitch changes between individual units (Glutz & Bauer 1988).

Each male has a wide and extensive repertoire of units in its song, usually in excess of 100 and mainly differing between neighbouring males. The units can be grouped into 12 types which include the following and intermediates: rattling, rasping sounds which are given in rapid succession; discrete whistles of constant pitch and others of variable pitch comprising of two or more subunits; units with rapid frequency modulation; varied and complex harsher sounds. Some units indicate simultaneous use of two internal tympanic membranes. The song always commences with a harsh introductory phrase (Cramp 1988).

Males rarely repeat song-types within one bout of singing and switch units irregularly so that changes in pitch are more marked, producing a richer, more melodious, varied and less monotonous song than in European Stonechat (Schwager & Guttinger 1984). The song can also contain mimicry of a wide number of bird species with song phrases being copied complete or abbreviated such as the *dju* call of Common Bullfinch *Pyrrhula pyrrhula* or the long final rattle of Chaffinch *Fringilla coelebs* song. Other species mimicked include Corn Bunting *Miliaria calandra*, European Goldfinch *Carduelis carduelis*, European Robin *Erithacus rubecula*, Common Redstart, Common Whitethroat *Sylvia communis*, Meadow Pipit *Anthus pratensis*, Skylark *Alauda arvensis*, Willow Warbler *Phylloscopus trochilus* and Sedge Warbler *Acrocephalus schoenobaenus*. Species mimicked are usually breeding neighbours but quite often they can be woodland species that do not occur in Whinchat breeding habitat. A breeding male in one locality 'learned' to imitate the calls of Common Swift *Apus apus* and the song of Common Nightingale *Luscinia megarhynchos* and these were copied by another male and thus passed into the repertoires of half the locality's population of Whinchats (Schmidt & Hantge 1954). The mimicry is so good as often to be indiscernible from the species mimicked. Whilst the female is incubating the male's song becomes louder and longer (Gray 1974).

In addition to territorial singing there is a Courtship song and an Excitement song. The latter consists of quietly but rapidly uttered harsh strangled motifs and is usually given in interactions with other males (Schmidt & Hantge 1954). The bird adopts an exaggerated posture with drooping, quivering wings, fanned tail which is constantly flicked up and down and head thrown back to show off the breast and white areas on the wings and tail. The Courtship song is approximately equidistant in volume between the Territorial and Excitement song and is almost a subsong. It sounds like *ziwuziwu* and is uttered during the brief pair-formation period and before copulation. The song is usually delivered from an elevated perch such as bush, fence, small tree or phone wires, occasionally in a song-flight and exceptionally whilst feeding or on the ground. The song-flight is similar to that of European Stonechat with the male flying up singing for a few seconds, body held erect and tail spread to display the tail pattern, then returning to a perch. Song commences 85–100 minutes before sunrise, continuing intermittently during the day and exceptionally until after dark (Frankevoort & Hubatsch 1966). However, captive birds were heard to sing in the twilight and also until late at night (Bechstein 1858).

Male and female have a Warning call or contact call which is a Bullfinch-like whistled *dju* or *fiu*. Indeed the imitation of Bullfinch referred to above may be the Whinchat incorporating its contact call into its song. Sometimes there are variations up to a harsh, clear *sah* which is weaker and lower pitched than the equivalent call of the European Stonechat. It serves to warn of an intruder approaching the nest and is often alternated with another call, a strangled clicking or more toneless hard note described variously as *zk zk*, *tk tk*, *tec tec* or *tack tack* which can often be given in quick succession *tack-tack*, *tack-tack*. It is not as hard or sharp as the European Stonechat equivalent but the combination of the two calls serves the same purpose as in that species, and can be described as *fiu-tack fiu-tack*; the *fiu* warns the young in the nest and the *tack* draws the attention of the predator to the bird uttering the notes. In the case of a human intruder, these calls commenced when the intruder was c.100m away from the nest and increased in frequency and intensity the nearer he came. During incubation only the male utters the warning calls but once the young are hatched both parents utter the calls.

There is also an anxiety call described as *chup* or *tuup* used in situations where the bird is subject to considerable stress. It is uttered by both sexes and is similar to the flight call of Chaffinch *Fringilla coelebs* although somewhat louder (Ruttledge 1961). Fighting males have also been heard to utter a screeching call (Schmidt & Hantge 1954). Disturbed birds also utter a churring *rrr* or *dschrr* which is sometimes extended in to a longer rustling sound (Glutz & Bauer 1988). A similar call is uttered by nestlings when a parent brings food to the nest.

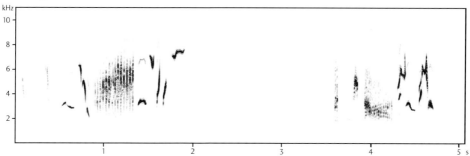

Whinchat *Saxicola rubetra* NSA02511 Song. Somerset, England 15 May 1973. *R. Savage*.

FOOD

The Whinchat mainly eats invertebrates. It regularly takes spiders (Araneida), small snails (Gastropoda) and worms (Oligochaeta). It also often takes beetles (Coleoptera), Hymenoptera and Diptera, these forming a predominant part of its diet, plus grasshoppers (Saltatoria), earwigs (Dermaptera), bugs (Hemiptera): comprising Pentatomidae, Cicadellidae, Aphidoidea, and Lepidoptera of the families Noctuidae, Geometridae and Arctiidae (both imagines and larvae). On migration stopovers in autumn, berries such as *Rubus* often become an important food item (Brensing 1977). Other prey recorded from the Palearctic include mayflies (Ephemeroptera), dragonflies and damselflies (Odonata), ants (Formicidae), bees (Apoidea), and woodlice (Isopoda). Migrant birds have been observed feeding on blackberries (*Rubus fruticosus*) in autumn at Dungeness Bird Observatory, Kent, southern England in 1960 and 1961 (Scott 1962).

Of 709 identifiable prey items brought to almost fledged nestlings in Poland at the end of July, 24.8% were imago and 15.9% larval Lepidoptera and sawflies (Tenthredinidae), 14.5% craneflies (Tipula), 12.8% grasshoppers, 5.8% flies, 10.6% unidentified insects and 9.7% spiders, with snails, dragonflies/damselflies (Odonata), beetles and wasps (Vespidae) all under 5% (Steinfatt 1937).

In Switzerland the food brought to 15 broods at 900–1,000m a.s.l. and 5 at 1,400–1,500m was studied, 4,198 and 1,531 prey items respectively, belonged to the following groups (rounded percentages): Hymenoptera 27/60%,(almost exclusively Symphyta larvae, mainly Tenthredinidae), beetles 27/2%, Diptera 21/12%, Lepidoptera 14/19%, (mostly larvae), Saltatoria 3/3.5%, Heteroptera 1/0.1%, Gastropoda 3/2%, Araneida 2/2%, Oligochaeta 1/0%. Although very abundant, moths *Odetia atrata*, scorpion flies (Panorpidae and Mecoptera), rove beetles (Staphylinidae) and leaf beetles (Chrysomelidae) as well as dung flies (Scatophagidae) were completely avoided (A. Labhardt in Glutz & Bauer 1988).

Among the largest prey items recorded is a mole-cricket *Gryllotalpa* (Oggier 1984). In the Ukraine 14 stomachs contained 98% insects, mainly Coleoptera (70%) which included 27 species of ground beetle (Carabidae) (Kuzmenko 1977). Young in a nest near Leningrad were given mainly whole, medium-sized insects including hard beetles, but smaller young were given softer prey such as small spiders and sawfly larvae (Prokofieva 1980). Items fed to young 7–10 days old measured 8–16mm (Glutz & Sauter 1962). Birds were recorded in the Ural River floodplain as virtually exclusively eating beetles but occasionally orthopterans and bugs, also snails and worms (Dement'ev & Gladkov 1968). The diet of nestlings and adults is probably supplemented with grit, as a captive bird lacking this in its diet was unable to stand but became perfectly healthy when given grit in its food (Bechstein 1858).

MOVEMENTS

The Whinchat is a long-distance trans-Saharan migrant with a winter distribution not dissimilar to that of Northern Wheatear, wintering throughout the rainy season on open grassy steppes, savanna and agricultural land mainly in equatorial and tropical West and East Africa as well as more northerly parts of southern Africa. In years when the rains fail in the wintering areas, returning populations reach Europe in poor condition and probably suffer increased mortality (Bastian *et al.* 1997). There are records of birds north of the Sahara in winter but these are exceptional, although encompassing a wide area, with records from northern and western Algeria, southern Morocco and Tunisia, throughout the Mediterranean and the western seaboard of Europe as far north as the UK and Fennoscandia.

There are two main wintering regions in Africa, with a distinct gap of around 10° longitude in Central Africa between the two where it is only recorded on passage, e.g. Chad (Newby 1979–1980). The first area extends from the West African savannas of southern Mauritania, Senegal, Gambia (where it is generally uncommon), Guinea, Sierra Leone (common in October–April in the rolling savanna plains of the north: Serle 1949), Liberia (common in the north and not uncommon in south), southern Mali, Ivory Coast, Ghana and Nigeria (an abundant winter visitor to the southern half of the country as far as the coast [Calabar] and mainly passage migrant in the north apart from the Jos Plateau [>1,220 m], where it also winters in numbers: Elgood *et al.* 1966), to Cameroon and northern Gabon. The second area extends from the north-east Democratic Republic of Congo and southern Sudan (south of 6°N) to south-west Ethiopia, Uganda and west and central Kenya, south through the Democratic Republic of Congo (east of the Congo River), Rwanda, Burundi and western Tanzania to Malawi (south to 13°S) and northern Zambia (south to 15°S).

It winters in a wider latitudinal belt in West Africa than the majority of Palearctic migrants, although the northern edge of its wintering range in West Africa lies slightly further south than that of Northern Wheatear and excludes most of the semi-arid zone from Senegal to Niger, Chad and central Sudan. However, it apparently penetrates further south into suitable cleared, cultivated and open areas in other vegetation belts in the equatorial coastal zone of West Africa, with a few reaching north-east Gabon (Brosset & Erard 1986). In East Africa it winters from southern Ethiopia southwards. Britton (1980) states "It winters commonly, sometimes abundantly in western Uganda, north-west Tanzania south to Kibondo, and north-east Uganda at Kidepo Valley National Park (NP). Elsewhere in Uganda, and in the Lake Turkana basin in north-west Kenya, it is mainly an uncommon passage migrant in October–November and late March–early April. It is regular at Lakes Nakuru and Naivasha but is rare east of the Kenya–Tanzania Rift Valley having been recorded from Nanyuki, Thika, Nairobi, Tsavo NP (East and West) and Arusha NP". It has been recorded as a very rare vagrant from south-east Kenya at Ngulia, Mombasa. Small numbers winter in western Tanzania south to Ufipa and Njombe, and in western Kenya, particularly Nyanza province on the north-east edge of Lake Victoria where it is sometimes numerous on passage. Further west and south the wintering area extends to eastern parts of the Democratic Republic of Congo (Keith *et al.* 1992).

Smaller numbers regularly reach as far south as northern Malawi and north-eastern Zambia east of 28°E, arriving in Zambia in November and departing late March (Aspinwall *et al.* 1998). It has been recorded from Samfya on 28 March 1970 and Ndola in the Copperbelt on 11 February 1972, and some may winter as far south as Lusaka at 15°25´S. On 7 January 1972 two birds were found in an area of open waste grassland and small cultivated plots 3km west of Lusaka. Subsequently six and possibly as many as ten were found in the same area on 16 January (Tucker 1972). It has been recorded as far south in Zambia as Chilanga about 17km south of Lusaka (Benson *et al.* 1971). Further south it has been reported twice as a rare vagrant to Namibia: a specimen was collected at Swakopmund on 21 January 1925, with a video-recorded record from Mahango Game Reserve, Caprivi Strip, on 5 November 1998 (N.J. Redman *in litt.* 2000). In Botswana's Okavango Delta a record of four birds at Qhaaxwha airstrip on 22 September 1984 was not accepted by the Botswana Bird Club but one of a bird at Xaxaba on 27 March 1987 was (Harrison *et al.* 1997). There are two unconfirmed reports from Zimbabwe, at Cashel in the eastern highlands where four birds were found on 25 December 1949 and others or the same birds being seen there on 2 April 1950 and a few days earlier (Irwin 1987); moreover, there is an accepted record of a male in full breeding plumage at Lonsdale Farm on 1 January 1991 (Hustler *et al.* 1992). In Transvaal [Meumalanga] South Africa, there is an accepted record of two birds 3km south-west of Diepgezet asbestos mine on 25 March 1987, and unconfirmed sight records from Himeville in KwaZulu-Natal January 1961 and three birds seen together at Umfolozi Flats, Zululand, February 1961 (Clancey 1964, Maclean 1985). Birds wintering in eastern, central and southern Africa and those on passage through Ethiopia and the Middle East are considered to be migrants from the eastern parts of the range in eastern Europe and the former USSR.

Birds leave their breeding areas in northern Europe and Asia from early August and September. Peak numbers on passage in western Europe occur in early September. There appears to be a general simultaneous departure over a broad front from west to east, with the general direction being south and south-west. Observatories on the east and west coasts of the UK and in continental Europe all report similar peak passage timings. Recoveries of birds ringed in western and central Europe show that they have moved south-west to western Iberia. Recoveries come from two main areas, (1) western France and northern Spain on the south-western edge of the Pyrenees and (2) western Iberia, especially Portugal (Cramp 1988). In the UK a suggestion of a double peak of passage birds may refer to the departures of first and second broods (Riddiford & Findley 1981). The Alps do not appear to provide an obstacle to the broad front migration, with birds being recorded up to 2,963m. From the more eastern parts of its breeding range birds head more south-south-west, but from the UK they head south to western France and northern Spain before turning south-west. It would then appear that most European Whinchats need to make a sharp turn, which evidently takes place before they arrive on the coast of North Africa or further inland, as they are encountered in about equal numbers across the Sahara from west to east and there are no records of large numbers on the Atlantic coast of Morocco and only comparatively few records from the Canary Islands (Moreau 1961, Bannerman 1963). Eastern populations cross the Middle East and Arabian Peninsula also on a broad front and reach Africa almost exclusively west of Somalia. There are 11 records (only two for autumn, 18 and 20 September, and nine in spring, 20 April–12 May) from Somalia, all west of 46°E, and western Somalia is considered to be the eastern limit of its migration route in both spring and autumn (Ash & Miskell 1998).

Birds ringed in Finland were shown to move either south-west through Iberia (15 recoveries) or south-south-west through Italy (10 recoveries), and two individuals from Finland had reached northern Italy by August. Autumn recoveries of Finnish-ringed nestlings demonstrated an uneven geographic distribution by age. Of 11 recoveries from Italy, or between Finland and Italy, nine were juveniles; but of 14 recoveries of Finnish-ringed birds in the western part of the Iberian Peninsula only five were juveniles (Glutz & Bauer 1988). Two nestlings ringed in south-west Poland were also recovered in northern Italy in August. Two recoveries of birds ringed in Nigeria from Libya and Poland respectively, together with a report of a bird ringed in April in Tunisia and subsequently found wintering in Togo, suggest that birds wintering in this region originate from central Europe (Elgood et al. 1966, Zink 1973). Fidelity to migration stopover sites was also demonstrated for Tunisian migrants: at Gabes in Tunisia 0.84% of migrants ringed were subsequently recaptured there (Moreau 1972).

The species has been recorded as an exceptional vagrant from the Selvagem Islands (Schmitz 1909) and it has recently been recorded for the first time from the Cape Verde Islands, where two were on the island of Sal on 30 September 1999 (Hazevoet 1999). Autumn birds have been recorded as vagrants from the Seychelles – a single individual at Bird Island on 5–7 November 1982, the first for the Malagasy Region (Phillips 1984) – and Novaya Zemlya in Arctic Russia (Dement'ev & Gladkov 1968). The species is an occasional autumn (September–October) migrant on the Faeroes but does not occur every year (the highest total for one day was an exceptional 30 at Akraberg and Sumba on the island of Suduroy on 21 September 1982 and possibly a similar number the next day on the island of Nolsoy), but there have only been two spring records, on 1 May 1898 and 28 April 1983 (S. Sorensen in litt. 2001). In Iceland there were 65 records involving 81 birds in the years 1947–1998. There are two records from the north coast and one from Grimsey off the north coast. All other records are from the south coast, with almost annual occurrence in the period 1971–1998 (not 1974, 1976, 1986, 1989 or 1990). In some years there is more than one record per year, notably 1981 when 14 records involved 26 birds, followed by 1982 with seven records of 12 birds. These two years were exceptional (see Faeroes) and more normally there are 1–3 records per year, each record normally of a single individual. In 1999 there was probably only one seen, but in 2000 there were seven (G. Petursson in litt. 2001), and between 16 and 20 October 2001 no fewer than 13 were recorded (Y. Kolbeinsson in Birding World 14). It is interesting that in direct contrast to European Stonechat, which has only ever been recorded in spring, all Iceland records apart from a female on 23 May 1972 have been in autumn, falling between 11 September and 24 November with a marked peak in the last three weeks of September.

The first real evidence of migratory movements in western, central and northern Europe is in early July, and departure from the breeding areas commences in earnest from early August onwards. In the northern UK on Fair Isle and in the Baltic region the peak time for passage is between mid-August and early September, whilst in the rest of western and central Europe it is from the last week in August to the first week in September. Median passage dates for two Baltic and one central European country are Finland 15 August; Estonia 24 August; and Switzerland 24–28 August. In Estonia at Sorve Bird Observatory from 1998 to 2000 passage commenced in the first ten days of July and ceased by 10 October, the main bulk of migrants moving south in August with peak passage recorded in the ten-day period 21–31 August (T. Pettay *in litt.* 2000). Autumn departure from the Russian Federation is during the first half of September (Bashkira, Kharkov, Grodno at the beginning of September, Kalinin, Ryazan and Moscow in the middle of September) with birds from Novgorod leaving in the second half of September. Departure is a slow process and in western Siberia passage migrants have been recorded at Semipalatinsk and in the Kyrgyz steppe as late as mid-October (Johansen 1954). Birds in the northern Caucasus leave earlier, from the last ten days of August, with passage continuing in most of the above areas until the end of September (Dement'ev & Gladkov 1968).

In the UK late migrants regularly occur throughout October and exceptionally in November. For example in Sussex, southern England, in the years 1982–1996 at least 533 were recorded in October and in the years 1962–1999 17 in November. Individuals in December, January and February (probably wintering in the case of the latter two months) are extremely rare. In Sussex, 1962–1999, there were only two, one on 2 December 1981, the other from 7 November to 4 December 1999. Indeed in the UK from 1864 to 1972 there were only eight records in January (Hudson 1973). However, three in January 1980 and two in January 1981 were reported wintering in Scotland (Allsop & Hume 1981, Thom 1986). Some of the birds recorded in November and later months in the UK have shown pale plumage characters, suggesting they may be from the eastern areas of the species' range. The individual in Sussex recorded in November–December 1999 was described as "decidedly pallid" both above and below, apart from a warmer tone on the central breast (D. Smith *in litt.* 2000). A similar individual was again recorded in Sussex on 6 October 2001 (E.U. pers. obs. 2001).

The majority of birds have left central Europe by the first ten days of October, with records in the second half of that month and early November being very scarce. In Germany the latest up to 1988 was 16 November 1974; Netherlands 28 November 1925; and Austria 30 November 1974. Wintering records, as in the UK, are exceptional and there is a possibility that some may refer to misidentified Siberian Stonechat. There are presumed records of wintering birds from Sweden 16–22 November 1981; Norway 28 December 1983–14 January 1984; Belgium 6 January 1985; Slovakia 9 January 1931; Spain 11 January 1919; and Switzerland 18 January–15 March 1975 (Glutz & Bauer 1988).

Passage through the Mediterranean region sees birds passing through the Camargue not much later than in central Europe. In Greece they are a common migrant from mid-August to mid-October with a peak in mid-September. On Corsica they are less common than in spring, occurring between mid-August and the end of October (Thibault & Bonaccorsi 1999). On Crete they have been seen as late as mid-November. They are one of the commonest prey species of Eleonora's Falcon *Falco eleonorae* off north-east Crete in autumn (Ristow *et al.* 1986). On Sicily they are present from mid-August to late October although less common than in spring, with a peak in September (Iapichino & Massa 1989), and similarly in Malta (Bannerman & Vella-Gaffiero 1976). On Cyprus they mainly occur in the second half of September. They are widespread on passage in Turkey with the main passage through the Bosporus around mid-September, but very few are seen in Jordan or Iraq. In Bahrain they are scarcer than in spring, occurring mainly in September–October with stragglers in November (Nightingale & Hill 1993). In Oman they also occur in September–October (Gallagher & Woodcock 1980) and in southern Yemen and Socotra from September to early November (Martins & Porter 1996).

Passage in Israel is relatively protracted. The Whinchat is a common migrant throughout the country with early arrivals in the period 13–27 August and the majority of birds occurring between mid-September and mid-October, with a peak between 25 September and 5 October. In some years two dense waves are noted in the second half of September (peak 22nd–28th) and the first half of October (peak 4th–8th). Stragglers have occurred as late as the first half of December (Shirihai 1995). In Egypt it is a common migrant from early September to late October, peaking from mid-September to mid-October with early migrants in late August (27th), and there are numerous records up to late November (Goodman & Meininger 1989). In the coastal areas of North Africa birds appear between mid-September and the second half of October, with early arrivals in late August and stragglers in November. They cross the Sahara on a broad front although fewer birds are recorded from the central sector (Keith *et al.* 1992) and the first arrivals in West Africa are generally in mid-September with passage continuing until November.

Throughout the Gambia it is a common passage migrant on open ground in October–November, with the earliest arrival being 13 September and occasionally single birds remaining to winter (Gore 1990). In Sierra Leone it is quite common from January to late April with the latest dates being 22 and 23 April 1935 when it was still very common on the Little Skarsies River (R.R. Glanville in Bannerman 1936). In the savanna zones of Liberia birds arrive at the beginning of October in the north-west and at the end of October in the south-east. Arrivals continue with a gradual rise in numbers on selected sites up to a maximum of 200 birds per km² in December declining to 15 per km² in January. In the south-east in the forest zone the highest numbers are in February with departure in March and April (Gatter 1997). In

Ghana it is locally common and widespread, being present from October to April in forest clearings and the coastal thicket zone from the Cape coast east to the Accra and Keta Plains. It extends northwards through the Volta Region to the northern savanna where it is present from late September to early May (Grimes 1972). It has also been recorded from the Ivory Coast in late November, and there are various old records from Togoland and Benin (Bannerman 1936). Most birds overfly northern Nigeria completely to their wintering grounds in lower-lying (<610 m) southern Nigeria, where it is one of the most conspicuous winter migrants. In the Enugu area between 23 September to 8 May and at Ibadan from 9 October to 30 April it was found to be common in farmlands. In the north at Kano small numbers of migrants are only noted in mid-September and mid-April (Elgood *et al.* 1966). In East Africa birds arrive earlier, with first arrivals in Ethiopia from 26 August, in central Sudan from the beginning of September, in northern Kenya in October–November and in Rwanda in early October (the bulk at the end of October). Arrivals in Zambia and Malawi are from late October/early November to December. It is generally solitary on its wintering grounds, but in favoured areas large numbers can be found together albeit maintaining loose individual territories.

Return migration in East Africa mainly begins in February from Zambia, and in the second half of March to mid-April in the Democratic Republic of Congo, Uganda and Rwanda, with the last bird being seen in Rwanda on 12 April. The main exodus in Kenya is from the end of March to early April, and in Sudan and Ethiopia it falls in the middle of April, with stragglers up to early May (Glutz & Bauer 1988). In Somalia northward migrants have been seen from 20 April to 12 May (Ash & Miskell 1998).

In the Gambia, West Africa, spring migrants appear as early as February and March with the majority passing through between mid-March and the end of April, the latest date being 9 May (Gore 1990). Birds were last seen in Sierra Leone on 22 April (Serle 1949) and in Liberia on 24 April 1982 in the south and 30 April 1984 in the north (Gatter 1997). Birds do occur, however, in May, for example on 21 May on the Nigerian shore of Lake Chad (R.J. Dowsett 1968 in Glutz & Bauer 1988) and 24 May in Gambia (Jensen & Kirkeby 1980). The earliest arrivals on the Mediterranean coast are in the first half of March with the main passage occurring in North Africa from the end of March to mid-May and stragglers occurring into early June. In Libya it is common on the coast at Tripoli and Cyrenaica from late March to May with peak numbers in mid-April, while at Serir in the desert it was also recorded from late March to May, with 50 present in late April 1970 (Bundy 1976). On Malta it is very common between the end of March and the end of May and present in far larger numbers than in autumn. Exceptionally large numbers can occur, such as 1,000+ at four localities on the island on 25 April 1970 (Bannerman & Vella-Gaffiero 1976).

Observations appear to support the fact that European Whinchats migrate to their breeding grounds by a more direct route than they do when migrating to their wintering grounds. In Portugal they are regular in autumn from the second week in September until mid-October, but are never seen in spring (Tait 1924). However, in Menorca they are especially frequent in both September and April–May (Ramos 1996). The species is generally more conspicuous in spring, especially between Tunisia and Egypt and eastwards as far as the United Arab Emirates. Recoveries of birds ringed at Cap Bon, Tunisia, indicate a route through northern Italy north to Scandinavia as well as through southern Italy north-east to Nizhniy Novgorod in Russia (Zink 1973).

Peak migration on the north Mediterranean coast is some two weeks later than in North African. In Greece it is present from early April to mid-May, peaking in the second half of April, although birds can still be passing through northern areas such as Paxos in early June (EU pers. obs.), whilst it may arrive in Crete from late March onwards (Handrinos & Akriotis 1997). On Corsica it is mainly seen in spring from 19 March to 5 June, with the majority of records occurring from late April to mid-May, occurring up to 1,500m even with snow on the ground, roosting in cultivated fields, grassland and low maquis in groups of 10–100 (Thibault & Bonaccorsi 1999). In Sicily it is a fairly common migrant from early April to late May with a peak in late April–early May; it has been recorded irregularly as early as mid-March and, intriguingly, in January and February (two in January 1971, one on 19 February 1977 and two on 2 February 1983), but it is not known whether these were wintering birds or very early migrants (the 19 February bird was judged a migrant) (Iapichino & Massa 1989).

In Egypt it is common from early March to late May with some birds arriving in early February, such as at Quseir on 2 February 1983. As there are no winter records for December or January it is presumed that this bird was an early migrant. Passage peaks from early April to early May, with the latest bird being seen on 23 May 1971 at Bahig (Goodman & Meininger 1989). Timings are similar in Israel although birds are less frequent before the end of March. Numbers are smaller than in autumn except in southern and eastern areas. In parts of north and central Israel the species is totally absent. There are three distinct influxes, (1) second–third week of April (peak 11–19 April), (2) last week of April–first week of May (peak 26 April–3 May), (3) second half of May (peak third week of May). The second influx is the largest. In most years numbers decrease significantly after mid-May but in some years May passage is as strong if not stronger than in April and continues to mid-June (Shirihai 1995). In eastern Saudi Arabia it is a regular but scarce migrant found during April and May with an extreme date of 29 June 1984 at Abqaiq (Bundy *et al.* 1989). It is also recorded from Bahrain, where small numbers in ones and twos occur from late March, with most in April and stragglers into early May (Nightingale & Hill 1993). It is recorded from southern Yemen from mid-April to early June (Martins & Porter 1996).

In central Europe earliest arrivals can be before mid-March. In Switzerland in 1977, the earliest was two birds both recorded on 27 February near Lucerne and Wengimoos/Bern respectively (A. & M. Brun & W. Schaub respectively in Glutz & Bauer 1988). In the Netherlands 7–8 birds were near Lauwersmeer on 12 March 1983 (Glutz & Bauer 1988) but generally most birds arrive between the last ten days of March and the first ten days of April. Main passage in Switzerland and southern Germany commences in mid-April and peaks in early May, with arrival on breeding territories occurring at the same time but continuing, like passage into the second half of May, with sometimes even higher levels towards the end of May or in early June. Arrivals on breeding areas and peak migration in northern and eastern parts of Germany are only slightly later.

Arrivals in the UK coincide with those in northern parts of central Europe. First arrivals on the south coast of England are in mid-April with the mean first arrival date in Sussex on the south coast of England, 1970–1993, being 12 April. Arrival dates appear to be shifting forward, as the mean arrival date for the ten years 1989–1999 in Sussex is now 28 March. Individuals do exceptionally arrive earlier, with the earliest date in Sussex being a male on 18–25 February 1995 (Patton 1995) and in Peebles, Scotland, on 13 March 1983 (Thom 1986). Walpole Bond (1938) found it unusual to encounter more than 6–8 migrant individuals together in spring in Sussex. Often individuals are encountered singly. However, a flock of 28, mostly males were observed on 29 April 1948 in the Cuckmere Valley, Sussex and another flock of 15 on the same day was nearby on the cliffs at Crowlink (Harber 1948). Peak passage in the UK is usually from mid- to late April through to mid-May, and dispersal to breeding areas is rapid throughout the UK with birds, even in Scotland, arriving from mid-April onwards and most occupying territories by mid-May. In southern Scotland birds arrived on their breeding areas between 25 April and 10 May, with males preceding females by 3–8 days (Gray 1974). Passage in the UK continues throughout May and is at its peak on Shetland and Fair Isle (where it does not breed) around mid-May, with birds presumably bound for Scandinavia continuing to arrive into early June with an extreme date of 27 June on Fair Isle (Williamson 1965).

In northern Jutland the peak is in mid-May, in southern Sweden the mean first arrival date is 7 May, central Sweden 8 May and Norway 6 May (Oslo) and 16 May (Mosjoen/Nordland). In Finland the mean arrival dates are similar. Migrants are not seen until early May and reach a peak between 20–25 May on Åland and near Tauvo (Glutz & Bauer 1988). In Estonia the mean arrival date from observations over 1977–1986 is 5 May with the earliest birds arriving 13–20 April (Leibak *et al.* 1994). In Armenia the earliest arrival dates are 13 March 1979, 16 April 1974 and 28 April 1971. Generally it arrives from late April to early May (Adamian & Klem 1999). In the Russian Federation early arrivals are at the end of March (North Caucasian Wildlife Sanctuary), with the majority arriving between mid-April and early May. In North Ossetia it appears in the first ten days of April, around Kiev 14–28 April, in the Minsk Region 29 April, while the mean arrival date in the Novgorod region is 2 May (extreme dates 25 April and 10 May) and around Arkhangelsk in late May. Further east at southern Bashkira it arrives in early May and around Ufa the main arrival is 7–9 May. There is little information concerning the Asian parts of its range but migrants occur on Cheleken in late April or the first half of May and around Tomsk in West Siberia it was first noted on 14 May (Dement'ev & Gladkov 1968). Further north of Tomsk it occurs around 20 May while further south passage birds were on the Irgiz on 3 May.

Up to 1983 birds ringed in autumn in the UK were recovered in France, Spain and Portugal but none were recovered in North Africa. However, in spring they have been recovered in Algeria, Morocco and Tunisia. This may suggest that birds cross the Sahara in autumn in one flight from southern Europe (Iberia) but that they often make landfall in North Africa on spring migration (Cramp 1988). G.L. Bates in Bannerman (1936) held the opinion that the species migrated non-stop over the desert and dry country south of the Sahara as he did not see it on a journey along the entire southern border of the Sahara from Nigeria to Senegal except at Zaria and Sokoto at the end of March and beginning of April. Mean minimum flight distances based on ringing recoveries were calculated to be 81–88km per day (maxima 94km per day over 20 days and 86km over 39 days (Hilden & Saurola 1982 in Glutz 1988). A nestling ringed in Tayside, Scotland, in June 1999 was found dead in Ghana on 21 September 2000, a distance of 5,460km, representing the furthest recovery of a UK-ringed Whinchat (Clark 2001).

Birds generally migrate in small groups or flocks (5–30) and most migration is nocturnal. Numbers on Fair Isle varied from 10 to 30 (occasionally 50) per day, with exceptional aggregations such as 500 on 4 September 1956. As many as 500–1,000 descended at Beachy Head, East Sussex, on 21 September 1980, after a night of south-east winds and rain.

Birds put on fat reserves before migration. Average weights for autumn migrant birds on the Col de Bretolet in Switzerland were (August) males (n=64) 16.7 g, females (n=59) 16.1 g, first-years (n=55) 15.4 g; September adults (n=19) 17.3 g, first-years (n=72) 17.7 g (Labhardt 1984). In central Nigeria birds averaged 14.5 g in October–November but during spring migration in March–April in successive years they averaged (n=37) 20.4 g and (n=20) 18.7 g respectively (Smith & Cox 1972). In northern Nigeria from September to February weights were in the range 13.5–15.0 g (mean 14.2), but in April they rose to 15.4– 23.0 g (mean 19.2 g) (Fry 1971).

BEHAVIOUR

The Whinchat usually hunts prey from a low level perch flying down to the ground to seize prey and then returning to the same or another suitable perch. Occasionally it will make aerial sallies to catch airborne prey. Birds on the ground move in a series of rapid hops with a rather upright carriage.

Three migrants on the south coast of England in October, observed for around one hour, fed entirely on the ground running and hopping in a fashion similar to that of the Northern Wheatear. It was considered that this behaviour was an adaptation to the high winds (Force 6) prevailing at the time (EU pers. obs. 2001).

The species usually roosts on the ground in thick vegetation or low down in tangled vegetation around the base of bushes. Occasionally it roosts in family parties in autumn but only singly in wintering areas. It is rather crepuscular remaining active until dark (Witherby *et al.* 1948). Perched Whinchats move their tail slowly up and down and flick the outer part of the wing (carpal joint to tip) as well as bobbing the whole body on flexed legs. With increased excitement or anxiety these actions become more pronounced and the feathers of the crown are raised and lowered.

In wintering areas such as Sierra Leone birds are loosely territorial, each maintaining a small territory which is readily abandoned if conditions become unsuitable or a more productive habitat becomes available, such as newly formed farm patches (Serle 1949). However, in Ghana it did not exhibit any territorial behaviour (Grimes 1972).

There is circumstantial evidence that some birds may form pairs before spring migration. In Sierra Leone pairs were observed in early April prior to migrating north (Serle 1949).

An unpaired territorial male on its breeding territory always performs courtship behaviour to any female that enters his territory. The male perches c.3–4m from the female jerking his tail continuously and occasionally singing in short bursts. The female responds by soliciting copulation and the male turns towards the female. He then flies to within 30–40cm of her, moving closer with rapid wing-flicking. When c.15–20cm away he holds his body horizontal with head raised, and slowly opens his wings before leaping next to her, holding this posture. (This posture is also adopted when male and female meet accidentally

Whinchat courtship (a) Male flies to female landing some 30–40cm from her and then moves towards her whilst rapidly flicking wings. (b) Some 15–20cm from female the male raises its head whilst keeping its body horizontal, slowly opening wings and raising and lowering tail. (c) He then leaps right up to female maintaining open winged posture. (d) Female defensively threatens with open bill. (e) Female who is ready to copulate flies off closely followed by the male. (After Glutz & Bauer 1988.)

at the nest when feeding young.) The female responds by opening her bill in mock threat, then flies off closely pursued by the male (A. Labhardt *in litt.* in Glutz & Bauer 1988). This may be followed by displacement behaviour such as mock preening or looking at the feet, brief feeding bouts and angled ascent by male in song-flight. After a few feeding flights the male, with plumage sleeked, would perform several flying leaps over the female alternately left to right, right to left (W. Daunicht in Glutz & Bauer 1988).

Mating takes place within the territory. Multiple copulations can take place with short pauses between each act. Birds will also copulate on the ground, fence posts or in a low bush and females will occasionally approach the male inviting copulation whilst he is giving subdued song. After copulation the female may remain motionless for some time (Horstkotte 1962, Thalman 1981).

Territories occupied by breeding pairs are defended by the male with song and flight-displays. The male may fly towards an intruding male in undulating 'threat' flight and follow this by perching several metres away with wings spread and tail fanned and delivering the 'excitement' variation of its song (see Voice). On other occasions, he may fly slowly towards the intruder, spiralling upwards when getting close and giving the excitement song but then breaking off and flying down to the ground, often with a subsequent chase taking place. Either of these actions may be followed by an aerial fight with much bill-snapping or a chase in which the defending bird flies around the intruder at high speed in tight circles. The chase is interspersed with pauses during which the antagonists sit silently facing each other. Occasionally the dispute is resolved in the grass with physical contact and often with screeching calls. After these interactions the male often performs somersaults and rolls whilst flying back to rejoin its mate. This was observed several times during May in pairs breeding in Scotland (Gray 1973). Aggression and fights are particularly fierce between late-arriving males attempting to reoccupy their previous year's

Whinchat courtship Male (a) with compressed plumage sometimes performs display dance in which he performs flying leaps alternately left and right over the perched female (b). (After Glutz & Bauer 1988.)

Whinchat mating behaviour The male (a) flies towards the female (b) and performs a hover dance in front of female holding his body almost vertically and describing parabolic to semicircular flight trajectories around her. The female responds by inclining her body forward, raising and partly expanding the tail whilst quivering partially opened and dropped wings. (After Glutz & Bauer 1988.)

territory and a male that has already taken it (Schmidt & Hantge 1954, Muller 1985). If near its territorial boundary the occupying male may perform a display-flight. Having dropped its wings and fanned its tail when perched it will take off and pass in front of the intruder as slowly as possible in a light hovering flight with tail lowered and head raised. This evidently shows to maximum effect the contrasting black and white tail and wing patterns. Unlike threat flights, display-flights are only given in the period between pair formation and start of breeding. The male sometimes also displays to another male at the territorial boundary by hovering and presenting his back to the neighbour (W. Daunicht in Glutz & Bauer 1988).

Interactions between paired birds include gaping and courtship feeding. A male was seen on two occasions to take food to the incubating female and another male fed a female brooding young 1–2 days old (Groebbels 1950, Schmidt & Hantge). Where it is found in association with Northern Wheatear and European Stonechat on migration and in breeding areas, the Whinchat is submissive to both species although a captive bird displayed aggressively to European Stonechat in a neighbouring aviary (Greig-Smith 1982c, F. Weick in Glutz & Bauer 1988), but it dominates Meadow Pipit *Anthus pratensis* and Reed Bunting *Emberiza schoeniclus* (Phillips 1970). It is more aggressive towards avian predators in the breeding season than European Stonechat. Red-backed Shrike *Lanius collurio*, Common Cuckoo and Magpie have been observed to be attacked and driven away from the vicinity of the nest (Groebbels 1950, Horstkotte 1962). Outside the breeding season it is generally less wary of humans than European Stonechat but when breeding it commences giving intensive alarm calls when the intruder is still 100–150m from the nest, often with other unpaired territorial males joining in (Steinfatt 1937). Exceptionally, mock attacks are made on a human intruder (Geroudet 1957). If an observer at a nest prevents an adult from feeding its young the bird may lie flat on its perch in apparent conflict between escape and attack, its plumage

Whinchat aggression towards Common Cuckoo Male (a) lands very near to cuckoo with compressed plumage and leans forward with its head turned towards or parallel with the cuckoo (b). It then takes off vertically to overfly the cuckoo, hovering for around one second. Holding its body horizontally directly above the cuckoo at the apex of its flight trajectory (c). Having performed this manoeuvre it returns to its perch close to the cuckoo for several seconds (d) and then performs display hover directly in front of cuckoo (e) and again returns to perch close to cuckoo. Dive bombing attacks also occur (f). (After Glutz & Bauer 1988.)

alternately sleeked and ruffled. A similar conflict has been observed in the presence of Common Cuckoo (W. Daunicht in Glutz & Bauer 1988). When a male does attempt to drive off a cuckoo it approaches and lands very close with sleeked plumage, leaning well forward with its head turned towards the cuckoo or parallel to it. It then takes off vertically to hover for c.1 second directly over the cuckoo, then returns to the perch for some seconds, repeating this 'display hover' a number of times until the cuckoo departs. It will also dive in flight at a cuckoo. Similar behaviour has been observed with Magpies (W. Daunicht in Glutz & Bauer 1988).

A pair of Whinchats confronted with a stuffed cuckoo showed slightly different behavioural reactions to it. The female, after initially attacking it with her mate, ceased after less than a minute and returned to her nest and eggs. The male continued attacking for a few minutes and then stood quietly on the back of the dummy for up to five minutes, occasionally eating a feather plucked from it. If, however, the male was disturbed from this position he would immediately return with a full-blooded attack. The attacks were directed mainly at the head and around the eyes of the cuckoo. During these attacks the birds showed no apparent fear of humans and would attack the dummy even whilst it was being held in the hand (Edwards et al. 1949). Fledged young pestering their parents are repelled by threat-gaping from the adults.

Whinchats perch mainly on the tops of bushes and tall plants in open ground, flying in low flight from one to another with rapid wingbeats and a jerky flight. They also perch on trees and wires but rarely in the cover of foliage (Witherby et al. 1948). Song is delivered from a perch such as a sapling, bush, post, fence, telephone wires, tall vegetation or even a slight rise in the ground (Walpole-Bond 1938).

In Belgium migrating groups of Whinchats observed between 15 August–30 September 1980 were found to move along and feed from wire fences, apparently using a cooperative intensive feeding strategy for increasing predation success in all members of the flock. In this study birds were perched on barbed wire and would dive close to the wire into the grass and then return to the wire. After a while they flew along the wire just above the grass to another perch. They always flew in the general direction of movement to the head of the group. It was considered that there was an intraspecific strategy for increasing prey susceptibility to the benefit of all the flock. By flying just above the grass along the fence to the head of the group, each bird flushed insects that could be located by other perched Whinchats.

Only birds at the back of the group are moving, while a bird that has arrived at the head of the group only starts diving after it has been overtaken by another individual. After a certain number of food turns (defined as a dive into the grass independent of the success of the action) the food supply at a particular place will be exhausted, causing neighbouring birds to compete with each other. They will then move to the head of the group and, as a consequence, to unutilised feeding areas. The larger a group is the more feeding efficiency is enhanced, as more birds pass over a feeding area and flush more insects. This could decrease the time between food turns and as a consequence increase the number of food turns taken per unit of time. Smaller groups have less competition between members and consequently birds move less often. The upper limit to group size may be influenced by the amount of prey available (Draulans & van Vessem 1982).

MOULT

Adults undergo a complete post-breeding moult before migration, commencing in late July or early August and completing by late August to early September. The moult period in the UK and Finland lasts around 50 days (Ginn & Melville 1983, Lehikoinen & Niemela 1977). More southerly populations may moult slightly later and take slightly longer. Juveniles undergo a partial post-juvenile moult between June and August, rarely in September, involving the smaller body feathers. Around 75% moult all the lesser coverts, while 25% retain some; 33% moult all median coverts with 67% retaining one to rarely all juvenile median coverts (Jenni & Winkler 1994), and 80% moult two or three of the inner greater upperwing-coverts (coverts 09/10 occasionally also 08 and exceptionally 07). Sometimes some rectrices are moulted but juveniles retain all the remiges, most of the wing-coverts and the majority of the rectrices.

This is the only species in the genus definitely known on current knowledge to undergo a pre-breeding moult. All birds undergo a partial pre-breeding moult on their wintering grounds in February, March and early April prior to northward migration. In Sierra Leone they commence this in early March and it is complete by early April before the birds depart north (Serle 1949). In Ghana adults are in breeding plumage by late March and April (Grimes 1972). Exceptionally birds arrive in Europe with feathers still growing on the sides of the breast, belly, flanks, back and uppertail-coverts. Both first-year birds and adults renew a majority of the head and body feathers (with exceptions being mainly in the area of the rump and uppertail-coverts), from a third to two-thirds of the lesser wing-coverts and (subject to much variation) median secondary coverts 02–08, although most frequently 05–08. They also moult one or two inner greater coverts (09–10), but retain all the remiges and rectrices although exceptionally the second and third pair of tail feathers are sometimes moulted (Ginn & Melville 1983, Glutz & Bauer 1988).

CONSERVATION

Currently the Whinchat is not under threat and is listed as a Species of European Conservation Concern (SPEC) in Category 4 which is for 'species whose global populations are concentrated in Europe, but which have a Favourable Conservation Status in Europe'. Species are considered to be concentrated in Europe if more than 50% of their global breeding or wintering population occurs there (Tucker & Heath 1994).

Numbers in the years 1970–1990 remained mostly stable in eastern Europe and Fennoscandia, which account for c.90% of the total population of the world although the species is in decline in most of the rest of Europe. Overall c.20% of the population was in decline, 1970–1990, mainly in north-west and central Europe (Tucker & Heath 1994). The situation in the last ten years does not appear to have changed much. Although as with many other species it has lost habitat owing to scrub encroachment, afforestation and building, the main cause of its decline is the steady transformation of grassland into arable farmland and the increasing intensification of managed grassland. Small fields are amalgamated into larger, more 'economic' units. Meadows formerly cut for bedding and fields rich in herbaceous perennials and damp pastures have been and are being drained. These have been transformed through the use of massive amounts of chemical fertiliser into fodder meadows which are cut early and several times a year, or else into pasture with a thick monocultural grass cover, both possessing little biodiversity.

Most north-western and central European grasslands are now maintained in this manner but are also potentially the most important breeding habitat for Whinchat. The main grass-cutting period for silage in western and central Europe falls between early May and mid-July, which coincides with the Whinchat's peak breeding activities. This is the main reason for this species's decline in these areas (Bastian & Bastian 1996). In western and central Europe nest losses to early and repeated cutting of meadows and other grassland are much more critical to this species than losses caused by adverse weather or predation by corvids. Populations with a high breeding rate should in principle be able to compensate for high mortality rates, and a computer simulation indicated that constant annual predation rates of 45–50% can be compensated for, even in bad weather, if there are no additional losses caused by agriculture practices (Bastian 1989); but it also indicated that losses caused by agriculture and accompanied by drastic changes in vegetation and arthropod fauna can barely be compensated for even when other mortality factors are excluded (Bastian *et al.* 1994). In Poland preliminary studies of a small population on 315ha of agricultural land indicated that drainage of small wetlands within the study area, e.g. ditches and reedbeds, resulted in a decline in the population, and this has also been noticed in other intensively farmed areas which have had small areas of wetland drained (Tryjanowski 1995). Many birds confronted with rigidly maintained short-grass meadows, virtually devoid of biodiversity and consequently food supply, do not even bother to attempt to settle and breed in such impoverished habitat.

A study of the populations in south-western Germany made three general recommendations: (1) to preserve remaining large populations through special efforts; (2) to create a larger and more varied food supply through the large-scale adoption of 'extensive' (i.e. non-intensive) farming practices; and (3) to commence such farming practices on large grassland areas by lowering nutrient concentrations through sympathetic cutting or grazing, creating a more diverse vegetation with consequently a richer, more diverse invertebrate fauna (Opperman 1999).

Long-term climate changes such as increasing drought in the Sahel wintering areas of the Afrotropical region may have an eventual effect on numbers surviving to return to breed in the Palearctic region. There is some evidence that conditions for successfully overwintering in this area are becoming more difficult (Ledant 1986).

STOLICZKA'S BUSHCHAT
Saxicola macrorhyncha

Plate 2

Pratincola macrorhyncha Stoliczka, 1872, *J. Asiat. Soc. Bengal,* 41, p.238—near Rápúr, Wagur district, and near Bhúj, Kutch [= India]

Etymology *macrorhyncha* from Greek *macrorhunkhos* meaning long-billed or large-billed

Alternative names Stoliczka's Chat, Stoliczka's Whinchat, White-browed Bushchat

TAXONOMY
Monotypic.

IDENTIFICATION
Larger than Siberian Stonechat *S. maura,* being 15cm/5.9 inches in length. Sexes dimorphic. Appears slimmer and longer, less rounded, with distinctly longer wings, tarsi and tail than Siberian Stonechat. The bill also appears long and more substantial, similar to Isabelline Wheatear *Oenanthe isabellina.* The species' overall structure combined with its pale appearance in fresh plumage is more reminiscent of *Oenanthe* or even *Anthus* than *Saxicola.* The male in breeding plumage has a combination of black/brown crown, lores, ear-coverts, mantle and wings, with white patches on the inner upperwing which are often hidden on the closed wing, predominantly white upperwing primary coverts, distinctive long white supercilia often meeting on the forehead, whitish uppertail-coverts, pale buff underparts and a large amount of white in the tail, with all but the central rectrices having mainly pure white innerwebs. The female in breeding plumage differs from the male in that the head and mantle remain pale sandy-buff with longitudinal brown streaks; the white in the rectrices is replaced by buff; the white on the inner upperwings is largely absent; and the rump and uppertail-coverts remain chestnut-buff. Juveniles are darker brown on the upperparts spotted with buff, and the buff throat, breast and flank feathers are narrowly fringed with brown giving a mottled appearance to the underparts.

Confusion species Roberts (1992) considered it very similar in general appearance to the Whinchat *S. rubetra,* although the latter does not occur as far east as Pakistan. Its plumage is certainly superficially similar to Whinchat, especially with the large supercilium, but both sexes are distinguishable by the different, attenuated profile owing to the longer bill and tail in proportion to the body, the different pattern of white or buff in the tail, the all-white chin and throat, the unmarked rump and uppertail-coverts, and the darker mantle and scapulars of the male in summer plumage.

Roberts also considered juvenile (meaning first-year) males virtually inseparable in the field from females or subadult males of the allopatric White-tailed Stonechat *S. leucura* (for differences see under the latter species). The only *Saxicola* sympatric with *S. macrorhyncha* is Siberian Stonechat in the form of the two subspecies *maura* and *indica.* Males of these in both fresh autumn and worn summer plumage can be distinguished as follows from male Stoliczka's Bushchat: *S. macrorhyncha* is larger and slimmer with proportionately long wings, tail and bill, whereas *S. maura* is more rounded and short; chin and throat are white in *macrorhyncha,* greyish-black or solidly black in *maura*; the tail shows a large amount of white on the innerwebs in *macrorhyncha* especially when it flies, but the visible part is all black in *maura*; the supercilium in *macrorhyncha* is long, narrow and white, often but not invariably meeting on the forehead and extending to the rear of the ear-coverts, whereas it is absent in adult male and never as prominent or long in first-year male *maura*; the outer four primary coverts are white and the others have all-white outerwebs in *macrorhyncha,* while the primary coverts are black fringed with white in *maura,* consequently appearing the reverse of *macrorhyncha,* more black than white; the underparts of *macrorhyncha* are pale buff with a slightly stronger yellowish-buff tone on the upper breast, whereas in *maura* they are darker chestnut-buff in winter and rufous-buff on the breast and white on the rest in summer; the underwing-coverts of *macroryhncha* are buff-white in fresh plumage, becoming silky-white in summer, but in *maura* they are black.

Female and first-winter male *S. macrorhyncha* can be confused with female and first-winter male *S. maura* but differ as follows: *macrorhyncha* structurally show same differences to *maura* as listed above; *indica* is the smallest of all *S. maura subspecies* and is noticeably smaller than *S. macrorhyncha*; the bill in *indica* is delicate, noticeably short and laterally wide at the base; in *S. macrorhyncha* it is longer and slightly more substantial without any noticeable lateral widening at the base; female *S. macrorhyncha* usually has no white patch on the inner upperwing greater coverts, while *S. maura* has a small white patch on the innermost upperwing greater coverts; the innerwebs of the tail feathers of female *S. macroryhncha* are buff, and in first-winter male off-white (extending along at least the basal 50%), both contrasting respectively with the darker outerwebs, while the rectrices of *S. maura* are uniform brownish-black; the supercilium in *macrorhyncha* is prominent and extends from the bill to the rear of the ear-coverts, while in *maura* it is narrower, weaker and less extensive, often only reaching half-way along the upper ear-coverts; chin and throat in female and first-year male *macrorhyncha* are white or buff-white, *maura* is similar but usually with some black in first-year male as well as on the forehead and lores (this may be minimal or absent on some individuals); the breast to undertail-coverts of *macrorhyncha* are pale buff with a faint but stronger tone of yellowish-buff on the breast, but are darker chestnut-buff in *maura*; rump and uppertail-coverts of female *macrorhyncha* are pale chestnut-buff all year with faint dark streaks on the uppertail-coverts, while in female *maura* they are similar in colour with no dark streaking but can show small amounts of pale buff or white in early spring. The underwing-coverts are buff on both *macrorhyncha* and female *maura*, but some first-year male *maura* can show black underwing-coverts as early as September.

DESCRIPTION

Adult male fresh plumage The overall impression is of a pale, sandy-buff bird with relatively featureless plumage until it flies, when the white on the wings and tail become apparent. The forehead, crown, nape, mantle, back and scapulars are dark brown broadly fringed with pale sandy-buff, leaving only dark centres to the feathers which creates a streaked, somewhat pipit-like appearance. The rump is white but this is much obscured by extensive pale chestnut-buff tips. The uppertail-coverts, which are noticeably long, are silky-white with some having an oval brown spot along the shaft and extensive chestnut-buff tips. There is a long buff-white supercilium which meets or nearly meets at the front of the forehead and extends unbroken above the eye, broadening slightly over the ear-coverts and tapering onto the sides of the nape. The lores, malar region, cheeks and ear-coverts are dark brownish-black, the feathers broadly fringed with pale buff, giving this area a grizzled, streaky appearance, as much of the dark colouring is obscured. The chin and throat are pure white merging into pale yellowish-buff on the breast. The rest of the underparts are a paler version of the breast colour apart from the long undertail-coverts which are creamy-white with broad chestnut-buff tips.

The outerwebs of the rectrices, apart from the central pair (01), are buff becoming dark brown for c.25–50% of the distal part of the feather, and are narrowly fringed sandy-buff. The central pair are often entirely dark brown, fringed sandy-buff, on both webs. When closed, the tail appears dark brown, as the central pair of tail feathers have no or only a very little white at the base of the innerweb (12–18mm) which is in any case obscured by the uppertail-coverts. The innerwebs of the other tail feathers are mainly white. The innerweb of the outermost pair (06) sometimes have an irregular subterminal brown band but the remaining feathers (apart from the central pair) only have a small and variable patch of brown showing next to the feather shaft near the tip, with the next-to-central pair (02) having a slightly larger patch of brown. The amount of white in the tail can vary amongst individual birds but is always extensive. The outermost tail feathers (06) are often pure white on the innerwebs, while the greatest amount of white is found on 05–03. One individual had 48mm of white on the innerweb of 03 out of a total feather length of 55mm, whilst another had a completely white innerweb on the same feather. One typical specimen had the following amounts of white on the innerwebs of the tail feathers:

Tail length 55.5mm

6) 45.0mm; 5) 50.5mm; 4) 51.0mm; 3) 47.0mm; 2) 42.5mm; 1) 12.5mm

The remiges are dark brown. The tips and fringes to the outer edges of the secondaries are pale chestnut-buff, stronger in tone than the sandy-buff fringes to the head and upper body feathers. This gives the impression of an elongated buff panel in the middle of the closed wing. The tertials are dark brown broadly fringed and tipped paler chestnut-buff than the secondaries; this forms quite a striking feature as the dark tertials contrast with the much paler mantle and scapulars. The outerwebs of the primaries are also narrowly fringed pale chestnut-buff together with the tips. The upperwing lesser, median and greater coverts are almost black with broad pale buff fringes and tips. The buff tips to the greater coverts form a distinct wing-bar on the closed wing. The two innermost upperwing greater coverts (09–10) are white, although this can vary, with some showing white only on the innerweb of the second innermost (09) and others with the inner two wholly white and the innerweb of the third innermost (08) white. There is also some white on the innermost median coverts. The upperwing primary coverts are predominantly white, the outer four (06–09) all white with a small, brownish-black, oblong distal spot on the innerweb, whilst the remaining inner ones show progressively more black, on mainly the innerwebs. The underwing-coverts and axillaries are buff-white.

Adult male in breeding plumage The head and upperparts of the body, apart from the rump and uppertail-coverts, become progressively darker, almost sooty-black. It is uncertain whether this is achieved by abrasion of the pale feather fringes or by a pre-nuptial moult of the body feathers and most of the wing-coverts, or even a combination of both. Observations by W.G. Harvey (2002) of a male on its possible breeding territory from February 2001 onwards suggest that possibly some feathers are moulted, as the transition from winter to breeding plumage appeared too rapid to be attributable to feather abrasion alone. The rump and uppertail-coverts are pure white, although the speed at which the chestnut-buff tips and oval streaks abrade varies amongst individuals. A bird in late January showed extensive chestnut-buff blotches on the rump and uppertail-coverts, whilst another in early February had a pure white rump and uppertail-coverts. The lores, malar region, cheeks and ear-coverts become pure black. The upperwing lesser, median and all but the innermost greater coverts are pure black. A specimen in BMNH had black lesser, median and greater coverts with only very narrow buff fringes by 28 January 1898. There was also black exposed on the sides of the throat and the ear-coverts, although still with some buff fringes. This darker plumage contrasts markedly with the long pure white supercilium, central chin and throat, upperwing primary and inner greater coverts. The upper breast becomes white whilst the lower breast retains a small amount of yellowish-buff contrasting markedly with the pure white of the upper breast, throat and chin. The buff-white flanks and belly increasingly have the black feather bases showing through, creating an irregular appearance. The undertail-coverts are white with a faint buff tinge.

The pale fringes and tips to most of the rectrices and remiges wear away leaving them dark brown/black but not quite as dark as the mantle and scapulars. Some secondaries still retain narrow pale buff crescentic tips and, variably, some greater upperwing-coverts also retain buff tips but much reduced in size. The bill, legs and feet are black, and irides dark brown.

First-year male This is similar in many respects to the adult male in fresh plumage. The first-year differs in appearing greyer-buff and, in first breeding plumage, less dark brown/black on head and upperparts; the white in the tail is more restricted and tinged with tawny-buff. The upperwing primary coverts are dark blackish-brown and show no or only a little white restricted to the outer edges. The inner two greater coverts show a restricted amount of white often suffused with buff. The white of the chin and throat is duller. In summer plumage the unmoulted remiges and rectrices progressively appear browner and more worn than at similar stages on the adult male, and the remiges contrast more markedly with the black of the mantle and scapulars.

Adult female in fresh plumage Similar to the male in fresh plumage but lacks the white on the inner upperwing greater coverts and in the tail. Forehead, crown, nape, mantle and scapulars are dark greyish-brown with broad pale sandy-buff fringes, leaving only the centre of the feathers dark and thus creating a similar streaked appearance to the male. The rump and uppertail-coverts are pale buff but the latter show a pale chestnut tone and some feathers have faintly discernible darker brown shaft-streaks. The supercilia meet on the forehead, as in the male, but extend to only just beyond the ear-coverts and are more buff than white. The lores, malar region, cheeks and ear-coverts are a paler buff-brown. The chin, throat, breast, belly and flanks are a pale creamy-buff, slightly more strongly buff on the lower breast, but never showing the greater contrast found in the male. The ventral area and long undertail-coverts are a pale chestnut-buff to creamy-white. The closed tail appears dark brown with discernible pale buff outer edges. The spread tail pattern is similar to the male, but the white is replaced by pale buff on the innerwebs (females never show any pure white in the tail). The areas of buff on the tail are also far less extensive, usually only reaching a maximum from the base of 33–34mm on the innerwebs and decreasing towards the central pair (01), which are entirely dark brown with no pale buff base. The outer pair (06) also have a pale buff outerweb for their entire length.

The remiges are dark brown with buff tips and broad buff fringes to the outerwebs. The buff fringes to the secondaries form a distinct pale panel on the closed wing. The tertials are dark brown with broad pale buff fringes and tips. The upperwing primary and greater coverts are dark brown with no white on them, but all have broad pale buff tips and fringes to the outerwebs. The tips on the greater coverts form a noticeable buff bar on the closed wing. A few specimens show a very small amount of white at the base of the innermost two greater coverts (09–10) and a white outer fringe to the innermost median coverts. The underwing-coverts and axillaries are whitish-buff with largely concealed dark grey bases.

The bill is blackish-brown, paler horn at the base of the lower mandible, and the legs and feet are black. The irides are dark brown.

Adult female in worn plumage The forehead, crown, neck, mantle and scapulars show similar sandy-buff fringes to fresh autumn plumage, but overall the plumage of the upperparts appears slightly darker as the long pale fringes slowly wear off to reveal more of the darker brown centres to the feathers. It is also possible that there is a pre-breeding moult of these areas in which the pale autumn feathers are replaced by slightly darker ones.

The pale fringes and tips to the remiges and rectrices also abrade, but there is no acquisition of the male's black lores, malar region, cheeks and ear-coverts in breeding plumage and the upperwing lesser, median and greater coverts are dark brown, not black. The rump and uppertail-coverts also remain buff.

First-year female Virtually indistinguishable from the adult female. The remiges and rectrices in summer plumage appear more worn and faded but the difference is marginal.

Juvenile Slightly darker brown above than the female and, owing to different patterning of the feathers, less obviously streaked brown and buff. The feathers on the forehead, crown and nape are dark brown with narrow diamond-shaped creamy-buff streaks or spots to their centres, giving a striped look of thin buff streaks on the head. The mantle and scapulars are also dark brown with larger, more oval, creamy-buff distal spots. The buff spots are bordered with dark brown/black fringes and tips, giving the mantle and scapulars a complex speckled appearance. The lower mantle and rear scapulars have larger spots and more distinctive dark fringes. The rump and long uppertail-coverts are creamy-buff. There is a buff supercilium extending from the bill to above the ear-coverts. The lores, malar region, cheeks and ear-coverts are pale buff with hair-like white streaks. The chin and throat are buff-white. The breast and flanks are yellowish-buff with narrow pale brown fringes creating a scaly appearance. The belly, ventral area and undertail-coverts are pale buff. The rectrices are dark brown with chestnut-buff tips and fringes to the outerwebs of all but the central pair (01) (on which they are much reduced or entirely absent). The outerwebs of the outermost pair (06) are entirely chestnut-buff. Juveniles can be sexed by the tail pattern as they show either male or female patterning on the innerwebs, even in juvenile plumage.

The remiges are dark brown with prominent greyish-white crescentic tips on the inner secondaries, decreasing in extent on the outer secondaries and inner six primaries. The tertials are dark brown with extensive pale chestnut-buff tips and fringes to the outerwebs. The pale outer edges of the tertials combine with the pale fringes to the outerwebs of the inner secondaries to form a prominent pale panel on the closed wing. The upperwing lesser coverts are dark brown with extensive buff fringes obscuring all but the dark centre of the feathers. The upperwing median coverts are similar but with triangular buff-white tips. The upperwing greater coverts are dark brown with large pale buff tips creating a noticeable wing-bar and darker buff fringes to the outerwebs. The upperwing primary coverts are dark brown with extensive buff tips and fringes to the outerwebs.

Measurements

	Male	Female
Wing	75.0–79.0 (mean 76.7)	71.5–77.0 (mean 74.4)
Tail	53.0–58.5 (mean 55.8)	50.0–59.0 (mean 54.3)
Bill	14.5–16.0 (mean 15.6)	15.0–17.0 (mean 15.8)

[Own measurements BMNH 2000/2001]

Footnote: Hybrid individual(s) in Goa (based on notes by Paul Holt, Vivek Tiwar, and Dan Zetterstrom per R. Millington) A male bird in the Carambolin grasslands on the coastal belt of central Goa about 7km south-east of Old Goa was at first identified as a first-winter male Stoliczka's Bushchat. However, other suggestions were that it might be a hybrid between Stoliczka's Bushchat and either Siberian or less probably White-tailed Stonechat, or even between Whinchat and Siberian Stonechat. Superficially it most closely resembled Stoliczka's Bushchat but subtle differences pointed to it not being a pure *S. macrorhyncha*. It was first recorded on 10 December 1996 and remained throughout that winter, reappearing on 14 November 1997 until at least mid-February 1998. It was again present from 3 November 1998 into April 1999 and was apparently also present in winter 1999/2000.

The upperpart plumage was dark with the feathers of the crown, nape and to a lesser extent the hindneck having conspicuously dark centres with paler buff-brown fringes, giving the crown and nape a heavily streaked appearance with the hindneck more uniform. There was a distinct, broad, whitish supercilium running from the base of the bill over the eye to the rear of the ear-coverts, reaching almost to the sides of the nape, but not as long as on a Whinchat. The supercilia met over the top of the bill, usually appeared to flare slightly behind the eye, and were almost as deep as the depth of the eye. Lores and ear-coverts were variegated but predominantly dark, the former appearing blackish and sharply demarcated from the pre-ocular supercilia. There was a random mix of black and brown feathering on the ear-coverts although the upper ear-coverts were predominantly black and glossy with the lower ones showing many browner feathers. Chin and sides of throat were white forming a conspicuous striped pattern that continued onto the neck-sides and wrapped around the lower border of the ear-coverts. The ear-coverts were almost completely surrounded by a combination of this whitish throat-/neck-stripe and the long supercilium. The pale sides to the neck also showed irregular darker streaks giving a mottled, scruffy appearance.

The underparts were marked by an extensive apricot-buff wash slightly more intense across the centre of the breast. The long undertail-coverts were whitish. The apricot-buff wash extended in a neat wedge up the centre of the throat as in Whinchat. The tail showed some white or greyish-white on the base of the innerwebs of a couple of outer feathers. It was not extensive and was seen most clearly when the bird fanned its tail. The remiges were dark with narrow pale brown fringes to the primaries and secondaries similar to the fringes to the scapulars and mantle feathers. The upperwing primary coverts were also neatly edged with pale brown. The median upperwing-coverts appeared particularly small and were glossy black. The innermost two greater upperwing-coverts were white at the tips, although the exact extent of white was not determined. The underwing-coverts were dark but not black as in a male Siberian Stonechat.

Much interest has been shown in this individual and opinion varies from it being a normal or aberrant Stoliczka's Bushchat, a hybrid of that and other *Saxicola* species, a hybrid of two other *Saxicola* species, or even a new species altogether. It has also resulted in further claims of Stoliczka's Bushchat being seen in other parts of Goa such as at Baga in February 1999 (P. Anand *in litt.* 2000).

It should be pointed out that Goa is far out of range of Stoliczka's Bushchat, which is judged to be a mainly sedentary species; this in itself diminishes the probability that the bird in question is or was a pure *S. macrorhyncha*. Moreover, it is unlikely in an area that has been relatively popular for birdwatching and in recent times has been much visited that this can be a new species to science. This leaves a hybrid origin as the most likely explanation, although the parent species remain debatable.

D. Zetterström *in litt.* to R. Millington gave the following reasons why he thought it was not a pure *S. macrorhyncha*: (1) there was not enough white in the outer tail feathers (obvious in male *S. macrorhyncha*); (2) there was too much colouring on the chin (none in *S. macrorhyncha*); (3) the bill was too stout (long in *S. macrorhyncha*, rather than heavy); (4) the ear-coverts were too solidly dark (paler centre to ear-coverts on *S. macrorhyncha*); (5) the throat was too coloured in the centre (in *S. macrorhyncha* it is wholly off-white contrasting with the orangey breast); (6) the legs were too short (longer, more wheatear-like in *S. macrorhyncha*); (7) the upperwing primary coverts were too dark (they form a distinct pale patch on *S. macrorhyncha*).

The chances of the bird being a hybrid *S. macrorhyncha* x *S. rubetra* are extremely remote owing to the wide disparity between the two species' usual ranges; thus it would be highly improbable that a pairing would have occurred between these two species. The evidence is also strongly against it being a *S. rubetra* x *S. maura*. In size the bird observed by P. Holt was 10–15% larger than Siberian Stonechat and appeared more attenuated. Despite having undertail-coverts extending almost half-way down the tail, the bird also appeared proportionately longer-tailed than Siberian Stonechat, with the rectrices appearing subtly slimmer and longer. The bill was noticeably long, heavy and bulky-looking. Both putative parent species have relatively short tails and bills, and both are structurally short and stocky-looking and could not be described as attenuated.

On the other hand, Holt's description, together with available photographs, suggests that this individual might well be a hybrid Stoliczka's Bushchat x Siberian Stonechat or (less possibly) White-tailed Stonechat. The predominant colouring, structure and facial pattern is similar to *S. macrorhyncha* – long supercilium meeting on the forehead, flaring behind the eye and extending to rear of ear-coverts; streaking on crown and nape; white sides to chin and throat; white on inner greater upperwing-coverts; long whitish undertail-coverts; larger size; more attenuated appearance; long bill; and longer tail, with some white on the innerwebs of the outer feathers. Two subspecies of Siberian Stonechat occur in the known range of Stoliczka's Bushchat, *S. m. maura* and *S. m. indica*, and a cross-breeding with either of them could have given rise to the overall apricot-buff wash to the bird's underparts, the restricted amount of white in the upperwing primary coverts, the pale neck-patches, and black lores and ear-coverts. The behaviour of this bird in perching on elevated grass stalks, then dropping into the grass and returning to its elevated perch, as well as regularly changing perches, is also more indicative of *S. maura* or *S. leucura* than *S. macrorhyncha*.

DISTRIBUTION AND STATUS

Historically the species has been recorded from Pakistan, west of the Indus River near the Afghanistan border at Bolan [Bibi Nani] and Chaman in Baluchistan (although possibly these records are unreliable), whilst east of the Indus it has been recorded in both Sind and Punjab. In India it has been recorded from Haryana (Hissar district), western Uttar Pradesh (Aligarh), south-eastern Rajasthan and Gujarat (Deesa, Kutch and Kathiawar). There are also two very old specimens in BMNH, collected by R. Swinhoe on 19 April 1881 from Kandahar and 24 April 1881 from Dubrai, both in southern Afghanistan (Swinhoe 1882, Ticehurst 1926). Paludan (1959) did not find the species in his surveys in Afghanistan and described its status there as uncertain, with only one reliable record; it is unlikely that it is present in Afghanistan now.

The historical records show that this species has been the subject of a long, continuous decline, and it is now considered a rare and localised endemic species to the low-lying arid north-western and semi-arid parts of India. It inhabits mainly the relatively restricted, semi-arid area of the Thar Desert on the western borders of Rajasthan and Gujarat next to the Pakistan border. This area has been the main source of records in the last 20 years (Rahmani 1996). It is apparent that the species has experienced a considerable contraction in range and a decline in numbers, probably owing to loss of suitable habitat, and it has disappeared from marginal areas in its former distribution owing to habitat alteration. However, W.G. Harvey (2002) relocated it in one of its historical haunts, with two males holding separate territories 30km and 60km south-west of Delhi, and one male being joined by a female. This area has been chronically underwatched, and it could well hold a breeding population as it still retains large areas of scrub and exposed flats. Conversely, these three birds may have just been taking up temporary territories on their way from their presumed wintering area to their breeding area, as they had all gone by 2 April, although the time they remained on their temporary territories seems protracted.

Whistler (1922) cautioned that this species would be adversely affected by the increase in irrigation in India, and this prediction has come true. Northern areas of the Thar Desert in Haryana and Punjab, and Ganganagar in Rajasthan, have been lost to cultivation. Rahmani cites the example of Aligarh district in Uttar Pradesh, India, a historical area for the species which used to be semi-arid with vast areas of scrub and wasteland but which is now totally converted into irrigated agriculture. Similar actions in Pakistan were highlighted by Holmes & Wright (1968–1969): "Huge expanses of formerly monotonous scrubby desert have been replaced by lush fertility that would have been inconceivable 40 years ago". The species' inability to adapt to such dramatic changes probably contributed to its demise in that country. In the mid-nineteenth century only some 4% of Sind received sufficient irrigation to permit cultivation, but by 1921 it had reached 16% and by the late 1960s it was almost 100%, although actual cultivated areas were less than this (Holmes & Wright 1968–1969). However, there may be other factors contributing to its decrease. For example in India it is no longer found in the Banni grasslands area of Kutch district or in the Jodphur area of Rajasthan, although both still retain large areas of apparently suitable habitat in the form of scrubland (Rahmani 1996).

In Pakistan, even almost a century ago the species was considered rare and localised, with Ticehurst (1922–1924) describing it as a very local desert-loving resident in Baluchistan, and Whistler (1922) reporting that in Jhang district in 1918–1919 it was very local and nowhere abundant despite large areas of suitable habitat. Hume (1878a) stated that it occurred in "Sind (Thurr and Pakhur [Thar Parkar] districts, and probably elsewhere)". In the early twentieth century Ticehurst failed to find it in these areas nor even locate the specimens Hume had taken, although he accepted that Hume's records were probably valid. There is another specimen in BMNH from R. Meinertzhagen's collection *said* to have been collected in February c.1937 from Rohri, Sind, but this now cannot be trusted (Collar *et al.* 2001). There is also a specimen in BMNH labelled 'Punjab' which was possibly collected in the Salt Range (Collar *et al.* 2001). There are early unconfirmed records from Bibi Nani [Bolan] and Chaman in Baluchistan (Ticehurst 1926, Rahmani 1994). A pair considered to be this species was observed in the Pat Desert, Sind, in February 1963–1965 (Holmes & Wright 1968–1969). Roberts (1992) failed to find it anywhere in its former haunts in Jhang district despite many visits and 28 years spent in southern Punjab, and considered it probably extinct in Pakistan, although no recent survey has been conducted there and, like Harvey, someone may chance across overlooked birds.

The list below for both Pakistan and India is compiled from historical and contemporary records and is based on information from a number of sources but especially that supplied by Collar *et al.* (2001).

PAKISTAN
Sind
Thar Parkar district	undated (Hume 1878a)

Punjab
Pahrwhal	Gujarat district January 1943 (specimen in BMNH)
Lalian	Jhang district February 1919 (specimen in BMNH)
Winoka	Jhang district February 1919 (Whistler 1922)
Nurpur Canal escape	Jhang district July 1919 (Whistler 1922)
Khiwa	Jhang district 1917/ juvenile female and adult male August 1919/ 1920 (11 specimens in BMNH)
Mukhiana	Jhang district December 1917 (Whistler 1922)
Mochiwala	Jhang district January 1918 (Whistler 1922)
Ludha Mani	Jhang district 19 September 1919 (Whistler, juvenile female in BMNH)
Dab Kalan	Jhelum River, Jhang district December 1918 (specimen in BMNH)
Shadan Lund nr the Indus	Dera Ghazi Khan December 1938 (specimen in BMNH)
Jampur nr the Indus	Dera Ghazi Khan February 1937 (specimen in BMNH)
Bhowana untraced	Jhang district August 1919 (female in BMNH, Whistler 1922)

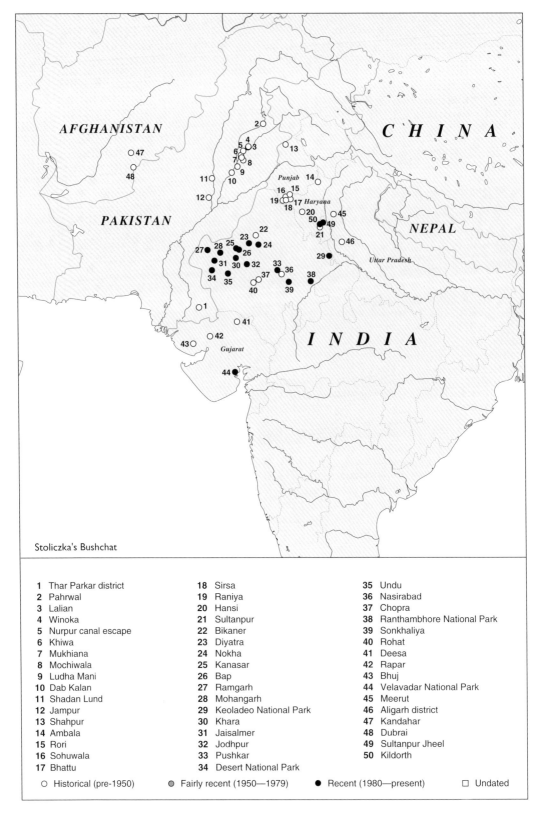

Stoliczka's Bushchat

1	Thar Parkar district	18	Sirsa	35	Undu
2	Pahrwal	19	Raniya	36	Nasirabad
3	Lalian	20	Hansi	37	Chopra
4	Winoka	21	Sultanpur	38	Ranthambhore National Park
5	Nurpur canal escape	22	Bikaner	39	Sonkhaliya
6	Khiwa	23	Diyatra	40	Rohat
7	Mukhiana	24	Nokha	41	Deesa
8	Mochiwala	25	Kanasar	42	Rapar
9	Ludha Mani	26	Bap	43	Bhuj
10	Dab Kalan	27	Ramgarh	44	Velavadar National Park
11	Shadan Lund	28	Mohangarh	45	Meerut
12	Jampur	29	Keoladeo National Park	46	Aligarh district
13	Shahpur	30	Khara	47	Kandahar
14	Ambala	31	Jaisalmer	48	Dubrai
15	Rori	32	Jodhpur	49	Sultanpur Jheel
16	Sohuwala	33	Pushkar	50	Kildorth
17	Bhattu	34	Desert National Park		

○ Historical (pre-1950)　　● Fairly recent (1950—1979)　　● Recent (1980—present)　　□ Undated

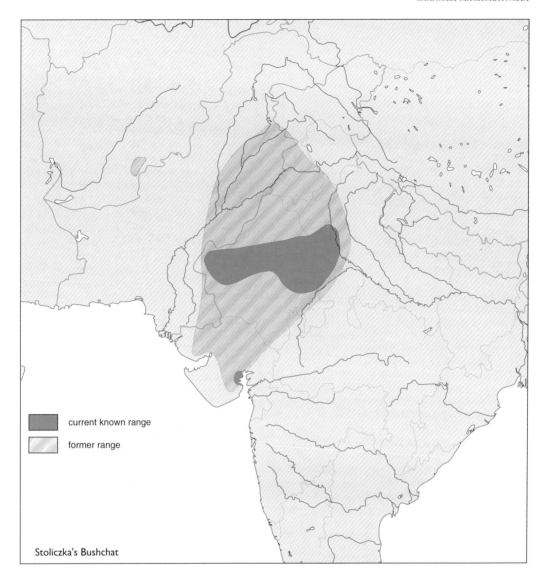

current known range

former range

Stoliczka's Bushchat

In India, at Jodhpur the species was found to be common and in some areas 'locally abundant' during the winter after a very dry period (Hume 1878a), and Whistler (1938) collected over 30 specimens at the end of January and in the first week of February, stating that "it is extremely common in the thin stunted scrub jungle that here and there studs the sandy, semi-desert, waterless tracts that occur all around Jodphur". During his visit to Kutch, Stoliczka (1872) found only two, possibly indicating that it was uncommon there. It was described as possibly resident, rare and very local but not uncommon in some areas (Ali & Ripley 1968–1998). Rahmani (1996) states it was only reported 15 times between 1975 and 1996, 14 times from Rajasthan and once from Gujarat.

Rahmani (1996) conducted four surveys during 1993/1994 in Rajasthan, concentrating mainly on the Thar Desert. The first (2 February–13 March 1993) located four birds on the border of Jaisalmer and Barmer districts. The second (15 July–23 August 1993) located one in the Desert National Park (Jaisalmer district). The third (12 January–12 February 1994) was the most productive, with 81 birds found in 16 sites. (In the area of Diyatra in Bikaner district 25 were seen over a 45km transect in one day and, on another, 13 were seen on six line transects of 1.5km each.) The fourth (17–23 May 1994) located none in the Jodhpur, Jaisalmer and Barmer Districts. Altogether, the species was located on only nine of 38 transects. This study resulted in 86 individuals being sighted at 18 different sites. Rahmani (1996) suggests his recent surveys show it may not be as threatened as previously thought, because in certain areas such as Diyatra, Desert National Park, Nokh and Khara it was found to be fairly common. However, he adds that he failed to find it near Jodphur where it was extremely common over a hundred years ago (Hume 1878a), and although he possibly did not survey exactly the same areas it must now be considered overall to be very localised. There are also two records cited in *Birds of Pakistan* (Roberts 1992): B. King saw it in the Desert National Park (date unspecified) and R. Grimmett saw a male and probably a female in the Sudasari Bustard enclosure in Desert National Park on 17 February 1982. In fact many birders and bird tour groups now regularly encounter this species in this park.

On 5 February 2001 W.G. Harvey found an adult male apparently recently arrived holding territory at Sultanpur Jheel 30km south-west of Delhi in the south-east part of Haryana state. This was the first record since 1915 for Haryana; the last birds recorded specifically at Sultanpur were in January and February 1878 (Hume 1878a). A second individual, thought to be a first-winter male, was found by Harvey at Kildorth, Haryana, on 28 February 2001, 30km due west of Sultanpur, again holding territory. Harvey considered that the species may be overlooked as the wasteland areas these birds were inhabiting are not watched in summer. A female was discovered in the adult male's territory on 11 March by N. Devasar. On 14 March the adult male had disappeared but the female was present at least until 19 March. Both the first-winter male and the female were still present on 2 April 2001 but were not seen afterwards despite searches (Harvey 2002).

INDIA
Punjab
Shahpur c.1878 (specimen in BMNH, Hume 1878a)

Haryana
Ambala November 1866 (specimen in BMNH; Whistler 1915)
Rori – Sirsa subdivision, Hisar district March 1915 (specimen in BMNH Whistler 1915)
Sohuwala [Sahuwala], Sirsa subdivision, Hissar district, winter 1914 (Whistler 1915)
Bhattu [Bhutto] December 1867 (specimen in BMNH)
Sirsa c.1850 (specimen in BMNH) c.1878 (Hume 1878a)
Lumba [Lumbee], Sirsa, November 1876 (specimen in BMNH)
Raniya [Ranian], nr Sirsa subdivision, Hisar district, November 1914 (specimen in BMNH, Whistler 1915)
Hansi, Hisar district c.1878 (Hume 1878a)
Sultanpur, Gurgaon, January and February 1878 (Hume 1878a two specimens in BMNH)
Sultanpur Jheel, south of Sultanpur National Park, 30kms south-west of Delhi, one adult male 5 February–c.14 March (W.G. Harvey 2002); 1 female joined adult male 11 March remaining until c.2 April 2001 (W.G. Harvey 2002)
Kildorth 30km west of Sultanpur one first-year male 28 February–c.2 April 2001 (W.G. Harvey *in litt.* 2001)

Rajasthan
Bikaner c.1878 (Hume 1878a)
Diyatra area, Bikaner district 'at and near' Tokla eleven individuals 16–18 January 1994 (Rahmani 1996)
Niagoan five individuals 18 January 1994 (Rahmani 1996)
Hadda 20 individuals 18 January 1994 (Rahmani 1996)
Nokha area, Jodhpur district, 12 individuals 28 January 1994 (Rahmani 1996)
Kanasar, Jaisalmer district two individuals 28 January 1994 (Rahmani 1996)
Kanasar – Bap area, Jaisalmer two individuals 29 January 1994 (Rahmani 1996)
Bap area Jodhpur district nine individuals 25–26 January (Rahmani 1996)
Ramgarh – Asatur area, Jaisalmer district two individuals on 16 February 1994 (Rahmani 1996)
Mohangarh, Jaisalmer district one individual on 10 December 1992 (Rahmani 1996)
Near Keoladeo National Park, at Koladahar one individual on 24 February 1988 (Rahmani 1996)
Near Khara village between Phalodi and Pokharan, Jhodpur district, in western Rajasthan on 2 August 1978. An adult male with several flying juveniles was seen (van den Berg *et al.* 1981).
Khara-Savreej, Jodhpur district five individuals 8 February 1994 (Rahmani 1996)
Jaisalmer c.55km east of, March 1876 (specimen in BMNH)
Jaisalmer c.20km south-east of, at the 'Fossil Park' one female November 1988 (B. Watts *in litt.* 1999 to Collar *et al.* 2001)
Jaisalmer 30km east of, one in December 1994 (P. Undeland *in litt.* 1995 to Collar *et al.* 2001)

Jodhpur district – many around Jodhpur February 1876 and January 1878 (Hume 1878 25 specimens in BMNH) including near the Magna/Mogra road, February 1878, (three specimens in the BMNH), and the 'Rohut road' [Rohat], February 1878, (two specimens in the BMNH). One collected Jodphur on 16 December 1948, specimen in AMNH. Recently more difficult to find in the vicinity of Jodhpur but two were found in the district at Sewada on 27 January 1994 (Rahmani 1996)

South-west of Pushkar one to two in November 1999 (K. Evans *in litt.* 1999 to Collar *et al.* 2001)

Desert National Park, Jaisalmer district: one female 6 March 1985; one female 18 February 1987; one female 27–30 January 1990; one individual 11–18 December 1992; one individual 25 July 1993 near Phulia; 13 in the Sudasari area 1–4 February 1994 (three Sam Bustard Enclosure/five Sudasari – Khuri road/one Nibha and four Sudasari); one 16 February 1994; near Sam one 17 February 1994 (Rahmani 1996); Sam Bustard Enclosure one in January 1982 with subsequent sightings by other observers (C.R. Robson in Collar *et al.* 2001). One adult male 9 February 1999 (K.D. Bishop *in litt.* 2001); near headquarters of DNP along the north boundary fenceline toward Sam one female 28 March 2001 (D. Roberson *in litt.* 2001)

Near Undu, Jaisalmer–Barmer crossing four on 12 February 1993 (Rahmani 1996)

Nasirabad, Ajmer district January 1900 & January 1936 (two specimens in BMNH)

Chopra [Chopsa] c.35km from Jodhpur, January 1878 (specimen in BMNH)

Ranthambore National Park 5 13 February 1986, 1987; one female 14–16 February 1992 (Rahmani 1996)

Sonkhaliya [Shokaliya, Sonkalia Bustard Closed Area], Ajmer district two January–February 1993 (Rahmani 1993), three January 1996 (P. Alstrom, U. Olsson & D. Zetterstrom *in litt.* 2000 to Collar *et al.* 2001)

Rohat [Rohit], Pali district December 1948 (eight specimens in FMNH, UMMZ and AMNH); Sariska Sanctuary (unmapped) no date (Rahmani 1995)

Gujarat

Deesa [Disa] 12 November 1875 (Butler 1875–1879 specimen in BMNH)

Rapar [Raipur] in Nagar district, Kutch "beginning of 1872" (Stoliczka 1872)

Near Bhuj early 1870 (Stoliczka 1872)

Velavadar National Park, Bhavnagar district ten individuals 28 December 1992–1 January 1993 (Rahmani 1996)

Rahmani (1996) mentions that "No individual of this species has recently been found in Kutch district, especially in the Banni grasslands"… "Mr Himmatsinhji a very experienced Kutch ornithologist has never seen this species during 50 years of active birdwatching".

Uttar Pradesh

Meerut January 1913 (specimen in BMNH)

Rooija [Rooiya] Aligarh district November 1877 (specimen in BMNH), but now absent (Rahmani 1995)

BREEDING

No information. No nest, eggs or unfledged young have ever been found or recorded. Observations of recently fledged young and adults in early-mid August together with Harvey's observations in Haranya in March would suggest that the breeding season is possibly between April/May to July.

There are also two juvenile females in BMNH collected by Whistler on 14 August 1919 at Khiwa in Jhang district, Punjab, and on 19 September 1919 at Ludhamahni, [Ludha Mani] also Jhang district, Punjab, Pakistan. Both these birds are unlikely to have moved far from their birthplace, as it is usual for the post-juvenile moult to be completed before any long-distance movement is undertaken, assuming they were not resident. Similarly, there is an adult male in full breeding plumage shot by Whistler on 14 August 1919, also at Khiwa, which may well be one of the parents of the juvenile shot at the same location on the same date. It is usual for post-breeding moult in *Saxicola* spp., to be completed before migration so presumably the adult bird was near or on its breeding areas.

HABITAT

Stoliczka's Bushchat is highly adapted to an arid semi-desert biotope with subtropical thorn scrub (Roberts 1992). It is found in similar habitat to Desert Wheatear *Oenanthe deserti* and Greater Short-toed Lark *Calandrella brachydactyla* (Ali & Ripley 1968–1998, Rahmani 1995). In the Thar Desert it occurs in dry, sandy areas with low (50–70cm high) herbs and shrubs, and widely scattered bushes, ground cover varying from 25–50%, generally around 35%, and shrubs consist of *Crotolania burhia, Aerva persica, A. pseudotomentosa* and *Cassia italica*; the dominant bush being *Capparis decidua*, with, in a few areas *Calotropis procera* and

Leptadenia pyrotechnica (Rahmani 1996). It has also been found inhabiting an abandoned field in a desert area (Holmes & Wright 1968–1969). Whistler (1922) found one or two individuals in cultivation but always in the vicinity of waste ground. All recent records are from dry biotope. Harvey (2002) found two males inhabiting areas of typically short (less than 0.5m high) tussocky dry grass, cut over by fodder cutters or lightly burnt, in extensive areas of very short, overgrazed grass and bare sandy ground. Occasional taller grass and stunted acacia scrub up to 2m high were used as lookout and feeding perches. The birds' territories were within 0.5km of villages and regularly visited by grazing cattle and humans cutting grass for cattle fodder.

Whistler (1922) found them in the Jhang district in Pakistan in the early 1900s in two kinds of biotope:

> "Its favourite haunts are the wide plains of a hard, sandy soil, fertile when ploughed and irrigated, but normally of the consistency and appearance of a 'made up' tennis court. They are bare of grass for the most part, but are studded with the small desert plants of Uck and Karil (wild Caper), and diversified with small sand dunes and broken ground... A few pairs also inhabit the Nurpur Canal escape, where the running off of volumes of waste canal water has produced great reed beds surrounded by jungles of 'Pampas grass'."

Rahmani (1996) observed that this latter area is more typically habitat of White-tailed Stonechat, the female of which superficially resembles female and juvenile *S. macrorhyncha*. Moreover, Roberts (1992) found that a female *S. leucura* in BMNH had been misidentified by Whistler as *S. macrorhyncha*. However, there is also a definite adult male in BMNH shot by Whistler on 25 July 1919 at the Nurpur escape channel. The label attached to the specimen states "...by a reedbed near a marshy channel running through grass jungle in the canal escape... Supposed female of same species wounded but lost. Scarce resident". No-one else (including Rahmani) has found it in reedbeds and it has been suggested that Whistler was possibly mistaken in his identification. However, I follow Collar *et al.* (2001) in judging there to be no valid reason to reject Whistler's records from Nurpur as there is at least one correctly identified specimen from the site (see above) and Whistler seemed well aware of the differences in the two species, describing Stoliczka's Bushchat as easily distinguished and resembling a female wheatear, rather than resembling the local subspecies *indica* of Siberian Stonechat. *S. leucura* is very similar to Siberian Stonechat, so by implication Whistler should have been able to tell this species from Stoliczka's Bushchat, and indeed he identified several pairs of both species in the area.

VOICE

There is little information apart from a description that it uttered "a little sharp *chip chip* now and then" (Hume 1878a). During January 1994 Rahmani found that while perched on a bush the male uttered a soft, low, musical "song", *twitch-chhe chee chee*, lasting for up to a minute. While singing the throat was distended. The song was only audible from 10–15 m, so it was considered not to be uttered for territorial or display purposes. It was also uncertain whether the female also uttered a similar note or song (Rahmani 1996). Harvey (2002) described a subsong as "...sustained, quiet, but musical and varied. Audible over 20m it was uttered for up to 30secs. It contained a few harsh and several 'conversational' phrases and was most reminiscent of a Northern Wheatear *Oenanthe oenanthe* song". This bird was also heard to give a soft-sounding deep *prupp prupp* call.

FOOD

Hume (1878a) wrote "I found nothing but insects recognisable in the stomachs of those I examined, though in several there was nearly digested matter that might have been the pulp of seeds". Whistler (1922) found that the stomach of one individual contained beetles, larvae and green vegetable matter whilst another contained larvae, carabids and other beetles. Ali & Ripley (1968–1998) and Roberts (1992) state that its food consists of insects. Harvey (2002) observed two males feeding mainly on ants in February.

The species seeks its prey mainly on the ground but will also use perches on bushes as a lookout for prey. After hopping along the ground for a couple of minutes it flies up to perch on tall seed stems of cane grass *Saccharum munja* or thorn bushes *Prosopis spicigera* (R. Grimmett in Roberts 1992). Rahmani (1996) found it spent much time either picking items from the ground or making aerial sallies to catch small flying insects. He never saw it take seeds or other vegetable matter. In July 1993 a female was observed picking up *Camponotus* ants, eating them on the ground and then returning to a perch on top of a bush. T.J. Roberts (in Rahmani 1994) stated that its foraging behaviour was similar to Siberian Stonechat, and he recorded two types of behaviour, picking from the ground and aerial sallies. One bird was frequently seen hovering for 2–3 seconds to catch an insect, and it was seen to fly up to 20m to catch a flying insect; on average 17 seconds elapsed between sallies and it always returned to a favoured perch at the top of a *Capparis* bush after consuming the insect either on the ground or in the air. When on the ground the species' behaviour was reminiscent of a wheatear, hopping around for 1–2 minutes seizing prey (Harvey 2002). Rahmani in January 1994 noted that aerial sallies were made mainly at noon or in the evening when innumerable small insects were flying. During the cold winter mornings when most flying insects are inactive, birds were seen picking small beetles and ants from the ground. Birds feed throughout the day, even at midday and some individuals were seen feeding 30minutes af ter sunset. Harvey (2002) states it perches frequently on low vegetation such as grass tufts and thorn bushes up to 0.5m high, making sallies to catch airborne insects or flying down to seize invertebrates on the ground. It usually returned to the same perch after a prey capture attempt. It was able to locate insects at least 20m distant. Harvey found the opposite of Rahmani in that it fed aerially more in the early morning but by midday often fed on the ground, running after prey up to 10m away. In periods of 30–60 minutes it fed every 1–3 minutes.

MOVEMENTS

There are conflicting opinions from the relatively few observers of this species as to whether it is sedentary, moves locally or is migratory. Until its breeding grounds are found it is unlikely that its true movements will be known. Ali & Ripley (1968–1998) and Roberts (1992) considered it sedentary, as did Ticehurst (1922–1924) and Whistler (1922). This may not be correct, however, as the territorial males observed by Harvey and Devasar in 2001 were not resident and appeared to have migrated possibly to breed in the area they were found in or else were passing through on their way to more distant breeding grounds. Rahmani (1996) made a suggestion following his four surveys over different months that it undergoes some local or possibly even long-distance movement, perhaps in response to rainfall levels. His evidence included 13 individuals present in January 1994 in the Desert National Park but none in the same area in May. It is at present unclear whether birds remain in the Thar Desert or leave, although Harvey's observations suggest the latter. An individual some 40km from the Thar Desert on 25 July 1993 could have been a resident bird or possibly an early returning migrant. A survey by Rahmani of literature revealed that previous observers had found it common in the winter months in certain areas but no-one was sure whether it was resident. Hume (1877a) had requested ornithologists in southern and western India to look out for it in the "next cold season" and in a following paper Hume (1877b) surmised that it must breed somewhere in central Asia. Later still (1878a) he stated:

"All my birds were killed at the end of January and during the first week of February when the weather was singularly cold and the generative organs were entirely undeveloped... Also I may say that I am by no means sure from further enquiries that this is a migratory species. One would naturally suppose it to be so, but natives (who are not to be relied on in regard to any small birds) assured me that they breed in Jodphur during the scanty rainy season (only about 4 to 6 inches rainfall) that they have there".

In the Hissar [Hisar] district of the Punjab (now in Haryana) Whistler (1922) found it not uncommon in the period 19 November–10 March. However, in the Jhang district he was confident that it was strictly resident based on the fact that he found pairs in April and July and obtained birds in juvenile or first-year plumage in August and September. Ticehurst (1922–1924, 1926) considered it resident and very local. Dharmakumarsinjhi (1954) described it as a winter migrant to Saurashtra. Rahmani states that most of the records for which the month is known appear to be of individuals collected or seen in winter, except the two from Afghanistan and Whistler's records from Hisar. The records from Afghanistan possibly resulted from seasonal or irruptive movements in response to rainfall levels. Rahmani thought it likely that during the summer this species moves from the Thar Desert to more northern latitudes and speculated that it returns to breed with the onset of rains, based on the fact that he saw a female or juvenile near Khuri on 25 July, and an adult male with several juveniles was seen on 2 August in the Khara area of Jodphur district (van den Berg et al. 1981). Both these sites are located in the middle of the Thar Desert. However, these birds could just as easily be returning from their breeding grounds to winter. The discovery by Harvey of two males holding territory south-west of Delhi indicates this species is at least partly migratory, possibly leaving the Thar Desert in spring to breed and returning in the monsoon around July–August. The situation is still far from clear and an intensive ringing study and possibly a chance encounter of breeding birds would be needed to provide some clarification of the situation.

BEHAVIOUR

Hume (1878a) always found the species perched on an exposed twig at the top of a stunted thorn bush, and Whistler (1922) also noted it perching on the tops of bushes and stems. He described it as fairly tame at times and at others excessively wild. Van den Berg et al. (1981) found it fairly tame. Rahmani (1996) found most individuals he observed very tame, allowing approach to 3–4m although some were very wary and did not allow him closer than 50–100m. Harvey (2002) described an adult male south-west of Delhi as "ridiculously" tame, allowing approach to within "six feet" and often flying towards an observer. A second first-winter male 30km away was rather less tame, as was a female that joined the first male although still allowing approach to around 4m.

An interesting and as yet unexplained behaviour was apparently first witnessed by P. Holt (*in litt.* 2000), who reported that a male he observed near Jaisalmer, Rajasthan, in the Desert National Park in 1985 "behaved in a very distinctive fashion. It was exclusively terrestrial, unaccompanied and usually stood bolt upright with its tail held almost perpendicular and nearly touching the ground. Whilst maintaining this exaggerated position it swayed rapidly from side to side as if displaying". Rahmani also observed such behaviour in which birds would puff up their underparts causing the white of the breast and belly to become more conspicuous, sway from side to side, making themselves appear larger than normal. This behaviour was shown by many birds present during January and February and always took place on the ground while the birds were foraging and was never seen when they were perched on bushes. In some instances the performing bird picked at something, moved and swayed again, then picked up another item, repeating the performance two or three times before flying back to a perch. Rahmani came to the conclusion that this was not an intraspecific sign of aggression as the nearest neighbour was 200–400m away and the birds concerned could only see each other when perched on top of bushes. However, Harvey (2002), who observed a bird give this 'puff and roll' behaviour six times in one hour, thought that it was an aggressive response associated with the presence of a pair of Siberian Stonechats, as it was performed immediately before or after it chased one or both of the latter away. When these birds were not around there was no display. Both male and female birds showed this behaviour. Harvey described the display as follows:

> "The bird stops still on the ground, puffs up all his underparts from chin to vent making himself ridiculously large and round and then, while quite stationary but on very erect legs, appears to roll his body from side to side … It is really a roll rather than a shaking or a wobbling and seems quite tightly controlled. But it lasts no more than 10–15 seconds".

Individuals appear to be very faithful to favoured areas. Rahmani observed one that always remained in an area no larger than 0.2ha. This bird returned to one particular *Capparis* bush and even appeared to have one particular favoured branch on the bush in the shade which Rahmani estimated, by the faecal staining evident, to have been used for many days or weeks, possibly months. Even when disturbed it would return immediately to the bush when the disturbance ceased. Harvey (2002) found two territorial males each exceptionally loyal to very small 0.2ha territories and also showed strong attachment to favoured perches, flying around an observer to get back to a favourite perch.

Aggressive interaction has been noted between this species and Desert Wheatear *Oenanthe deserti* possibly owing to their similar choice of prey (Rahmani 1996). Conversely Whistler (1922) noted that it was "on good terms with Desert Wheatear, neither shy nor pugnacious in its presence". The Desert Warbler *Sylvia nana* is often found in close association but no aggressive encounters have been observed between the two species (Rahmani 1996). Harvey (2002), observing two individual males, one adult, the other a first-winter and both apparently holding territory, noted that the adult was extremely intolerant of other species in its feeding territory. It drove off Crested Lark *Galerida cristata* and Greater Short-toed Lark *Calandrella brachydactyla*, Tawny Pipit *Anthus campestris* and especially Siberian Stonechat, yet it did not show aggression towards Isabelline Wheatear *Oenanthe isabellina*. The first-winter individual was more tolerant and allowed the close approach of both Hume's Short-toed Lark *C. acutirostris* and Crested Lark but was aggressive towards Siberian Stonechat. A female that joined the adult male was aggressive towards Siberian Stonechat and Crested Lark.

MOULT

Examination of specimens in BMNH revealed an adult female collected on 10 August 1919 from Bhowana, Jhang district, Punjab, Pakistan in full wing and tail moult. Primaries 01–04 were new but not fully grown, while 05–10 were old. All the secondaries were old apart from 01 which was new but not fully grown. Tertial 07 was new. The tail was in moult with all feathers new and approximately two-thirds their normal length. The upperwing greater, median and primary coverts were also new, as were the uppertail-coverts. The rest of the body plumage was old.

A male collected on 14 August 1919 also in the Pakistan Punjab had heavily abraded remiges and rectrices but showed no sign of moult. Harvey (2002) observed both a male and female newly arrived in February 2001 on what was suspected at the time to be their breeding territory and judged that these birds underwent a pre-breeding moult of at least the body feathers and possibly the wing-coverts, as the speed of their transition to breeding plumage appeared too fast to be caused by feather abrasion. Whistler

(1922) also considered that males at least acquired their breeding plumage by a combination of moult and abrasion.

This species would not be alone in the genus if it did have a partial pre-breeding moult as Whinchat also undergoes a partial moult in its winter quarters prior to spring migration. However, from the little information available concerning the individuals seen by Harvey it would appear that they were migrating while also possibly undergoing a partial moult which would be unusual.

CONSERVATION

Stoliczka's Bushchat is listed as a Globally Threatened Species under IUCN criteria. It is classed as Vulnerable (Collar *et al.* 1994, 2001). The main threat is habitat alteration. Rahmani (1996) states it is not hunted or trapped and there is presumably no threat from hybridisation with the congeneric Siberian Stonechat, even though there may have been cases of hybrids involving these two species (see above).

It is vital that its breeding areas be found so as to undertake an estimate of its numbers and also to ascertain if these areas are threatened by development or improvements and need protection.

Only a tiny fraction of the Thar Desert is protected, mainly in the form of the Desert National Park. Even this area is under threat from habitat alteration caused by the proposed construction of an irrigation canal (Rajasthan Canal) through the park. This would result in an increase in use and disturbance by humans in the area. Currently there are an estimated 30,000 people already living within the park (Rahmani 1998). Although not specifically protected this species is afforded some protection as it inhabits areas within the Desert National Park such as Sam and is also found at Sonkhaliya, both of which are protected areas for the Great Indian Bustard *Ardeotis nigriceps*. It has also been found in Keoladeo National Park, Ranthambore National Park and Velavadar National Park. Rahmani (1998) suggests that the Desert National Park would be better protected by resettling people outside its boundaries with suitable compensation, banning irrigation, redefining the boundaries and developing core areas. Grassland/pasture plots should be developed in the command area of the proposed Rajasthan Canal where cultivation is unsustainable. Rahmani (1998) suggests that the proposed route of the canal should be re-aligned and that an environmental impact study be made before any construction takes place. Proper protection of desert habitat in both Gujarat and Rajasthan would benefit this species as well as a number of others (Collar *et al.* 2001).

A two-year project is the minimum necessary to study the biology, ecology and distribution of this species and the following are the main aspects to pursue: (1) a status survey in its range at different seasons, with special emphasis on visiting areas in the same seasons where it was historically recorded; (2) a study of its local and/or migratory movements by marking birds; (3) a study of its habitat requirements and the effect of canal irrigation systems; and (4) a study of its general biology (food, territoriality, breeding season, clutch size, nesting success, predators, songs etc.) (Rahmani 1996).

Saxicola insignis Gray & Gray, 1846, *Cat. Mamm. Birds Nepal Thibet*, pp.71, 153—Nepal
[Although the type specimen, from the two initially collected, was listed by Gray & Gray (1846) and Blyth (1847) as collected in Nepal, A.O. Hume (1877a) corrected this stating that "Jerdon says 'This species has only as yet been found in Nepal, and probably comes from the most northern districts, perhaps, as Mr Blyth hints, from Thibet'. This is quite a mistake – Mr Hodgson distinctly records on his plate that this occurs in the plains only, and both his specimens were obtained (on January 10th) at Segowlee, a well known Cantonment in the plains of the Champurun district, some 16 miles south of the Nepal frontier and on the main road to Khatmandoo" (=Sagauli, Bihar State, India).]

Etymology *insignis* from Latin meaning notable, extraordinary, remarkable

Alternative names Hodgson's Stonechat, Hodgson's Chat, White-throated Bushchat, White-necked Bushchat

TAXONOMY
Monotypic.

IDENTIFICATION
Size 16–17cm/6.3–6.7 inches. Sexes dimorphic. Much larger than Siberian Stonechat *S. maura* or any other members of the genus apart from Buff-streaked Bushchat *S. bifasciata* of South Africa, with a distinctly longer tail in proportion to the body and a large bulbous head with corresponding larger and heavier bill than *S. maura*. It appears less agile and more deliberate in its movements. Male plumage pattern is similar to Siberian Stonechat with black on head and upperparts, but differs in having a white chin and throat at all times joining with very extensive white neck-patches which almost meet on the hindneck and extend onto the upper mantle. The rump and underparts from breast to ventral area are rufous-orange in fresh plumage and the visible part of the tail is black. The wings also have an extensive area of white covering all the inner upperwing-coverts and extending onto the base of the secondaries and most of the primaries, which shows as a very large white patch on the black wing both when the bird is perched and especially when it flies.

Females are greyish-brown on the head and upperparts with darker brown streaking. A distinct buff supercilium extends at least mid-way along the upper edge of the ear-coverts. The chin and throat are buffish-white and the rest of the underparts are a uniform pale orange-buff. The rump and uppertail-coverts are chestnut-buff. The wings and tail are dark brown with an area of white on the wings covering similar areas to that on the male but less extensive.

Confusion species Three other *Saxicola* species occur in its wintering range: Siberian Stonechat *S. maura*, White-tailed Stonechat *S. leucura* and Pied Bushchat *S. caprata*.

It differs from all subspecies of Siberian Stonechat in several respects. It is considerably larger (3.5–4.5cm) with a longer tail in proportion to the body and, owing to its size, slightly heavier movements, almost like a small thrush; *S. maura* is smaller, more compact, with a shorter tail and lighter, quicker movements (this is difficult to judge in the field unless a direct comparison can be made, and should be used in conjunction with other criteria); in fresh-plumaged *insignis* the feather fringes of the mantle and scapulars are greyish-buff, creating a darker appearance to the upperparts and more contrast with the rufous-/orange-buff underparts, whereas fresh *maura* has sandy-buff fringes to the mantle and scapulars, giving a paler appearance and less contrast with the pale chestnut-buff underparts; male *insignis* has a white chin and throat at all times, while male *maura* has a variable dark grey to black chin and throat in fresh plumage (some first-year males can be very pale, occasionally showing no black on the head including the chin and throat, but in fresh plumage they usually show at least some dark grey feather bases on the throat); female *insignis* has a buff chin and throat very like female and occasional first-year male *maura* and in this case this is not a reliable identification feature used in isolation; male *insignis* has a very extensive amount of white on the upperwing-coverts extending onto the secondaries and primaries, and the female has a smaller but still extensive amount of white also on the inner upperwing-coverts, but only on the inner primaries and outer secondaries, which is very striking in both flight and when perched, whereas male *maura* has much less white on the wing, this being confined to the inner four upperwing greater coverts and never on the secondaries and primaries; female *maura* also has white on the upperwing but only on the two or three inner upperwing greater coverts which, as in male *maura* appears far less extensive than either sex of *insignis*; both sexes of *insignis* also have the upperwing primary coverts solidly white with the black bases hidden by the black alula, but male *maura* has the upperwing primary coverts predominantly black with prominent white fringes and tips. Thus any male stonechat with black visible on the primary coverts is unlikely to be *insignis*. Male *insignis*, possibly first-winter, often shows irregular dark spotting across the upper breast in winter, while *maura* is unspotted below at all times.

Hodgson's Bushchat differs from White-tailed Stonechat as follows: *S. insignis* shows same structural difference from *S. leucura* as it does from *S. maura*; the tail of *insignis* is all black (male) and dark brown/ black (female), while the inner webs of the tail in *leucura* are predominantly white (male) and buff contrasting slightly with the darker brown outer webs (female); chin and throat are white in male *insignis*, black in male *leucura* (even in fresh plumage); the wing-patch on *insignis* is far more extensive in both sexes than in male or female *leucura*, which have a similar white upperwing-patch to *S. maura*); the underparts of female *insignis* are mostly orange-buff, whereas on female *leucura* they are very pale buff with only the breast showing a stronger orange-buff colouring.

Pied Stonechat *S. caprata* is 2.5–3cm smaller and structurally similar to but not as small as *S. maura*; males are predominantly black, with white under- and uppertail-coverts, rump and upperwing-patch, and are unlikely to be confused even in winter plumage when the black feathers have extensive brown fringes. Females differ from female *S. caprata* as follows: *insignis* is overall paler greyish-buff, showing marked contrast between upper- and underparts, with noticeable darker streaking above and orange-buff and unmarked below; *caprata* is darker brown both above and below, and appears more uniform brown overall with less contrast, usually showing only a little dark streaking above and noticeable darker streaking below; *insignis* has a buff-white chin and throat, appearing lighter and showing greater contrast with the orange-buff upper breast, while *caprata* is greyish-white on chin and throat and consequently this area is darker, showing less contrast with the grey-brown upper breast; *insignis* has much white on the upperwing-coverts, outer secondaries and inner primaries, while *caprata* has no white on the upperwing-coverts or remiges, being uniform brown; *insignis* has a prominent buff supercilium extending from the bill to the rear of the ear-coverts, while *caprata* usually lacks a supercilium (it can be ill-defined and faint on some individuals, rarely extending much beyond the eye).

DESCRIPTION

Adult male fresh plumage Forehead, crown, nape, lores, malar region, cheeks and ear-coverts black with broad greyish-buff fringes. The mantle and scapulars are black with long grey-buff fringes and, to a lesser extent, grey-white fringes on the lower mantle and scapulars. The fringes on all the above upperpart feathers obscure much of the black apart from the centre of the feathers, thus creating a streaked appearance. The lower back is mainly pale grey with pale brown fringes and reduced black centres to the feathers, thus showing a less streaked appearance. The rump and uppertail-coverts are white with scattered large buff-orange tips, especially to the uppertail-coverts, creating a marked contrast between the darker mantle and black tail. The chin and throat are white with narrow indistinct buff-orange tips extending up the centre of the throat and marginally onto the centre of the chin. The white of the throat extends laterally onto the sides of neck and the white almost meets in a full collar at the rear of the neck. The white feathering on the neck is obscured to a varying extent by buff and/or black fringes to some of the feathers, giving it a mottled appearance. The breast, belly and flanks are pale buff-orange with a slightly greater depth of colour on the upper breast. Many of the feathers have pale buff fringes. The undertail-coverts are white. Two specimens in BMNH also show black speckling across the upper breast, possibly adopted on moulting from juvenile plumage to first year. The tail is black with prominent broad chestnut-buff tips and similar-coloured narrow fringes to the outer webs of the rectrices. The outer pair of rectrices (06) have large pale buff to white tips and broad fringes to the outer webs. The bases of the rectrices are white including the central pair. The white extends only for c.10–25mm and is not visible in the field, being hidden by the uppertail-coverts. The largest amount is at the base of the second innermost pair (02), which is up to 25mm, and the amount of white at the base of each tail feather then declines gradually until the outermost pair (06). The white is present on both webs but extends further down the outer web.

The primaries are black with white bases on 02–09, the white being present on both webs. The largest amount of white is on 04 (almost 50% of the feather), followed by 03, 02=05 and then the white decreases descendantly up to and including 09. These white bases form an angled white flash separated from the inner white covert-patch by the black outer greater coverts. There are pale grey-buff or grey-white crescentic tips to the primaries and similar-coloured narrow fringes to the outer webs on the inner primaries. The innermost four secondaries (03–06) have white on the feather up to 50% from the base, slightly more extensive on the outer web and with a black central shaft-line. The remaining outer two are completely black and all have broad grey-white to buff tips and fringes to the outer webs. The grey-white to buff tips of the secondaries, when bunched on the closed wing, form a noticeable large distal pale spot, and the pale fringes also form a distinctive panel on the centre of the closed wing. The basal third of all three tertials is white, the rest black; they are narrowly fringed pale buff. There is a large area of white on the inner upperwing. Most of the upperwing greater coverts are white; only the outermost few are black. The inner median and lesser upperwing-coverts are also white. The upperwing primary coverts are predominantly white with black bases hidden by the black alula. The underwing-coverts are black with buff-white tips. The axillaries are black at the base with long white tips. The bill, legs and feet are black, and irides dark brown.

Adult male summer plumage As the plumage wears, the rump, uppertail-coverts, chin, throat and neck-patches become pure white. The neck-patches become extremely prominent, extending in a broad band around the neck and virtually meeting on the hindneck (only just divided by a small line of black feathers often tipped with white or buff). The white on the hindneck also extends variably onto the upper mantle, accentuating the extent of the neck-patches and contrasting with the largely black feathering on the mid- to lower mantle and scapulars. The upper and lower breast become a brighter rufous-orange contrasting with the pure white of the throat and chin. The sides of the breast, flanks, belly and ventral area become pure white as the buff-orange fringes wear away. With extreme wear the feathers on the belly and lower flanks can show the black bases. The lower back loses its brown fringes and becomes pale grey merging into the extensive white on the rump and uppertail-coverts. The pale grey-buff fringes to the feathers of the head and upperparts wear away revealing progressively more black, and the pale fringes and tips to the remiges, rectrices and wing-coverts also wear away to leave these black. The tertials and one or two of the innermost secondaries are often the last to lose the greyish-white tips, and these often show as a conspicuous pale spot on the closed wing even when the rest of the plumage has lost most of its pale fringes.

First-year male The forehead, crown, nape, mantle and scapulars are dark brown/black with broad grey-buff fringes and tips. The rump and uppertail-coverts are white, broadly tipped buff-orange (which is more extensive than on the adult male and often obscures much of the white). A broad buff supercilium extends from the bill over the eye to the rear of the ear-coverts. The lores and malar region are dark brown/black broadly fringed with grey-buff but the cheeks, around the eye and the ear-coverts are blacker owing to narrower pale fringes and contrast with the paler forehead, crown and nape. The chin and throat are buff, being paler buffish-white in the centres. The sides of the throat are darker buff with slightly darker brown mottling. The neck-patches are far less extensive than on adult male and appear merely as a pale suffusion, the white being almost totally obscured by broad, greyish-buff fringes. The upper breast has a narrow band of small diffuse black/brown spots and streaks formed by irregular black feather centres. These also extend in some individuals onto the extreme base of the throat and there are sometimes isolated, slightly larger black spots on the fore-flanks. This spotting appears to abrade by late winter, with one specimen showing spots on 27 October but another showing no spotting by 14 February. The breast, flanks and belly are dull buff-orange with very narrow, hardly discernible pale brown fringes. These areas are duller than in the adult male (this is especially noticeable on the breast). The ventral area and undertail-coverts are buff, slightly paler than the rest of the underparts. The remiges, rectrices and tertials are dark brown (not as black as the adult male). There is no pale base to the tail. The rectrices have prominent buff fringes to the outer webs and cinnamon-buff tips to all but the innermost pair (01) in fresh plumage. All the secondaries are broadly tipped buff-white and only primaries 01–04 also show pale tips, but less extensive than on the secondaries. The flight feathers lose their pale fringes and tips with wear and become gradually more brown and worn as the year progresses, so that there is a marked contrast between these and the black mantle and scapulars in summer plumage. There are similar white patches on the upperwing to the adult male but not quite as extensive and less well defined; the white does not extend as far down the webs of the secondaries as in the adult male. The upperwing lesser and median coverts are black, contrasting with the browner upperwing outer greater coverts. The lesser coverts have broad greyish-white fringes but the median coverts have none or only very narrow off-white fringes to the outer webs. The alula is dark brown with the largest feather having a greyish-white fringe suffused with buff on the outer web extending round the tip and slightly onto the inner web. Only the inner upperwing greater coverts 06 and tertials 07–09 show extensive white areas, whereas in the adult male it is inner upperwing greater coverts 04–06 plus tertials 07–09. The outer greater coverts 05–01 show no white apart from white fringes to the inner webs and a narrow buffish-white fringe to the outer web. The upperwing primary coverts also show less white than the adult male, with only the extreme tips and fringes to the distal part of the feathers showing white. The underwing-coverts are black with extensive white tips. The axillaries are greyish-white with roughly the distal third white. The underwing pattern, as in the adult male, reflects the pattern of the upperwing.

In Nepal the plumage of wintering immature males was considered indistinguisable from adult males by March (Baral 1998).

Adult female Forehead, crown and nape dark brown with broad pale grey-buff fringes in fresh plumage which gradually abrade. The mantle and scapulars are dark brown but the long grey-buff fringes obscure much of the brown, creating a streaked appearance which is less marked as the feather fringes wear away. The back is mainly pale grey-brown. The rump and uppertail-coverts are pale buff-orange forming a marked contrast between the back and the dark brown tail. There is a broad buff supercilium running from the base of the bill over the eye to the rear of the ear-coverts. The lores, malar region, cheeks and ear-coverts are brown with extensive narrow buff tips and fringes, creating a mottled effect. The chin is white and the throat is pale chestnut-buff to buff-white. These areas become whiter with wear, extending slightly onto the sides of the neck to form small narrow indistinct patches on the neck. The breast, belly and flanks are a uniform pale buff-orange although there is a fractionally stronger colouring on the breast which contrasts slightly with the paler buff throat. The contrast becomes more marked as the throat wears whiter; the flanks and belly also then show more contrast as the lower breast becomes buffish-white with wear. The undertail-coverts are creamy-buff. The rectrices are dark brown and have prominent pale buff tips and fringes to the outer webs except for the central pair which have much smaller tips. A specimen collected in March had lost all pale tips and fringes to its tail. There is no pale base to any tail feather. The remiges are dark brown with the base of primaries 01–07 white (02–05 show most white); primary 08 has a minute amount of white at the base of the outer web whilst 09–10 show no white. All the secondaries 01–06 have buff-white bases (the male shows no white on secondaries 01–02) but much less extensively than in the male and obscured by the upperwing greater coverts and primary coverts (except for a small area where the primaries are more exposed in flight, at the point where the greater coverts meet the primary coverts). The white is not pure as in male but often suffused with pale buff in fresh plumage, especially on the secondaries, but it becomes purer in worn plumage. The white is present on both webs of the feather but is slightly more extensive on the outer web. The secondaries have prominent grey-white tips and narrow buff-white fringes to the outer webs. The pale tips to the secondaries form a noticeable distal pale spot when the wing is folded. The inner two tertials are dark brown, the longest (07) having a narrow grey-white fringe on the outer web. The majority of the upperwing greater coverts are dark brown with narrow grey-buff fringes to the outer webs. They also have broad pale buff tips forming a noticeable wing-bar. The median coverts are also dark brown with prominent buff tips, more extensive on the inner 01–04 medians and forming a less distinct and shorter second wing-bar. The inner 4–5 greater coverts have white outer webs forming a large white patch on the inner wing. The inner median coverts are white, forming an extension to the white on the inner greater coverts. The upperwing lesser coverts are dark brown broadly fringed with buff and one or two innermost coverts can show some white. The alula is dark brown with the largest feather showing a prominent white tip and fringe to the outer web. The upperwing primary coverts are predominantly white with the extreme bases dark brown mainly hidden by the alula. The underwing-coverts are creamy-buff with darker grey centres. The axillaries are almost entirely creamy-buff with only the extreme base dark grey. The bill, legs and feet are dark brown, almost black, and irides dark brown.

First-year female Similar to adult female. The underparts are, however, duller and paler, being buffier with little orange tint and no stronger orange tones on the breast and ventral area. The upper breast has some blackish-brown spots as in the first-year male, and only the centre of the throat is white with the sides buff with darker mottling. The rump and uppertail-coverts are uniform buff-orange and show no white. The remiges and rectrices are paler grey-brown, not dark brown as in the adult female, and as the year progresses show more wear through abrasion. The pale areas on the primaries and secondaries are buff, not white. The secondaries are tipped greyish-white. The outer upperwing greater coverts are dark brown broadly tipped buff. The inner greater coverts only show some pale greyish-white on the fringes, more diffused and much less extensive than in the adult female. The underwing-coverts and axillaries are pale buff and the underwing reflects the pattern of the upperwing. The bill is horn-brown, the legs and feet dark brown almost black, and irides dark brown.

Measurements

	Male	**Female**
Wing	81.5–88.6	80.1–84.0
Tail	54.9–66.0	54.0–58.1

[Kozlova 1930a]

	Male	**Female**
Wing	89.0–91.5 (mean 90.4)	85.0–86.5 (mean 85.8)
Tail	59.5–61.5 (mean 60.7)	55.5–57.0 (mean 56.3)
Bill	15.5–17.0 (mean 16.1)	16.0–17.0 (mean 16.5)

[Own measurements BMNH 2000]

DISTRIBUTION AND STATUS

Found in the central Palearctic and Oriental regions. It breeds locally in the subalpine and alpine parts of western and central Mongolia and in adjacent areas of the Russian Federation and possibly Kazakhstan. It migrates through western and central China to winter in the Gangetic plains and duars of northern India and the terai of Nepal. Its distribution and status are still imperfectly known both in its breeding and wintering areas. From known information its global distribution is apparently restricted to an area from between 49° 43´ and 25° 36´N and 76° 50´ and 106° 02´E (Collar *et al.* 2001).

There is only one known regular wintering area that supports a relatively high number of this species, at Sukla Phanta in Nepal. The few other current wintering areas only support irregular single-figure numbers.

Everywhere it occurs, both in its breeding and wintering areas, it is now considered to be rare and very local. From the comparatively little information available it is probably the scarcest species in its genus. Under IUCN criteria its population is considered globally threatened and it is classed as Vulnerable (Collar *et al.* 1994, 2001). In fact the main numerical values triggering this classification – that there are fewer than 10,000 individuals and that it has declined by more than 20% in ten years or three generations – may appear over-optimistic. At any rate it is likely that there are considerably fewer than 10,000 individuals. Obtaining a true picture of the population is not eased by the facts that (a) on their breeding grounds they seem to be in small, widely scattered and localised breeding colonies, none of which has been studied since 1979 (probably owing to the difficulties of locating them in huge areas of mountainous and relatively inaccessible terrain), and (b) their current wintering grounds are also relatively unknown apart from two areas in Nepal. The facts that it is now absent from most of the areas, especially in northern India where it was historically recorded, and that the total wintering population in Nepal is estimated at no more than 110 individuals, point to a continuing decline in a species which apparently was always comparatively scarce. Baral (1998) was probably correct in suggesting that its status under IUCN criteria should be revised from Vulnerable to Endangered; Collar *et al.* (2001) retained it in Vulnerable on the basis that populations may be overlooked, but acknowledged that if intensive fieldwork failed to confirm this then its elevation to Endangered would indeed be warranted.

It has been recorded definitely from only seven countries, the Russian Federation, Kazakhstan, Mongolia, China, India, Nepal and Bhutan. The species is listed by Rashid (1967) and Husain (1979) as occurring in Bangladesh but this needs to be substantiated. It is definitely known to breed in two countries; north-west Mongolia and the adjacent areas of the Russian Federation, and there are records in the breeding season from adjacent areas of eastern Kazakhstan but without definite proof of breeding (Knystautas 1993). The information concerning breeding areas is comparatively sparse and no breeding site appears to have been visited and reported on since 1979.

Kozlova (1930a,b) stated that, based on specimens in the Zoological Museum of the Academy of Sciences in Russia and in Prof. Sushkin's private collection, one may assume with certainty that it breeds in the alpine zones of the following Mongolian regions: River Bujantu [Buyant Gol]; the upper reaches of the Dsapchan [Zavkhan Gol], in the Hangay [Khangayn Nuruu], the environs of Lamen-gegen and the south slope of the Seiljughem mountain chain [Siylkhemiyn Nuruu]. The evidence for breeding in Kazakhstan is not adequately substantiated, and if the species ever bred there it may now no longer do so, as there are no records since the 1930s. In the collection mentioned by Kozlova there is an adult male collected by Slovstov near Saissan-nor [Lake Zaysan] in what is now north-east Kazakhstan. The specimen is undated but Kozlova judged by its plumage that it was collected in summer and because of this, even though it was not in typical mountainous habitat, it was presumably on its breeding grounds (Kozlova 1930a).

Kozlova was dubious about the true locality for this bird, partly because it is a mountain species in the breeding season. Sushkin (1938) mentions that Khakhlov told him that he had once seen a pair which he presumed were on spring passage near to the *mys topolevyi* [poplar promontory] at Lake Zaysan in Kazakhstan. The fact that they were paired and near to a known breeding area in north-west Mongolia may indicate that these birds were breeding, although sadly again no dates are given. Dement'ev & Gladkov (1968) also quote Khakhlov as stating that they breed in small numbers 'here and there' north of Lake Zaysan but confirmation was again lacking.

Sushkin (1938) stated that it was probably distributed in the alpine zones of the mountain ranges in north-western Mongolia, from the south-eastern limit of the Altai, possibly including the Mongolian Altai and south-east to the Ala Shan [Helan Shan]. He based this statement on three records of individuals located in summer in Mongolia. The first was found by Berezovskiy & Kolomiytsev on the upper reaches of the Buyant Gol in the Hangay mountains [Khangayn Nuruu], north-east of Uliastay at an altitude of around 2,300m, although no dates are given. The second was a juvenile collected by Przheval'skiy in the Ala Shan range of mountains in August 1880. This location is also considerably to the south of any known breeding area in north-west Mongolia, in what is now Ningxia Autonomous Region of China, and probably indicates that the bird was already on migration to its wintering area. Kozlova (1930a) reported that it had completed its moult from juvenile to first-winter plumage. However, there is a recording in the National Sound Archive of an adult male in song display flight on 15 May 1991, near Nanping (Camp IV) in Sichuan Province which is relatively near to the bird collected by Przheval'skiy in 1880. This may indicate that there is an unknown breeding population in this area. The third specimen was collected by Sushkin himself on 13 August 1914 in the upper reaches of the Sary-Dzhamaty River on the southern slopes of the Saylyugem mountains [Siylkhemiyn Nuruu] in north-western Mongolia at about 2,500m. It was a juvenile male which had almost completed its moult into autumn plumage but retained evidence of nestling plumage on the scapulars, lower throat and upper breast, suggesting that it was locally bred. On 12 August what was possibly an adult was seen in flight in the same area. Searches failed to locate any others (Sushkin 1938).

Kozlova (1930a), on an expedition mounted by the Academy of Sciences to the high mountains of the south-western Hangay [Khangayn Nuruu] in north-west Mongolia in the summer of 1929, said that there was a large breeding colony (population) but it would have to be left to future expeditions to determine the exact extent of the breeding area. She found it breeding in "quite large numbers" (and collected no fewer than 32 specimens on this expedition (Kozlova 1932) on the southern slopes of the permanently snow-covered peak of Otchon-Tengri [Otgon Tenger Uul, 4,021 m] and also to the south-west of this peak, in the Cholute mountains (untraced) and to the east, along mountain slopes flanking the Bombotu valley. It was present in a narrowly defined area in the subalpine meadow zone between 2,430 and 2,600m. She went on to say that on the banks of the Bogdoin Gol on the south side of Otchon-Tengri it was so common that she no longer wanted to collect it.

In July 1979 a joint Soviet/Mongolian expedition surveyed the Monho-Hayrhan [Mönkh-Khayrkhan Uul] massif in the Mongolian Altayn Nuruu. Small numbers of pairs of *S. insignis* were found breeding between 2,800 and 3,100m on the northern macro slope of the glacial massif. Some pairs were relatively densely located with 3–5 pairs carrying food to their young in nests up to "only a few tens of metres apart", whereas others were up to 1–2km apart. At this same location two fledged young were seen on 31 July on an ascent to the Ulan-Daba [Ulaan Dabaa] Pass. Along the Khudzhirtyn Gol there were no *S. insignis*, and only one pair was located in the Borgiyn Gol basin on the north slope at 2,500m (Kishchinskiy *et al.* 1982).

The Russian Federation expeditions in 1970 and 1971 went to an area near the village of Tashakta [Tashanta] on the southern part of the Chuyskaya steppe in the Gorno-Altayskaya Autonomous Region, which borders north-west Mongolia. The area studied was the northern foothills of the same Saylyugem mountain range [Siylkhemiyn Nuruu] as Sushkin studied in 1914, up to an altitude of 2,100m (Panov 1976). This area was almost 1,000km north of where Kozlova found the species breeding. The impression gained was that Hodgson's Bushchat was extremely sporadic in its breeding distribution and the birds that were found represented a small local population. Searches of other suitable locations nearby, such as the Yustyt River valley, 10–15km north or Kosh-Agach even slightly further north, were unsuccessful, as were searches southwards along the Chukskiy [Chuyskiy] highway. It was considered that the area in question represented the northern limit of the species' breeding range. The number of breeding pairs in the population was only 4–10 with up to three males being heard from any one spot. One bird was seen at this location in 1974 (Neufeldt 1986) but between 1 June and 7 July 1977 another expedition to this exact area (and certain suitable-looking adjacent ones) sadly failed to locate any birds despite targeted searches. The demise of this population may not be unrelated to the fact that 'professional' zoologists collected ten specimens from this population over a period of 5–6 years (Loskot 1986).

Some Russian ornithologists have suggested that it is still an irregular breeder in the Russian Federation (M.V. Cherkasova pers. comm. to Ponomareva & Vinokurov 1984). It may well be that the site found by Panov represented an irregular extension north of its normal range in north-west Mongolia, and that therefore it may not occur on a regular basis in the Russian Federation. Its apparently strict breeding habitat and nest-site requirements (see below) probably limit its capacity to expand its breeding range, as does its apparent low productivity. However, there are vast areas that remain unexplored and it is probable that undiscovered colonies exist.

Its wintering areas are in southern Nepal and the adjacent northern Indian states of Uttar Pradesh, Bihar, West Bengal, Karnataka and Assam (Ali & Ripley 1968–1998, Sharma *et al.* 1997). It occurs or formerly occurred in the Gangetic plains from north Haryana, Uttar Pradesh to Bihar (terai) through the Nepal terai, to the foothills in northern West Bengal and Assam (duars) (Hume 1877c,d, 1878b,c, 1880a,b, Vaurie 1959, Ali & Ripley 1968–1998, Narayan & Rosalind 1997, Sharma *et al.* 1997). However, many of the records are very old and Baral (1998), whilst listing a number of other old records (see below), pointed to the fact that the only recent records for this species are from Nepal and Assam. It was collected from Umballah [Ambala] on 14 November 1866 (Beavan 1865–1868) and also on 17 December 1922 (Jones 1927); from Cawnpore [Kanpur] in February (Marshall & Marshall 1875), from Gorakhpur and Basti districts of Uttar Pradesh in October and December 1878 (Hume 1878a) and from Segowlie [Sugauli, Bihar] on 10 January, this being the type locality given in Gray and Gray (1846). It has also been recorded

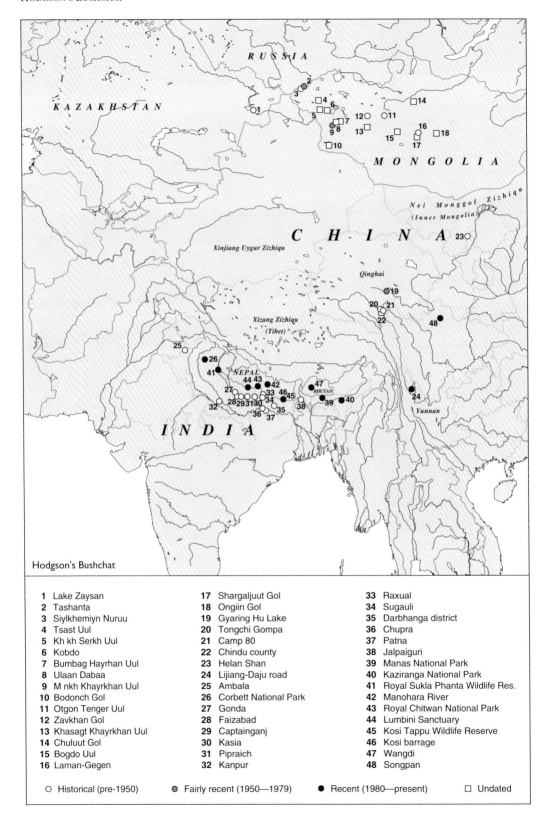

Hodgson's Bushchat

1 Lake Zaysan	**17** Shargaljuut Gol	**33** Raxual
2 Tashanta	**18** Ongiin Gol	**34** Sugauli
3 Siylkhemiyn Nuruu	**19** Gyaring Hu Lake	**35** Darbhanga district
4 Tsast Uul	**20** Tongchi Gompa	**36** Chupra
5 Kh kh Serkh Uul	**21** Camp 80	**37** Patna
6 Kobdo	**22** Chindu county	**38** Jalpaiguri
7 Bumbag Hayrhan Uul	**23** Helan Shan	**39** Manas National Park
8 Ulaan Dabaa	**24** Lijiang-Daju road	**40** Kaziranga National Park
9 M nkh Khayrkhan Uul	**25** Ambala	**41** Royal Sukla Phanta Wildlife Res.
10 Bodonch Gol	**26** Corbett National Park	**42** Manohara River
11 Otgon Tenger Uul	**27** Gonda	**43** Royal Chitwan National Park
12 Zavkhan Gol	**28** Faizabad	**44** Lumbini Sanctuary
13 Khasagt Khayrkhan Uul	**29** Captainganj	**45** Kosi Tappu Wildlife Reserve
14 Chuluut Gol	**30** Kasia	**46** Kosi barrage
15 Bogdo Uul	**31** Pipraich	**47** Wangdi
16 Laman-Gegen	**32** Kanpur	**48** Songpan

○ Historical (pre-1950)   ◉ Fairly recent (1950—1979)   ● Recent (1980—present)   □ Undated

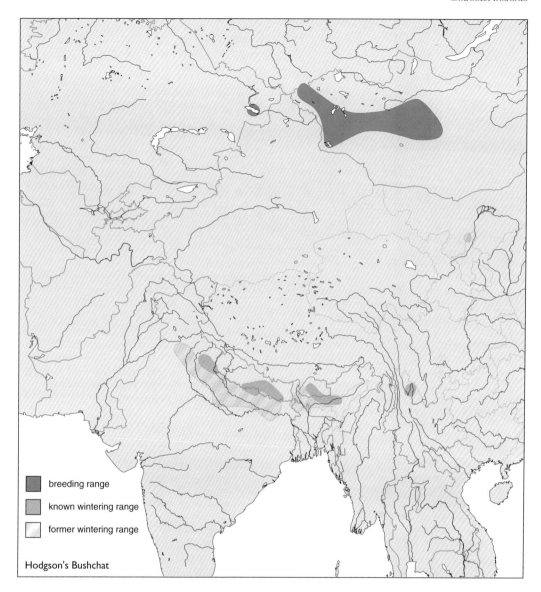

breeding range

known wintering range

former wintering range

Hodgson's Bushchat

in April from the lower hills of Sikhim [Sikkim, West Bengal] and the Bhutan Doars [duars], [Assam/ West Bengal] (Oates 1890). There is a possible record from Ataria [Atrauli] 32km north of Lucknow in the spring of 1897 (Jesse 1902–1903). E.W. Cleveland is quoted by Hume (Hume 1878a) as stating:

> "It takes a good deal of patient fagging to find these birds as they occur rather sparingly in these districts (Bustee and Gorakpur)... Judging from my own experience, I should say that in the course of a ten-mile ride across a stretch of flat open country, thickly dotted with cane fields (their favourite haunts) one would scarcely meet with more than a single pair of these birds, whereas upwards of twenty *P. indica* (*Saxicola maura indica*) would be seen in that distance".

At least ten specimens were shot in this area in a relatively short period around 1878, suggesting that it was reasonably distributed throughout northern India before its habitat was degraded. Hume could write in 1880 "the bird is to this day, not uncommon along the plains country at the base of the Himalayas, stretching from the Bhutan Doars [Assam/West Bengal] at any rate to the Bustee [Basti] and Gorakpur [Gorakphur] Districts".

The following century saw a steady conversion of natural grassland to agricultural use and other artificial habitats with a consequent large decline in numbers. It was described as a winter visitor to Jalpaiguri district (Inglis *et al.* 1920). A specimen was also collected in the north of the Gonda district [Oudh] (Hume 1880b). None of the areas in India listed above are now thought to hold a regular wintering population and there have been no records from the areas in Uttar Pradesh, for example, since the nineteenth century. It is now a rare and irregular species in India apart from in Assam. Collar *et al.* (2001) state "on the basis of current information the regular Indian wintering population might be estimated as under 100 birds. This could, however, be misjudged…". Assam, which still retains large areas of grassland, much of it unsurveyed, is now the only area providing regular contemporary records in India and may hold a larger wintering population than is currently known (Baral 1998). However, in Kaziranga National Park (26° 32´N, 93° 00´E) it is scarce and irregular (Sarma *et al.* 1997) and in Manas Wildlife Sanctuary (26° 43´N, 90° 59´E) it is only regularly present in small numbers (Narayan & Rosalind 1997). At Manas Naryan & Rosalind (1997) saw the species every year between 1986 and 1989. A few were first seen in March 1986 at the Kasimdaha grasslands near Basbari. This constituted the first record of *S. insignis* for north-eastern India and the state of Assam. In 1986 the last sighting was on 24 April, which is later than the last date of 10 April given by Ali & Ripley (1968–1998). In 1987 the first sighting was on 28 February in the same area and birds were present until the fourth week of April. In 1988 they did not appear until the third week of April and other birds were seen at Kapurpora on the Manas River. In 1989 they were again only seen in April and had disappeared within two weeks. These sightings suggest that the Manas area acts as a staging post for this species on its spring migration (Narayan & Rosalind 1997). However, the impact of recent damage caused by Bhodo tribal guerillas is unknown and further investigation of the whole area is needed as there is insufficient information (K.D. Bishop *in litt.* 2001).

As mentioned above it has also been reported from Kaziranga National Park situated on the floodplain of the Brahmaputra River, southern bank, in the Nowgaon and Golaghat districts of Assam, which is a further range extension eastwards (there is some ambiguity about both of these records – see under Assam below): four or five birds were seen at the Baguri Range in the park on 13 April 1995, and a single bird was then seen in the same area on 29 April 1995, which is the latest date it has been recorded from India (Sarma *et al.* 1997). K.D. Bishop (*in litt.* 2001) has never found this species in ten 4–5 day trips made during February–April between 1985–2001, in north-east India. He searched for this species without success in north-east India during February/March 2001 in suitable-looking habitat along the Noa-Dihing River, adjoining Namdapha National Park and in and around Digboi and Dibru-Saikhowa National Park, but considered an extended, more thorough search might prove successful.

There are five localities from which this species has recently been recorded in Nepal: Kathmandu Valley, Royal Sukla Phanta Reserve [Sukla Phanta], Lumbini, Chitwan and Kosi [Kosi Tappu and Kosi Barrage]. Kathmandu Valley was the site of an isolated record of two immature males considered to be on migration, collected along the Manohara River, Kathmandu, at 1,380m on 9 October 1982; Lumbini was also a single record of an adult male collected in February 1995 and subsequent searches failed to find any other birds. Chitwan contains four localities – Meghauli, Patna, the Narayani River and just outside the park north of Sauraha – where this species has been recorded. Records suggest that Meghauli and Patna are the two most important of these. It is not known if the birds seen at Meghauli are wintering or migrants. It is also suspected that there may be a small wintering population in grasslands close to the Makhali River which forms the border between west Nepal and India, but there has been no investigation of this area as yet (Baral 1998).

Kosi Tappu has only a single record of a bird on 5 October 1987, and the species has not been seen since in this area. It is known to winter regularly in only two places in Nepal. The first is the Kosi Barrage (Dam) area in south-eastern Nepal, the other being Sukla Phanta in the west of Nepal. This species was only definitely recorded in Nepal as late as 1975, when two males were seen south of the Kosi Barrage on 11 April (Fleming *et al.* 1984); but there were 82 records, 1975–1998, only ten of which were outside the two regular wintering areas (Baral 1998).

Prior to 1997 the only area where the species had been recorded regularly wintering was the Kosi Barrage where 10+ (six males and four females) were recorded on 17/18 March 1982 (Martins *et al.* 1983). This area unfortunately lies outside the nearby Kosi Tappu Wildlife Reserve. The area has suffered from steady habitat degradation and alteration by monsoonal floods, as well as by human disturbance and cattle grazing. Recent reports from this area note a decline in wintering individuals with no more than two present, and none at all in the winter of 1997/1998 (Baral 1998).

However, a survey in the Sukla Phanta area of Nepal found one male on 9 and 13 November 1997 with two there on 14 November. Two more extensive surveys in December 1997 and March 1998 produced daily counts of up to six individuals with a maximum of 26 (23 males and three females) on 11 December 1997. It is of interest to note that of the total of 23 males only four were considered immature.

The maximum count in March was 18 individuals on 18 March (Baral 1998). A total of 29 individuals was counted in December from Sukla Phanta and Chitwan combined. There is one report from Sukla

Phanta of 50 individuals present on 17–19 March 1993 (Irvin 1994) but this record has been questioned by local ornithologists who also visited the area several times during that year (Baral 1998).

Extrapolation of these figures to the amount of suitable habitat still available gave a maximum number of 110 individuals likely to be wintering in Nepal in 1997/1998. The preponderance of males found suggests that females occupy different habitat, are less conspicuous and therefore under-recorded, and/ or are genuinely fewer in number. The scarcity of records from other areas in Nepal may point to a decline owing to the destruction or degradation of its traditional grassland and wetland habitat, which has experienced a dramatic decline in the last 30 years (Baral 1998).

List of known records by country A full review of localities with coordinates is also provided in *Threatened Birds of Asia* by Collar *et al.* to whom I would like to acknowledge my gratitude for their assistance. However, there are a few errors and omissions in their text which I have corrected in the following list, as well as adding some additional detail which became available after their work was published.

The first name for a location is the one used in the original report. Names in parentheses [...] are those in current use.

KAZAKHSTAN

A pair at *mys-topolevyi* ['poplar promontory'] on the northern shore of Lake Zaysan, "collected in spring" (Khakhlov undated in Sushkin 1938).

A single male in summer plumage collected at Saissan–nor [Lake Zaysan] Slovstov – specimen in Severtsov collection, 6511 (10136) – undated in Kozlova 1930a,b.

RUSSIAN FEDERATION
Altay Republic

South of Tashanta in foothills (2,100m) of Saylyugem [Siylkhemiyn Nuruu] range of mountains, with c.5–10 pairs, June 1970/1971 (Panov 1976), and one male, June 1974 (Neufeldt 1986).

MONGOLIA

There is much variation in publications concerning location/place names in Mongolia and it is impossible to find any source which is regarded as the definitive source for names in Mongolia.

Gol = river; Nuur = lake; Nuruu = mountain range; Uul = mountain

Bayan-Olgiy province

Saylyugem mountains, Siilhem mountain [Siylkhemiyn Nuruu], one juvenile male collected and possible adult seen on southern slopes (2,500m) of the mountain range near the Syry-Zhamata [Sary-Dzhamata] River in August 1914 (Sushkin 1938). (This record is mistakenly listed in Collar *et al.* (2001) as in Uvs Province.)

Tsast Uul, undated (Fomin & Bold 1991). This record is mistakenly listed in Collar *et al.* (2001) as in Khoud Province.

Khovd province

Khokh Serkh mountain [Khokh Serkh Uul], undated (Fomin & Bold 1991).

Kobdo (40km south of), undated (Kishchinskiy *et al.* 1980 in Stresemann & Portenko 1982).

Bumbat Mountain [Bumbag Khayrkhan Uul], undated (Bold 1997).

Ulaan Davaa [Ulaan Dabaa], undated (Bold 1997).

Munch-Chajrchan-Ula [Monkh Khayrkhan Uul], 'several' pairs and families 2,800–3,100m; two fledged young, near Ulaan Dabaa pass, 2,600m; one pair Borgiyn-gol River basin, 2,500m, July 1979 (Kishchinskiy *et al.* 1982, Fomin & Bold 1991).

Bodonch Gol, undated (Bold 1997).

Jargalant Khayrchan Uul, pair with recently fledged juvenile and another male, 2,500m, July 1995 (Bräunlich 1995). The species might be widespread in suitable habitat in this area and the adjacent Altay [Mongolian Altayn Nuruu] and Bombat Khairchan [Bumbag Khayrkhan Uul] (Bräunlich 1995).

Zavkhan province

Near Otgontenger, Otkhon-tengri snow peak [Otgon Tenger Uul], south-west Khangayn Nuruu, three males and one female, June–July 1929 in MCZ and ZMB (also Fomin & Bold 1991). These specimens are undoubtedly included in the list below of 32 specimens collected by Kozlova in and around Otgon Tenger Uul between 22 June and 19 July 1929.

Total 32 specimens collected (Kozlova 1932):

Foot of Cholute mountains south-west of Otgon-tengri [Otgon Tenger Uul], where Kozlova collected four adult males and two adult females, 22 June 1929; one adult male and one adult female, 24 June 1929; four adult males, 27 June 1929;

Bogdoin-gol valley at southern foot of Otkhon-tengri [Otgon Tenger Uul] 4 adult males and one adult female 29 June 1929; 4 adult males 30 June 1929; 2 adult males 1 July 1929; one adult male 4 July 1929; one adult female 5 July 1929; 3 adult males 7 July 1929; one adult male and one adult female 8 July 1929; one adult male 19 July 1929.

Valley of Bombotu-gol, Buyantu river basin near Otkhon-tengri [Otgon Tenger Uul] one pullus (sex unknown) 19 July 1929.

[The Kozlova records are omitted from Collar *et al.* (2001)]

Zavkhan river [Zavkhan Gol] upper reachesundated (Fomin & Bold 1991).

Khokh Nuur east of Otgon Tenger Uul in Khangayn Nuruu at 47° 32′N, 98° 32′E one male collected at 2,600m 9 June 1997 and now in USNM collection.

Gov'-Altai province

Khasagtkhhairkhan Uul [Khasagt Khayrkhan Uul], undated (Fomin & Bold 1991).

Arkhangai province

Chuluut Gol, undated (Bold 1997).

Bayankhongor province

Bogd mountain [Bogdo Uul], undated (Bold 1997).

Lamen-gegen [Laman-Gegen], east Khangay, on the upper Tujn-Gol, one juvenile collected near the monastery, July 1926 (Neufeldt & Vietinghoff-Scheel 1982, Stresemann & Portenko 1982).

Shargaljuit River [Shargaljuut Gol], undated (Bold 1997).

Ovorkhangay province

Ongin Gol [Ongiin Gol] at its eastern extremity (Shargalzhuut), undated (Fomin & Bold 1991, Bold 1997).

CHINA
Qinghai Province

Jialing Lake [Gyaring Hu lake], Madoi county, October 1960 (specimen in ASCN, also Xian Yaohua *et al.* 1964, Cheng Tso-hsin 1987).

Drechu Gomba [Tongchi Gompa] 'Camp 79', six males, 4,200m, April–May 1935 (Dolan 1938) Schäfer 1938, Schäfer & Meyer de Schauensee 1939, Vaurie 1972, three males in AMNH collected 2 May 1935 at Ching-Hai [Qinghai Nanshan Mountains] presumably from six listed above).

'Camp 80' on upper Jalung Kiang steppe, c.50 birds (of which only one was a female) recorded 4,600m, April 1935 (Schäfer 1938).

Chindu county, undated (Cheng Tso-hsin 1987).

Ningxia Autonomous Region

Ala Shan, Alxa [Helan Shan mountains] at or near Bajan-choto [Dynjuanin], an immature male having completed post-juvenile moult collected August 1880 (N.M. Przheval'skiy in (Kozlova 1930a,b), Cheng Tso-hsin 1987, R.L. Potapov *in litt.* to M.G. Wilson 2001).

[The record of several first-winter individuals collected at same location by Przheval'skiy in Aug–Sept 1880 (Neufeldt & Vietinghoff-Scheel 1982) is incorrect (R.L. Potapov *in litt.* to M.G. Wilson 2001)]

Yunnan Province

Km 47 along the Lijiang-Daju road, April 1988 (S. Jensen *per* C.R. Robson *in litt.* 1991 to Collar *et al.* 2001).

Sichuan Province

Road to Nanping (Camp IV) east of and along the highway, at a pass 50km north of Songpan at 3,400m (32°42′N 103°42′E), 16 May 1991, one male singing (recording in British Library National Sound Archive).

[This record not included in Collar *et al.* (2001)]

INDIA
Haryana

'Lallroo' [Lalru], one in November 1866 (Beavan 1865–1868). This record was omitted by Baker (1922–1930) which may suggest either an oversight or withdrawn record (Collar *et al.* 2001).

Ambala, December 1922, one female collected (specimen in BNHS, Jones 1927).

Uttar Pradesh

Corbett National Park, one male, February 1989 (Bose *et al.* 1989).

Avadh = Oudh [Gonda], one undated (*Stray Feathers* 1880b).

Avadh = Oudh [Gonda], one male, undated, possibly the same as above (Jesse 1902–1903).

Fyzabad [Faizabad], Gorakhpur, 5 December 1878, one adult male collected (specimen in BMNH).

Kaptanganj [Captainganj], 'Zillah Bustee' (Basti district), 27 October 1878, one juvenile female collected (specimen in BMNH; also see Hume 1878b). One adult female, 14 December 1878 collected (specimen in BMNH).

Kassia [Kasia], Gorakhpur, 29 December 1878, one juvenile male collected (specimen in BMNH).

No location, Gorakhpur, 17 December 1878, one adult male collected (specimen in BMNH).

Piprach [Pipraich], Champaran (currently a district of Bihar), December 1878, one male (specimen in BMNH).

Cawnpore [Kanpur], one female in February, year unspecified (Marshall & Marshall 1875, Jesse 1902–1903, specimen in AMNH).

Bihar

Raxaul, 17 March 1937, one female collected (specimen in BMNH; labelled by R. Meinertzhagen (Meinertzhagen has been found to have re-labelled specimens of other species that he stole from other museums so it is possible the location on this label is bogus.)

Segowlee [Sugauli], two males collected (including type specimen), 10 January, year unspecified (Hume 1877c).

Location unknown, Tirhut district, one collected 20 December 1902 (specimen in AMNH).

Baghourie [Baghownie], Darbhanga district, one in December 1902 (Inglis 1901); one male 24 January and one male 20 November 1923 collected (specimens in BMNH); March and December 1909, three males collected (specimens in BNHS).

Chapra [Chupra], 'Rajaputee', Saran district, October–November 1897, male and female collected (specimens in BNHS).

Patna, one male, 19 March 1937; two males, 26 November 1937; one male, 19 December 1938, all collected (specimens in BMNH).

West Bengal

'Lower Hills of Sikkim', 5 April 1873, one abnormally small adult male collected (specimen in BMNH).

Jalpaiguri undated (Inglis *et al.* 1920); four on 7–8 January 1931, two males collected (specimens in BMNH).

Assam

Manas National Park, 1987 (Rahmani *et al.* 1988) unspecified number February–April 1986–1989 (Narayan & Rosalind 1997).

Kaziranga National Park, 1–5 individuals 13–29 April 1995 (Sarma *et al.* 1997, Baral 1998). This record appears to be slightly ambiguous and not wholly verified as the record from P. Sarma states that "On 13 April 1995 four to five bushchats which were *seemingly* different to *S. maura* were noticed in Baguri range of Kaziranga National park by the second author (M. Barua). Later, on 29 April, the third author (V. Menon) saw a single individual of the same species in Baguri Range". There does not appear to be any detailed description available and M. Barua in conversation to K.D. Bishop some time later did not mention this record.

Also unconfirmed records as follows (courtesy of Collar *et al.* 2001):

Spring 1897, possible record of one at Ataria, north of Lucknow (Jesse 1902–1903).

Motipur, one individual possibly this species June 1899 (Inglis 1901).

NEPAL

Royal Sukla Phanta Wildlife Reserve, regular wintering population (Baral 1991, 1995, 1997, 1998; also see Baral [1998] for complete list of occurrences 1991–1998); c.50 individuals seen 17–19 March 1993 (Irvin 1994) considered dubious (see Baral 1998); six on 12 March 1997 (Giri 1997); maximum of 26 on 11 December 1997 and 18 on 17 March 1998 (Baral 1998); three females January 1999 (J. C. Kovacs *in litt.* 1999 to Collar *et al.* 2001).

Manohara River, Kathmandu valley, 1,400m, two immature males, 9 October 1982 (Fleming *et al.* 1984, Nepali 1986).

Royal Chitwan National Park, at Meghauli 50–100m, one on 23 March 1986 (Holt *et al.* 1986); two, 16–26 April 1991 and three in January and November 1994 (Drijvers 1995); at Patna, one male, 30 November 1997 (K. Pokharel pers. comm. to Baral 1997) and one male, 7 December, and two males, 18 December 1997 (B. Mahato pers. comm. to Baral 1997); one unconfirmed record at Naryani River of one in spring 1993/94 and December 1994 (Smith *et al.* 1996); north of Sauraha just outside the park boundary, one male in December 1997 and January 1998 (K. Pokharel pers. comm. to Baral 1998).

Lumbini Sanctuary, one adult male collected in February 1995 (H.S. Nepali pers. comm. to Baral 1995) although none was seen on subsequent visit in March 1998 (Baral 1998).

Kosi Tappu Wildlife Reserve, one in October 1987 (Heinen 1988), one male in March 2000 (*Danphe* 9 [2000]: 1–2).

Kosi Barrage, 50–100m, two males, 11 April 1975 (Fleming *et al.* 1984); 10+ birds, 17–18 March 1982 (Martins *et al.* 1983); two males and 1–3 females on 9 April 1983 (Alström & Olsson 1983); five males and three females, 14 February 1984 (Redman *et al.* 1984); three in March 1986 (J.N. Dymond *in litt.* 1999 to Collar *et al.* 2001); five on 10 February 1987 (Juliusberger 1987); one male on 31 March 1994 and 3–6 April 1995 (Drijvers 1995); one first-year male in March 1996 (Daulne & Goblet 1996); two adults and one first-year male on 23 March 1996 (Davidson & Heywood 1996); maximum of two birds south of the barrage, undated (H. Choudhary *in litt.* 1996); Chisapani (unmapped), 1 August 2000 (*Danphe* 9 [2000]: 3); see Baral (1998) for complete list of sightings 1975–1998.

BHUTAN

Wangdiphodrang [Wangdi], 2km north at Bajothang beside the Sang Chu, one male April 1999 (B. Carrick and P. Holt *in litt.* 1999 to Collar *et al.* 2001).

MOVEMENTS

Hodgson's Bushchat migrates in autumn mainly through Tibet and central China to winter in northern India and Nepal. Ali & Ripley (1968–1998) give first arrival and last departure dates for India as 27 October and 10 April, although birds can also leave earlier in March or later in April (see above). In Nepal it is said to occur between November and late April (Inskipp & Inskipp 1991). In Sukla Phanta single males have been noted as early as 9 and 13 November 1997, with two males being seen there on 14 November. However, there are records of birds being seen in autumn in Nepal as early as 5 October at Kosi Tappu and in spring as late as 6 May at Sukla Phanta, both dates being considered exceptional (Baral 1998).

In Qinghai province, China, it was recorded at 'Camp 79', Drechu Gomba (33° 25´N, 97° 03´E), with six males in breeding plumage present at 4,200m on 2 May 1935 (Vaurie 1972), while on the upper Jalung [Yalu River] at 'Camp 80', (33° 25´N, 97° 15´E) in the Kiang steppe, amongst 50 birds recorded (presumably here and at other camps) only one female was noted. These birds were at elevations up to 4,600m between 19–25 April, mainly in undulating country on mountain slopes or in swampy valleys (Schäfer 1938, Schäfer & Meyer de Schauensee 1939). The reason for the apparent imbalance in sex ratios is unknown; the sex ratio on the wintering grounds is also biased towards males. It may be that males are more obvious than females, use different habitat or follow a different migratory route or schedule to the females. The species appears to mainly migrate through central areas of China where it is considered a very rare migrant. It has been stated that it migrates along the Jalung [Yalu River] and Yangtse River (Schäfer & Meyer de Schauensee 1939). Meyer de Schauensee (1984) mentions that in spring in China it migrates through west and southeast Qinghai province and western Sichuan. It was also recorded during an avifaunal survey of Qinghai between 1959 and 1962 (Xian *et al.* 1964). Cheng Tso-hsin (1987) records it on migration at Gyaring Lake (October 1960) and Chindu county, both in Qinghai, and also from the Alxa region in the Inner Mongolian Autonomous Region. It has been recorded twice considerably to the east of other records; on the Lijiang–Daju road at km 47 in Yunnan Province (S. Jensen *in litt.* to C.R. Robson 1989, in Collar *et al.* 2001); 50km north of Songpan on the road to Nanping on 16 May 1991 (British Library NSA). The single record from Bhutan was of a male presumably on spring migration at Bajothang, 2km north of Wangdiphodrang [Wangdi] in April 1999 (B. Carrick & P. Holt 1999 in Collar *et al.* 2001).

BREEDING

Little detailed information is available. What there is comes mainly from Kozlova (1930a) and Panov (1976). It would appear that the breeding population consists of small, localised and widely scattered colonies numbering 2–10 pairs in each colony. In the Hangayan Nuruu [Khangayn Nuruu] Kozlova (1930a) found that several pairs breed together and up to 2–3 males can be heard singing at the same time.

Panov (1976) described the breeding territories in the Russian Federation as small and contiguous with up to three males being visible and audible from one spot. In 1970 the distance between two nests in adjacent territories did not exceed 300m. Males vigorously defended their territorial boundaries chasing off intruding males. In north-west Mongolia 3–5 pairs were carrying food to their young only "tens of metres" apart (Kishchinskiy *et al.* 1982). Kozlova (1930a) mentions that it is not difficult to locate where a pair of *S. insignis* are breeding as both birds always remain close to the nest. However, the nests themselves were described as very difficult to find and built in very deep rock crevices (Kozlova 1930a).

Nest sites in the Gorno-Altayskaya Autonomous Region in the Russian Federation were located in shallow ravines or gullies through which flowed freshwater streams, prone to drying out. All four nests found in this area were located in the base of the earth walls of these gullies, hidden in holes or crevices approximately 300mm deep, very well concealed by overhanging grassy turf. The nest itself is a bulky structure with substantial walls; the base is built into a shallow depression. The front of the nest looks like a truncated cone, as the base is noticeably wider than the upper edge that forms the rim of the nest cup. The nest is 140–190mm wide at the base whilst the nest cup has a diameter of 105mm and is 40–55mm deep. It is constructed of dry grass lined with a small amount of wool, feathers and, less commonly, dry moss. The front wall is often very bulky, being anything from 20–70mm thick. Panov thought that the structure of the nest was perfectly suited to the harsh climatic conditions prevailing in the breeding habitat, with night temperatures even in late June approached 0°C.

Breeding of pairs in the small colony studied by Panov appeared to be fairly synchronous. Two nests found on 27 and 28 June 1970 respectively contained four and five nestlings, both broods ready to fledge. On 28 June 1971 two pairs were each accompanying recently fledged young, while two other pairs both had nestlings approximately eight days old in the nest. Kozlova (1930a) found one nest with five eggs completely unincubated on 24 June whilst at a nest in another site on 27 June the young had just recently fledged. In the Mono-Hayran massif in Mongolia a pair were still feeding young in the nest on 18 July whilst fully fledged young from other nests were also in evidence (Kishchinskiy *et al.* 1982). From the limited data available Panov suggested that the clutch usually consists of only four eggs (despite the small sample and the two records of five eggs/nestlings) as a consequence of the habitat, which is relatively poor in invertebrate prey. Dement'ev & Gladkov (1968) suggest the normal clutch is five.

The eggs are greenish-blue, speckled and streaked with ochre-brown (Kozlova 1930a), or marked with red-brown spots, which are often densest at the larger end forming a cap or ring. The size of eggs is 20.8–21.0 x 15.9–16.0mm (Kozlova 1930a). Incubation is by the female only with the male remaining in close attendance; there is no information on the incubation period but it is probably around 14 days. Panov (1976) reported that the young are fed by both parents when in the nest and after fledging, with the female appearing to take the larger role. However, Kozlova (1930a, 1932) stated that the male takes no part in either incubation or feeding the young even after they have fledged, although he remains close to the nest and young at all times. This seems unlikely as this species' breeding behaviour is very similar to that of *Saxicola maura* in which the male and female share the feeding of the young both in the nest and for a short time after they have fledged. The first young in north-west Mongolia fledged at the end of June. The young when they first left the nest after fledging were unable to fly well but perched conspicuously on the tops of small birches *Betula exilis* waiting to be fed (Kozlova 1932).

It is not known if the species is double-brooded although it is likely that pairs that fail will make repeat attempts.

HABITAT

In its breeding range Hodgson's Bushchat inhabits alpine and subalpine zones at 2,000–3,100m (Kishchinskiy *et al.* 1982, But'ev 1983). Kozlova (1930a) described its breeding habitat requirements as quite strict, saying that it favours areas with many gorges near mountain streams where there are also rocky outcrops or scattered boulders. It perches on rocks or the tops of shrubs like willows (*Salix arbuscula*) and birches (*Betula exilis*). At lower altitudes it shared its habitat with Twite *Acanthis flavirostris*, Rock Sparrow *Petronia petronia* and Rufous-tailed Rockthrush *Monticola saxatilis*, whilst at higher altitudes it was found with Altai Accentor *Prunella himalayana*, (Red-spotted) Bluethroat *Luscinia svecica* and Willow Ptarmigan *Lagopus lagopus*.

At the site studied by Panov (1976) in the Russian Federation the birds frequented a hilly semi-desert plateau at 2,100m with very poor, sparse grassy vegetation and scattered low shrubs and bushes. On the surrounding slopes and near the tops of the rounded hills there were ancient outcrops of rocks. The distinguishing features of the site where this species was found, and what set it apart from other similar areas, were the shallow ravines and gullies with small streams flowing through them. Observations of captive birds showed that the species is unlikely to be found breeding in areas not containing fresh water. It seems very fond of water, drinking frequently and bathing regularly. It is also very particular concerning the quality of the water and will not drink or bathe in anything apart from fresh water. This may partly explain why it is attracted to sites for breeding that have flowing fresh water and shallows available. A male in breeding condition, on 10 June 1974, near to the site discovered by Panov, was in a hollow with a small pool formed by a temporary stream, surrounded by towering crags. This had attracted a number of species to come to bathe and drink (Neufeldt 1986). In north-west Mongolia pairs were found in subalpine meadows at 2,430–2,600m (Kozlova 1930a) and also in wet alpine meadows at a higher elevation than the colony in the Russian Federation, at 2,800–3,100m, with scree and huge rocky outcrops on steep slopes. This habitat was judged much wetter than where Panov found his colony. Juvenile birds were also found in a rocky wet meadow by a stream at 2,600m and once on a moraine in the steppe (Kishchinskiy *et al.* 1982). Ponomareva & Vinokurov (1984) note that these habitats are virtually unaltered by any human economic activity. Migrants in Tibet inhabited sections of a river with steep banks, tussocky bogs in side valleys and stone prayer walls (Schäfer 1938).

Its wintering habitat in northern India and the terai of Nepal is mainly relatively large, open phantas.

This habitat formerly covered much of the Gangetic plain but is now restricted to a few isolated areas in northern India and southern Nepal, which in some cases are now nature reserves.

In India in winter it has been stated to inhabit rank dry or wet grassland, reeds and tamarisks alongside rivers, and also canefields (Ali &Ripley 1968–1998). In Bihar it frequents sugarcane, 'ekra' (*Erianthus ravaneae*) grass and other open grassland areas (Inglis 1951–1969). Baker (1924) and Oates (1890) described its winter habitat as "flat open country thickly dotted with canefields". In Assam (Manas National Park) it occupies vast open grasslands dominated by *Saccharum narenga* and *Imperata cylindrica*, interspersed with tall elephant grass and very few trees and bushes (Narayan & Rosalind 1997).

In Nepal Fleming *et al.* (1984) stated that it was found in reeds at Kosi Barrage and at the edges of fields in the Kathmandu Valley. At Sukla Phanta, now the main known wintering area, the climate is subtropical and drier than in other protected lowland areas in Nepal. In Chitwan , which supports a smaller wintering population, the climate is humid and damp and the grassland soil is moist throughout the year owing to the high humidity. Kosi Tappu and the nearby (8km) Kosi Barrage are subject to annual flooding, and grassland can disappear to be replaced by alluvial deposits. The vegetation at Kosi Barrage comprises mainly *Saccharum spontaneum* and isolated low (3 m) tamarisk bushes *Tamarix dioica*. In Sukla Phanta individuals were found inhabiting open grassland using stems 3–5m high as perches. They frequented both burnt and unburnt grassland but would avoid dense grassland lacking any bare patches and concentrate on areas adjacent to dirt roads or small areas of bare ground. After grass was burnt they exhibit a preference for the burnt rather than unburnt areas showing a preference for those areas that still retained a fair amount (15–75%) of unburnt tall stems over 1m high on open ground. (Baral 1998).

At Chitwan they inhabited newly formed *Saccarum spontaneum* grasslands. Parts of the grassland were heavily grazed by livestock but others had sufficient tall stems and open, bare areas to attract individuals. At Kosi Barrage in the 1997/1998 winter, no birds were recorded despite the availability of apparently suitable habitat of *Saccharum spontaneum* with widely scattered low tamarisk bushes and open bare areas. The species has also been reported from mown grass along with other *Saxicola* at a race course (Jones 1927). Studies at Sukla Phanta showed that within some grasslands there were certain areas which appeared to be preferred, even though they appeared identical, and it was suggested that the microhabitat requirements of this species would need further study (Baral 1998).

VOICE

Comparatively little information. Ali & Ripley (1968–1998) state that its alarm note is a metallic *teck teck*. Panov (1976) noted breeding males giving a *tru-trup-tru* threat call both on the ground and in the air when involved in aggressive territorial interactions with another male. He also stated that when the nest is approached both male and female fly very close to the observer giving alarm calls similar to but slightly different from that of Siberian Stonechat. In low-intensity excitement birds give muffled clicking sounds; as the alarm increases, clear rhythmic ticking sounds are given as well. At the most critical moments another note resembling a drawn-out 'snore' or rattle is occasionally given. The male will occasionally sing quietly and briefly as a displacement reaction when disturbed (Panov 1976).

The male's song is described by Panov (1976) as very attractive. Kozlova (1930a) describes it as sweet-sounding but rather monotonous, as it is delivered without variation. It is a fairly stereotypical whistling phrase given several times in succession with brief pauses. Males sing generally from a high perch such as a rock or top of a willow shrub or arctic birch. They also sing quite often in flight, ascending at a slight angle and hovering in one place for several seconds, appearing to hang in the air with regular wingbeats, then making a slow gliding descent (Kozlova 1930a, Panov 1976). They sing throughout the breeding cycle and when with young sing especially in the morning and on clear, warm evenings (Panov 1976). Kozlova (1932) mentions that males sing vigorously in the last third of June and up to the middle of July. Observations of captive birds noted that young males commenced singing as early as three weeks after

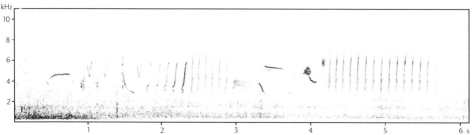

Hodgson's Bushchat *Saxicola insignis* NSA 57496. Song. Sichuan, China 16 May 1991. *McCallum – Borror Lab. of Bioacoustics.*

leaving the nest. At this stage the song is continuous and includes clear drawn-out whistles, a peculiar chirping on high and low notes and a special muffled "croaking" sound (Panov 1976). The distress call of nestlings is a clear ringing *tsri-tsri-tsri*.

FOOD

Little information. Consists of invertebrates, mainly insects taken from the ground. The stomach contents of a bird collected on 10 April consisted of beetles, larvae and green vegetable matter, whereas one collected on 12 December contained larvae, carabids and other beetles (Whistler 1922). Ali & Ripley (1968–1998) describe its food as insects, comprising mainly beetles and their larvae. A specimen in BMNH is labelled as having "several tenebrionid beetles *Gonocephalus elongatum*" in its stomach. One individual in Nepal was seen to capture a moth in flight (Baral 1998). There may also be some vegetable matter included in its diet – as in *S. maura* the vegetable matter may be involuntarily ingested when it seizes invertebrate prey from vegetation.

BEHAVIOUR

Fleming *et al.* (1984) described this species as shy and solitary in its wintering areas whilst Schäfer & Meyer de Schauensee (1939) also described them as very shy. However, wintering males in Sukla Phanta, Nepal, allowed approach to within 10m (Baral 1998). On migration they were also considered shy and rather solitary, and when approached they would fly for up to 50–80m and land only on an elevated perch. The flight was described as "rapid, elegant and low over the ground" (Schäfer 1938).

Hume (1878b) considered them to be always solitary and well spaced in their winter habitats, but at Sukla Phanta 2–3 males would sometimes be perched within 2m of one another. Females were observed to perch on their own, most often some distance from any males but on occasions down to 5m. The difference in Hume's observations to those in Sukla Phanta may partially be explained by the loss of much of this bird's winter habitat in India and Nepal, which might cause a greater density in the remaining suitable habitat.

Birds in their breeding areas in Mongolia are described as completely indifferent to man and easy to shoot (Kozlova 1932). After one of a pair is shot the other appears very quickly and, once noticing that its mate is absent, displays much anxiety, giving constant contact calls for a considerable period (Kozlova 1930a).

In their breeding areas pairs defend small, contiguous territories with the distance separating nests not exceeding 300m. The males vigorously defend the territory boundary, chasing intruding males in flight and on the ground, uttering threat calls. Anxious breeding birds jerk and flick their tails upwards whilst simultaneously fanning them slightly. Occasionally they move the tail sideways as well. They also flick up the wings, with one wing always raised higher than the other; at times of peak anxiety one wing may remain in a raised position for a few seconds (Panov 1976). This may be a form of distraction display.

Birds in their winter habitat appear to establish small feeding territories and interact aggressively with other species in their genus. There appeared to be some overlap in habitat preference between *S. insignis* and Siberian Stonechat and White-tailed Stonechat. It was frequently recorded in association with both these species and less often with Pied Bushchat in winter in Nepal. A male Siberian Stonechat was seen chasing a male *S. insignis* and on later dates this same *insignis* individual was seen on at least five occasions to chase a Siberian Stonechat. Another male *S. insignis* in the space of an hour was seen to chase a male White-tailed Stonechat twice and a male Siberian Stonechat once. Birds in Assam also defended winter grassland territories, which they maintained for days on end against any intruding Siberian Stonechats. However, winter territories seem to be less well defined and less aggressively defended against other *S. insignis* than breeding territories. Birds also apparently defend temporary territories on migration, with birds in Manas National Park in Assam, India, driving out Siberian Stonechat. In Assam between 1986 and 1989, the birds seen were either single or in loose pairs which might suggest that some birds pair before migration.

The main feeding strategy adopted by birds in winter at Sukla Phanta and Assam was to survey the ground from an elevated perch and drop onto prey on the ground. In Assam they perched on grass or shrubs c.75–125cm high (Narayan & Rosalind 1997). The average time spent on the ground appears to be longer than for other *Saxicola*: at Sukla Phanta each attempt to seize prey on the ground lasted a mean 30 seconds, although birds would on occasion remain there for over a minute. In Sukla Phanta on 3 January 1997 a male was observed for one hour whilst it fed. In that time it dropped to the ground eight times, remaining there for a total of 19 minutes, and perched for the rest of the time. Unburnt stems on burnt grassland were the main perches. This male changed its position 49 times, utilising stems shorter than 1m 11 times and stems taller than 1m 38 times (Baral 1998). Migrants in Tibet were described as hopping nimbly on the ground when feeding (Schäfer 1938).

On another occasion a wintering bird was observed on ploughed land feeding in a thrush-like manner "running with its head lowered close to the ground and then raising its head while stationary" (Baral 1998). In Sukla Phanta all *Saxicola* species present, including *insignis*, were noted to follow walking observers and occasionally persons on bicycles. It was thought that they also followed herds of Swamp Deer *Cervus duvauceli* in a similar fashion in response to the fact that large moving objects were likely to disturb and flush insects (Baral 1998).

Hodgson's Bushchat also utilises flycatching techniques (although less than other *Saxicola* that inhabit Nepal). One was observed in Sukla Phanta chasing a moth about 30cm above the ground (Baral 1998).

Wintering birds in Sukla Phanta appear to remain in the same area for the whole winter, with (presumably – but without ringing studies not conclusively – the same) individuals being noted in the same locality day after day. A similar situation was evident at Manas National Park in Assam (Narayan & Rosalind 1997). It is also not known if the same individuals return to occupy the same wintering areas in subsequent years. Each day in the late afternoon all the individuals in the study area in Sukla Phanta moved from their territories and slowly flew in a south-westerly direction, presumably to a communal roost site.

MOULT

No specific information. Dement'ev & Gladkov (1968) state it is the same as other species in its genus.

CONSERVATION

Under IUCN criteria the species is treated as a globally threatened species classed as Vulnerable (Collar *et al.* 1994, 2001). Baral (1998) has suggested that its status should be revised to Endangered.

No survey has been undertaken of its breeding areas since 1976 but it is unlikely to be threatened by either the current low level of human population or development. Its breeding habitat in the Russian Federation was considered by Ponomareva & Vinokurov (1984) to be virtually unaltered by human influence. There is little specific knowledge of its current breeding areas and the fact that it appears to nest in small groups, and none has been studied since the 1970s, makes it difficult to devise a protection plan if one were needed.

The species's decline is probably attributable to the extensive loss of habitat in its wintering areas where much grassland and wetland have been destroyed or modified for agriculture and grazing. Grassland is one of the most threatened ecosystems in the Indian subcontinent. The increase in human and livestock populations places tremendous pressures on grasslands and very little natural grassland is now left owing to general degradation and disturbance from cultivation, overgrazing, harvesting of grass, fires, forestry and miscellaneous irrigation and dam projects (Rahmani 1988, Collar *et al.* 2001).

The main threat to this species in Nepal is loss of habitat. In the last 30 years there has been a rapid decline of grassland habitat. Burning, ploughing and grazing have each had an effect on this species. Every year in Nepal during January all grasslands inside protected areas are cut, burnt and trampled by more than 100,000 people. Baral (1998) recommends this activity to be monitored and restricted in areas that support globally threatened species. Controlled and carefully timed burning may benefit the species by maintaining suitable grassland habitat and creating an apparently preferred pattern of cleared and uncleared areas, but it would still be prudent to minimise human impacts as the species appears able to inhabit grassland that is not burnt annually. Ploughing and grazing create an unsuitable habitat by reducing the grass height below the optimum range for this species. Such areas can be returned to suitable grassland within a year if protected, being colonised rapidly by *Saccharum spontaneum* or *Imperata cylindrica* grasses. Flooding has also had an impact on this species' habitat. The restricted grassland areas south of Kosi Barrage are not protected and consequently suffer much disturbance from fishermen and cattle and also degradation from recent heavy and frequent flood damage. Baral (1998) also suggests other pressures which may have a disproportionate effect on an already threatened species: these are hunting and collecting for museum specimens in both its wintering and breeding areas as well as on its migration stopovers (see Kozlova in Distribution above) and pesticides used on crops (Baral 1988, Collar *et al.* 2001).

In Nepal Baral (1998) has suggested extending and managing areas of protected grassland such as at Sukla Phanta Wildlife Reserve in Nepal for the benefit of all grassland species. Heavily grazed areas quickly regenerate into quality grassland habitat if given sufficient protection and sensible management (see above). Open areas to the east of Sukla Phanta are ideal for this. Such schemes should involve the local community to develop a sustainable utilisation by both people and wildlife. The Nepalese government should also be asked to confer full legal protection to the species under the National Parks and Conservation Act. Similar actions should be considered in India and China. Baral (1998) also recommends education programmes to create public awareness of conservation problems in Nepalese grasslands. An intensive survey should be carried out of all potential natural grassland areas in the Gangetic plains during winter to attempt to identify key sites for the species and then protect them.

In the Russian Federation it has been proposed by Ponomareva & Vinokurov (1984) that surveys should be undertaken to locate where the species is breeding, and seasonal reserves or sanctuaries should be established to protect not only this but the whole complex of montane-steppe species. This equally applies to Mongolia.

Pratincola dacotiae Meade-Waldo, 1889, *Ibis*, p.504, pl.15—Fuerteventura, Mauritanice, Dacos [= Fuerteventura Island, Canary Islands] = *Saxicola dacotiae dacotiae*.

Saxicola dacotiae murielae Bannerman, 1913, *Bull. Brit. Orn. Club* 33, p.37, Allegranza Island [Canary Islands]

Etymology *dacotiae* named after the type locality '*Dacos*'. Jobling (1991) believed '*Dacos*' to be a Roman adaptation of an ancient Mauretanian (Moroccan) name for one or more of the Canary Islands.

murielae named in honour of the wife of D.A. Bannerman, proposer of the subspecies

Alternative names Canary Island(s) Chat, Fuerteventura(n) Chat, Canary Chat, Meade-Waldo's Chat

TAXONOMY

Polytypic. Traditional systematists considered this species to be closely related to the European Stonechat *S. rubicola*, and recent DNA research confirms this (Wink *et al.* 2001, 2002). Volsøe (1951) suggested that it was no more than a distinctive subspecies of the European Stonechat, but this was vigorously dismissed by Bannerman (1963) who at the same time admitted there was undoubtedly a connection between the two. Voous (1977) accepted it as a separate species. Hall & Moreau (1970) stated that it forms a superspecies with European Stonechat, Réunion Stonechat *S. tectes*, and White-tailed Stonechat *S. leucura*. Sibley & Monroe (1990) suggested that it may be more closely related to Whinchat *S. rubetra* and best omitted from the superspecies grouping of Hall & Moreau. This would now appear to be erroneous.

Collins (1984) was of the opinion that although the supercilium of both sexes is reminiscent of Whinchat the Canary Island Stonechat lacks the white triangular sides to the base of the tail and its voice and habitat differ markedly. The Réunion Stonechat *Saxicola tectes* from Réunion in the southern Indian Ocean is stated by Collins (1984) to be virtually identical in plumage and possibly closely related despite being separated from *S. dacotiae* by both the continent of Africa and the equator. Meade-Waldo (1889a), who first discovered the Canary Island Stonechat near Tuineje on Fuerteventura on 25 March 1888, and whose name was originally given to the species (Meade-Waldo's Chat), stated that the Réunion Stonechat was its nearest relative. Collins suggests that this could be an example of convergent evolution, both species, in isolated environments, having arisen from a common ancestor in the form of the European or African Stonechat. Slightly more tenuous is his alternative suggestion that the two populations are all that is left of a formally widespread species in Africa that was later replaced by the African Stonechat.

Two subspecies have been recognised, the nominate *S. d. dacotiae* and the somewhat poorly differentiated *S. d. murielae*, which was first discovered by Bannerman in 1913 and named after his wife (Bannerman 1913, 1914). He even gave it a specific English name, Muriel's Chat (Bannerman 1963). Bannerman considered that the 12 specimens collected exhibited enough difference in plumage from *S. d. dacotiae* to allow them to be assigned to a separate subspecies (see below). *S. d. murielae* supposedly inhabited only two small islands in the Canary Islands group, Alegranza and Montaña Clara. Bannerman first encountered it on the tiny islet of Montaña Clara in June 1913 where the only birds seen were a probable family party of four or five birds. Two specimens were collected from this group, with the rest disappearing, and at the time they were considered to be of the nominate subspecies *S. d. dacotiae*. Aware that it had never been recorded from this islet or on the nearby larger island of Lanzarote, Bannerman considered the birds he saw on Montaña Clara to be wanderers from Fuerteventura. However, on learning that this same bird was present in even greater numbers on the slightly larger neighbouring island of Alegranza he began to doubt if this was correct. On his return to the British Museum he compared the 12 specimens collected from both islands with *S. d. dacotiae* and declared that they represented a separate valid subspecies *S. d. murielae*. He also decided that the family party he saw on Montaña Clara must have bred there and that the parents had originally flown from Alegranza. On Alegranza he recorded it as plentiful (via information from his taxidermist) throughout the island, usually occurring in family parties of three to five. A resident of that island also related to Bannerman's taxidermist that it bred and was present all year round on the island (Bannerman 1963). It has never been recorded since from either island, although a period of 43 years elapsed before anyone else searched these islands. Detailed searches of Graciosa and Montaña Clara in 1956 (Etchécopar & Hüe 1957, Hüe & Etchécopar 1958), Graciosa, Montaña Clara and Alegranza in 1970 (Lovegrove 1971), Alegranza in 1981 (H. H. Bergmann in Collar & Stuart 1985) and of Alegranza and Montaña Clara at a later unspecified date (Pérez Padrón 1983) all failed to locate a single bird or any resident who knew of it.

Collar & Stuart (1985) were doubtful of the validity of this subspecies. They pointed to the fact that although Bannerman acknowledged the anomaly of his original records this was only compounded by the fact that Bannerman may not actually have seen any of these birds alive. Bannerman possibly saw the family party on Montaña Clara but the specimens were shot by his taxidermist, who was accompanying him on this trip. He did not visit Alegranza, leaving this to his taxidermist, who collected the specimens – and his subsequent reports were based entirely on the information given to him by his taxidermist. No apparent verification of the ornithological competence of the resident questioned on Alegranza was apparently sought. The conjectures in subsequent reports by Bannerman of the eventual destination of the surviving birds on Montaña Clara were also somewhat uncertain. First it was suggested that they flew directly to the 'mainland', presumably meaning the coast of North Africa, then later in the same report that they had flown to Alegranza (Bannerman 1919–1920). Much later, Alegranza was rejected as a possible destination owing to headwinds, and it was stated the birds must have crossed the narrow stretch of sea to Graciosa and possibly thence crossed to Lanzarote (Bannerman 1963). However, this species has never been recorded on either of the latter two islands.

Observations of *S. d. dacotiae* in the field on Fuerteventura in April, when they would be in fairly worn plumage, have indicated the plumage of this species can vary amongst individuals (Shirt 1983). Others have also noted such variability in plumage (von Thanner 1905, Polatzek 1908–1909, Volsøe 1951), and subsequent examination of museum skins has revealed that *S. d. dacotiae* can also, in fresh and slightly worn plumage, appear very similar to *S. d. murielae*. One of the main distinguishing criteria for *S. d. murielae*, the lighter shade of the crown feathers, has also been invalidated by the discovery that the colour of these feathers in *S. d. dacotiae* is also variable (Cramp 1988). A strong doubt does remain that the birds on Montaña Clara – and Alegranza – may just have been wanderers from Fuerteventura – or possibly an overspill of population from Fuerteventura which occasionally bred on these islands – and therefore the taxonomic status of the birds collected by Bannerman merits further investigation.

IDENTIFICATION

Size 12.5cm/4.9 inches. Sexes dimorphic. Similar in behaviour and size to European Stonechat. Structurally slightly different to European Stonechat in appearance, with a slightly longer, narrower tail in proportion to the body and a slightly longer bill in proportion to the head.

The plumage of males can be rather variable. The adult male in breeding plumage is dark brown or black on the head and upperparts with a narrow white supercilium reaching beyond the eye. The chin, throat and sides of breast are white with an extensive white collar extending from the throat and almost joining on the nape. The inner upperwing has a small white patch often almost concealed by the scapulars on the closed wing. The rump is greyish-brown with dark streaks and the uppertail-coverts are similar but often also show white. The tail is black and the underparts from breast to undertail-coverts are buff-white with a stronger tone of cinnamon-chestnut on the breast. In fresh plumage the grey-brown fringes to the upperparts, especially the head, obscure most of the darker colouring, and the underparts are less white and warmer buff-pink in tone.

The female is streaked grey-brown above, lacking the black head of the male but showing a broad, pale buff-white supercilium, and has a smaller white patch on the inner upperwing, often invisible except in flight. There is no white neck-collar but the chin and throat, as in the male, are pure white. The rump is pale tawny-brown. The rest of the underparts are buff in fresh plumage but in worn plumage are more off-white with only a slightly stronger tone of yellow-buff on the upper breast and foreflanks.

Confusion species European Stonechat (regular in winter) and Whinchat (occasional on migration) both occur on the Canary Islands including Fuerteventura.

Both male and female *S. dacotiae* can be distinguished from the former as follows. There are subtle structural differences: *S. dacotiae* has a less rounded, flatter crowned head, longer, slimmer tail in proportion to the body, and marginally longer bill, giving a slightly sleeker, elongated profile than in *S. rubicola*. Male and female *S. dacotiae* of all ages have a pure white chin and throat. *S. rubicola* males have a wholly black head including chin and throat, whilst females usually show greyish-buff to buff-black on the throat, and never pure white. Both sexes of *S. dacotiae* show a prominent but shortish, mainly white, occasionally buff-white supercilium, all year; female *S. rubicola* occasionally may show a faint buff supercilium but never as distinct or pale as *S. dacotiae*. Male *S. dacotiae* is pale cinnamon-buff on the underparts with a slightly richer tone on the breast, whilst the female is whitish-buff on the underparts. *S. rubicola* male is much darker rufous-orange on its underparts and the female is correspondingly darker orange-buff with a stronger tone to the breast. The feathers on the upperparts of *S. dacotiae* have extensive greyish-buff fringes to the upperparts, while *S. rubicola* has these fringes more rufous-brown, creating a browner, darker tone to the upperparts and not as grey or pale as in *S. dacotiae*.

An adult female or first-year Siberian Stonechat *S. maura*, although not yet recorded from the Canary Islands, would pose greater identification problems to separate from female *S. dacotiae*, as it also shows a pale supercilium, buff-white chin and throat, and pale upperparts and underparts. The main identification difference, apart from structural, is the area of rump and uppertail-coverts: *S. maura* have extensive, buff-orange and unmarked (in fresh plumage when most likely to occur) rump and uppertail-coverts; S. dacotiae has only the lower half of the rump and the uppertail-coverts tawny-buff and the patch is therefore less extensive and slightly darker in tone and, usually with dark brown streaks on longer uppertail-coverts. S. maura upperwing primary coverts are prominently edged and tipped white in fresh plumage; S. dacotiae has upperwing primary coverts edged pale brown or grey and therefore the contrast between the white and grey or brown is not nearly so obvious. There is also a greater contrast between the darker greyish-brown upperparts and the paler underparts of S. dacotiae than is found in Siberian Stonechat.

S. dacotiae can be separated from Whinchat by its paler, greyer-fringed feathers on the upperparts; S. rubetra has darker, buff-fringed upperparts with much more contrast owing to black spotting with white fringes on many of the upperpart feathers. Moreover, S. dacotiae has a long but often broken and narrow buff-white supercilium, usually most prominent from above the eye to the middle of the upper ear-coverts, whereas S. rubetra has a long, broad, unbroken buff to white supercilium at all times of the year, extending from the bill to the rear of the ear-coverts and present on all ages and sexes. In autumn S. dacotiae has pale whitish, pinkish or yellowish-buff, unmarked underparts, while S. rubetra has darker orange-buff underparts with noticeable spotting on the breast and flanks; S. dacotiae has a pure white chin and throat running into extensive white neck-patches, while S. rubetra has a buff chin and throat which join to less extensive buff neck-patches; S. dacotiae has a paler buff and less definitely marked rump and uppertail-coverts with only thin dark brown streaks, while S. rubetra has darker buff rump and uppertail-coverts with prominent black spotting fringed with narrow white crescents. S. dacotiae has a longer tail in proportion to the body which is uniformally dark greyish-brown, whereas S. rubetra has prominent white triangular patches at the base of the black tail, which is also considerably shorter in proportion to the body.

DESCRIPTION

Saxicola dacotiae dacotiae

Adult male fresh plumage, July–November The black on the forehead and crown is virtually concealed by extensive olive-grey or grey-brown feather fringes. The mantle, scapulars, back and rump are brown rather than black, but again obscured by greyish-olive to grey-brown feather fringes. The uppertail-coverts are white with large rufous-orange tips obscuring much of the white. There is a large white spot above the lore joined to the supercilium. The supercilium is white, long and fairly narrow, extending from the base of the bill to behind the eye, and is often speckled with grey-brown towards the rear. The supercilia meet at the front of the forehead. The lores are greyish-brown and sides of head black with grey-white fringes, giving a slightly grizzled appearance. The chin and throat are white and they join with the extensive white neck-patches, which are often partially obscured with greyish-brown fringes. The breast, sides of breast, flanks and belly are pale pinkish- or yellowish-buff with the strongest colouring on the upper breast. The ventral area, rear flanks and undertail-coverts are white. The rectrices are dark grey to black edged with pale buff to off-white on the fringes of the outerwebs and on the tips. The remiges, tertials and upperwing primary coverts are grey-black, narrowly fringed with buff-brown on the outerwebs and tips. The outer upperwing lesser, median and greater coverts are black with pale greyish-brown tips, and there are also pale grey-brown edges along the outerwebs of the greater coverts. The inner, upperwing lesser, median and greater coverts are white, forming a white panel on the inner wing (this is often obscured by the scapulars unless the bird flies). The underwing-coverts and axillaries are white. Bill, legs and feet are black to dark brown; irides are dark brown.

Adult male in worn plumage, January–May Abrasion to the feather tips and fringes results in the forehead, crown, cheeks, ear-coverts and hindneck becoming progressively more solidly black, with only a few greyish-brown fringes remaining. The supercilium becomes whiter, more defined and narrower but less extensive, often only present in front of the eye and as a narrower line above the eye but not extending to the rear of the ear-coverts. However, on one individual in BMNH (collected on 2 March) the supercilia are whiter and broader behind the eye and greyish-white and narrow in front. On a very few individuals it can be absent completely. The mantle, scapulars, back and rump become streaked dark brown and pale greyish-brown. The longer uppertail-coverts are also greyish-brown with darker shaft-streaks on the longer coverts with often extensive white showing on the shorter coverts, although not on all individuals. The chin and throat remain pure white and still join to the pure white neck-patches which often almost meet on the hindneck. The upper breast becomes a yellowish- to chestnut-buff, showing a distinct and greater contrast than in fresh plumage to the lower breast, flanks and belly, which lose their colour and become buff-white. The pale fringes and tips to the rectrices and remiges progressively wear off, as do the ones on the upperwing lesser, median and greater coverts, leaving all these feathers brownish-black apart from the white inner upperwing-coverts.

First-year male Forehead and crown, malar region, cheeks and ear-coverts never as black as adult in worn plumage usually retaining many brown feather fringes. The underparts become almost uniform dull white

123

in well-worn plumage with no stronger contrasting colouring on upper breast as in adult male at similar stage. In fresh plumage it shows a greater contrast than adult between yellowish-buff upper breast and the remainder of the underparts which are buffish-white. Rectrices, remiges, tertials, upperwing primary coverts, some outer upperwing greater coverts are retained from juvenile plumage and consequently are more worn and browner than in adult male in worn plumage.

Adult female in fresh plumage, July–December The forehead, crown, mantle and scapulars are greyish-brown or greyish-olive with darker brown feather centres creating a streaked appearance. The lower rump and uppertail-coverts are pale tawny-brown with some dark streaking, contrasting with the greyer upperparts. The lores and cheeks are grizzled greyish-buff. The ear-coverts, sides of neck and sides of breast are greyish-brown faintly streaked with buff. Some birds show a hint of white on the foreneck where the white feather bases are partly exposed. There is an indistinct, but long, buff supercilium extending from the bill to behind the ear-coverts. The chin and throat are buff-white. There is no white neck-patch but a suggestion of paler white or buff feathering in this area. The breast and upper flanks are pinkish-buff fading to a paler buff-white on the belly, ventral area and undertail-coverts. The remiges and rectrices are similar to the adult male but the white inner upperwing-patch is considerably less extensive with often only the innermost (10) greater upperwing-covert white. Underwing-coverts and axillaries creamy-white. Bill, legs and feet black-brown. Irides dark brown.

Adult female in worn plumage, January–May The head and upperparts are grey-brown with more noticeable darker streaking, and the uppertail-coverts lose much of their tawny-brown fringes, becoming more uniform with the rest of the upperparts. The sides of the head, neck and breast turn greyish-brown with paler spots and streaks. The buff supercilium becomes paler and slightly more distinct but never pure white as in the male. The breast and upper flanks are pale buff-yellow, the rest of the underparts buff-white. The pale edges and fringes to the remiges, rectrices and upperwing-coverts wear off, leaving these feathers grey-brown.

First-year female Very similar to the adult female but in fresh plumage the underparts are more uniform pinkish-buff and in worn plumage uniform whitish-buff. In both plumages there is not the evident contrast between the stronger pinkish-buff to buff tones of the adult's upper breast and the rest of the underparts, which are much whiter. Often there is no white at all on the inner upperwing greater coverts. The remiges and rectrices as well as the tertials, upperwing primary coverts and some outer upperwing greater coverts are retained from juvenile plumage and appear much more worn and brown than in an adult at a similar time of year.

Juvenile The upperparts are similar to the female in tone, being a dull greyish-brown. The forehead and crown have small indistinct buff-white streaks. The mantle, scapulars and back have slightly larger pale buff spots with thin black fringes. The rump and uppertail-coverts are unspotted and are pale buff-brown. There is an indistinct narrow buff-white supercilium extending from the bill to above the eye. The lores and cheeks are buff-white grizzled with grey flecks. The ear-coverts are dark greyish-brown flecked with fine buff-white streaks. The chin and throat are white. The breast is chestnut-buff with irregular dark brown fringes, creating a distinct scaly band across the breast. The rest of the underparts are paler buff. The remiges and rectrices are greyish-black with narrow pale buff fringes to the outerwebs and pale buff tips. The upperwing-coverts are greyish-brown with pale buff spotting on the upperwing lesser and median coverts. The upperwing greater coverts have prominent pale chestnut-buff tips which often extend down the shaft in a triangular shape on the inner ones. The innermost upperwing greater coverts can also show a small, variable amount of white. The tertials show prominent pale chestnut-buff fringes and tips. The underwing-coverts and axillaries are buff-white.

Measurements (*S. d. dacotiae*)

	Male	Female
Wing	60.0–63.5 (mean 61.3)	61.0–64.0 (mean 62.8)
Tail	45.5–49.0 (mean 47.7)	46.0–49.5 (mean 47.3)
Bill	15.4–16.5 (mean 16.1)	15.6–16.1 (mean 15.9)

[Own measurements BMNH, 2000]

Saxicola dacotiae murielae

(Based on description by Bannerman 1914)
Virtually identical to *S. d. dacotiae*. In worn plumage differs in having the crown lighter, more reddish-brown, lacking a marked contrast with the rest of the upperparts. The underparts from upper breast to belly are a uniform pinkish-buff with slightly stronger colouring on the upper breast. The breast is more yellowish-buff, the belly and flanks much paler, often almost white, giving a less uniform appearance. In fresh plumage the dark bases to the crown feathers are smaller and much less pronounced than in *S. d. dacotiae* and the breast and belly are pinkish-buff rather than whitish.

DISTRIBUTION AND STATUS

This species has one of the most restricted and localised ranges of any bird in the western Palearctic. It is a single-island endemic, now only known to occur on Fuerteventura in the eastern group of Canary Islands. It has apparently occurred in the form of the subspecies *S. d. murielae* (see above) on the islands of Alegranza and Montaña Clara in 1913, based on Bannerman's single visit. It was suspected of breeding on Alegranza based on reports from residents and a family party was seen on Montaña Clara although it was not proved that breeding took place there. It has not been recorded from either island since or before 1913, and it is remarkable that it has never been recorded from the larger and closer island of Lanzarote, which is separated by only 10km of water from Fuerteventura.

Early on, it was also considered that a small population of this species inhabited the Sous in southern Morocco, which is adjacent to the eastern Canary Islands (Tristram 1890, Meade-Waldo 1893, Bannerman 1919–1920), but Volsøe (1951) demonstrated that this was erroneous.

It is rarely found on the large plains of Fuerteventura but is restricted to the hilly areas where it occurs in steep valleys and along dry or semi-dry watercourses with thinly scattered shrub growth (barrancos). It also occurs locally on the seashore on the south coast, on open slopes which drop down to the sea when these have a growth of *Euphorbia*, around the edges of lava fields and in areas of permanent standing water, such as reservoirs, and sometimes in gardens. When it was first discovered the species was considered to be restricted to and thinly distributed in the southern half of Fuerteventura only (Meade-Waldo 1893). By 1914 it was recorded from Corralejo in the extreme north to the Jandía Peninsula in the extreme south of the island (von Thanner 1914), as well as from Barranco de Rio Cabras in the east (Polatzek 1908–1909) and Barranco de la Peña in the west (Bannerman 1914). It was also found at several inland sites such as La Oliva in the north (Polatzek 1908–1909) and Tuineje in the south (Meade-Waldo 1889a). It is unclear whether the apparent extension in its distribution is a result of population growth or just increased observation and coverage. Some of the early observers were categorical that it did not occur in certain areas between 1902 and 1904 where it was subsequently discovered (Polatzek 1908-1909, von Thanner 1908). By 1914 it was considered that the population was stable because there was no more suitable habitat available (von Thanner 1914).

Population size based on an extensive general survey on the island in 1979 was estimated by a 'reasoned guess' at 50–150 pairs (Collar & Stuart 1985). Collins (1984) considered there were probably 100–200 pairs. Collar & Stuart stated that the species was found throughout the island but only locally, its occurrence being very much determined by the availability of suitable habitat, most of which was on the coast and most birds were in the southern half of the island. However, in 1985 the formally designed sample survey called for by Collar & Stuart gave a considerably larger, revised estimate of 750±100 pairs (Bibby & Hill 1987a,b).

In the Bibby & Hill study a distribution map was produced showing where it was likeliest to find this species on Fuerteventura, based on predictions arising from the study. This suggested that concentrations were likely in the main mountains of the Jandía Peninsula in the south, an area around Pajara on the west coast, and a less continuous chain to the east. Areas of predicted low density or absence were: both of the coastal plains, especially in the north and east, the main central plains, and the sand-covered isthmus connecting the Jandía Peninsula to the rest of the island. The distribution of known records compared well with the predicted distribution as did the areas where none was recorded with the predicted areas of absence. There was also a scattering of occupied squares evident

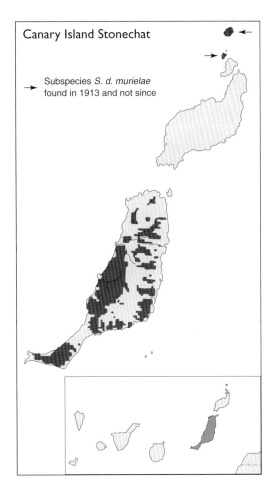

Canary Island Stonechat

Subspecies *S. d. murielae* found in 1913 and not since

along the eastern mountains. The main predicted area in the study not supported by actual sight records was the concentration in the western mountains. The lack of records from this area was probably due to the fact they were not adequately explored in the study or casually at other times.

There is no evidence that the species has declined in the period since it was first discovered and the population appears to remain stable and widely distributed throughout the island. There is a possibility that the population varies from year to year. For example, in Barranco de la Peña in 1913, it was described as plentiful and very numerous (Bannerman 1914, 1922) but a survey in 1957 found only one specimen (Hooker 1958). The likelihood of population fluctuations is also supported by findings in 1984 that very few birds were present in certain known sites for the species (Collar & Stuart 1985).

BREEDING

The breeding season commences very early, often in January. Polatzek (1908–1909) shot a female about to lay an egg on 15 January. Meade-Waldo (1889b) found young as early as mid-February, which would mean that the eggs of that nest would have been laid around mid-January. Three almost fully fledged young were found in a nest on 16 February (von Thanner 1910) whilst another nest had three eggs. The survey by Bibby & Hill in 1985 found fledged broods with 63% of the sample of 84 pairs and deduced that egg-laying must have commenced in mid-January.

The breeding cycle, in the form of males starting to sing and pairs prospecting nest sites, commences with the onset of the first heavy rains of winter and is possibly connected to the length of daylight. When the rains commenced on 7 January 1981 the first young were seen on 13 March, but in the following year the rains did not start until 12 February and young were not seen until 28 March. Those birds that nest in lusher, wetter areas such as near reservoirs may be less reliant on the rain (Collins 1984). Generally most egg-laying occurs in February and March (von Thanner 1905, Polatzek 1908–1909). The female selects the nest site and builds the nest without assistance from the male, although he will accompany her as she collects nest material. Nests are usually on or near (below 0.5m) the ground, either open from above or concealed under overhanging rocks or indeed in holes in rocks, such as are found in the sides of barrancos, or in holes in walls (one in such a location was at head height); others are under stones or placed below thin bushes such as *Salsola vericulata*, *Launaea arborescens* or *Lycium intricatum*, this latter bush being especially favoured (Meade-Waldo 1889b, von Thanner 1905, 1910, Polatzek 1908–1909, Bannerman 1963, Collins 1984). The nest is a firmly built cup with an inner diameter of about 5cm, and is built of grass stems and roots lined with goat hair or wool. The head-height nest in a wall consisted of mainly soft grass stems with a mass of wool, hair and fibres worked into them, and was lined with a thick pad of brown and white wool together with black and brown/white hairs. Another nest consisted entirely of black goat hair. Some nests are more loosely constructed than others. Nests in bushes are said to have the exterior exclusively built of plant stems (Bannerman 1963). Nests can sometimes be lined with feathers. Polatzek suggests that the lining is renewed for second breeding attempts but it is highly unlikely that the same nest is used twice. European Stonechat *Saxicola rubicola*, to which this species is closely related, regularly has two or three broods and a new nest is built for each nesting attempt. Successive nests of one pair were found 25m apart (Collins 1984). Nests in adjacent territories were found to be 100–400m apart, with most more than 200m apart (D.R. Collins in Cramp 1988).

The female lays one egg a day and incubation commences with the laying of the last egg of the clutch. Incubation is by the female only and lasts 13–15 days. The usual clutch consists of 3–4 eggs with extremes of 2 and 5 (Bannerman 1963). However, all three nests found by Collins in 1981 contained a full clutch of only three. When the female leaves the nest to feed she is accompanied by the male. She can remain up to 30 minutes off the nest and when she returns she is accompanied by the male. He will occasionally visit her when she is sitting. On one occasion a male actually fed the female on the nest just as the young were hatching, and also fed the same female when she was off the nest (Collins 1984).

The eggs are subelliptical, smooth and glossy. Their colour is usually a pale green-blue with fine freckling or mottling of pale reddish-brown, often forming a thicker zone towards the broader end (Bannerman 1963). Other eggs collected had a bluish olive-green colour with pale grey and red-brown spots lying close together and often merging with one another, being strongest at each end of the egg (Polatzek 1908–1909). Eggs collected by Bannerman measured 17.5 x 14.5mm, 17.5 x 15.0mm, and 18.0 x 15.0mm; eggs collected by Polatzek were 16.0–18.0mm in length and 13.5–14.7mm in width.

Another sample of 14 eggs gave an average measurement of 17.8 x 14.1mm (16.0–18.8 x 13.5–14.7).

In 1979 12 pairs had their number of young specifically recorded. This revealed five pairs with one, four with two and three pairs with three young (Shirt 1983). A later survey in 1985 found the average number of young from 47 broods was 2.3±0.2. They divided the island into three bands in relation to latitude. The mean brood size was significantly higher in the central band compared to the northern and southern bands. The central band showed the highest brood size, averaging 2.6±0.2, followed by the northern with 2.3±0.2 and the southern with 1.9±0.2. Differences in brood size may possibly be influenced by food supply and available ground vegetation which in turn is possibly influenced by rainfall, which is greatest in the centre of the island and least in the south (Bibby & Hill 1987a).

The young remain in the nest for 16–18 days, are fed by both parents, and after fledging remain hidden under dense scrub for the next few days until they can fly adequately. Both male and female feed and care for the young when in the nest and when fledged.

The species is considered to be generally single-brooded, with second broods unusual (Bannerman 1963). Second breeding attempts may depend on how wet the year is; possibly in drier years all pairs will only have one brood. The first definite record was of a pair in 1980, which was particularly wet, having consecutive nests only 20–30m apart. The second brood hatched around 5 April, 23 days after the first brood had fledged (Collins 1984). An adult and young collected on 24 May (Polatzek 1908–1909) were considered to be probably a second brood, as were young being fed by a pair on 21 May (Witt 1971), but there was no definite proof. In the winter of 1995/1996, which was especially wet, Muller (1999) found a pair of birds in a barranco near Fayagua on 19 February feeding two fully fledged young. He estimated the age of the young to be between one and two months old; therefore the start of incubation must have been between mid-December and mid-January. Whilst observations continued on the feeding of the first brood, which was done mainly by the male, the female was found to have another nest with four eggs. The young hatched on 1 March. This constitutes only the second definite record of a double brood for this species. From various observations it appears the breeding season can extend from mid-December to late May, with the peak activity in March and April.

HABITAT

Fuerteventura is 1,653km^2 in extent. The island landscape is an arid mixture of stony plains, sand-dunes and large areas of eroded mountain ranges. "The island was formally well wooded with lush grassland some 500 years ago but has suffered long term desertification due to low rainfall and overgrazing by numerous goats which prevents revegetation and ensures that the desertification process continues" (Bibby & Hill 1987a). Shirt (1983) divided the island into four main types of vegetation related to substratum and availability of water, all types being composed mainly of xerophytic shrubs or herbs, with less desert-adapted species occurring near reservoirs and in the lower parts of barrancos: (1) stony plains with a vegetation comprising virtually exclusively of *Launaea arborescens* and *Salsola vermiculata*; (2) sandy plains and dunes with *Omnix natrix*, *Frankenia laevis*, *Euphorbia paralias* and *Lotus lancerottensis*; (3) malpais with the predominant vegetation being *Euphorbia obtusifolia* and *Senecio kleinia*; (4) areas with more water with good stands of *Sueda vera* and *Tamarix canariensis*.

Bannerman (1963) stated that *S. dacotiae* frequented both secluded barrancos and open hillsides. Polatzek found it in fields and gardens near a village. Bannerman also wrote of one barranco which had a small salty perennial stream. This was bordered by numerous small bushes and coarse rushes growing amongst the rocks, and *S. dacotiae* was found in comparatively large numbers there. In another vegetated barranco, also with salty water, it was frequenting tamarisk. Later surveys confirm the reports of these and other older accounts, with birds found to prefer rocky hillsides, edges of malpais (lava flows), barrancos and cultivation near slopes (Shirt 1983). Scrub typically comprises aulaga *Launaea arborescens*, saltwort *Salsola vermiculata*, box-thorn *Lycium intricatum*, the succulent spurge *Euphorbia obtusifolia* and ragwort *Senecio kleinia*. Some birds also occur locally on the seashore on the south coast where the dominant scrub species are *S. vermiculata* and the glasswort *Salicornia fruticosa*, and around a few areas of permanent water (Collar & Stuart 1985). On Jandía in the extreme south-west, a pair were found in a barranco dominated by *Launaea arborescens* and the threatened spurge *Euphorbia handiensis*. In another barranco it was common, perching in bushes of *Nicotiana glauca*, but was absent from an adjacent unvegetated barranco (Collar & Stuart 1985). Barrancos were noted as especially favoured by this species compared to other habitat (Shirt 1983). Bibby & Hill (1987) found that census squares occupied by *S. dacotiae* were generally higher, steeper and with greater barranco length than unoccupied ones. All these habitats share two characteristics, rocky slopes (providing suitable nest sites) and fairly well developed semi-desert scrub (providing an adequate supply of invertebrate prey during the long dry season, as well as nesting material) (Collins 1984).

The survey by Bibby & Hill in 1985 listed the number of territories in which different species of frequently occurring shrub species were recorded (n=102 territories). They were as follows:

Launea arborescens	59	territories	(58%)
Euphorbia obtusifolia	29		(28%)
Salsola vermiculata	22		(22%)
Lycium intricatum	38		(37%)
Nicotiana glauca	33		(32%)
Sueda spp.	7		(7%)

This survey also showed that territories were on average predominantly located on stony ground (41.3%). Rocks composed 22.4% and boulders 22.7% of the ground surface. Sand and soil together composed 24.0% of the ground surface. Vegetation covered on average 18% of the ground in *S. dacotiae* habitats although in most locations it only covered 10–15% of the ground. The average vegetation height was 46cm with an average range of 22–101cm. The average slope of the terrain in which *S. dacotiae* was located, combining data for birds on slopes with those on flat terrain (valley bottoms and coastal malpais), was 24.5°. However, 31 (32%) of the 97 cases in which slopes were recorded, were for *S. dacotiae* in valley bottoms or coastal malpais. The average slope of the terrain excluding these was 34.8°. Birds were thus generally found in areas with relatively steep, mainly stony slopes, of which less than a fifth was covered in vegetation averaging less than 50cm in height (Bibby & Hill 1987).

Contrary to earlier reports by von Thanner (1905), Polatzek (1908-1909) and Bannerman (1963), the majority of areas with *S. dacotiae* were found to be more than 200m from buildings (96%) and 200m from cultivation (95%). They were found in the immediate proximity of walls in 26% of cases and a further 5% were within 50m of a wall. Walls were absent in their habitat in 66% of cases. Water was absent from 85% of locations but was present within 200m in 3% of cases and within 50m in 12% of locations, these tending to be in steep barrancos where ground water had accumulated after recent rains (Bibby & Hill 1987a). The findings of this survey appear to confirm Bannerman's statement in 1963 that "water is much esteemed by this chat but does not appear to be essential".

FOOD

No detailed survey of diet has been undertaken but it would appear to consist of invertebrates caught on the wing or on the ground (Bannerman 1963). Food is stated to be mainly flies (Polatzek 1908-1909, Löhrl 1987) and von Thanner (1905) recorded birds showing a preference above all else for an unidentified large, white-bodied fly.

The following are stated to be important constituents of the diet: small Hymenoptera (ants and ichneumons), Diptera (flies), Lepidoptera larvae and Chilopoda (centipedes) (Collins 1984). Beetles (Coleoptera) and spiders (Araneae) are also taken (Pérez Padrón 1983).

Food brought to young consisted of mainly terrestrial insects such as grasshoppers (Orthoptera), adult Lepidoptera and a fly (Muscidae) (D.A. Hill in Cramp 1988). A male feeding fully fledged young was observed to feed them exclusively on flies (Diptera), which it fed to them singly (Muller 1999).

VOICE

The calls and song are similar to that of the European Stonechat. The usual call is a sharp stony *chep* often repeated a number of times. Meade-Waldo (1893) considered this call to be much louder and sharper than in *S. rubicola* but Collins (1984) found no difference. Collins also noted a thin high-pitched *sit* note used in conjunction with the *chep* call during the breeding season. This may be similar to the two-note call that is used by European Stonechat to alert young in the nest to potential danger. The high-pitched note of this call warns the young, whilst the lower note is used to attract the predator towards the adult and away from the nest.

Only the male sings, commencing immediately after the first winter rains. The song is described by Collins (1984) as a rather scratchy *bic-bizee-bizeeu* with variations such as *bizee-beeu*. It is given from a perch or, much less frequently, in a song-flight. The flight song is different to that given from a perch. During these flights two different notes are uttered, the first being a mellow, lark-like *liu*, the other a loud rasping *screeiz*. The notes are combined into a repetitive phrase of *liu liu liu screeiz* while the bird dances up and down. After a few minutes the male drops down onto a prominent perch (Collins 1984).

Newly fledged young utter a thin wheezy *zirr* call which serves as a locating and begging call (Collins 1984). Birds are most vocal during the breeding season. Before nesting, pairs will sometimes come close to an observer uttering a few *chep* calls before disappearing. Once nesting commences they remain silent

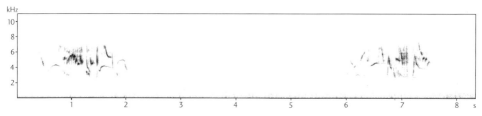

Canary Island Stonechat *Saxicola dacotiae* NSA cc25951. Song, Fuerteventura, Canary Islands, 25 December 1994. *C Chappuis.*

and inconspicuous unless an intruder comes too close to the nest. Both sexes then react by calling intensely giving the *chep* or *chup* note singly or in sequences of 2–3 calls and flying close to the intruder flicking their wings and tail. Meade-Waldo (1889b) in contrast stated that the species was singularly quiet even when its young were being handled, flying from bush to bush occasionally uttering a low *chut chut* call. In contrast with the European Stonechat (Greig-Smith 1980), no difference appears to exist in the intensity of calls before or after the eggs had hatched (Collins 1984). Males will call the female off the nest with the *chep* call if an intruder is perceived to be too close to the nest.

MOVEMENTS

Entirely sedentary. It has never been recorded outside of the eastern Canary Islands and apart from Bannerman's records from Montaña Clara and Alegranza in 1913 it has only ever been recorded on Fuerteventura.

Collar (*in litt.* 2002) suggests that an exceptionally rainy breeding season could result in high productivity of birds and create a surplus. As the island dried out during the summer the competition for declining resources might tempt some of the population to disperse across the short stretches of sea to smaller islands. It could well be that Bannerman in 1913 found not a new subspecies but the relics of an emigrant population from Fuerteventura. some may even have remained to breed on these islands as long as a covering of green vegetation remained forming separate temporary populations to the main one on Fuerteventura. It may still happen in some years with exceptionally good rains and birds may even reach southern Lanzarote unnoticed as Lanzarote and the smaller islands in the eastern canaries are comparatively underwatched.

BEHAVIOUR

The Canary Island Stonechat is monogamous in the breeding season, with the pair-bond lasting throughout, but there is a suggestion that pairs are sometimes assisted by unmated males. From 84 pairs observed in one study, six (7.1%) were accompanied by an additional male. There was no sign of aggression between the males in these groupings but it was not possible to establish for certain if there was an element of co-operative breeding or even a polygamous mating system during the breeding cycle (Bibby & Hill 1987). In two cases a pair was seen in close association with another pair.

Some recently fledged parties of young were each accompanied by their parents and an additional male or female or by two adult males (Bibby & Hill in Cramp 1988). Young remain with and are fed for a longer period by their parents than is the case with European Stonechat, presumably as a consequence of the restricted food supply in the generally inhospitable conditions of an arid island, and also because many pairs appear to be single-brooded. When abundant winter rains provide more amenable conditions and consequently a richer food supply, second broods are probably occasionally completed. Such conditions may also influence clutch size and breeding success (Muller 1999).

The species is territorial during the early breeding season but becomes less so over time, and pairs wander into adjacent territories without encountering aggression. Young birds of a first brood were also not driven from the territory by their parents when a second brood was being raised (D.R. Collins in Cramp 1988).

In suitable habitat such as barrancos there can be four pairs per km². The highest densities in one study were also in a barranco in the south of the island, with nine adults and 9–10 juveniles present in a 2km stretch (Shirt 1983). Outside the breeding season the species can be found in pairs, singly or in scattered groups often consisting of adults and juveniles.

Males have been observed displaying to females in the early part of the breeding cycle. The male flicks his tail slowly, then flies at the female who responds by hopping about excitedly and flicking her wings. The male then bows forwards with bill pointing down under his breast exposing the black of the nape. The two birds then flutter together just above the ground before resuming normal behaviour. Although similar to European Stonechat this courtship differs in that the male faces the female rather than turning his back to her (Collins 1984).

Males have been seen to show antagonism towards Spectacled Warbler *Sylvia conspicillata* in the breeding season. Pairs also give alarm calls when Great Grey Shrike *Lanius excubitor* is present in their territories and will mob this species if it gets too close to the nest or young (Collins 1984).

The Canary Island Stonechat catches prey on the ground or in the air. To catch airborn insects it flutters upwards from its perch, usually returning to a fresh perch. In catching terrestrial prey it flies down and usually hops after it but on occasions will run for short distances (Collins 1984). Food for the young is usually looked for on the ground, but birds rarely remain there for long (Bannerman 1963). They use a variety of perches as vantage points to find prey. These vary from small bushes, walls, stones and on occasions roof tops. When sitting on a perch the species constantly raises its tail up and down (Bannerman 1963), which in one recent observation involved "holding its tail slightly depressed and then cocking it slightly" (B. Small *in litt.* 2001). Its flight is described as almost always low over the ground (Löhrl 1987).

There is a similar association between Canary Island Stonechat and *Sylvia* warblers to that found in European Stonechat and Dartford Warbler *S. undata*. Both Sardinian Warbler *S. melanocephala* and Spectacled Warbler *S. conspicillata* have been observed following feeding *dacotiae* individuals (B. Small pers. comm. 2001)

MOULT

Little information. Probably similar in sequences and strategy to European Stonechat although timing different. Adults have a complete post-breeding moult. Moult commences from late April to May and is completed in June or July, although more investigation is needed. First-year birds appear to start moulting earlier than adults. Juveniles have a partial post-juvenile moult involving the head, body and some upperwing-coverts, although some outer greater coverts are retained. This moult commences shortly after fledging from mid-February to late April, but again more research is required (Cramp 1988).

CONSERVATION

Although formerly treated as threatened (Collar & Stuart 1985), the species is now judged under IUCN criteria to be Near-Threatened (Collar *et al.* 1994, Stattersfield & Capper 2000). Despite its relatively small overall population it does not appear to be at risk, and based on recent estimates it may even be experiencing a positive population trend. It is widespread on Fuerteventura and there are good concentrations in some of the more remote and inaccessible areas. Agriculture has been declining since the eighteenth century, and most farming is at subsistence level. The continuance of current non-intensive farming methods combined with the species' preference for marginal cultivated areas and land unsuitable for farming means agriculture cannot be seen as an adverse influence.

The continued unrestricted expansion of the tourist industry and its related infrastructure has resulted in a small overall loss of habitat and is making the birds more accessible to birders and consequent disturbance; of more concern is that this may present an unquantifiable but potentially serious danger of exploitation from egg collectors. Persecution of small passerines by hunting and trapping generally does not occur on Fuerteventura.

Four introduced mammals may also augment the natural predation rates by indigenous birds. Cats possibly restrict numbers near villages and habitation. Rats *Rattus* and Vagrant Hedghog *Erinaceus algirus* probably take eggs and young (Collar & Stuart 1985). The introduction in 1965 of North African Ground Squirrel *Atlantoxerus getulus* may also have a detrimental effect on numbers, although there is no proof of this (J.A.L. Gutierrez in *Atlas de las aves de Espana* 1997); currently they do not appear to be affecting the species' population.

The long-term and continuing desertification of Fuerteventura appears to potentially pose the most serious ongoing threat. Loss of soil cover and further degradation of vegetation may reduce suitable habitat. The species has been fully protected by law since 30 December 1981.

Collar & Stuart (1985) and Bibby & Hill (1987a,b) proposed various measures to protect it. Several areas should be given protected status, most importantly the Jandía mountains which are relatively less degraded by goats and where a good variety of indigenous and endemic flora still survives. Several of the major barrancos where it occurs should be given protected area status. A detailed investigation of the western mountains should be made, as these were predicted by Bibby & Hill (1987a) to contain good numbers of this species. An accurate and thorough assessment of numbers and distribution should be made in order to monitor long-term trends in population.

Tucker & Heath (1994) ten years later agreed with the above concerning protected areas and identified the main conservation requirements as further detailed study of the species' biology and monitoring of its numbers. They also recommended the large-scale elimination of grazing animals, especially goats, although recognised that this would be difficult to achieve. The widespread distribution of the species over Fuerteventura makes it difficult to devise an adequate conservation strategy. They suggested that key sites should be protected. Only three sites at the time of their publication were recognised and likely to be approved by Parliament. These were the Parque Natural de Jandia, Parque Rural de Betancuria and Paisaje Protegido de Malpais Grande. The Jandia Peninsula identified by Bibby & Hill in 1985 and Tucker and Heath (1994) still had only partial protection as of 2000 (Heath & Evans 2000).

Moro Tabaiba and Morro Rincones, both of great importance to this species, were still entirely unprotected as of year 2000 as were many other areas with high densities of this species. This is especially so on the rocky slopes of the interior of mountains. Heath & Evans (2000) identified a number of other threats to the species including agricultural intensification and expansion, illegal hunting, industrialisation and urbanisation, recreation and tourism. Domestic waste disposal results in increasing rat (*rattus*) populations which prey on breeding birds and feral cats also pose an increasing threat.

Possibly a thorough search could be made of suitable areas on Lanzarote with a view to ascertaining if it is still present or suitable for introducing this species. Harsh penalties for egg collecting or wilful disturbance should be available.

THE COMMON STONECHAT COMPLEX
European Stonechat *Saxicola rubicola*
Siberian Stonechat *Saxicola maura*
African Stonechat *Saxicola torquata*

Motacilla torquata Linnaeus, 1766, *Syst. Nat.*, ed. 12,1, p.328—Cape of Good Hope [= South Africa]

Etymology [*torquata* from Latin *torquatus* meaning collared or necklaced]

Alternative names Stonechat, Collared Stonechat, Collared Bush Chat, Collared Indian Bush Chat, Black-headed Chat

TAXONOMY

To date it has been generally accepted that Common Stonechat is a single species comprising in excess of 20 subspecies. At least 43 subspecies have been proposed at one time or another but a considerable number are now discounted. One of the standard works based on traditional taxonomy, Peters's *Check-list of Birds of the World* (Ripley *et al.* 1964) admits a total of 25. However, this includes the now separated species Réunion Stonechat *S. tectes*. Keith *et al.* (1992) in *The Birds of Africa* also do not include two Afrotropical subspecies listed in Peters: *S. t. adamauae* from the mountains of northern and western Cameroon, and *S. t. pallidigula* from Cameroon Mountain and Fernando Po Island. In the present work, *S. tectes* is accepted as a separate species and *S. t. adamauae* and *S. t. pallidigula* are included as subspecies of African Stonechat.

In 1991 the South African Ornithological Society (SAOS) published a second updating report to the *SAOS Checklist of Southern African Birds* (Clancey 1980). This report viewed an extralimital subspecies accepted by both Ripley *et al.* and Keith *et al.*, *S. t. promiscua*, as confined to parts of the eastern Tanzanian highlands. The southern African populations associated with it in the *Checklist* were now transferred to a new race, *S. t. altivaga* (Clancey 1988). This gives a revised total of 25 subspecies.

Sibley & Monroe (1990), in *Distribution and Taxonomy of Birds of the World,* set out to classify families and key generic groups based mainly on evidence of phylogenetic relationships derived from DNA studies. Although not specifically looking at birds on a species by species basis they did list suggested proposals for taxonomic classification and names of individual taxa. In their publication in 1990 they suggested a split into two species, Common Stonechat *Saxicola torquata* and Siberian Stonechat *Saxicola maura.* They further suggested that the name *Saxicola torquata* should be restricted to the two western Palearctic subspecies plus those in the Afrotropical and Malagasy regions, while *Saxicola maura* (Siberian Stonechat) should apply to the six eastern Palearctic subspecies. This was based not on any DNA evidence but on the fact that some authorities consider them separate species, due to lack of intergradation where their ranges meet, and differences in morphology. Sibley & Monroe also hinted that the Afrotropical subspecies *S. torquata albofasciata* may merit specific rank, and suggested the name Ethiopian Stonechat. In addition, they classified the then subspecies *S. t. tectes* as a full species. In an update, Sibley & Monroe (1993) revised some of their earlier classifications. They reverted to the traditional taxonomic classification, including Siberian Stonechat as *S. t. maura*, a subspecies of the Common Stonechat.There is no apparent reason for this and possibly it was done because there was no hard evidence to justify their original suggestion. Possibly the vexed question of whether there is intergradation in the Transcaucasus, where the subspecies *S. t. rubicola* and *S. t. armenica* meet, made them more cautious and revert to the traditional historical classification.

They did, however, add in their 1993 review that these two taxa were accepted as species by others or exhibited characteristics that suggested such status. Many birders do now use the name Siberian Stonechat when describing one or all of the eastern subspecies, and some have unofficially regarded these eastern subspecies as forming a separate species. Sibley & Monroe did not have the benefit of the research findings of Wittman *et al.* (1995) or Wink *et al.* (2001, 2002) whose DNA studies show that their original assumptions in 1990 were correct as far as they went. The British Ornithologists' Union (BOU) does not yet support this view; indeed, the only national representative body that does is the Netherlands (see below).

I propose that the Common Stonechat *Saxicola torquata* should be treated as three species, European Stonechat *Saxicola rubicola*, Siberian Stonechat *Saxicola maura* and African Stonechat *Saxicola torquata*, as this reflects more accurately the current and recently available facts than does the existing accepted taxonomic classification.

The current position concerning the Common Stonechat complex is far from satisfactory as no definitive mtDNA study has been made of the entire complex of subspecies. However, based on available biological criteria plus the mtDNA studies of Wittman *et al.* (1995) and Wink *et al.* (2001, 2002), the 25 subspecies can at the least be split into three separate species.

Eight subspecies are currently recognised throughout the Palearctic: two in the western Palearctic and six in the eastern Palearctic. The two western subspecies are partially migratory, whereas the six eastern subspecies are totally migratory. Of the latter, *S. m. przewalskii* (and possibly a second, *S. m. indica*) are also marginally found in the Oriental region. A further 15 subspecies are found in the Afrotropical region, 14 south of the Sahara in Africa and one in south-west Arabia, with two others found in the Malagasy region on Madagascar and Grand Comoro Island.

There is some disagreement about whether Saudi Arabia and Yemen qualify to be included in the Palearctic or Afrotropical zones (Campbell & Lack 1985). I have preferred the latter as geographically it is closer to Africa and the subspecies concerned shows a greater affinity, based on plumage and ecology, to African Stonechat than it does to European or Siberian Stonechat

Historically, the species Common Stonechat and its subspecies have all been proposed and recognised by the taxonomists involved using what is now termed the Morphological Species Concept (Haffer 1992), which ignores any evolutionary or genetic consideration but attempts to classify birds as species or subspecies simply on the basis of their physical similarities or differences. This is a flawed method as there is no absolute correlation between the degree of physical similarity of two animals and their biological interactions or evolutionary relatedness (Burkhardt 1987; Carter 1951; Knox 1994).

The differences between the three species based on traditional Biological Species Concept (BSC) taxonomic criteria are enumerated in detail under the various headings in this account and the following three species accounts ,and it is apparent that there are considerable differences in plumage, moult (at least in the case of Siberian Stonechat), voice (Urquhart unpublished), ecology, habitat and morphology. The Phylogenetic Species Concept (PSC) evidence also points to considerable genetic divergence amongst the three species.

Although BSC is still regarded as the established method for deciding taxonomic classifications it has one distinct disadvantage which has been widely recognised. Collinson (2001) put it succinctly stating that

"when two closely related taxa are absolutely separated geographically, with no way of determining whether hybridisation between the two in the wild is either possible or disadvantageous, there is no scientifically sound method of classifying them with respect to each other under the terms of the BSC. In such cases as these, the conventional approach of taxonomists using the BSC is to make a subjective judgment based on perceived differences in morphology, genetics, ecology or reproductive behaviour as to what would happen if the two forms were to come into contact again in the future".

This puts the taxonomist in a hypothetical situation where it has to be judged whether the two taxa would hybridise widely and intergrade, in which case they are subspecies, or if not then they are species. This is unsatisfactory in the least but this is what has been done in arriving at a classification of one species called Common Stonechat with 25 subspecies. There is now strong evidence that this classification is no longer acceptable.

A frequently given reason for being cautious about considering a split of Common Stonechat is the vexed question of dealing with allopatry and also the uncertainties due to integradation where the respective ranges of two subspecies meet. Two of the new species, European Stonechat and Siberian Stonechat, are considered to come into contact in adjacent and possibly overlapping areas in the Transcaucasus such as northern Armenia through the subspecies of European Stonechat *Saxicola rubicola rubicola* and the Siberian subspecies *Saxicola maura armenica*. Both are superficially alike with similar life histories. However, they exhibit diagnostic differences: *armenica* has a white base to the tail, all-white rump and uppertail-coverts and larger measurements. They also differ in the habitat they prefer, with *armenica* found in montane habitat and *rubicola* lowland. Vaurie (1959) could find no evidence of intergradation but Beaman (1997) suggested that they do from personal observation in north-east Turkey and the Transcaucasus region (although no real evidence was provided and it was suggested that further investigation would be required). There is in fact little or no evidence of widespread intergradation or that any resulting hybrids are breeding widely. Although there may be some intergradation between birds of the two subspecies involved it is in my opinion not widespread and not of great significance.The respective subspecies, although adjacent geographically, are in the main separated altitudinally with *armenica* found from c.825–1900m whilst *rubicola* is mainly found only up to 600m with some populations in central Europe occasionally reaching 700-800m. The four easternmost subspecies of Siberian Stonechat, *S. m. maura, stejnegeri, indica* and *przewalskii*, which cover a huge area to the east, do not come into contact with European Stonechat, from which they are separated by around 1500kms. Current information also indicates that they do not come into contact with the two Siberian Stonechat subspecies in the Transcaucasus *armenica* and *variegata*, from which they are separated by around 600kms. It is possible that *armenica* and/or *variegata*, the latter with marked plumage differences, may be a separate species in their own right; these are the only subspecies of Siberian Stonechat which come into contact with European Stonechat.

Similarly, African Stonechat is widely separated from European Stonechat (which only breeds in the coastal countries of north Africa) and Siberian Stonechat (which only comes into contact with African Stonechat in the form of the two Caucasian subspecies *variegata* and *armenica*, when on their wintering grounds in north-east Africa). It does seem perverse to assume that these three proposed species with wide geographic separations and with minimal evidence of intergradation where two subspecies meet, should be assumed to be the same species based on hypothesis, when the available facts, both biological and genetic, indicate the opposite.

Although no comprehensive, detailed DNA analysis of the entire European, Siberian and African Stonechat complex has yet been attempted, two significant steps have been taken concerning the use of DNA techniques. The first was when Wittman *et al.* (1995) published the results of a mtDNA sequence study into geographical differentiation and speciation in the Common Stonechat. (*Please note that the following taxonomic classifications and English names are those in use at the time of the study and therefore differ from my proposals.*) They examined Common Stonechats from three different subspecies, inhabiting three different continents and whose breeding areas did not overlap. These were *Saxicola torquata rubicola* from Europe, *S. torquata maura* from Asia and *S. torquata axillaris* from southern Africa. They also examined seven separate European populations of *S. t. rubicola*. Variation within the European populations of *S. t. rubicola* was less than 0.3% but the genetic distances between the three subspecies from Europe, Asia and Africa was much greater, varying from 2.7 to 5.7%, suggesting that they might be treated as separate species. In fact, at the time these results were published, the 5.2–5.7% of DNA sequence divergence between the African subspecies *S. t. axillaris* and the European subspecies *S. t. rubicola* was the greatest genetic distance so far reported for a subspecies of any known species. It was even greater than the distance shown for sibling species such as Common Nightingale *Luscinia megarhyncha* and Thrush Nightingale *L. luscinia*, which have a variation of 4.7%, and Pied Flycatcher *Ficedula hypoleuca* and Collared Flycatcher *F. albicollis*, with a variation of 3.4%. In the case of *S. t. maura* and *S. t. rubicola* the sequence divergence at 2.7%, although less than *S. t. axillaris*, still demonstrated a comparatively large genetic distance. The sequence divergence, different plumage characteristics and allopatry all indicate that Siberian Stonechat *S. t. maura* should be classified as a species.

It was suggested by Wittmann *et al.* (1995) that if substantial genetic distance is a criterion for species status then the current status of stonechats from Africa and Asia in relation to those from Europe should be reviewed, especially as there are also differences in morphology, behaviour, distribution and habitat preference.

Although both the then classified *S. t. axillaris* and *S. t. maura* have been hybridised with *S. t. rubicola* and have produced fertile offspring (Gwinner *et al.* 1987, 1995), this would still not invalidate their claim to species status under the modern species concepts propounded by Prager & Wilson (1975) and McKitrick & Zink (1988). Gwinner (1991), who also worked on the Wittman DNA study, had earlier proposed that African Stonechats are derived from Palearctic species or subspecies that migrated to Africa, similar to *S. t. variegata* which migrates from the Caucasus to Ethiopia. African Stonechats also have similar responses to photoperiodic changes as their European counterparts, and they could have retained a similar photoperiodic responsiveness as an ancestral trait (Gwinner *et al.* 1983; Gwinner & Dittami 1985).

The hypothesis that African Stonechats are derived from Eurasia was also proposed by others such as Voous (1960), Hall & Moreau (1970) and Glutz & Bauer (1988). It is also consistent with fossil records of stonechats from the European region in the Pleistocene/Holocene periods (Brodkorb 1978). However, Wittman's analysis indicated that *S. t. axillaris*, the African subspecies chosen for the study, became separated from a common ancestor before either *S. t. rubicola* or *S. t. maura*. The genetic evidence therefore suggests that Gwinner's hypothesis that *maura* was a direct ancestor of *axillaris* is incorrect.

Largely based on Wittmann *et al.* (1995) the Dutch Committee for Systematics (*CSNA*) in 1998 (Sangster *et al.* 1998) unilaterally split the species Common Stonechat into three species: European Stonechat *Saxicola rubicola*, Siberian Stonechat *S. maura*, and African Stonechat *S. torquata*. They also decided to treat the race *S. t. hibernans* as a synonym of *S. rubicola* and likewise *S. t. stejnegeri* with *S. maura*. The remaining subspecies *S. t. variegata, armenica, indica* and *przewalskii*, pending further DNA analysis, are considered by the Dutch to be conspecific with *S. maura*. At the time of writing The Netherlands is the only country officially to adopt this new classification. The results of research (published in this book) by Wink *et al.* (2001, 2002) (who also participated in the Wittman study in 1995), confirm the research by Wittman *et al.* (1995) and confirm the Dutch decision to accept a split of Common Stonechat into three species. However, as will be noticed there are some differences in the Latin binomen used for the proposed new species. The Dutch have used the binomen *Saxicola rubicola* for the two western Palearctic subspecies *hibernans* and *rubicola*, whereas Wink *et al.* has used the binomen *Saxicola torquata*. As stated earlier I have accepted both the English name and Latin binomen used by the Dutch for the two western Palearctic subspecies. Wittmann *et al.* (1995) and Wink *et al.* (2001, 2002) both use the binomen *Saxicola axillaris* for African Stonechat. This would only be correct if subspecies *S. t. torquata* from South Africa was grouped with the European populations. A grouping including *S. t. torquata* with the rest of the African populations under African Stonechat *S. torquata* is far more likely than a grouping of *S. t. torquata* under European populations (Sangster *in litt.* 2002).

Hall & Moreau (1970) placed the single species Common Stonechat *Saxicola torquata* in a superspecies grouping with Réunion Stonechat *S. tectes,* White-tailed Stonechat *S. leucura* and, with some doubts, Canary Island Stonechat *S. dacotiae.* Their reservations were due to the fact that *S. dacotiae* had a similar head pattern to Whinchat *S. rubetra* but shared with *S. torquata* a similarity in wing formula, and the fact that it does not have a pre-breeding moult; Sibley & Monroe (1990) reflected these reservations by stating it may be more closely related to *S. rubetra* and should be left out of the *S. torquata* complex. However, it may prove that the earlier systematists were correct, as the mtDNA researches of Wink *et al.* (2001,2002) have found a close relationship between European Stonechat *S. rubicola* and the Canary Island Stonechat *S. dacotiae.* It should also be noted that Hall & Moreau mentioned that *S. leucura* may prove to be not specifically distinct, but no mtDNA work has been done on this or any other species in the genus *Saxicola* occurring in the eastern Palearctic and Oriental regions.

Subspecies

Listed below are the currently accepted subspecies of the three species of 'Common Stonechat'. Because little or no mtDNA research has been done on many of the subspecies I have retained them until more information is available. It is probable that some subspecies may just be synonyms, e.g. *S. r. hibernans, S. m. stejnegeri* and *S. m. indica.* Others may well be species in their own right such as *S. m. variegata, S. m. przewalskii, S. t. albofasciata, S. t. sibilla* and *S. t. voeltzkowi.*

European Stonechat *Saxicola rubicola*

Western Palearctic

> *Saxicola rubicola rubicola*
> *Saxicola rubicola hibernans*

Siberian Stonechat *Saxicola maura*

Eastern Palearctic

> *Saxicola maura variegata*
> *Saxicola maura armenica*
> *Saxicola maura maura*
> *Saxicola maura indica*
> *Saxicola maura stejnegeri*
> *Saxicola maura przewalskii*

African Stonechat *Saxicola torquata*

Afrotropical

> *Saxicola torquata felix*
> *Saxicola torquata albofasciata*
> *Saxicola torquata jebelmarrae*
> *Saxicola torquata moptana*
> *Saxicola torquata nebularum*
> *Saxicola torquata adamauae*
> *Saxicola torquata pallidigula*
> *Saxicola torquata axillaris*
> *Saxicola torquata promiscua*
> *Saxicola torquata salax*
> *Saxicola torquata stonei*
> *Saxicola torquata clanceyi*
> *Saxicola torquata torquata*
> *Saxicola torquata oreobates*
> *Saxicola torquata altivaga*

Malagasy

> *Saxicola torquata sibilla*
> *Saxicola torquata voeltzkow*

IDENTIFICATION Based on European Stonechat *Saxicola rubicola*

Size 12.5cm/5 inches with some variation amongst the subspecies. Some subspecies of Siberian Stonechat and African Stonechat average slightly larger. Sexes dimorphic. The three species are small, robust and compact birds with short, rounded wings and a short, fairly square tail. Their legs are slender and, in proportion to body size, long. They have a bold and engaging character and are rarely still for long, moving frequently, full of nervous energy, restlessly flicking their wings and fanning their tail when perched and flying low over the ground or vegetation with rapidly whirring wings from one prominent perch to another or to the ground to seize prey.

The male European Stonechat has a dark brown/black head which appears somewhat large, round and neckless. The chin and throat are also dark brown/black. There are prominent patches of white on the sides of the neck, upper sides of the breast and on the inner upperwing. The breast and underparts are rufous or chestnut-brown and the upperparts including the tail are dark brown to black. The rump and uppertail-coverts are rufous-brown to orange-buff in fresh plumage, becoming white with black and orange streaks as the feather tips wear. Among the three species' there are subtle and complex variations amongst the various subspecies concerning size as well as the amount of white on the neck, the inner upperwing, the rump, uppertail-coverts and base of the rectrices; the extent of rufous or chestnut on the breast and the rest of the underparts; the general colour tone (pale or dark) on both upperparts and underparts.

Females are very much duller, with no black on the head, dull grey-brown upperparts and orange-buff, slightly rufous underparts. The chin and throat are generally pale buff, darkening with wear in the majority of subspecies but not in Siberian Stonechat subspecies *S. m. maura* and *stejnegeri*. They show little or no white on the neck but do have white on the inner upperwing, although less prominent and extensive than on the male. The rump and uppertail-coverts are usually orange- or buff-brown in the Palearctic and white in African Stonechat. As with the males there is considerable variation amongst the various subspecies concerning size and the general overall colour tone of the plumage.

There is a distinct juvenile plumage, evident from fledging until individuals commence to assume a plumage similar to that of the adults towards the end or after the breeding season is over. Juvenile plumage is superficially similar to that of the female, the upperparts being dark brown but with profuse buff streaks on the head and larger buff spots on the rest of the upperparts. The underparts are rufous-buff and the sides of the breast and flanks are finely spotted and mottled with brown and grey respectively. The rump and uppertail-coverts are rufous-buff with irregular black spots and streaks.

Confusion species In the western Palearctic the only possible confusion species is Whinchat *Saxicola rubetra*. For differences with other members of the genus, all of which occur in the eastern Palearctic, Oriental and Afrotropical regions, see under each particular species. For differences from the eastern races of Siberian Stonechat likely to occur in the western Palearctic, see below and under the Siberian Stonechat section in this chapter.

European Stonechats can be told from Whinchat by subtle differences in structure – the overall body shape is more rounded, with slightly longer tail and shorter wings (primary projection only c.50% that of overlying tertials) in proportion to the body, large round head with somewhat neckless appearance. By contrast, *S. rubetra* appears more attenuated although with slightly shorter tail in proportion to the body, but has longer primary projection (c.75% that of overlying tertials) with flatter back and crown accentuated in the latter case by the prominent supercilium; European Stonechat males and all African Stonechat males have an unmistakable completely dark brown/black head, throat and chin at all times of the year, even in fresh autumn plumage. Male Whinchat shows a different head pattern and has a prominent supercilium at all times of year, creamy-buff in autumn but white and strikingly long and broad in spring/summer plumage, and also a distinct white line running from the base of the lower mandible under the lores and below the eye. The chin and sides of throat are white, forming a noticeable white stripe under the black cheeks and ear-coverts. Male *S. rubicola* have only dull grey-white fringes and tips to the upperwing primary coverts in fresh plumage, while adult male *S. rubetra* have a variable but usually extensive amount of white on the upperwing primary coverts (= >50% from base); all male *S. rubicola* have no visible white at the tail-base (the two Caucasian subspecies of Siberian Stonechat *S. m. variegata* and *S. m. armenica* show white but in a different pattern), while all male *S. rubetra* show prominent triangular white or occasionally buff patches at the base of the tail.

Female *S. rubicola* can, as with the male, be told on structure. Females of European and African Stonechat can be confused with male, female and first-winter Whinchat, which in fresh plumage superficially resemble each other. The head of female *rubicola* is darker brown and generally lacks a prominent supercilium, while the head of *rubetra* is paler with a prominent long, broad, buff-white supercilium; in *rubicola* the overall tone of the upperparts is darker and the underparts are a stronger pink to orange-buff, whereas

135

rubetra appears more prominently streaked and spotted above. The upperparts of *rubetra* are paler with more contrast between the black feather-centres and pale fringes, and there are white crescentic tips to the mantle and scapulars. The underparts are also paler, appearing more tawny-buff; *rubicola* throat colour varies from pale buff in fresh plumage to darker brown/black in worn plumage, while *rubetra* is white or pale buff throughout the year. *S. rubicola* at all ages and in both sexes has white on the inner upperwing greater coverts, although this is reduced on females and juveniles and therefore often not very obvious until the bird flies; *rubetra* has much less extensive white on the inner upperwing greater coverts and on first-year birds the white is absent from all areas. *S. rubicola* has a completely dark brown tail; *rubetra* has prominent white triangular patches at the base of the tail and for all ages, although some (presumably first-year) individuals can show only inconspicuous buff patches.

In autumn, first-winter and adult female, as well as some first-winter male Siberian Stonechat of subspecies *S. m. maura* and *stejnegeri*, can look very like Whinchat. Differences are again in structure, with the same differences as in the other subspecies, although primary projection (c.75%) is roughly the same as *S. rubetra*; *S. m. maura* and *stejnegeri* usually show a pale supercilium but it is indistinct, thinner and shorter in length, whereas *S. rubetra* always shows a broad distinct supercilium extending at least to the rear of the ear-coverts. *S. m. maura* and *stejnegeri* have an extensive pale orange-buff rump and uppertail-coverts, sometimes with some white admixed but always without dark streaks or spots (also *S. torquata* females have unmarked white rumps and uppertail-coverts); *S. rubetra* rump and uppertail-coverts are darker rufous-brown and prominently streaked and spotted with dark brown or black, and do not show any white at any time of the year. *S. m. maura* and *stejnegeri* have a dark brown/black tail with narrow greyish-white edges and tips, while *S. rubetra* has prominent white patches at the base, but caution here is required as some birds have a less distinct buff colour and females of *S. m. variegata* show an extensive buff base to the tail, but in a different pattern more like Northern Wheatear *Oenanthe oenanthe*. *S. m. maura* and *stejnegeri* mantle and scapular feather tracts are pale and relatively plain with comparatively indistinct darker brown streaking on the centres of the feathers, while *S. rubetra* is always more strongly marked with dark brown/black spots and streaks to the centre of the feathers, often with white fringes. *S. m. maura* and *stejnegeri* underparts lack any markings on breast and flanks, while *S. rubetra* has brown spots and streaks on the breast and flanks.

Juvenile *S. rubicola* has a dark brown tail, while *S. rubetra* shows white or buff triangular patches at the base of the tail. *S. rubicola* is dark grey-brown above with profuse buff streaks on the head and spotting on the mantle and scapulars; *S. rubetra* is paler, warmer brown in the same areas with very pale shaft-streaks to the feathers. *S. rubicola* underparts are darker with a strong rufous-buff tone to the breast and paler buff on the rest of the underparts with narrow brown tips to throat, chin, breast and flanks; *S. rubetra* is pale creamy-buff on the entire underparts with indistinct narrow darker brown tips only on the breast and flanks.

Leucism and Albinism Records of leucistic individuals or of complete or partial albinism concerning European and Siberian Stonechats in the Palearctic are apparently very rare, possibly owing to under-recording. I have only found one record for the western Palearctic and that was of a partially 'albino' female European Stonechat breeding in northern England in March 1998 (J. Callion pers. comm. 2001). Glutz & Bauer (1988), however, record that both partial and completely white individuals of African Stonechat have been seen in various populations in the Afrotropical zone. An albino specimen that associated with Red-collared Widowbirds *Euplectes ardens* was collected in the Drakensberg Mountains, KwaZulu-Natal, South Africa on 15 January 1981. It was totally white with a dark bill and legs and red eyes (Little 1984).

Hybrids There are to date only two confirmed records (i.e. accepted by the National Records Committee of the country concerned) of pairing and breeding with another species. These both concerned Siberian Stonechat, were both with Whinchat and were recorded from Finland. The first record was of a male Siberian Stonechat *S. m. maura* paired with a female Whinchat raising five young at Joensuu in 1986. The second was of a female Siberian Stonechat, again of subspecies *S. m. maura*, paired with a male Whinchat and raising four young at Siilinjärvi in 1997.

There is also an Austrian record of a probable pairing of a female Whinchat and male Stonechat (subspecies unknown but presumably *S. r. rubicola*) successfully raising young in 1994. It was speculated that this mixed breeding was influenced by a locally isolated Whinchat population combined with a simultaneous failure in initial colonisation of the same area by European Stonechat (Uhl 1998).

There are also at least two currently unsubstantiated records of suspected hybrid individuals of European Stonechat x Whinchat in Germany. A possible hybrid male was holding territory in 1996 and was said to show plumage characters reminiscent of Canary Island Stonechat *S. dacotiae*, and a possible female hybrid was in Baden Wittenburg in 1998.

Two cases of hybrid breeding were suspected in Norway in 1994 although neither was accepted. A pair comprising a male European or Siberian Stonechat and female Whinchat was discovered, observed carrying food, and photographed over 12–15 July at Mortenses on the Varanger Fjord. The nest or young could not be found before the observers had to leave the area. The second record was of a bird submitted as an individual of the Siberian Stonechat subspecies *S. m. maura/stejnegeri* seen on 30 September. This record was rejected owing to the possibility that the bird, for which photos were supplied, might have been a hybrid European or Siberian Stonechat x Whinchat!

The resulting progeny of any such pairings certainly pose identification problems but occurrences appear to be rare. Although to date there has been only two accepted records of pairing with another species there is every likelihood that it has happened at other times in the past and will occur again in the future (see under Stoliczka's Bushchat for details of a strange stonechat from Goa which was probably a hybrid Siberian Stonechat x Stoliczka's Bushchat – see photo). The possibility of hybrids should always be borne in mind if an unusual *Saxicola* is seen.

Intergradation There is probably intergradation between the various races in the Palearctic. This supposition seems to have been widely accepted although surprisingly no-one has yet supplied definite proof. The two European Stonechat subspecies *S. r. hibernans* and *S. r. rubicola* are so similar that it would be very difficult to prove if they did or did not intergrade but it is probable, as stated earlier, that they do where their respective ranges meet. With regard to the easternmost limit of the range of *rubicola* in the eastern Caucasus and Armenia, it was stated by Vaurie (1959) that where it came into contact with *S. m. variegata* and *S. m. armenica* there was no evidence of intergradation. This statement has been contradicted by Beaman (1994) who states he encountered intermediates between the subspecies of European Stonechat *S. r. rubicola* and Siberian Stonechat *S. m. armenica* in north-east Turkey and the Transcaucasus – but see my comments under Taxonomy.

In autumn at Eilat, Israel, it has been found that besides typical individuals of the three Siberian Stonechat subspecies *maura*, *armenica* and *variegata*, quite a few individuals showed plumage characters intermediate between *maura* and *armenica*, with wing measurements and tail patterns intermediate between the two subspecies. Others had the tail pattern of *armenica* and the wing measurements of *maura* or showed intermediate characters between *armenica* and *variegata* (Shirihai 1995). This seems unusual concerning *maura* as its range on current knowledge is widely separated from both *variegata* and *armenica*.

The ranges of *S. m maura* and *S. r. rubicola* are fairly widely separated so it is unlikely that they intergrade. However, there is a recent record of successful breeding between these two subspecies in Germany in 1997 (see under Distribution *S. m. maura*). This was probably the result of a returning migrant *maura* that had wintered in western Europe (see under Migration *S. m. maura*) that paired with a local *rubicola*.

The ranges of *S. m. maura* and *S. m. stejnegeri* do overlap in Central Asia and the two probably intergrade where they meet. Vaurie (1959) said he had seen specimens intermediate between these subspecies. Vaurie also asserted that the ranges of *maura* and *indica* were connected to those of *armenica* and *variegata* but this is not correct. The subspecies *indica* probably intergrades with *maura* where their ranges meet and may be synonymous with *maura*. Clines connect *S. r. hibernans* to *rubicola*, *S. m. maura* to *indica* and *stejnegeri* to *przewalskii* (Vaurie 1959).

I would question whether *przewalskii* is connected to *stejnegeri*. It is so much darker than *stejnegeri*, considerably larger and breeds south of *stejnegeri* range so would possibly be expected to be lighter in colour, not darker, as evidenced with the *hibernans/rubicola* cline. The range of *przewalskii* also comes into contact (over a much larger area than *stejnegeri*) with both *maura* and *indica* but there is no sign of intergradation with these two subspecies which are markedly paler and smaller.

DISTRIBUTION

The range of European, Siberian and African Stonechat extends over three continents, Europe, Asia and Africa, from the Arctic Circle to the very tip of South Africa and as far east as Japan. They are found breeding between latitude 71°N in the forest tundra of Siberia (Krechmar 1966) and 35°S at Cape Agulhas on the southernmost tip of South Africa.

In Europe European Stonechat is generally distributed only up to 53°N. It extends further north regularly in Europe only in the UK, Ireland, Netherlands, Germany, Denmark, Norway, Sweden and, sporadically since the 1990s, Finland.

In the Palearctic zone it is distributed widely through the temperate and boreal zones, breeding over most of Eurasia from Norway, Finland and southern Denmark in the north, west through UK, France, Spain and Portugal and south to most of the larger Mediterranean islands but excluding Malta and Cyprus. In North Africa it is found in Morocco, Algeria and Tunisia. It stretches east across northern Europe to southern Poland, the Ukraine and Belarus and east across southern Europe to Turkey and Transcaucasia. The range of Siberian Stonechat in the form of the two subspecies *S. m. armenica* and *variegata* adjoins the

European Stonechat range in the Transcaucasus ranging north to western Kazakhstan and south through Iran and Iraq. There is a gap over a large area of western Russia before Siberian Stonechat is found again from northern and eastern European Russia, the eastern Kirghiz Steppe in Kazakhstan stretching east across Siberia to China, Korea and central and northern Japan. It extends north in Siberia as far as the middle and lower reaches of the Ob, Yenisey and Lena Rivers and southwards to Afghanistan, northern Pakistan, much of India (including the Himalayas from eastern Kashmir to Arunachal Pradesh), Myanmar [Burma], Thailand, Laos and Vietnam.

In the Afrotropical region African Stonechat breeds discontinuously from north-west Senegal down to Gabon and lower Congo. In East Africa it occurs from western Sudan down to Kenya and northern Tanzania. In central and southern Africa it is found from the Democratic Republic of Congo south through Angola, Zambia, Mozambique and Zimbabwe to the southern coast of South Africa. There is a separate subspecies found in Yemen and south-west Arabia, and in the Malagasy region there are two isolated subspecies found in Madagascar and on Grand Comoro Island.

BREEDING

Palearctic region The western European populations around the Mediterranean from North Africa to southern Europe, and also in south-central Europe, commence laying around early March. An early nest with fresh eggs was found in southern Spain on 28 February (Stenhouse 1921). In the more northerly European countries, i.e. UK, Belgium, Germany and Netherlands, laying generally commences from the end of March to mid-April. In above-average mild and dry winters, laying can commence earlier such as in mid-February in southern Switzerland and mid-March in the UK. In eastern Europe and throughout Asia to Japan breeding commences later, from about the end of April to mid-May. There is little information for the Siberian Stonechat subspecies *variegata* and *armenica*. There is a record of pairs feeding young as early as the last third of May at Tatvan in Turkey (Kumerloeve 1969) and a record of a nest in Armenia in late May with 3–4-day-old young suggests that laying may commence around the end of April. Records of adults with fledged young in July and August suggest that two broods are attempted (Adamian & Klem 1999). The Siberian Stonechat subspecies *maura* can possibly commence breeding in the south of its range from the end of April but the majority commence from early to mid-May and it is just possible some of the population in the west of the range may manage to raise two broods, second nests being commenced in mid-June. Near Tomsk in 1912 the earliest full clutches were on 19 May but the usual dates for this same area fall in the period 1–20 June (Johansen 1954). When they first arrive in this area they are restricted to the warmest, just thawed areas on the banks of the Yenisey River, occasionally hunting insects on the ice piled along the riverbanks. During the first third of June they occupy their breeding sites, and commence laying from mid-June. Consequently it would be unlikely that more than one successful breeding attempt would be possible (Rogacheva 1992).

In Kashmir Bates & Lowther (1952) found eggs in the third week of July at both extremes of its altitudinal range. The more easterly subspecies *stejnegeri* commences laying from mid-May, continuing breeding until at least July in Japan (Fujimaki *et al.* 1994) and rarely into August (Brazil 1991). Certainly in Japan and probably elsewhere in the Far East the species raises two broods. The subspecies *indica* commences breeding from mid-March and continues up to July with two broods being normal (Ali & Ripley 1968–1998). There is no information concerning *przewalskii* but it is possible that it attempts two broods in the south of its range.

Afrotropical region Unlike European Stonechat, the African Stonechat is mainly single-brooded, although occasionally birds which have lost their eggs or young before fledging will make a second attempt. In Kenya a study between August 1981-February 1983 of around 50 pairs of *S. t. axillaris* found re-nesting occurred in only four pairs which had lost their clutch before fledging. No other pairs produced second clutches (Dittami & Gwinner 1985). Another study of *axillaris* in Arusha N.P, Tanzania, 1993–1997, found that 13 out of 23–32 pairs attempted second broods in two favourable breeding seasons (Scheuerlein 2000).

In southern Africa the African Stonechat is a spring and summer breeding species with a peak in October in the majority of areas but later from October–December at higher altitudes in KwaZulu-Natal, Lesotho, Swaziland and eastern Transvaal [Mpumalanga], where more severe winter weather conditions probably delay breeding (Harrison *et al.* 1997).

Laying dates for the Afrotropical region are: Senegal/Gambia, March; Mali, January; Sudan, May; south-east Sudan and Ethiopia, April–May, with birds also reported in breeding condition in the latter countries in February, March, June and September but not definitely proved breeding (it is possible that there may be two breeding seasons, February–June and September or, less probably, a very prolonged breeding season: Urban & Brown 1971); Cameroon, January–February (Bannerman 1936); Uganda, February–March; Kenya, January–June (mainly March–May), birds around Lake Nakuru on the Mau escarpment, Kinangop Plateau and around Ol Kalou breeding during the rains from March to the end of June (Dittami & Gwinner 1985), with birds in the Chyulu Hills, Kenya, and northern Tanzania (Mts Meru and Kilimanjaro, Ngorongoro Crater highlands, Usambara, Uluguru, Udzungwa and Southern Highlands) breeding during the rains from September to February (van Someren 1939, Baker & Baker in prep. in Scheuerlein 2000); southern Democratic Republic of Congo, August–September; Malawi and Zambia, August–November; Zimbabwe, July–December (mainly August–November); South Africa, Transvaal [Mpumalanga], August–December (mainly August–October); KwaZulu-Natal, August–December; Lesotho, September–December (Keith *et al.* 1992).

Other subspecies There is no information for the subspecies *S. t. felix*, *sibilla* or *voeltzkowi*.

Sexual system European, Siberian and African Stonechats are sexually mature and breed in the year following their birth, usually forming monogamous pairs which remain together throughout the breeding season unless one of the pair dies or is usurped (Johnson 1961,1971b).

Records of polygyny are extremely rare. On Jersey, Johnson (1961, 1971b) recorded three occurrences concerning European Stonechat in a remarkable sequence from 1955 to 1957.

1955: A male divided his time between an incubating female in one territory and another, darker female in a territory 400m away. Two days after the brood from the male's first territory fledged the male was observed carrying food to a second nest containing six almost fully fledged young. By back-calculating from the known ages of the young it was possible to deduce that the first egg in the second nest was laid around two days after that in the first nest. The male had been consorting with two females simultaneously, accompanying them on their feeding trips between incubation stints and sharing in the feeding of both broods. The original female commenced a second nest and laid a second clutch of eggs whilst the second female left the area shortly after the young from her first nest fledged, leaving the male to carry on feeding them.

1956: A male was recorded breeding with three females, two colour-ringed, the other unringed. He held three separate territories each occupied by one female, and was observed copulating with two of the females and in courtship display with all three. By the end of April he was feeding the unringed female's young, escorting one of the ringed females when she left her eggs to feed, and displaying to the third female who laid her first egg around 6 May. On 2 May the unringed female disappeared after her young were predated and the male carried on dividing his time between his remaining two females, helping to rear both broods successfully. Once the young of these broods had dispersed the male reverted to a monogamous pairing with one of the ringed females and they successfully reared a second brood. Not surprisingly after these efforts the male was usurped by a young male paired to a young female and he and his mate disappeared.

1957: The young pair referred to above remained in the territory during the winter and split up in early March when the male was replaced by another male. The female laid her first egg around the 22 March. The new male was also accompanying another colour-ringed female who laid her first egg approximately five days later. The females in this trio successfully raised two broods each and both attempted a third, one failing and one succeeeding. Throughout this time the same male was in attendance, dividing his duties at all stages of the breeding cycle between the two females. Johnson remarked that unlike monogamous pairs the two females, when they met at the edge of their territorial boundaries, showed no animosity towards each other. The incidence of such behaviour may be linked to seasons when the breeding densities are low and males that do not have adjacent territorial boundaries do not have to invest so much time in defence of their territory. This allows them to take advantage of any surplus population of females in the immediate vicinity. Similar behaviour has also been suspected but not proved in the Netherlands and Germany (Glutz & Bauer 1988). In the UK males have been observed associating with two females prior to breeding but one of the females always disappeared before breeding commenced (Greig-Smith 1979). There is a record from Germany of polyandry in which a female associated with four males in succession, three of which assisted her in the raising of the brood. There is also a record of possible polyandry from South Africa where a female raised a brood of three nestlings assisted by two males, one of which appeared to be subordinate to the other (W.R. Tarboton *in litt.* 2000). It has been suggested that such situations most probably occur when there is an imbalance in the sex ratio of a population (Ziegler 1966). In Germany it has been suggested that an unbalanced sex ratio is normal amongst European Stonechat populations; in one study in Koblenz, 186 'bachelors' and single birds were found alongside 884 pairs over a period of 12 years (Glutz & Bauer 1988).

Both European and Siberian Stonechat and also African Stonechat populations appear to have a transient population of unpaired birds discreetly present in and around breeding territories, as birds which lose their partner usually acquire a new mate within a day or two. In Kenya, where individuals of pairs were known to have died, the remaining birds would re-mate within a few days with a 'surplus' first-year bird from the previous breeding season, indicating that there were transient birds present looking for either a prospective mate or a territory (Dittami & Gwinner 1985). The brief absence of a male, caught for ringing, from a breeding pair in the Netherlands resulted in his mate being courted by another male literally within minutes (Agatho 1960-1961). Sometimes the male of an established pair is ousted by another where the breeding population has surplus males (Ziegler 1966).

Before the young hatch there is a marked division of labour, with the male exclusively involved in defending his territory and mate whilst the female selects the nest site, builds the nest, lays and incubates the eggs. When the young are hatched the male commences to assist the female in feeding the young, although a minority of males will only make a token effort.

Nest-site selection A study by Greig-Smith 1979 in southern England found that the distance between successive nests (up to three in a season) varied between 10 and 145m, with the mean distance moved being 95m in 1977, 96m in 1978 and 81m in 1979. In Westfalia, Germany, the distance between successive nests was mostly less than 40m (Ziegler 1966) and in the Netherlands a minimum distance of 1m was recorded between successive nests (Frankevoort & Hubatsch 1966). Johnson (1971b) recorded a pair on Jersey that built three successive nests in a line approximately 1m apart, doing this for two years running in 1957 and 1958.

On heathland in southern England, Greig-Smith (1984) found that breeding took place in four types of vegetation: bracken, purple moor grass, heather, and gorse. Birds tended to move from the former two after June when the vegetation put on rapid growth, even though nesting success increased for nests under these plants, probably owing to the increased cover from predators. Heather and gorse did not change greatly in structure but were increasingly favoured by European Stonechats after June even though nests sited in them were less productive than nests in bracken and tended to fledge fewer young than earlier in the season. A possible explanation of this behaviour is that the subsequent post-fledging survival of nestlings may depend to a degree on their weight on, or just prior to, fledging. From four nestlings that survived to return and breed three had been the heaviest in their broods whilst the fourth had been the lightest in a brood of six. After June and the increased leaf growth in bracken the peak weights for nestlings reared in this vegetation did not increase but for nestlings reared during the same period in nests in heather and gorse they did. Of five nestlings that fledged in captivity three were described as 'large and vigorous' and the remaining two as 'small and stunted'. Despite a constant effort from the parents in feeding these latter two, they both died two days after fledging (Doughty 1970). Nest sites in Jersey are most commonly at the foot of north-facing slopes with the entrance facing between north-west and north-east to avoid direct sunlight (Johnson 1971a). However, other observations in UK and Germany suggest that there appears to be no favoured aspect, and nests have been found on slopes as well as on the level, often only sheltered from the sun by the natural vegetative cover in which they were concealed. Glutz & Bauer (1988) remark that nests are often placed on slopes formed by dykes or embankments, interpreting this as a deliberate strategy to attempt to remain dry during heavy rain. Walpole-Bond (1938) drew attention to the fact that the nests he found in Sussex in southern England were almost invariably situated near to or right by a small track of some sort. Nest-seekers in the UK have found this fact to be extremely helpful (EU pers. obs., J. Callion pers. comm. 2000). Other observers have also recorded this throughout the UK. An analysis of 674 British Trust for Ornithology (BTO) Nest Record Cards for the years 1977–1989 revealed that in 87 instances (12.9%) the recorder felt it relevant to mention this fact, although not specifically requested to do so on the card (E. Urquhart unpublished). It is possible that many more nests in the sample were in a similar situation but the recorder did not think to mention it.

The reason for this apparent preference remains unclear, but it could be an anti-predator measure, as a track is more likely to be followed by a ground predator and, being relatively free of vegetation, would allow an incubating bird or the vigilant male slightly earlier sighting and warning of a predator's approach to the nest site than if it was through thick vegetative cover. In Germany it was considered that building nests on the top of a ditch or on an embankment or near tracks provided both a clear free flyway to the nest and cover from danger. Birds were often seen to use these features to conceal themselves when feeling threatened. The borders between low and higher vegetation were put to similar use (Flinks and Pfeifer 1993). J. Callion (pers. comm. 2000) notes that birds in northern England nest near larger tracks and suggests that these tracks, if frequented by large domestic animals or humans, might act as a deterrent to ground predators. Davis (1974) suggested that by flying along a track just above the ground between the surrounding vegetation the bird's return to the nest could be disguised from avian predators more successfully than if it was above the surrounding vegetation.

The female usually chooses the nest site and does so alone, inspecting potential sites every 1–2m, disappearing into the vegetation for up to 3–4 minutes. Generally the male remains at a discreet distance, but still follows her. Once the site is chosen he will often accompany her back close to it and display excitement when she brings nest material, although usually still not visiting the actual site. However, Doughty (1970) found that in captivity the male made the initial inspection of the nest site, visiting and inspecting at least four potential nest sites. Before entering each site he would hold his wings high and quiver them whilst simultaneously uttering what Doughty described as a *eurring* sound, and when actually on the nest site he gave a high-pitched warble. This appeared to encourage the female as she was often seen to respond to these calls and actions and to visit the site the male had chosen. Once the actual nest site had been selected the female became the dominant partner in this area of their territory, with the male always giving way. Agatho (1960–1961) mentions that in the wild the male, once the site is chosen, may fly into the nest site for a couple of seconds, which he interpreted as acting as a stimulus to the female to commence nest building. Doughty observed that the male of a captive pair would always fly to the nest site to investigate if the female, whilst building, remained at the site for any length of time. Greig-Smith (1979), from 52 observations of nest building, noted that on 51 occasions it involved only the female but one involved a male carrying nest material, which he considered an indication that males did not usually assist in nest building but might indicate that males are involved in the selection of the nest site. There are other observations of males carrying nest material; once in Cornwall, England (Parrinder & Parrinder 1945) and twice in the southern Netherlands (Agatho 1960–1961). Agatho interpreted this behaviour as a stimulus for the female to build, citing the example of a male that sang for over an hour above the nest site and, failing to get a response from the female, collected a dry leaf and flew to his mate with it. The female immediately commenced building. A similar action was noted by Doughty with the captive male flying in a fast direct flight towards the female with a piece of dead bracken in his bill. During nest building the male will sometimes feed the female, approaching her with rapid, even wingbeats with the wings being held beneath the body (E.N. Panov *in litt.* 2001).

The nest is usually built into a shallow depression in or on the ground below thick vegetative cover or sometimes into the debris and litter of leaves and twigs at the base of low bushes. In these latter cases it can appear to be above the ground. All races, both Palearctic and Afrotropical, utilise similar nest sites. In seasons with a high population nests of different pairs can sometimes be in a cluster or very close together, but not colonial. This has been recorded from both Europe and Asia. In optimum habitat in Japan the mean for distances between nests was 110m (n=53) with extremes of 50–163m; in less suitable habitat the mean was 179m (n=30) with extremes of 50–321m (Fujimaki *et al.* 1994). The nest is invariably very well hidden, although exceptional nests above ground level, such as in gorse bushes in the UK, can be relatively exposed. Some nests deep in vegetation can have what can only be termed an entrance tunnel up to 25cm long and 2–3cm wide created by the adults' comings and goings.

Atypical nest sites in the UK have included trenches, ditches, quarry faces, a heap of pine seedlings and a small reedbed, whilst in Germany nests have been found in mouse holes and under clods of earth. A nest located on 25 September 1993 in the Orange Free State [Free State], South Africa, was built in a rusty tin can lying between clumps of grass on a roadside verge (van Niekerk 1994). Nests in central Siberia were under a log and under a broken pail (Rogacheva 1992).

The overwhelming majority of nests are on the ground. Of 1,327 nests in the UK recorded by the BTO Nest Record Scheme, 84.8% were at ground level. Only 14 nests (1.1%) were recorded above 60 cm, the highest of which were two at 200cm in the crown of a gorse bush and on a wall respectively and a third 250cm up in gorse and bramble (E. Urquhart unpublished). In the Netherlands nests have been found at a maximum height of 1.7m in corn sheaves and 2.2m in hayricks. A nest in Cameroon was 1m above ground in a bank by a road (Bannerman 1936).

In Germany (Westfalia) birds breeding in pasture had to change their nesting site during the breeding season due to vegetative changes. First and early second broods were usually in ditches but for late second and third broods pairs moved to meadows with lower plant heights, as the vegetation in the ditches had grown too dense and tall. In meadows with upright perches such as fences or old plant stalks from the previous year, nests were sited under broad-leaved plants such as *Rumex* or *Cirsium* near to such perches. On heather moorland nesting continued throughout the season owing to its slower growth, but in cultivated fields pairs also often moved, as the cereals became too high (Flinks & Pfeifer 1987b, 1993).

Nest building Observations in the UK indicate that the female usually builds in the early morning, but J. Callion (pers. comm. 2000) has recorded several instances of females in the north of England building in the late afternoon. The female collects nest material from within the territory, often within a 10–15m radius of the nest site, although if there is a ready source of material outside her territory and not in another adjacent territory, she will utilise this source also. The male remains in his territory when the female makes such forays but will go to the very limit of his territory to observe her. There is a remarkable record of a female in northern England visiting an active Carrion Crow *Corvus corone* nest when the adults were absent and removing sheep's wool to line her own nest (J. Callion pers. comm. 2000).

On Jersey, Johnson (1971a) found that nest building can take 4–10 days depending on climatic conditions, with cold weather sometimes inhibiting building. In Germany nests in April were built in 6–7 days but in May in only 3–4 days (Glutz & Bauer 1988). In Japan the mean for nest building (n=9) was 5.3 days with extremes of 4–10 days (Fujimaki *et al.* 1994). Johnson remarked on a facet of behaviour that can occur during nest building which he termed 'false incubation', where the female disappears for up to an hour in the vicinity of the uncompleted nest as if she were incubating eggs and then reappears with the male close by. Similar behaviour has been noted in southern Netherlands by Agatho, who observed that pairs would show a tendency to guard an empty nest or incomplete clutch of eggs. At the time of nest building pairs seem very sensitive to disturbance and desertion resulted in nearly all cases where an unfinished nest was disturbed by human investigation.

Nest composition The bulk of the nest consists of unwoven dry grasses and stalks up to 25cm long on the outside, often with moss and leaves added into it. Other materials used in the nest foundation include pine needles, seedpods of broom, bracken and heather, and such oddities as strips of rag, string and even polythene. The cup of the nest is then formed in the top of this foundation by the female turning and twisting her body to shape the material to her liking. Sometimes the rear of the nest will be less bulky than the front. The nest is constructed comparatively loosely and this, together with the often present moss, gives it an almost springy feel. The outer diameter of the nest is c.10–14cm and the height c.7cm. The cup is c.6–7cm in diameter and c.4–5.5cm deep. Virtually anything soft and locally available will be used to line the nest, including short fine grasses, animal hair, rabbit fur, thistle down, spiders' cocoons, sheep wool and various feathers. One female in the west of England lined all three of her nests with red wool which she collected from a rubbish heap in a nearby garden. Up to 400 feathers have been counted in one nest (Herrman 1987) but such a high number is unusual. The nest rim is rarely decorated; of 58 nests examined in southern England only one was decorated, with small blobs of sheep's wool (EU pers. obs.). Another nest in Jersey had chicken feathers inserted evenly around the rim, curving upwards and inwards. Nests constructed early in the season in Germany were considered to consist of more material than those constructed later in the season, which had thinner walls and a shallower cup (W. Schneider in Glutz & Bauer 1988).

Egg-laying Copulation occurs 1–4 days before the first egg is laid. Glutz & Bauer (1988) give an average in April of four days between nest completion and egg-laying. From May onwards any time lapse decreases dramatically and is rarely more than one day. Bad weather will cause a delay in egg-laying even if the nest is complete, with a maximum delay in one extreme case of 11 days. The female takes from 30 seconds to two minutes to enter the nest, deposit an egg and depart, usually laying the egg in the early morning between 06:00 and 07:00hrs. During the egg-laying period the nest is ignored apart from the daily visit to deposit an egg, the pair remaining in other parts of their territory. At this time of egg formation the female often spends long, inactive periods hidden in a bush (P.W. Greig-Smith in Glutz & Bauer 1988). An analysis of 724 BTO Nest Record Cards showed extreme dates in the UK for laying first eggs in a clutch from 16 March to 25 July – a protracted breeding season (E. Urquhart unpublished). The earliest recorded date for a first egg in the UK is 13 March 1998 from a nest in Cumbria, northern England (J. Callion pers. comm. 1999). There is evidence that the trend towards milder winters in the UK is prompting earlier breeding attempts. There is a record of a nest with young being found in north-west England on the extraordinarily early date of 26 February 1995 (Massey 2000). This would mean that the clutch was completed at the very latest on 12 February. The year 1995 was an unusually warm and early nesting season (Crick 2000). At the other extreme there are records for first eggs being laid for repeat breeding attempts as late as 1 and 12 August. In the UK the majority of eggs for first clutches are not laid before the second week of April (Fuller & Glue 1977). There appears to be some synchronisation of laying amongst pairs in a particular population. In a study in southern England the completion of first clutches became progressively more synchronised over a three-year period (1977–1979), declining from 42% variation to 13% (Greig-Smith 1979). Similar circumstances of synchronisation have been found in south-west England and the Netherlands. In central Europe the majority of pairs commence laying at approximately the same time as those in UK. In Belgium, The Netherlands and Germany it commences between the second and fourth week of April in normal years and mid-March if temperatures have been high in that month. In Catalonia, the Mediterranean regions of France and southern and western Switzerland, laying commences from the middle to the end of March, although in above-average mild and dry seasons birds resident in Mendrisiotto in southern Switzerland have commenced laying from around 15 February (Glutz & Bauer 1988). The breeding season also often extends into August in central Europe; for example in Westfalia, Germany, the latest third brood started was on 7 August with the young fledging on 9 September (Flinks & Pfeifer 1987b), whilst a nest with young about ten days old was found on 3 September in Luxembourg (Glutz & Bauer 1988). In central Siberia the mean date for first eggs over an unspecified number of years was 13 June. The earliest egg recorded was 1 June 1982 and of 45 cluches 18 were in the first third of June, 24 during the second and three during the last, one of which consisted of a second attempt after the first nest was destroyed by a dog (Rogacheva 1992).

In Japan earliest eggs laid were from 29 April and latest eggs for second broods 15 July. First breeding begins from late April (earliest nest built 25–28 April) to early May and second broods start from late June to early July (latest nest built 11–14 July) (Fujimaki *et al.* 1994).

There are three distinct periods of relatively concentrated egg-laying activity in UK; from mid-March to the end of April; a peak in mid-May to early June; and a smaller concentration from the end of June to mid-July.

Morgan & Davis (1977) state analyses of nest record cards have shown there is a propensity for recorders to complete cards for more nests in the early months than in later months of a breeding season (Summersmith 1952, Monk 1953), thus giving a false impression of the number of third broods attempted. Morgan & Davis (1977) made a special effort to locate third broods on heathland in Surrey, England over a two-year period 1972–1973 and found that from 30 pairs observed with first brood nests, 29 (97%) attempted a second brood and 15 (50%) a third brood. This was in marked contrast to the proportions of 32% for second and 10% for third brood nest record cards held by the BTO.

Clutch size The clutch normally consists of 4–6 eggs, the majority being of 5 with extremes of 2 and 7. Clutches of 7 are extremely rare. From 524 clutches recorded by the BTO only six comprised 7 eggs. Clutches of 6 are most likely to occur in the middle of the breeding season. In 1994 a female in Cumbria, northern England, laid three clutches of 6/7/6 eggs and all three nests were successful. The cumulative total of 19 eggs produced by this female in a single breeding season is the highest so far recorded in the UK and probably Europe (J. Callion in *Cumbria Bird Report* 1994). Also in 1994 a female in Aberdeenshire, Scotland, raised three broods which were all successful in fledging, giving a cumulative total of 17 young, while in 1995 another female raised 15 young from three broods (Thorpe 1999). In Germany there are also records of pairs raising 16 and 17 young in one breeding season (Glutz & Bauer 1988).

Of 197 nests in one UK study, clutches of 2 eggs comprised 1%, 3 eggs 3%, 4 eggs 10%, 5 eggs 63%, 6 eggs 22% and 7 eggs 1%, yielding a mean clutch size of 5.06 (Fuller & Glue 1977). A similar result was obtained by Greig-Smith (1979) in East Sussex, England, who found from 101 nests that clutches of 2 eggs comprised 1%, 3 eggs 3%, 4 eggs 25%, 5 eggs 46% and 6 eggs 25%, yielding a mean of 5.3. Another analysis of over 400 nests recorded between 1972 and 1996 gave a mean clutch size of 5.2 (H. Crick *per* BTO 1995). The trend in this latter analysis showed a significant linear increase from 4.9 up to 5.4. The reason for this increase is unclear but it may be due to a recovery from the effects of organochlorine pesticides in the 1950–1960s which adversely affected not only birds of prey but probably smaller passerines as well. Of 234 clutches in Germany (Westfalia), 1.7% consisted of three eggs, 5.5% four, 61.5% five, 29.9% six and 1.3% seven, resulting in a mean clutch size of 5.24 (Flinks & Pfeifer 1987). Of 42 nests in central Siberia, six contained 4 eggs, 10 contained 5 eggs, 18 contained 6 eggs, seven contained 7 eggs and one contained 8 eggs (Rogacheva 1992).

Clutch sizes of Siberian Stonechat in Hokkaido, Japan, also averaged higher than European clutches, with 6.3 for first clutches and 5.6 for second. It may be that the more compressed breeding season, which allows only two broods, results in larger clutch sizes (Fujimaki *et al.* 1994).

In the UK clutch sizes in the middle period from mid-May to early June (see under Egg-laying) tend to average the largest, possibly reflecting the time when food is optimally available. Mean clutch size for the first period was 4.92, the second 5.49 and the third 5.06 (Fuller & Glue 1977). On Jersey Johnson (1971b) found, from 61 nests, means for the same periods of 5.22, 5.48 and 5.15 eggs, whilst in Germany Flinks & Pfeifer (1987b) found the equivalent values were 5.16, 5.44 and 4.63. A captive study of individuals of the European Stonechat *S. r. rubicola* and the African Stonechat *S. a. axillaris* demonstrated that the number of eggs laid by females of the respective species differed markedly. Average clutch size for European Stonechats was 5.09 and for the African Stonechats 3.44. Hybrid females of these two species laid on average in the next year a clutch of 4.07 eggs which was intermediate between and significantly different from the clutch sizes of the European and African Stonechats. The study also found that the clutch size of a female of one species paired to a male of the other species did not differ from that of a female paired with a male of the same species as itself. The conclusion drawn from this study was that the difference in clutch size between the two species is to a large degree genetically determined. (Gwinner *et al.* 1995)

Number of broods European Stonechats in the UK regularly raise three broods in a single season when conditions are appropriate, largely facilitated by the fact that much of the population remains within the UK, either on or comparatively near to their breeding territories, and can, therefore, commence their breeding cycle earlier than returning migrant birds. Throughout the rest of the Palearctic range where the population is mainly migratory two broods are normal provided there are no repeated breeding failures, with a small percentage of pairs managing to raise three broods. In southern Switzerland, from a total of 160 pairs in a migratory population recorded over a five-year period, 18% were single-brooded, 64% double-brooded and 5% triple-brooded (Lardelli 1986). The birds raising three broods could, however, be residents which have only moved locally and remained within Switzerland over the winter. In the southern Netherlands many pairs raised two broods and attempted a third, but regular third broods were rare owing to a high failure rate (Frankevoort & Hubatsch 1966). A pair also raised three broods in Rendsburg, Schleswig-Holstein, in 1993, and as they can be present from late February/early March to October/November it was considered that they have the potential to raise three broods regularly. Observations indicated that some or all possibly overwinter in Schleswig-Holstein (Pfeifer 2000). There are only two known records of four broods being successfully raised in one season, both from Germany, in eastern Niedersachsen (Plucinski 1956) and Baden-Wurttemberg (Guldi 1965). However, if earlier nesting attempts fail, pairs will quite often make up to four breeding attempts and in some cases be successful with three. A new nest is built for every breeding attempt. In a study of 37 pairs in southern England it was found that 100% made a second attempt, 84% a third and 8% a fourth (Greig-Smith 1979). However, many birds that made only two breeding attempts raised the same number or even more young than those which made three. The difference is probably attributable to the quality of the parent birds and to the territory held. On Jersey, Channel Islands, it was found that in pairs suffering no predation or interference the interval between the start of first and second broods spanned 36–55 days, the mean being 46.3, and for second and third broods it was 40–47 days, mean 43.8 (Johnson 1971b). In southern England Greig-Smith (1979) obtained very similar means of 44 days and 43 days respectively, but individual intervals varied more than on Jersey, depending on weather conditions, with minimum and maximum intervals of 33 and 58 days for first to second broods and 30 and 50 days for second to third broods. In Germany (Westfalia) the interval between first and second broods was 41 days, and second to third 40 days (Flinks & Pfeifer 1987b). In the Netherlands the same periods showed 46 and 39 days (Bijlsma 1978). Interestingly, in Japan, where only two broods are attempted, the interval between successive breeding was similar to Europe, at 46 days (Fujimaki *et al.* 1994). The intervals between the start of laying for two successive broods are longer the later they start in the year. In Germany for 73 nests in May the interval averaged 42.5 days; for 105 in June it was 45.2 and for 37 in July it was 48.3 days (W. Schneider in Glutz & Bauer 1988).

In Arusha NP, Tanzania, only pairs of African Stonechats which succeeded in fledging their first brood before 28 October and retained at least some of the young up to the post-juvenile moult attempted a second brood. The interval between the first and second brood was on average 68 days (Scheuerlein 2000). The subspecies *axillaris* studied by Scheuerlein was found to have a similar prolonged breeding season (time between onset of laying and onset of moult) to the European Stonechat amounting to 152 days (±23 days, n=59). It differs in that it mainly produces only one brood per season and may raise two broods in favourable years. The prolonged season may be an adaptation to counteract losses from nest predation. Pairs have been observed to initiate up to seven laying attempts (Scheuerlein 2000).

Description of eggs The eggs are oval to subelliptical. The average of 148 eggs of European Stonechat subspecies *hibernans* was 18.7 x 14.4mm (extremes of 16.5–21.3 x 13.2–15.5mm) (Cramp 1988). An examination of egg measurements of European Stonechats from 5 European countries (UK, France, Netherlands, Belgium and Czechoslovakia) found those from UK were on average largest 21.3 x 14.4 and 20.6 x 15.7mm and smallest from Belgium at 16.1 x 13.1 (Glutz & Bauer 1988). Averages of two samples for the smaller Siberian Stonechat subspecies *S. m. maura* were 16.02 x 13.0mm and 17.1 x 13.2mm (Dement'ev & Gladkov 1968).

Fifteen eggs of African Stonechat subspecies *S. t. torquata* from Cape Town, South Africa, measured on average 18.5 x 14.5mm with a maximum of 19.4 x 15.0 and minima of 18.0 x 14.3 and 18.1 x 14.2mm (Vincent 1947).

A sample from UK of eight fresh and unincubated eggs gave extreme weights of 1.9–2.4g. The eggs are smooth and matt or slightly glossy. The base colour is generally pale turquoise-blue or greenish-blue; exceptionally, some are almost white, others yellowish-white and others unmarked pale blue; a very rare form is a pure bright blue. Usually there are red-brown or occasionally purplish spots or freckles of varying intensity overlaying the base colour. The spotting and freckling can be evenly distributed over the egg, or appear as a ring or even a cap at the larger end. The markings are very fine and numerous on some, large, blotchy and relatively few on others. Occasionally eggs in a clutch are not uniform but vary considerably in colour and pattern. Females that lay aberrant eggs do so consistently for all clutches.

Incubation Incubation is solely by the female and lasts 13–14 days, occasionally 15; an infertile clutch was incubated for up to 24 days before being abandoned (Glutz & Bauer 1988). In Japan the mean incubation time of Siberian Stonechats was similar to European Stonechat being 13.6 days (Fujimaki *et al.* 1994). Incubation generally commences with the laying of the final egg of the clutch, but sometimes with the penultimate egg. In bad weather the start of incubation may be delayed by 1–5 days with no apparent ill effects to the eggs. Despite some earlier references (Witherby *et al.* 1948) to the male actually incubating there is no real evidence for this. Observations of over 600 nests in the Netherlands over a ten-year period never produced a record of a male incubating, although males were seen flying onto the nest for a minute or less, which was interpreted as a stimulus to a mate that was reluctant to recommence incubation (Agatho 1960-1961). Very occasionally a male will feed the female on the nest. In Germany this was observed on 14 occasions (Mildenberger 1950) but not once in the Netherlands (Agatho 1960-1961).

Incubation stints vary from 20 to 60 minutes, the female leaving for 5–25 minutes to feed, accompanied by the male. Greig-Smith (1979) stated that such stints usually lasted no more than 30 minutes with a similar time spent feeding, and that stints tended to increase the longer incubation went on. The female is usually accompanied by the male on these feeding sorties; indeed, males will sometimes call a female off the nest to feed. She leaves the nest quietly and inconspicuously, using any available cover as she distances herself from the nest in an initial long flight of 50m or more. On settling she often indulges in a period of rapid preening, then proceeds to feed, moving steadily away from the nest. Johnson & Agatho both mention that the female appears to have a favoured feeding area within the territory to which she will go, such as a meadow or field. Incubating birds have been seen to feed almost 500m from the nest (EU pers. obs.). The female returns to the nest in a series of flights usually decreasing in length the nearer to the nest she gets, and often she does not bother to feed on the way back. Usually she makes one or two decoy descents into vegetation near to the nest site before settling in the nest. The male returns to a favourite perch near the nest site and occasionally hovers in front of the nest as the female settles on it. Whilst the female is incubating the male remains perched nearby and if approached by an intruder or potential predator he often flies towards it and attempts to lead it away from the nest by making short flights whilst remaining highly conspicuous and vocal. Low-level alarm calls (*trrack*) are given when the potential perceived danger is not great, but the nearer the intruder gets to the nest the more urgent the calls become, changing to a two-note *whit-trrrack*. The low-level call rarely causes the female to leave the nest, but the urgent call often results in her silently quitting the eggs and making a long flight to an inconspicuous vantage point. The male continues to make himself obvious and then flies off to join her. Johnson recorded an even more elaborate demonstration by the male in which he flies to a perch away from the nest and commences rising and falling in hovering flight before moving further away and dropping into cover, only to reappear even further away repeating the whole process.

Hatching On Jersey it was found that eggs hatch after 13 or 14 days, usually at night or in the early morning (Johnson 1971b). Ziegler in Germany, also found that they hatch at night or in the space of six hours in the early morning. Sometimes hatching appears to take place in two shifts roughly 12 hours apart. If incubation starts before the laying of the last egg of the clutch the interval between the hatching of the first and last chick may be up to 2.5 days (Glutz & Bauer 1988). Of 16 nests observed in Japan eggs either hatched on the same day or over a two-day period (Fujimaki *et al.* 1994). Unhatched eggs remain in the nest throughout the fledging period and no attempt is made by the adults to remove them. Hatching success is high. From 160 eggs laid in southern England over a two-year period 1987–1988, 71.8% hatched (EU unpublished information) and in Jersey from 332 eggs in 63 clutches between 1955 and 1958 81% hatched. Other studies in southern England have found up to 91% successfully hatched (Parrinder & Parrinder 1945, Dennis 1976). In Kenya from 97 eggs 70% hatched (Dittami & Gwinner 1985). In Japan the average for all clutches from 82 nests was 85.4% (Fujimaki *et al.* 1994).

Infertility is the main cause of partial losses in clutches, being most frequent in second and third clutches. Of 332 eggs examined by Johnson in Jersey, 13% were infertile and of 64 eggs that did not hatch 72% were infertile. In the Netherlands Frankevoort & Hubatsch give lower percentages with 8% of 2,153 eggs being infertile and in Germany, Schneider (in Glutz & Bauer 1988) found 9% of 1,140 eggs infertile, with 32% of successful clutches containing infertile eggs.

Feeding nestlings In the first 24 hours after hatching the nestlings are brooded constantly by the female apart from brief feeding spells, until their long but sparse, brownish-grey down is dry and can afford some insulation. Agatho states that both adults feed the young from the first hatching, but Johnson (1971b) thought it more usual for the male to concentrate primarily on territorial defence for the first 4–5 days. Conversely Greig-Smith (1979) mentions that the male may take the larger share in feeding the young in the first few days while the female broods. A male has on one occasion been seen to transfer food for nestlings to the brooding female (Frankevoort & Hubatsch 1966). In observations of a captive pair the male was seen to bring food to the brooding female in the first two days after hatching and she transferred it to the young. The female never left the nest to find food for the young in that time, only leaving to feed herself. On the third day she commenced finding food for the young (Doughty 1970). From personal observation and that of others, it would appear that either the male or female takes a disproportionate share of the feeding responsibilities during the first 3–4 days after which it evens out between the pair, although some pairs show an imbalance throughout the feeding stage. Greig-Smith in southern England between 1977 and 1979 found considerable variation in the effort of males in feeding their young.

The young are altricial on hatching and take 13–15 days to fledge. The first defecation occurs roughly 3–5 hours after the first feed, then at each or every second feed (Gwinner *et al.* 1987). Brooding, which is only done by the female, decreases gradually to around 50% of the time by the fourth day and by day six the female only broods the young at night and ceases to brood them at all by the eighth day. The parents hunt for food separately in their territory. If the adults are carrying food but for some reason, such as the presence of an intruder, are prevented from delivering it to the nest for any appreciable time they will often swallow it themselves. A male Stonechat called the female back off the nest just after she had gone down to feed the young. She responded instantly, flying back to a bush but retaining the food and returned to the nest when the alarm was over (EU pers. obs.). If the young produce a faecal sac whilst being fed the adult carries them well away from the nest, usually over 50m. When leaving the nest after feeding the young, the adult makes a long, elevated flight to another part of the territory. Feeding is usually accomplished by the adult perching on the rim of the nest but a male who had lost his mate once fed his four young while hovering in front of them (EU pers. obs.).

Birds of either sex who lose their mate during this stage of the breeding cycle are perfectly capable of raising the brood themselves. The male referred to above raised four young and Agatho recorded a male raising five young without a mate. In the relatively rare cases where the male plays a minimal role in feeding the young the female still usually manages to cope although such pairs usually only raise one brood. However, if adverse weather such as prolonged rain or cold occurs, broods where only one parent is feeding the young often perish. There is little information on the frequency of visits by parents to the nest. In southern England on at least two occasions parents with young 8–10 days old appeared to take a break from feeding duties. The pairs retreated to a part of the territory well away from the nest and fed and sat around in a relaxed manner. This lasted for approximately 45 minutes before the female unhurriedly worked her way back to the nest and collected food for the young when near the nest. Both pairs showing this behaviour had broods of four so may have had less pressure than those with 5–6 young to feed (EU pers. obs.). If the female ceases to feed the young the male also stops and accompanies the female.

Growth of nestlings On the fourth day of life nestlings are showing feather quills all over the body and by the fifth day the quills of the wing-coverts and remiges are fully formed and the eyes opening. On the sixth day all the dorsal surfaces are covered with feathers still in their quills. By the seventh day the feathers of the remiges and wing-coverts are 2–4mm out of the quills and by the eleventh day the feathering of the young is almost complete. Nestlings put on a rapid weight increase up to about their eigth day of life after which there is a slowing down and finally a decline in weight just before fledging around the 13th day. The majority of young reach their peak weight on the 11th or 12th day in the nest (Greig-Smith 1979). Young weigh 2g at birth and put on weight at an average of 1.5 g per day from days 2–7. After this the growth curve flattens out and peak weight is achieved on the 11th or 12th day, averaging 16g, although one nestling peaked at 19g. For each day the young remain in the nest after reaching the peak weight they lose an average of 1g per day (Glutz & Bauer 1988). The young from around the sixth day in the nest all face towards the entrance to the nest. They generally arrange themselves in two rows. The young in larger broods compete to form a hierarchy with the stronger, heavier nestlings seeking out a position at the rear of the nest with their heads and chests resting on their weaker siblings in front. It is presumed that the young at the rear gain a competitive advantage when the parent arrives with food as, being heavier, they can dominate over the backs of the birds in front and gain more food, consequently growing faster. Lighter nestlings run a greater risk of pre-fledging mortality and of only achieving a low fledging weight which can subsequently affect their chances of survival after fledging (Greig-Smith 1985).

Fledging The young leave the nest 13–15 days after hatching. Glutz & Bauer (1988) give a mean of 14.9 days from a sample of 114 nests in Germany. In Japan the mean nestling period was 13.4 days (Fujimaki *et al.* 1994). In Jersey from a sample of 22 nests the range was 12–16 days with four broods leaving at 12 days, eight at 13, seven at 14, two at 15 and one at 16 (Johnson 1971b). If weather conditions are unfavourable the young have been known to remain in the nest for up to 18 days, whilst another brood with little or no obvious disturbance left the nest at an estimated 10–11.5 days old (Niethammer 1938).

From the 11th day the young crawl out of the nest for short periods before returning to it to await a parent arriving with food. Exceptionally in Spain a brood of five which left the nest prematurely following disturbance were all found to have returned when the nest was checked two days later (De Garnica 1986). They may also return to the nest after having left it voluntarily: Johnson (1971b) cites one example where a brood left the nest at 13 days, only to return two days later. When the young are ready to leave the nest permanently the parents quietly entice them with soft *trrack* calls, hovering and perching close by. If undisturbed the young leave one at a time, moving into adjacent cover a few metres from the nest.

The young are capable of limited flight when they leave the nest but favour scuttling into the adjacent undergrowth. Agatho saw a young bird flutter 70m the day after it had left the nest. The young generally remain reasonably close to the nest site. In Japan they remained near to the ground for the first five days, then commenced perching on the upper parts of grasses and on poles, and moved 10–200m from the nest site (Fujimaki *et al.* 1994). In Germany fledged young were led by the parents to suitable cover for the first 2–3 days after fledging where they remained hidden deep in the vegetation until about 17 days old. From 17–19 days they perch 50–80cm up in the vegetation layer, crouching when threatened even though they are able to fly away. When a parent bird arrives with food they move towards it via plant stems. From 20 days old they perch on higher, more exposed perches and fly off when disturbed (Schneider in Glutz & Bauer 1988). In Japan the mean time from leaving the nest until independence (n=17) was lower, being ten days (Fujimaki *et al.* 1994). The distance young put between themselves and the nest site is variable. Some young remain close to the nest for up to seven days. Observations in Germany of 22 recently fledged young found that in the first five days the mean distance was 5.5m with only one individual being found more than 10m away (Ziegler 1966). However, others can be found as much as 200m away from the nest site by the first or second day out of the nest. It was suggested by Agatho that this difference was attributable to the amount of cover that each individual territory offered recently fledged young. The tail of the young bird is usually fully grown by the 25th day of life.

Success rate of broods Overall success rates for broods fledging (number of young fledged from number of eggs laid) is relatively high. In southern England it was 55% in 1987 and 79% in 1988 (EU unpublished information) and a figure of 64% was recorded by Johnson (1971b) in Jersey, whilst Greig-Smith (1979), also in southern England, recorded 59%. In Germany over a period of 13 years, 357 clutches resulted in 50% fledged young (Schneider in Glutz & Bauer 1988), and another sample of 237 clutches over ten years gave an average of 61.1% with a maximum of 72.2% and minimum of 33.3% (Flinks & Pfeifer 1987). Much higher success rates have been reported from widely scattered parts of the UK, such as 84% in Scotland (Dennis 1976), 90% in southern England (Morgan & Davis 1977) and 91% in western England (Parrinder & Parrinder 1945). In central Siberia 85% of young fledged from 32 nests, with 5% of eggs infertile and 10% predated (Rogacheva 1992). In Japan overall breeding success was 67.3% for nests before 1 June and 60% for nests after that date (Fujimaki *et al.* 1994). In Kenya, it was 58% (Dittami & Gwinner 1985). A study in Arusha NP, Tanzania, found success rates varied from 36% at 1,700m to 80% at 2,800m. The number of fledged young varied from 1.9±0.2 per pair to 2.5±0.1 per pair, much lower than in European Stonechat. Conversely, European Stonechat adults suffer much higher mortality than African Stonechats from eastern Africa, at 59% (Frankevoort & Hubatsch 1966, Flinks & Pfeifer 1984) compared to 24–35% in Arusha NP, Tanzania (Scheuerlein 2000). The mean number of young raised per pair in the Netherlands was 8.1 (range 6.2–10.2) per year over a five-year period and 5.7 (4.2–8.6) in Germany over an 11-year period (Glutz & Bauer 1988). Also in Germany birds which raised only one brood fledged on average 3.42 young, those with two broods 6.82 and those with three broods 9.65. In the UK averages in excess of 7–8 young fledged per pair per breeding season occur regularly, although a study in Ayrshire revealed that one-year-old birds breeding for the first time reared an average of 5.3 young throughout the breeding season but older pairs achieved 9.6 (Phillips 1968). There is, however, one exceptional example of a one-year-old female in southern England raising seven young from her first brood (Davis 1972).

A study in Rheinland-Pfalz, Germany, reported that of 109 nests found during the building stage 78% subsequently failed; of 39 found during the laying stage 51.3% failed; of 217 found during incubation 46.4% failed; and of 515 nests with young 17.7% failed (Schneider in Glutz & Bauer 1988). In the period 1972–1996 complete nest failure rates in UK significantly decline during the incubation stage but show a non-significant increase for the nestling stage. Why there is an increase in nestling stage failure is not readily apparent (H. Crick pers. comm. 2000).

Behaviour after leaving the nest Both adults feed the young after they leave the nest, dividing responsibilities for the scattered young between them. Very rarely the male will take full responsibility for feeding the young before they leave the nest, but usually this happens after 4–5 days when they can fly reasonably competently, leading them to another part of the territory. As soon as the male takes sole charge of the young, and if time allows, the female starts building another nest. She always builds a new nest for each breeding attempt whether the previous one was successful or not. The male will keep the young in loose contact, gradually feeding them less and less whilst leading them around the territory. At dusk he guides them to roost in suitable cover, which is often their former hiding place when they first fledged. Males are vulnerable to losing their mate to a stronger male during this period, as they are unable to guard them constantly, but the success rate of interloping males is generally low (H. Flinks *in litt.* 2001).

Whilst still looking after its own well-grown juvenile young, a male will on occasions 'adopt' other juveniles and tolerate their presence in the company of his own young. By a process of colour ringing it was found in Aberdeenshire, Scotland, that a male was chaperoning three of his own young together with two individuals from other unrelated broods, showing no aggression towards the unrelated birds. This was in mid-July, towards the end of the breeding season (Thorpe 1999). In Germany Schneider found from mid-June that unpaired males cease singing and 'adopt' independent juveniles from neighbouring territories. They remain with the juveniles constantly, acting almost as a surrogate parent. H. Flinks (*in litt.* 2001), based on experience elsewhere in Germany, considers such adoptive behaviour to be possible owing to delayed moult in early hatched individuals into first-adult plumage. He observed a colour-ringed juvenile female 80 days old and still in juvenile plumage establish herself in a family group of five fledglings which were being guarded by both parents, which showed no aggression towards her. Flinks judges that the benefit to juveniles of associating in these groups was an increased chance of survival against predators owing to elevated adult alertness against predators. If an early start to moult into first-adult plumage was normal, it would not be possible for individuals to take advantage of such opportunities.

In another 5–10 days the male drives the young away or just ignores them. In the latter case the young will remain on the territory until the next brood hatches and are then driven off by the male or leave of their own volition (Freitag 1943). Agatho mentions that young can be fed by the parents until they are 30–32 days old, and some can remain in the territory for up to four days longer, but all are gone before the next brood hatches. The young may disperse only as far as just beyond the boundary of their natal territory or move further afield. Greig-Smith (1979) found they moved 500–1,000m in the first 90 days. Independent juveniles form groups which roam around, sometimes briefly in association with apparently unmated adult Common Stonechats or even Whinchats. In Cumbria in northern England, flocks of juveniles at the end of the breeding season (late July to late September) always consisted *only* of moulting juveniles without any adult bird present (J. Callion pers. comm. 2001).

The final brood raised often but not invariably remains with the parents in the territory. The young of the single-brooded African Stonechat can remain with their parents for some time. In Kenya in a study of *S. t. axillaris*, which breeds in April and May, the young remained with the parents for 3–4 months up to September. By October most young had apparently dispersed well away from the study area (Dittami & Gwinner 1985).

Brood parasitism and nest predation Nests can be parasitised by cuckoos. In the former Soviet Union (West and East Siberia, the Far East and middle Asia) Siberian Stonechat *S. m. maura* has been found to be parasitised by Common Cuckoo *Cuculus canorus* (Malchevskiy 1987). In 1978 and 1980 in the Ternopol region in western Ukraine, two out of seven European Stonechat *S. r. rubicola* nests were found to have been parasitised. One on 24 May 1978 contained a three-day-old Cuckoo with four eggs strewn outside the nest. When the Cuckoo was six days old it was noted that the female European Stonechat left the nest after brooding the baby Cuckoo at 06:02hrs and commenced brooding the Cuckoo at night at 21:36hrs. During the intervening 15 hours 24 minutes she fed it 82 times and brooded it 27 times, these two activities comprising a total of 7 hours 38 minutes. The male visited the vicinity of the nest six times but never fed or brooded the Cuckoo, which died two days later. A second nest found on 16 June 1980 contained three almost fully feathered European Stonechat nestlings and an unhatched Common Cuckoo egg (Talposh 1996). In India *S. m. indica* is said often to be parasitised by Common Cuckoo and *S. m. maura* is also regularly parasitised by this species in Kashmir (Bates & Lowther 1952). However, in western Europe such parasitism is rare, with for example only two records from the UK and six records from a total of 553 nests in 10 years in the Netherlands (Agatho 1960-1961). In Germany between 1976 and 2001 from a total of 600 nests none were parasitised by Common Cuckoo even though this species was present in the area under study (H. Flinks *in litt.* 2001). In Japan *S. m. stejnegeri* is parasitised infrequently by both Common Cuckoo and Horsfield's Hawk-cuckoo *Cuculus fugax* (Lack 1963). On Hokkaido nine nests were found parasitised by Common Cuckoo between 1990 and 1994 (Kinoshita & Kato 1995). In southern Africa there are at least two records of the African Stonechat being parasitised by Red-chested Cuckoo *Cuculus solitarius* (Rowan 1983).

There is a remarkable record of a female Common Cuckoo on Hokkaido repeatedly diving into the nest of a Siberian Stonechat, killing all six two-day-old nestlings in the nest and destroying or removing the one remaining egg. It made no attempt to lay its own egg in the nest after this act, and had not previously laid an egg in the nest and made no attempt on previously visiting the nest to kill the young. The female Siberian Stonechat was actually standing on and pecking the Common Cuckoo whilst it killed the nestlings (Kinoshita & Kato 1995).

BTO Nest Record Cards reveal a variety of predators in the UK such as Red Fox *Vulpes vulpes*, Stoat *Mustela erminea*, Weasel *Mustela nivalis*, Brown Rat *Rattus norvegicus*, Adder *Vipera berus*, Grass Snake *Natrix*

natrix, Magpie *Pica pica* and Carrion Crow *Corvus corone*. Even domestic dogs and cats have been recorded destroying nests. In Central Siberia nests were predated by both dogs and stoats (Rogacheva 1992). Hedgehogs *Erinaceus europaeus* and snails have also caused nests to fail (Glutz & Bauer 1988). In the case of snails they apparently cause eggs and newly hatched young to stick together from the slime they exude, and also cause the death of newly hatched young by gnawing the nestlings' naked skin. There is a record of young being found dead from staphylococcal infection (P. Geroudet in Glutz & Bauer 1988). In Jersey the three main predators were Magpie, which accounted for 10.1% of all young hatched, various rodents (3.7%), and cats (3.0%). Sadly even human interference has been recorded, e.g. a BTO card for a nest in Hampshire, southern England, in 1989 reports "5 young taken for avicultural purposes".

The time taken to replace a predated nest can be very short. The female of a pair observed in southern England which lost their nest on 17 June had selected another site, built the nest and laid the first egg by 21 June (EU pers. obs.). In Arusha NP, Tanzania, females commenced a replacement clutch within 10 days of failure (Scheuerlein 2000).

In Arusha NP Fiscal Shrike *Lanius collaris humeralis* and Tropical Boubou Shrike *Laniarius aethiopicus* pose a high risk to fledged African Stonechat *S. t. axillaris*. The risk is especially high to newly fledged young, which are either incapable of flight or only possess rudimentary flying skills and consequently make easy prey. The prospects of successfully fledging juveniles in a Fiscal Shrike territory are low, with up to 70% of nests and broods being lost. The mortality rate increases as the season progresses, so that the chances of fledging a successful second brood are even lower (Scheuerlein 2000). However, Red-backed Shrikes *Lanius collurio* apparently had no effect on a population of European Stonechats in Schleswig-Holstein (Pfeifer 2000).

HABITAT

In the western Palearctic the European Stonechat inhabits temperate, steppe and Mediterranean zones. In mainland Europe it breeds from sea level up to 500–600m. Small numbers breed in the mountains of central and eastern Europe up to 700–800 m, and exceptionally up to 1,850m in the Italian Alps (Hagemeijer & Blair 1997). In Greece it has been found up to 1,600–1,800m (Handrinos & Akriotis 1997).

A variety of habitat has been recorded in mainland Europe and North Africa: in Belgium on the edges of railways and canals as well as industrial sites (Lippens & Wille 1972); in Luxembourg along sunny road embankments, wasteland, the environs of rubbish tips, slagheaps, sewage works and transitional areas from wetland to more elevated, drier sites (Melchior *et al.* 1987); in the Netherlands on farmland, heathland, peat moors, well-vegetated banks and coastal sand-dunes; in Germany on dry, sunny, stony hillsides, bushy slopes, sandy clearings in forests, heaths, wasteland and to a lesser extent moist moorland and in osier stands (Niethammer 1937); in Switzerland and Italy on sunny, eroded terrain with low vegetation such as in traditional vineyards and screes at the base of mountains usually below 600m; on the Iberian Peninsula in open garigue or maquis; on Majorca in thin scrub vegetation, the *Salicornia/Inula* scrub of marshes and throughout the lowland garigue and on mountain slopes up to 400m (Parrack 1973); on Corsica in low or recently burned maquis, vineyards, meadows, wetland fringes and cultivated fields up to 1,600m with occasionally isolated pairs up to 1,700–1,800m (Thibault & Bonaccorsi 1999); in Greece in a variety of open habitats, especially low sparse maquis, farmland with hedges or scattered low bushes and the edges of wetlands up to 1,800m (Handrinos & Akriotis 1997); in Morocco on the northern fringes of the Sahara in the larger river valleys as well as open desert with bushes; in Algeria in palmeries, gardens, scrub and oases in the desert; in Tunisia in thorny hedgerows, areas of cactus and cultivated fields.

In the UK it is found from sea level to generally below 300m. Analysis of 1,147 BTO Nest Record Cards from 1977 to 1996 showed 69% nesting below 122m; 23.7% between 122 and 305m and 7.3% above 305m. Of the total of 98 nests above 305m, 21.4% were above 400m. The highest recorded nest in this sample was at 460m/1,505ft from Llangollen, Wales (E. Urquhart unpublished). However, birds were seen breeding at 590m in Cumbria in 1996 (J. Callion pers. comm. 2001). This constitutes the highest recorded breeding in the UK.

In the UK European Stonechats show a preference for two main habitats: open, rough, coastal areas and inland heath, neither of which need to be damp or have standing water. Both will usually contain small shrubs such as gorse, as well as heather, bracken, bramble, open grass or any combination of these. Analysis of 1,399 BTO Nest Record Cards 1977–1996 revealed 61.9% frequenting these two habitats (E. Urquhart unpublished). A study of habitat in Cornwall, south-west England, in 1993 revealed a close association with gorse. Of 303 pairs located, 160 (52.8%) were in gorse. If all gorse and associated habitats were taken together, i.e. bramble, heather, blackthorn, bracken and privet, a total of 222 nests (76%) had some form of association with gorse (Lord 1994). The optimum height of scrub for siting the nest in this study was 80–130cm; tmereafter preference declined and was virtually non-existent at 220cm. A typical territory in the UK will consist of areas of scattered gorse bushes, some low and others of medium height.

There will possibly be bushes of other species of similar height to the gorse and some that are higher and are used as lookout posts. The undergrowth will frequently consist of bracken and/or heather, interspersed with open grassy areas. Areas with extensive, dense and overgrown gorse are avoided, as are areas where other plants such as heather and bramble predominate but are dense and overgrown.

Afforestatation of large areas of the UK has provided an albeit temporary habitat in which to live and breed. Lack (1933) demonstrated that European Stonechat numbers increased as the trees grew, reaching their maximum breeding density when the trees in plantations were four and five years old; after this they declined. The first ten years of this early successional stage can in effect provide suitable breeding and wintering habitat. In southern Scotland there is evidence that this habitat held a greater population than the traditional coastal sites in the same area (Phillips 1968). It was also found that the density of European Stonechats in forest plantations with heather undergrowth was considerably greater (8.9 pairs per km^2) than ones with grass (3.7 per km^2). The most suitable habitat of this kind is when the heather or bracken associated with the trees is fairly luxuriant and the trees are 4–5 years old. Trees around ten years old start to develop a canopy and the habitat becomes progressively unsuitable. At this stage some birds may continue to struggle on by inhabiting the edges of the plantation or in rides of half-grown plantations where the trees are 3–6m (Moore 1962).

Certain artificial habitats are also attractive such as railway embankments, golf courses, derelict industrial areas and waste ground. Winter habitat of resident birds in the UK is very similar to breeding habitat, and many birds will occupy habitat in winter that is also used, though not necessarily by the same individuals, in the breeding season. Other individuals will occupy areas that are not used for breeding such as gravel pits, wasteland, seashore and marshland.

Siberian Stonechats favour different habitats to the European Stonechat. They frequent a wider altitudinal range, with their breeding habitats ranging from broad valley bottoms with low scattered bushes to relatively open hill slopes. In western Siberia wooded steppe with luxuriant meadows and much fallow land is optimal habitat. Dement'ev & Gladkov (1968) state that in Russia the subspecies *maura* does not, as suggested by Stegmann, prefer dry meadows in all parts of its range and both it and *stejnegeri* often prefer damp meadows with moist soil and good herbaceous cover. In central Siberia it inhabits mainly dry tall grass meadows with scattered shrubs and is abundant in the forests and forest steppes on the borders of the Minusinsk depression (Rogacheva 1992). In the steppes it is rare around areas fringing water basins (Bezborodov 1979 in Rogacheva 1992). Apart from the meadows on the Yenisey River terraces, it is a rare breeding species on alpine tundra but common on subalpine meadows in the West Sayan Mountains along the Yenisey (Sokolov *et al.* 1983, Petrov & Rudkovsky 1985).

It has been found to be abundant in the montane steppe belt within depressions harbouring patches of dry meadows and meadow-steppe habitat. It is similarly abundant in the alpine tundra belt in dwarf arctic birch tundra as well as in grassy areas in valley forests. In the Us depression it is common on meadow-steppe slopes and floodplain meadows. It is abundant in marshes and depressions of the upper floodplain in the Poyma River basin bordering the Kansk forest steppe. In the forest steppe it is found on the edges of fields with small birch groves. In the taiga zone of central Siberia it is typically found in dry and floodplain hayfields and pastures along the Yenisey in the southern taiga subzone between 59° and 60°N. In the Angara area it is abundant in hayfields, pastures and transitional bogs on the terraces of the Chuna River valley. Forest areas devastated by *Dendrolimus sibiricus* which are being revegetated are also favoured. It also occurs on the stony sloping banks of the Yenisey that are colonised by forbs after the spring floods, as well as in burnt forest areas that are regenerating into meadows. Roadside and cattle tracks with tall weedy and interdigitating low grasses are less favoured than typical habitat of dry hay fields. Unmown meadows of tall grass do not appear attractive possibly because they do not have the complex variety of vegetation that includes open areas on which to forage, perches for observation and feeding or high densities of insect-attracting plants.

In the Karkaralinsk pinewoods it is found in glades, on the fringes of forests and dry pines growing on the stony slopes of mountains. In Semireche, as well as meadows, it may breed in thickets of chee grass mixed with such plants as liquorice, burnet and spurge, with nests sometimes in thickets of acacia shrubs, sea buckthorn and feathergrass steppe as well as completely dry and highly marshy areas. It also occurs in peatfields and vegetable gardens around villages (Dement'ev & Gladkov 1968).

As with the European Stonechat it is found at sea level but unlike that species it also occurs up to considerable elevations, for example in the Altai at 2,700m and Semireche at 3,100–3,200m. In Tadzhikistan it does not occur below 1,600–1,800m, remaining exclusively mountainous and possibly ranging as high as 3,000m or even 4,000m in the Pamirs (Dement'ev & Gladkov 1968). In Pakistan it ranges up to 3,880m, never breeding below 2,100m in Baluchistan but breeding down to 1,500m in the Murree Hills. It frequents a wide altitudinal range provided its habitat is a relatively open hill slope or a broad valley bottom with low scattered bushes. In winter it descends to irrigated cultivated land, stony scrub, uncultivated patches alongside riverine areas and the margins of lakes (Roberts 1992). In Kashmir it is a common species at lower and medium levels on rather bare stony hillsides with scattered stones, weeds and bushes for perches, and in dry cultivation with rank grass between the fields for nest sites. It ranges commonly up to 2,600m but is scarce at higher altitudes; it is occasionally found at elevations up to 3,050m at Baltal (Bates & Lowther 1952). In Afghanistan it has been found breeding at 1,700m (Paludan 1959). In addition to the habitat occupied by *maura* in Russia, *stejnegeri* is also stated to inhabit extensive moss bogs containing wild rosemary and small bushes of birch in the northern Maritime Territory. It is found on Sakhalin Island in the shrub-meadow complex formed on the floodplains of rivers and streams, in forest glades, on mountain slopes up to 1,500m and by the shores of lakes and sea coves. On Kunashir Island it is common amongst marshes with shrubbery, birches and willows in river valleys, fens with shrub birch stands and debris-strewn fellings (Dement'ev & Gladkov 1968). On Hokkaido, Japan *stejnegeri* is found from sea level to 1,400m in pastures, alpine meadows, cultivated fields, native grasslands, young plantations and vacant wasteland in urban areas (Fujimaki *et al.* 1994).

There is little information on the two Caucasian subspecies *variegata* and *armenica*. Dement'ev & Gladkov (1968) state that *variegata* breeds in chiefly dry, woodless mountain and steppe meadows but also occurs in reed thickets at the mouth of the Ural River and marshy lowland with bulrushes. Migrant *variegata* are quite common in wetland reedbeds in Armenia (V. Ananina per M. Wilson *in litt.* 2002). In Israel on migration, both the above subspecies prefer wetter habitats than European Stonechat, being found in reeds surrounding fishponds, along channels and around sewage pools (J. Smith *in litt.* 2001). In Armenia *armenica* is noted as breeding in the semi-arid areas and the zone of phryganoid vegetation from 825–1,400m and frequenting mountain steppe from the subalpine to alpine zones at elevations of 1,200–1,900m. In east and south-east Turkey it has been found on slopes with low *Quercus* scrub at Van Golu [Lake Van], fairly barren slopes near Ozalp, Hakkari, and also on the 'wastelands' of the Yuksekova Plain with its dense stands of blooming fennel and poppies (Kumerloeve 1969).

The subspecies *przewalskii* breeds in grasslands, meadows, upland pastures and hillsides. In Nepal it breeds on the Tibetan plateau above 2,745m and in Thailand above 1,600m in the far north-west, occupying cultivated areas and open grassland up to 2,000m in winter. In Laos resident birds on the Bolaven Plateau are usually found above 100m. Passage migrants can occasionally appear along logging roads and by grassy pools in the midst of dense forest (Duckworth *et al.* 1999). In Vietnam it is common up to 3,500m. On the Thainguyen Plateau in southern Vietnam wintering birds inhabit open grassland with individual trees, bushes and bamboo, remaining even during the dry season from November/December–May, and in Dong Nai province it is found in grassland near forest (M. Kalyakin *in litt.* 2001). In Malaysia and Borneo it occurs in buffalo pasture, paddyfields and marshes in the lowlands throughout the winter, and in Myanmar [Burma] it frequents open country on the plains. It has been found breeding up to 2,140m near the Panwa Pass on the Yunnan frontier in north-east Myanmar (Smythies 1986). In Japan it inhabits grassy highland plateaux and meadows at 700–1,800m as well as lower coastal plains, young plantations, cultivated land, neglected fields, open pasture and wasteground in urban areas; on migration it frequents woodland edges, riverbanks and reedbeds (Brazil 1991).

In Tibet *indica* is found between 365 and 2,900m in open country with scattered bushes. In India it breeds mostly between 1,500 and 2,500m, occasionally up to 3,000 m, in open country, terraced cultivation, pastures and scrubby, grassy hillsides. In winter it ranges from 2,200m down to the foothills of the Himalayas and further south moves to reedbeds, tamarisk jungle, scrub on stony wastelands and dry mudflats along tidal creeks and coastal sand-dunes (Ali & Ripley 1968–1998). In Pakistan it has also occasionally been found in sandhills on the southern edge of the Thar Desert (Ticehurst 1922–1924).

The majority of the African Stonechat subspecies inhabit highland montane areas (up to 3,200m), occupying similar habitats to those of the Siberian Stonechat, namely open country with scattered scrub, small bushes, alpine moorlands, coarse vegetation, cold, wet and windy mountain slopes, grassy hillsides, edges of montane forests, cultivated areas, marshy areas and the peripheries of swamps, but certain races also occur in lowlands: *S. t. moptana* inhabits the lowland floodplains of Niger, Mali and Senegal, *salax* is also found at low altitudes in Gabon and the lower Congo valley, and *clanceyi* is resident in the coastal sand-dunes of the western Cape (Clancey 1966).

S. t. salax reappears at high altitudes such as 1,500–3,000m in southern Sudan, Ethiopia, Cameroon and Uganda, although in the latter it also frequents flat marshy areas and swamp edges down to 1,100m. In Kenya and Tanzania it is found usually above 1,300m in rank herbage, cultivated areas and tea planta-tions, grassy hillsides and moorland, but it can also range as low as 800m in the Rukwa Valley, 550m at Mikumi NP and 500m along the Ngerengere River in Tanzania (Britton 1980, Zimmerman *et al.* 1996). It is mainly associated with high-altitude grasslands in southern Africa but can occur down to sea level in South Africa and Mozambique, in the latter in winter only. It is usually associated with comparatively moist, open areas with coarse grass and herbs and scattered bushes. In the Okavango, Botswana it is

151

restricted to the permanent wet swamp and floodplain. In eastern Zimbabwe it frequents montane grassland and is present generally above 900m and has been recorded up to at least 1,880m in the Chimanimani Mountains on the central plateau, in tall grass, reeds bordering streams, *Protea* and bracken scrub, small swamps and the centre of moist vleis (Beasley 1995). It is found at 650m in the Honde Valley and can ascend as high as 2,200m in the Inyanga Highlands. It has become common in developed areas in the south-east lowveld especially around sugarcane plantations. In north-western Matabeleland it is confined to the more permanent river valleys. It is also found along the Zambezi River west of Victoria Falls (Irwin 1987). Subspecies of African Stonechat in South Africa are mainly found between 1,000 and 2,000m although at the Cape they occur down to sea level (*S. t. clanceyi*). In KwaZulu-Natal *torquata* is common and widespread from sea level to high altitudes in the interior and was considered to be one of the few species to have adapted to the vast sugar belt (Clancey 1964).

FOOD

The food of European Stonechats comprises mainly insects, spiders and other small invertebrates. Items taken include woodlice (Isopoda), centipedes (Chilopoda), beetles (Coleoptera), earwigs (Dermaptera), lacewings (Neuroptera), damselflies (Odonata), grasshoppers (Saltatoria), sandhoppers (Amphipoda), small snails (Gastropoda), worms (Polychaeta and Oligochaeta), and their eggs. Apart from beetles the most predominant insect taxa includes Rhynchota, especially Heteroptera, Hymenoptera, Diptera (mainly Brachycera and the larger Nematocera) as well as adult and larval Lepidoptera (Glutz & Bauer 1988, Cramp 1988).

Nestlings tend to be fed softer prey such as spiders and caterpillars, whereas adults tended more towards hard, heavily chitinised beetles. Diet composition changes significantly as a function of nestling age.

From a total of 1,758 faecal samples taken from both adults and nestlings in Germany over the period March–October it was found that beetles were the commonest prey item, with 42.8% in adult faeces and 34.6% in nestling faeces; the respective proportions of Diptera was 21.1% and 12.7%, and those of the larvae of Lepidoptera, Tipulidae and sawflies (Tenthredinidae) were 8.1% and 19.1%. Other frequently taken forms were Hymenoptera, two-thirds of which comprised ants (Formicidae), Lepidoptera (adults) and spiders. Spiders, Scarabaeidae, Carabaeidae, Staphylinidae, caterpillars, Diptera, ants, Hymenoptera and Rhynchota were taken throughout the study period. There were some seasonal differences, with spiders being taken mainly in March and April. Scarabaeidae were most frequently taken in March/April and September/October, whilst ants, although taken throughout the year, were most commonly taken in August. Other groups were taken in shorter periods during the year such as Curculionidae in May/June; Elateridae in June/July; Cantharidae June–August; Lepidoptera July–October; and Saltatoria and Tipulidae August–early October. Mites (Acarina) were commonly found in both adult and nestling faeces, and had probably been taken mainly as parasites of dung beetles. Green plant matter was also found in faeces but was considered to have been involuntarily torn off when snatching prey from vegetation. Sand and grit particles up to 2mm in size were discovered in 10% of adult and 30% of nestling faeces (Flinks & Pfiefer 1987a).

Greig-Smith & Quicke (1983) analysed 121 nestling faeces collected between 11 May and 8 August in southern England which resulted in the following percentages of invertebrates being identified in the faeces.

Order	
Oligochaeta (earthworms)	15%
Araneae (spiders)	6%
Coleoptera (beetles) of the family Curculionidae – weevils	49%
Coleoptera other families	68%
Hemiptera (true bugs of the family Pentatomidae – shieldbugs)	40%
Hemiptera (other families)	11%
Diptera (true flies of the family Syrphidae – hoverflies)	15%
Diptera (other families)	46%
Hymenoptera (of the family Aculeata – bees and wasps)	18%
Hymenoptera (of the family Formicidae – ants)	8%
Lepidoptera (adult butterflies and moths)	39%
Lepidopteran and symphytan (sawfly) larvae	42%

Prey brought to the young varied from cryptic, relatively immobile invertebrates such as caterpillars found on the ground or vegetation to large fast-flying species of moth, butterfly and flies captured in flight.

A captive pair fed their young on two species of blowfly (Calliphoridae) – greenbottle and bluebottle – that were made available to them. They were selective in mainly feeding the young the softer, smaller, newly emerged greenbottles, rejecting the larger, fully developed flies of both species. By the time the young were eight days old the parents were willing to feed them fully developed bluebottles but still refused to take fully grown greenbottles. They also fed the young pieces of grit and cuttlefish bone (Doughty 1970). In a German study, prey size fed to nestlings varied from less than 2mm to 35 mm, with the majority being 7.5–10mm. A 5cm lizard was also fed to the young on one occasion (Flinks & Pfeifer 1987). There is some evidence that parents avoid certain insects such as ladybirds. A feeding adult in England in May 1976 only once chased a ladybird despite very many of these insects flying around, and a three-hour observation of a brood of nestlings revealed that no ladybirds were brought to the young during the period (Bibby 1978).

European Stonechats are opportunistic feeders and will exploit a wide range of invertebrate species according to the time of year, the habitat and the abundance of suitable food sources at certain times of the year. Two male European Stonechats on 29 December 1993 in the Negev Desert in Israel were observed each to prey on and eat a single scorpion *Scorpio maurus* (c.16–17mm not including the tail). The average size prey for European Stonechats in the desert was 5mm. Although usually nocturnal these scorpions are briefly diurnal after rains. The scorpion was seized in one case just anterior to the tail and thrown against a stone, retrieved and the process repeated. It was then struck with the bill and finally eaten except for the claw (Rodl 1994).

In spring and summer European Stonechats have a continuing, varying and abundant supply of invertebrate prey, but in winter the choice is restricted to a few invertebrate families supplemented by seeds. They have been found to take the seeds of Cruciferae, Brassicae and *Atriplex* (Leburier & Rapine 1936) and a variety of different berries such as blackberries and small fruits. A French study between 1981 and 1985 found ten stomachs contained both the fruit and seeds of Cotoneaster, Pyracantha, *Rhus coriaria* and *Vitus vinifera* (Debussche & Isenmann 1986). Small snails are also said to supplement the diet in autumn and winter (Dement'ev & Gladkov 1968). A female was observed hammering a snail on a wall in England in winter (Fisher 1979). A pair observed in December 2000 in Oxfordshire, England, survived a five-day freezing and snow-covered spell by feeding virtually exclusively on hibernating caterpillars which they found at the base of grass clumps (EU pers. obs.).

In southern Spain during autumn and winter 14 gizzards were examined and ants formed 54.3% of the total invertebrate species present whilst 92.8% contained ants. In spring a sample of three gizzards revealed only three ants (8.6%) in a total of 35 prey items. This would suggest that while ants form an important part of the diet in winter in southern Spain they are only eaten when alternative invertebrate food is scarce, and are quickly replaced by more nutritious prey in spring (Herrera 1984).

Similar findings were made in the Channel Islands where it was considered that ants formed the majority of prey outside the breeding season; in winter birds also fed regularly on the seeds of *Euonymous* and took sandhoppers on beaches (Johnson 1971b). Wintering birds (no differences between the sexes) in the Negev Desert, Israel, also preyed on a high proportion of hymenoptera between November and January (40% of food items), the dominant group being ants *Messor semirufus* and *Cataglyphis*. Beetles (mainly Scarabaeidae and Curculionidae) increased from 20 to 40% between October and February (Rodl & Flinks 1996).

In the UK wintering birds have been recorded hovering over water, picking unidentified prey items from the surface and, on occasions, actually dropping briefly into the water (Hodgson 1978). Individuals have also been seen to attempt to catch fish fry and shrimps. An African Stonechat in Zimbabwe in autumn was seen to dive into the water and secure a 3cm Green-headed Bream *Oreochromis macrochir* which it took back to its perch and swallowed whole (Hezekia 1987). Leburier & Rapine (1936) observed that birds in winter will carry on foraging well into dusk. Other birds have adopted tactics recalling European Robin *Erithacus rubecula*, and in the UK they have perched close to humans digging trenches or turning over soil, often using tools as perches on which to drop on newly exposed prey (Campbell 1980, Terry 1980).

Captive birds of both the European and African species have been fed on commercial insect food, hard-boiled egg, maggots and pupae, breadcrumbs, curds, beefheart, ground eggshells and mealworms.

The main method of feeding is to locate prey from an elevated perch which serves as an initial vantage point. Depending on both time of year and circumstances one of three main feeding strategies is usually adopted. In the first ('drop attack') the bird descends by flying, gliding or hopping to the ground, then picking off the prey or pursuing it briefly on the ground. In the second ('aerial sally') it sallies forth at an angled ascent up to 30m or makes a short fluttering pursuit-flight to seize the prey in flycatcher fashion. In the third ('aerial glean') it picks off the prey from surrounding vegetation, again whilst in flight (Moreno 1984).

In a comparison between two co-existing insectivorous passerines (Northern Wheatear and European Stonechat) found that during July–August in open, heavily grazed garrigue in northern Spain the commonest technique for European Stonechat (80% of 368 capture attempts) was 'perch to ground sallying', in which terrestrial prey is located on the ground during a stationary search period from an elevated perch. When prey is located the bird either flies or glides down to seize the prey. Other less favoured techniques were 'aerial sallying', which constituted 9%, and 'aerial gleaning', 6%. Moreno also described what he called 'flutter pursuit' in which a bird flies rapidly to the prey and then flutters after it along the ground or in the air, this constituting the remaining 5% of capture attempts. After one of these actions the bird either returns to its original perch or one some way distant.

Perches are often abandoned for another before a successful capture attempt. A study of foraging behaviour on an inland site in southern England (Greig-Smith 1983) found that rates of prey capture were very variable, ranging from 0–29 attempts in five minutes and showed no obvious seasonal trends or differences between the sexes. Birds will use any suitable perch strong enough to bear their weight, but the mean heights of perches in spring were 1m rising to 1.6m in summer, and males tended to perch slightly higher and closer to the top of vegetation in spring than did females. Both sexes were found to select perches higher than the mean available. In spring the birds' preference for perches was directly correlated to those giving the best chance of successful capture per visit, but in summer no preference was shown. Visits to perches lasted 18.9–27.2 seconds for successful prey capture attempts, and 21.5–26.6 seconds for unsuccessful attempts, and also showed a tendency to be longer the higher the perch was, up to a maximum of 2m, declining slightly above this height.

It was found that the time spent searching from each perch and the distance moved between perches was correlated with the height of the perch: the higher the perch the longer the time spent on it, as the bird had a greater area to search, but once that area was searched it had to move a greater distance to cover a fresh area. Individuals appeared to search an area systematically from a perch, covering the nearest areas first and then gradually covering areas further away, and distant prey were more easily detected from higher perches. This study suggested that birds were able to judge each perch independently according to its size, position and the area that could be covered and prey detected from it.

The Greig-Smith study also showed that in spring 'perch to ground sallying' was virtually exclusively used as a hunting technique and was also used when feeding in rainy weather. In summer, aerial sallies and gleaning were also employed as methods of feeding. The proportion of perch to ground attacks decreased from 100% in early March to around 30% in mid-June, then rose again to 40% by August. Sallying and gleaning commenced around mid-March and reached 30–40% of feeding techniques by mid-June. After this sallies fell to less than 20% by mid-August whilst gleaning attempts continued to increase slightly. The change to incorporate the other two techniques was noted to occur in conjunction with the emergence of new prey types and their consequent availability on the foliage within the territories and also with the increased number of flying insects available as the months became warmer. It was also noted that for feeding by perch to ground technique the lowest perches provided the greatest capture rates but for aerial sallies and aerial gleaning the highest perches were more successful.

Johnson (1971a) commented that birds will often hover several metres above the ground if there is no convenient perch, seeking potential prey. He stated that in winter this behaviour often replaced feeding from perches on Jersey, when birds were likely to stray from their normal habitat onto ground that was level and contained few suitable perches. A male was observed on Menorca to fly down onto sandy ground in dunes and commence turning over the sand in the search of prey (EU pers. obs.). A group of seven birds on the south coast of England were observed feeding in a field of short grass for about an hour, running and hopping on the ground after prey and only resorting to elevated perches when alarmed. This was judged to be a behavioural adaptation to the high winds (Force 6+) prevailing at the time (EU pers. obs.). Individuals have also been seen to find prey by following cattle and horses as they disturb the ground (J. Callion pers. comm. 2000).

VOICE

European Stonechats are mainly vocal during the breeding season, the male singing at the start of the season and to a varying extent throughout the annual breeding cycle. Both male and female utter a range of alarm and contact calls during the breeding season. They are far less vocal at other times of year, and are virtually silent during the winter.

Only the male sings. The song period commences approximately one month before nesting, which is usually around late February although it can be from early to mid-February if winters are mild. In the UK the peak song period is March and April. It then virtually ceases apart from brief peaks just before the start of a new breeding cycle. It generally ceases altogether at the beginning of July, with occasional birds singing as late as mid-October (Cramp 1988). Males sing in good weather throughout the day. A study of territorial males in southern England between March–September found males usually commencing at around 06:00hrs and continuing with approximately equal frequency at any time of the day until around 21:00hrs (Greig-Smith 1982a&b). In central Siberia from early May males were stated to "sing constantly day and night... After June 15 the singing intensity decreases" (Rogacheva 1992).

The song rate of individual birds varies, perhaps owing to individual characteristics of the bird concerned; and no song is heard during rain. However, the quality of habitat in which the territory is located and the relative abundance of food may also influence frequency of song. The amount and intensity of song from an individual will also vary according to the position and behaviour of pairs in adjacent territories. Singing is usually most intense when the male or female from an adjacent territory is close by. Indeed, in seasons when the population is high, singing is more frequent: on Jersey it was found to be virtually non-existent in periods of low population (Johnson 1971a). Song is normally only heard in spring and summer and does not form any part of territory or pair formation in autumn and winter. In a study of wintering European Stonechats in the Negev Desert, Israel, where they do not breed but form wintering pairs, no song or courtship display was noted (Rodl 1994). However, in an area of high breeding density in Spain arrivals of migrants in autumn would on some occasions cause resident males to sing in defence of their mate and territory (Johnson 1961).

At the beginning of the breeding season singing from most bird species is generally associated with attracting a mate and territorial defence. In the case of the European Stonechat many males often do not start singing – if they sing at all – until after they are already paired. Where the population is partially migratory change of pairs and assimilation of the migrant population into the resident one may be facilitated by song, with rival males 'outsinging' one another to decide which occupies a territory. Song may also serve to retain a mate against newly arrived males or even to attract a newly arrived female considered superior to a male's existing mate. There is, however, some evidence that song does have a function in attracting a female as a potential mate. Males that hold territories but fail to attract a mate have been found to indulge in higher levels of song than those who have a mate, for as long as they hold a territory. Unmated males were also found to sing most in the part of their territory that was closest to their paired neighbours. In the southern Netherlands where the population is migratory, Agatho (1960–1961) found that unmated males sing directly to females and do not sing unless in the presence of a female. Males whose partners died after nesting sang loudly and frequently for many days afterwards in an evident but usually unsuccessful attempt to re-mate.

Greig-Smith (1982a,b, 1983) found that males do not sing and feed from the same perches, nor do they usually sing and feed at the same time. Males sang from higher perches, such as the tops of small trees and bushes, than those from which they fed, with a mean of 0.9m for feeding and 1.8m for singing. The fact that the two activities were conducted from such different heights suggests that they were incompatible. It appears that males separate their feeding and singing activities into distinct periods, tactically allocating time to both activities in normal conditions rather than singing only when conditions for feeding are unfavourable. Most song is given from a perch; in a study in southern England over 97% was from an exposed perch at the top of a tree or bush, and indeed the higher the perch the more song phrases were produced per bout of singing from that perch.

Song is also delivered in a special flight which is generally very brief (less than 15 seconds) although occasionally lasting several minutes. The male flies up almost vertically from his perch on the topmost part of a bush and sings at heights of 3–15m often near the centre of his territory (Johnson 1971a). Other birds in southern England have been described as ascending as high as 30m (Hudson 1900) and in Germany up to 10–25m (Glutz & Bauer 1988). The flight itself is slow and erratic with slow wingbeats and brief spells of hovering. Sometimes the male will rise and fall vertically for 1–2m as if on a piece of elastic, keeping his body raised at an angle, the tail lowered and legs hanging down with toes pointed backwards. The white feather areas are displayed to maximum effect and on some occasions individuals have been heard to 'whirr' or 'rattle' their wings. At the end of the flight the bird drops suddenly at an angle almost to the ground, sometimes disappearing briefly behind vegetation only to reappear perched in a prominent

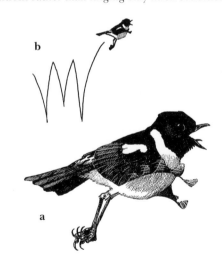

European Stonechat male song display flight (a) Brief flight whilst delivering song. Posture distinctive. Body held at an angle with legs conspicuously trailing, toes pointed backwards, tail fanned and depressed. White patches on neck, rump and wings prominently displayed. (b) Flight slow and erratic with periodic hovering or with bird rising and falling at steep angles as if on elastic, finally dropping in angled trajectory to perch. (After Glutz & Bauer 1988.)

155

position. Johnson considered that in some cases the song flight is an enhanced form of territory demarcation, but Freitag (1943) stated that, as it is different from song given from a perch, it could also have a courtship function. There is an intriguing comment by Walpole-Bond of song being occasionally given from the ground in England, although he did not list any specific instances.

European Stonechat During male's song display flight the female either reacts with indifference or shows interest following his movements intently (a and b). Finally, she may solicit copulation (c). (After Glutz & Bauer 1988.)

In a study by Greig-Smith (1979) on an inland heath in southern England, it was found that song from perches was given in association with two major contexts. The first was when there was no obvious associated activity with the female close by (52.1%) and the other when there was no associated activity with the male on his own (22.1%). It thus appeared that song was not associated with direct territorial disputes or confrontation with males in adjoining territories. Although there were occasional periods of countersinging between birds in neighbouring territories, this only comprised 10% of all song heard. It would appear in this study, from the small amount of evidence available, that singing could contribute towards deterring rival males from encroaching on the singer's territory before any dispute could arise. It was also found that song was most frequent at the start of the breeding cycle, declining gradually until the young hatched, and that song was timed to occur at the start of each new breeding attempt and also to that of neighbouring pairs. The peaks of song occurred when the female laid the first egg of a clutch or when a neighbouring female was at a similar stage. This would suggest that a male also sings to deter neighbouring males from enticing away his mate as well as enhancing his bond with her. It may also be that singing males are attempting to entice and mate with neighbouring females during their fertile period. Agatho (1960–1961) mentions situations where he observed a male whose mate was incubating eggs suddenly fly to the extreme border of his territory and sing vigorously if a neighbouring female was visible. Unmated males also sing as close as possible to a neighbouring pair's territory when the female of that pair is near egg-laying.

The song is a somewhat variable, monotonous, thin, fast warble superficially similar to a Hedge Accentor *Prunella modularis* but described by Walpole-Bond as prettier and more vivacious. It has been described as a rapid repetition of double notes, "the first clear and sharp, the next deeper or somewhat throaty, then the clear again, the sound rising and falling rhythmically" (Hudson 1900); frequency ranges over 3–7kHz. The song consists of discrete phrases, each lasting 1.0–1.5 seconds and separated by gaps of at least 2.0 seconds (Greig-Smith 1982a). The song sometimes lasts just for a few phrases but on other occasions it is longer and the phrases delivered in an unbroken sequence. The male sings an average of 6.3 phrases before changing perch. The phrases consist of approximately eight complex units (sounds) and individual males can have a very large vocabulary of units (up to 100), which subtly differ from neighbouring males. Whistling sounds form a considerable proportion of the song and it is these that produce the melodious content of the song (Schwager & Guttinger 1984). Songs given in flight are considered to be more melodious and varied than those from a perch (Frankevoort & Hubatsch 1966). Although not widespread or frequent, some mimicry has been detected in the song. Species involved include Great Tit *Parus major*, Winter Wren *Troglodytes troglodytes*, Yellowhammer *Emberiza citrinella*, Meadow Pipit *Anthus pratensis* and Eurasian Jay *Garrulus glandarius* (Cramp 1988).

Both male and female employ other vocalisations which serve principally as warning and distraction calls. The warning call is usually described as *whit* and is a high-pitched short modulated call averaging 59 msec and restricted to a narrow range of frequencies (4.5–5.7kHz). The distraction call is a relatively harsh *track*. This call is of similar length to the *whit* call but covers a wider frequency range (1.6–6.8kHz) (Greig-Smith 1980). A study of adult alarm calls in response to a human intruder during the breeding season and when young were in the nest found that the alarm calls comprised a mixture of both *whit* and

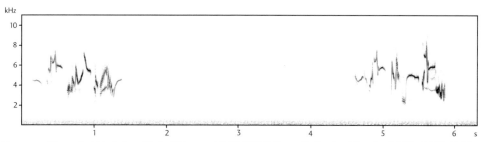

European Stonechat *Saxicola rubicola* (*hibernans*) **NSA 21025. Song. Sutherland Scotland 2 May 1988.** *R. Margoschis.*

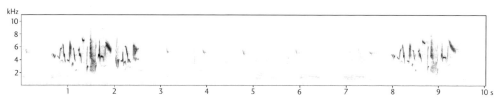

Siberian Stonechat *Saxicola maura maura* **Soviet Bird Songs. Song. Bratsk, Siberia, 5 June 1987.** *K. Mild.*

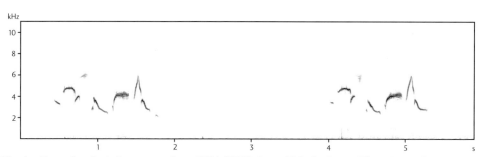

Siberian Stonechat *Saxicola maura stejnegeri* **NSA 61282. Song. Tukada, Japan. Victor Recording Co.**

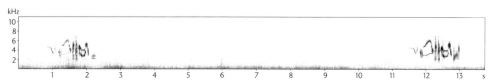

African Stonechat *Saxicola torquata* (*torquata*) **NSA 57617. Song. Cape Province, South Africa, 5 December 1979.** **D. Watts.**

trrack, often combined into a continuous alternating sequence (Greig-Smith 1980). A series of calls of only one type were exceptional. Experiments indicated that the *whit* call serves as a warning whilst the *trrack* call, combined with short flights and wing-flicking, is used to distract the predator away from the nest and towards the calling adult. *Whit* calls warn incubating females, young in the nest and recently fledged young of the presence of an intruder, and result in the young ceasing their begging calls and remaining silent until the danger has receded. Newly fledged young hide in vegetation remaining silent for as long as the calls are given by the adults. These *whit* calls are also uttered at a greater rate the nearer the perceived danger is to the nest or young and decline as danger recedes. Males can commence giving these calls when an intruder is 150–200m from the nest site (Frankevoort & Hubatsch 1966). The *trrack* call remains constant throughout and had no effect on nestlings. At the laying and incubation stages of the breeding cycle virtually no vocalisations are given. Once the eggs hatch both calls are given whenever the adults perceive danger. They increase in intensity as the young grow, reaching a peak of 40–50 calls per minute when the young are almost ready to fledge or are in their first week out of the nest. After this the calls virtually cease as another breeding cycle commences or the season draws to a close.

Alarm calls are not generally given in response to the presence of birds of prey; instead, the birds remain silent. However, they do give alarm calls when corvids are present and any other predator that actively searches at ground level. It was also found that pairs whose nest was predated demonstrated lower alarm call rates before suffering predation than successful pairs. Greig-Smith (1980) suggested that the different acoustic properties of the two calls make the bird calling *whit* more difficult to locate than when it is calling *trrack*. The *whit* call is also used by the male to call the incubating or brooding female from the nest either as routine or when danger threatens, although the female is more reluctant to leave the nest the closer the eggs are to hatching. However, when young are in the nest she leaves immediately on hearing the warning calls. The *whit* call is sometimes employed in courtship when the male is hovering above the female in a high state of sexual excitement. The *trrack* call is likewise used by males in courtship in spring and also when establishing pairs and territories in autumn (Johnson 1971a).

Various other calls have been heard occasionally, mainly in the breeding season. A very long drawn out note described as *wee-wee* was made by a male several times in succession early in the breeding season (March and April) when a rival male was threatening his territory and/or mate (Agatho 1960–1961).

E.M. Nicholson in Witherby *et al.* (1948) refers to a similar call heard in July, when what may be a similar note was uttered three times by a male near to its nest. The call was described as a loud scream lasting approximately 5 seconds and then being followed by two or three quiet *ticks*.

Another call is described by Cramp (1988) as a brief hoarse rattling *krrrr* used in song flights and when males indulge in territorial defence.This may be the same as the whirring and rattling of wings described by other observers. There is also a soliciting call by the female which is a thin quiet sibilant *seeseeseeseeseesee* inviting the male to copulate.

After the first few days of life nestlings beg with an insistent and continous *shree shreee shreee shreee*, which increases in volume as they grow (Greig-Smith 1980). Nestlings if fairly advanced will utter a short, shrill, high-pitched call if handled or disturbed by a predator, causing the rest of the young to abandon the nest and scatter into cover. Fledged and independent young have a contact/alarm call similar to the *trrack* of the adult, although somewhat harsher and slightly more trilled.

The sonograms published in this book for European, Siberian and African Stonechats indicate some difference in song between the species, and there is also an apparent difference in song between at least two subspecies of Siberian Stonechat *S. m. przewalskii* and *S. m. maura*. The songs of the three species when heard do demonstrate some noticeable differences. Research on this subject is currently being undertaken although it is only at a preliminary stage (Urquhart in press).

MOVEMENTS

In the Palearctic the Siberian Stonechat is migratory whereas the European Stonechat is migratory in northern Europe and Scandinavia partially migratory in UK and Ireland and resident in southern Europe and North Africa. Within the UK a majority remain to winter, residing on or near their breeding territory or making longer movements within the UK (Lack 1986). A minority migrate to southern Europe and the coastal countries of northern Africa. In mild winters that part of the population that remains and survives has the advantage over the migratory part of the population of being able to commence breeding earlier and making multiple breeding attempts. Occasionally the temperate maritime environment of the UK will bring prolonged severe spells of winter weather, causing considerable mortality amongst the resident population. The migrant population will then be in the ascendancy as it is they and their offspring that will maintain and increase the population until the sedentary part of the population regains the advantage, usually 3–4 years (Berthold 1993).

Although it can only be speculation, the now generally accepted warming of the climate may allow the sedentary populations to increase to such an extent that in future the European Stonechat may become entirely resident in the UK.

In the rest of northern Europe the species is mainly migratory, but this may also change with global warming. Berthold has predicted that this is what will happen with partially migratory species in northern Europe, such as Common Blackbird *Turdus merula*, Chaffinch *Fringilla coelebs*, Skylark *Alauda arvensis*, Common Bullfinch *Pyrrhula pyrrhula*, Hedge Accentor *Prunella modularis* and European Robin *Erithacus rubecula*, noting that they are virtually exclusively resident in the UK as a result of the favourable winter climate.

Within the UK the predominant movement is either westward or southward, many making for the temperate coastal areas to winter. Whilst many make for the coast, a smaller proportion move south-east and inland to occupy the more southern and central counties of England, turning up in autumn and winter on territories and in areas in which they are often unknown during the breeding season. There is a remarkable record of a female ringed as a nestling on 11 June 1991 in Northern Ireland which was subsequently seen at a sewage works in southern England (Bedfordshire) in January and February 1992, 441km south-east. By 19 April she was back at her birthplace incubating eggs.

The hypothesis that there exists a genetic control of partial migration states that the decision about whether a nestling will be migratory or sedentary is already decided in the egg by the combination of the parents' genes. It asserts that partial migratory behaviour is based on quantitative traits. Because of this, even if both parents are migratory they can produce sedentary young and vice versa, and a single brood can contain both migratory and sedentary nestlings. A brood of nestlings in northern England (Cumbria) demonstrated the phenomenon of different wintering strategies amongst siblings. Two nestlings from this brood ringed on 1 May 1992 were subsequently seen in widely differing parts of the UK. The first was seen at least until 2 February 1993 near to its natal area and was presumably wintering in the area. The other was last seen near its natal area on 23 September and then turned up on the south-east coast of Kent (Sandwich Bay Bird Observatory) 482km south on 5–6 November 1992; quite possibly it was intending to migrate across the English Channel, as it was not seen after 6 November (J. Callion pers. comm. 2001). The European Stonechat is generally considered to be nocturnal and solitary on migration, and a recent study of a wintering migratory population in Israel appears to confirm this (Gwinner *et al.* 1994).

However, aggregations of 12–40 birds can occur at migration staging sites in autumn or on their first arrival in wintering areas before the birds have established territories. There is also some evidence that pairs do occur on migration, with Moreau & Moreau (1953) relating how they observed migrant European Stonechats, often in pairs, moving in small numbers in late October along the north-east coast of Spain; and there is a record of a pair that arrived at the South Bishop Lighthouse in Dyfed, Wales, on 27 February 1976, obviously on migration and remaining for a few days before moving on (McCanch 1985). In the Kharkiv region of north-eastern Ukraine, 1992–1994, 56% of a migratory population of European Stonechats returning to breed were considered paired on their arrival (Banik 2001).

Direct observations of specifically active migration are rare, presumably because they are mainly nocturnal. However, Eagle Clarke (1912), reporting on a month of bird migration study at Eddystone Lighthouse off the south-west coast of England (Devon), recorded this species on the nights of 12–13 and 14–16 October when it was present in numbers and remained around the lighthouse for some time.

BEHAVIOUR

European and Siberian Stonechats in the Palearctic are short-lived and spend a large proportion of their life as one of a pair, although not necessarily with the same mate, and are strongly territorial for most of the year. There is no specific data for life expectancy in the Palearctic but up to 1996, of the 191 ringing reports and recoveries of UK-ringed European Stonechats, 75.9% were recovered before they were 12 months old and 16.6% between 12 and 24 months. In his study of the European Robin, which is broadly similar in lifestyle to the European Stonechat, Lack (1976) showed from an analysis of ringing recoveries that 29% of young were found dead before 1 August of the year in which they were born, while of those that survived to that date, 69% were recovered within the next 12 months. The oldest known European Stonechat in the UK is a nestling ringed on 22 May 1969 retrapped 11km away from its birthplace on 4 May 1974, giving it an age of 4 years, 11 months and 13 days. There are records from France and Germany of birds of 6 and 7 years old respectively.

In a sedentary population of African Stonechat *S. t. axillaris* from Kenya it was found that birds remained paired on their territories all year round. The pairs were stable, with partner changes occurring in only seven of the 34 pairs studied over a period of 18 months. Assuming the changes that did occur represented the death of a partner, individuals were also considered long-lived, as only seven of the 64 birds died over a period of 18 months (Dittami & Gwinner 1985).

In sedentary populations of European Stonechat pair-bonds can be maintained through the winter, and pairs formed in autumn can last through the following breeding season. Even outside the breeding season they form pairs and occupy winter territories which are often not used for breeding. In Belgium 64% of wintering birds were paired (van Hecke 1965) and on a heathland in southern England 62% were paired, with solitary birds usually being males (Greig-Smith 1979).

Winter pairs are often more unstable than those in the breeding season. Even on migration, territories are formed and defended wherever the birds stop to rest. In Spain Johnson (1961) noted that whilst they may not be paired on migration birds rapidly paired and defended territories in areas where they made migratory stopovers, with males chasing females from the resident population and displaying high levels of sexual excitement. A study in the Negev Desert, Israel, also demonstrated that birds formed pairs and established territories in wintering areas where they do not breed, although the pairs did not remain constant through-out the entire winter period, with a territory-holding male having different females as a mate during one winter. This study also demonstrated that the functions of pairing were different to those of the breeding season. The functions in winter appeared to be a reduction of individual defence effort needed to maintain a territory and an enhanced vigilance which would reduce the risk of attack from predators or competitors. These winter pairs did not migrate together when they left on spring migration. In 17 out of 22 pairs the second bird of the pair left 1–11 days after the first (Gwinner *et al.* 1994, Rodl 1994, 1999).

The boundaries of a territory are based on prominent features such as a wall, fence, phone wires or hedge and, provided there is no physical alteration to the existing topography, the territory will continue to be defined by such features even though the individual occupants change. Johnson (1971a) considered that when population density is at a periodic low the territory size is probably defined more by topography than by individual territorial behaviour of the males. Within the territory the most important requirement is a scattering of prominent perches provided by bushes and tall plants of suitable height, usually up to 1.5m. These perches are used to locate and drop on prey and as prominent positions from which the male can sing and guard its territory. They are also important because of the tactical relationship between male and female for most of the year in that they rarely lose visual contact with one another. Perches selected are either bare or with minimal leaf cover. Even among a favoured dense evergreen such as gorse, the bare and more exposed perches are favoured as these afford better visibility. Where walls, fences, posts and large boulders are features in a territory they will be used as perches just as often as natural vegetation, provided they are the requisite height. Small trees are occasionally used and are often a feature of a territory, but generally these serve only to give the male an overview of his territory. Usually he will spend most of his time on lower perches. Another important feature of a territory is that cover of some form – banks, slopes, gullies, undulations, walls or a line of bushes – should be available to allow low-level escape flights from intruders.

Winter territories are established from around mid- to late September in the UK, coinciding with pair formation which commences after the adults have completed their post-breeding moult and after late-bred juveniles have moulted into their first adult plumage. The establishment and occupation of these winter territories is usually completed by late October to early November, and they are then defended vigorously by the occupying pairs. In Jersey during this time of general pair formation the existing pair-bonds between adults that had bred also broke down and changes took place.

Pairs consist of individuals of the same age or of differing ages, with either the male or female being the older partner. Young may also pair with their parents. The greatest disparity in ages was of a first-year male in a polygynous *menage* paired to both a four-year-old female and a first-year female (Johnson 1971a). Initially after establishment or occupation of territories the male will perch conspicuously within and on the borders of the territory and vigorously affirm the territory's boundaries. The female is less conspicuous and perches lower, allowing the male to initiate each move of the pair within the territory. From around December the male becomes far less conspicuous and then in association with the female retains a low profile throughout the winter months, concentrating on obtaining food to survive the harshest months of the winter. In February territorial activity increases once again. In coastal Scotland territorial display was first noted on 10 February with changes in territory taking place up to March. The majority of pairs maintained their winter territory but two pairs comprising young birds that had been resident all winter were ousted, in one case by a newly arrived pair (Phillips 1968).

European Stonechat males of migratory populations returning to their unoccupied breeding areas in Germany are tolerant of other males so long as no females are present. As soon as the females arrive territories are immediately established and defended (Ziegler 1966). Males in Germany at least are thought often to arrive earlier than females but other observations suggest that females arrive at the same time or, at the latest, 1–2 days after the males (Mildenberger 1950).

In Jersey courtship commenced in early March with the male chasing the female around their territory in a high degree of excitement, making loud chacking calls and indulging in aerobatic flights.

Johnson (1971a) described the male's actions as follows:

"The vocalisation, directly and invariably associated with courtship is a loud, irregular, excited series of 'chack-chack-chack, chack-chack...'. This call is uttered suddenly as the male literally launches himself at the perched female. He then proceeds to chase her around the territory, still calling loudly and, even while in flight, displaying the white patches on his neck, rump and wings which appear to 'glow' with increased brilliance. When she comes to rest, he perches or crouches on the ground in front of her with his back to her, bill open, head down and wings slightly drooped and trembling, while she remains unconcerned. After a few seconds the white patches cease to 'glow' and the male relaxes and flies to another part of the territory. This display increases in intensity and frequency throughout early March."

Johnson (1971a) also described a form of low-intensity courtship encountered early in the season when the male, with little or no 'fluorescing' of the white patches, perched in front of the female and slowly raised and lowered his tail whilst simultaneously spreading and closing it fan-wise. When fully raised the tail was vertical at 90° to the male's back. In the same study on Jersey it was found that with the birds in an advanced state of excitement from around the end of March to early April the pair-bond appears suddenly to relax and, for a period varying from a few hours to 3–4 days, the birds in adjacent territories may be seen intermingling freely with little or no territorial behaviour. With this 'window of opportunity' changes in pairs occur and Johnson gave an example of where, from a population of eight pairs, the pair-bond ceased around 30 March and by 3 April two males had mated with new females from outside the study area, another male had mated a second female whilst retaining his existing mate, one female had paired with a new male, two adjacent pairs had exchanged mates, one pair occupied a new territory and only one pair carried on as before. This behaviour would appear to have been synchronised throughout the populations he studied and the pair-bonds are restored with either new or original partners as suddenly as they collapse. Although the above example is a particularly graphic instance of widespread changes of mates in a population, in the majority of populations studied by Johnson it was found that on restoration of the pair-bond most of the pairs remained as they were before the collapse of the pair-bond. Johnson speculated that this breakdown of pair-bonds may also, in areas where it is only a winter visitor, precede northward migration in spring (see Gwinner *et al.* 1994). Where populations are partially migratory such as on Jersey such breakdown may ensure integration into the population of newly arrived migrants with less disruption than if the pair-bonds remained intact and assist the pairing of sexually matched individuals. There was evidence of appreciable differences in the intensity of behaviour amongst individual birds and Johnson speculates that the breakdown of pair-bonds may allow realignment between 'compatible' males and females. However, such breakdowns have not been noticed by other major studies of European Stonechats (Agatho 1960-1961, Greig-Smith 1979) but would certainly merit further research.

As display and territorial activity increase in intensity more complex and varied courtship behaviour becomes evident. The male indulges in hovering flights over the female as part of his display often after having chased the female rapidly and persistently around the territory. Johnson (1971a) describes the courtship behaviour as follows:

> "In courtship display the male will hover 2–4 metres directly above the female, for 10 seconds or so, while she perches motionless on a fence or bush. Displaying his white patches, he may, if greatly excited, descend vertically to hover a few centimetres above her, or even facing her, calling incessantly with a steady 'whit-whit-whit…' If the female is responsive she will follow the male, flicking her wings and tail, when he suddenly flies to a nearby perch. In this event the female crouches near the male with bill open and head lowered, showing her white patches while fluffing out her feathers, trembling her wings and occasionally shaking her body. The male hovers above her, bill gaping and white patches displayed, descending gently to her for 2–3 seconds. After this both usually fly away to different parts of the territory and resume feeding or other activities. At times the hovering may be replaced with passes by the male across the female in level flight."

Glutz & Bauer (1988) describe a bowing display (see illustration).

European Stonechat courtship display Male indulges in bowing display whilst simultaneously raising and fanning wings and tail, either perched or on the ground (a and b). Conversely, male may adopt more assertive display raising his body vertically, raising head up and down, fanning and flicking tail downwards and wings outwards. The white on the neck, wings and rumps is fluffed out to maximum effect (c). Display often a combination of both. Female may stand her ground ignoring male's advances and sometimes threatening male (d) or may show inclination to mate by crouching submissively, fluffing feathers of mantle and rump and flicking tail downwards (e). (After Glutz & Bauer 1988.)

This latter behaviour of passing rapidly to and fro in horizontal flight is described as uncommon in Jersey, and it was only seen once during a four-year study in southern England (EU pers. obs.). However, Agatho described it as normal in the southern Netherlands.

Normally it is the male who initiates courtship display, but on 7 March Johnson (1971a) recorded a female hovering 10m above a male newcomer to the territory she occupied, calling *whit-trrack whit-trrack*. She then flew to an electricity cable followed by the male, who perched near her without any overt display. The two birds remained paired from then on, later being joined by a second female in a polygynous relationship. Johnson commented that this was a medium-intensity display pattern in which he would have expected the male to have taken the lead. Possibly the female's actions were stimulated by a shortage of males in the population. Agatho also often observed females giving a display every time their mates approached the nest if it contained young. Sometimes it was similar to the display she demonstrated in normal courtship, but frequently it was different and she stood as high as possible on outstretched legs, her body held horizontally, wings outstretched, quivering and held level with the body. The significance or reason for this display is unknown, but Agatho thought it might have a role in maintaining the pair-bond. A male in southern England (East Sussex), waiting with food whilst the female fed young in the nest, briefly crouched and bowed low on a perch above the nest quivering his wings rapidly whilst raising his spread tail to a 45° angle when she left (EU pers. obs.).

The size of a territory varies according to season. The winter territory is usually larger than the breeding territory. Published estimates of size have indicated wide variations within and between locations, possibly owing to the size of local populations in any given year and the availability of suitable habitat. A winter territory in Jersey was 7ha but had contracted to around 3ha in the breeding season (Johnson 1971a).

Observations by Parrinder & Parrinder (1945) in western England (Cornwall) showed 15 coastal breeding territories to vary between 75 and 2.5 acres each with 12 territories being approximately 2.0 acres each.

On Corsica up to 2.7 pairs per 10 ha were found breeding in lowland vineyards and fallow areas but only 0.1 pair per 10ha in low frutices above 1,000m (Thibault & Bonaccorsi 1999). Leburier & Rapine (1936) estimated that a pair required a breeding territory of around 1.0ha in Brittany, France. The sizes of 45 territories on inland heath in southern England (East Sussex) were generally larger, ranging from 0.8 to around 4ha (Greig-Smith 1979). In the Netherlands on uncultivated strips within farmland, breeding areas ranged from 1.0 to 4.8ha (Agatho 1960-1961). In Germany on pasture, 25 breeding territories were estimated to average around 2.9ha each (Flinks & Pfeifer 1993). In Japan breeding density was 0.8–1.0 nests per ha in suitable habitat (semi natural grassland) but only 0.4–0.5 nests per ha in less suitable habitat (cultivated fields and pastures) (Fujimaki *et al.* 1994). On Jersey 14 winter territories continuously occupied over the period 1950–1970 varied in size from 0.7 to 7.0ha, with only five being less than 2.0ha in extent (Johnson 1971a). In southern Scotland (Ayrshire) winter territories varied from 2 to 7ha (Cramp 1988).

There is a remarkable observation by Johnson (1961) from the south-east coast of Spain, where he found in early November one of the greatest concentrations of European Stonechats he had ever seen. He recorded pairs defending territories less than 46m across, and these abutted on one another for at least 16km along the coast and 400m inland. This would mean that these territories were less than 0.25ha in size. It is probable that the resident population at this time of year was considerably augmented by migrants from northern Europe, which would have put considerable pressure on resident birds to relinquish part of their territories.

In partially migrant populations winter territories have been described as an extension of the breeding territory. Phillips (1967) recorded a pair in southern Scotland (Ayrshire) leaving their breeding area and residing 500m further along the coast, returning to the breeding area in late February. Parrinder & Parrinder (1945) found that the extent of wandering in pairs from their study area extended to a radius of about 800m from the breeding territory. Phillips (1967) found that the winter pairs in his study area had territories measuring 228–685m in length and 68–91m in depth. He found no evidence of a build-up of numbers in winter caused by birds from inland areas moving to the coast. Rather, birds breeding on the coast remained for the winter paired and in territories roughly corresponding to the breeding territories, with usually the same number of territories as found in the breeding season. This contrasts with the findings of the Parrinders, where only seven winter territories were held in an area that normally held 14 breeding pairs. Other individuals or pairs move to areas that are not frequented in the breeding season (see Movements), with birds turning up many miles inland in areas where they have ceased to breed or never bred.

There are records of single, presumed first-year males holding territories in winter in habitat unsuitable for breeding but in very close proximity to and maintaining contact with an established pair. These single birds were considered possibly to be siblings of the pairs with which they maintained close contact (Phillips

162

1968). Moreover, pairs comprising first-year birds were confined to very small territories in the breeding season. Breeding densities in partially migrant populations in northern Europe can vary from year to year depending on how well a population has survived the winter. In southern England Greig-Smith (1979) recorded a 3.5-fold variation in density over the three years 1977–1979. In 250 ha there were 24 territories in 1977, 14 in 1978 and seven in 1979, giving a mean of 9.6, 5.6 and 2.8 pairs respectively per km², the fall in numbers being attributable to the severe winter weather in the latter two years. Another estimate in northern Europe is of 7.3 pairs per km² in Dorset in southern England (Bibby 1978). Higher densities have been recorded, such as 31.5 pairs per km² in Cornwall in western England (Parrinder & Parrinder 1945) and 179 pairs per km² over 14ha of waste ground in the Netherlands (Agatho 1960–1961). In years when such populations are at a peak it can appear that the species is almost semi-colonial, with nests very close to each other; but in reality each pair still maintains a territory, albeit much smaller and restricted than in years when the population is low. In central Siberia very high densities up to 560 birds per km² can be found in exceptionally favoured areas (S.M. Prokofyev in Rogacheva 1992). Generally the highest number of birds in favoured dry hayfield areas is 76 per km², ranging down to 8 per km² in marginal habitat (Rogacheva 1992).

In a study of 22 territories in coastal southern Scotland it was shown that territories were more consistently used for wintering than for breeding, but that for both seasons there was a continuum from occasional to regular occupancy. This study also demonstrated that there was a significant correlation between the percentage use of sites for breeding and for wintering, showing that certain of these territories were preferred in both seasons (Phillips & Greig-Smith 1980). Presumably the most favoured territories were those with the most acceptable features, as it is known that those territories with the optimum acceptable topographical features are those most occupied. An inherent preference for the same features in individual territories is manifest year after year by generations of European Stonechats, even though the individual birds concerned are statistically unlikely to survive for more than one breeding season.

Population density has an appreciable influence on breeding activity and behaviour. The success of a pair in reproducing and raising multiple broods depends to a large extent on how much effort pairs and especially the male have to make in defending the territory and driving off intruders: the less time spent on defending boundaries the better chance of breeding successfully. In periods of high density the pressure for territories is greater, resulting in more territorial disputes and increased vigilance by the pair occupying a territory, leaving less time to concentrate on raising young. Phillips (1968) found that intense display occurred on the borders of those territories held by first-year birds which were adjacent to territories held by older pairs. This constant territorial activity primarily upset the older, established pairs and contributed significantly to breeding failures among them.

In territorial interactions the male is more often involved than the female in aggressive encounters. Females do occasionally interact with females from adjacent territories but rarely show aggression towards other males. Greig-Smith encountered a number of conflicts between two females forming a triangular relationship with a male at the beginning of the breeding season, the disputes always eventually ending in the disappearance of one of the females. Davis (1972) also recounts how a female of an old established pair was very aggressive towards a younger female in her first breeding year in a territory 100m away, although the respective males took no part in these confrontations. Every time the younger female left her nest "a veritable ball of fury"' in the shape of the older female "would come hurtling across the common" to confront her. Similar behaviour has also been observed in northern England (Cumbria) when pairs were establishing territories, with one female flying 50m to confront another (J. Callion pers. comm. 2000). In Russia both sexes were found to defend their territory, and during territorial conflicts males would move along their common territorial boundary parallel to each other, hopping in "typical passerine manner", performing mock feeding movements. The tail feathers would be fanned slightly, sometimes asymmetrically, and the wings flicked out to the sides so fast as to be barely discernible. Conflict between males was silent but between females *trrack* or rattling *krrrr* calls were heard. No fights were seen between males but one was seen between females who became locked together rolling around on the ground in a ball of feathers. One of the males, observing this from some distance, immediately flew close to the conflict.

When establishing their territories males bob slightly and display their breast and white plumage areas, spreading their wings and arching them slightly forwards with the tail fanned. They utter short *krrr krrr* calls and move towards each other with a light tripping gait (Linsenmair 1960). Display in territorial interaction also includes wing-flicking, which exposes the white wing-patches, slow and fast tail-flicking, and fanning the tail. Greig-Smith (1979) mentions the fact that the male will often make complex vocalisations involving buzzing and whistling sounds. Territorial males in the breeding season will chase other intruding males, and sometimes in their excitement make physical contact, although this is not usual. Males do not usually show aggression towards intruding females, but sometimes can show aggression towards their mate. A male in a study area in southern England whose mate joined him at the very edge of their territory buffeted and chivvied her further back into the territory (EU pers. obs.). In the study of wintering pairs in Israel, it was found that aggressive encounters occurred between a territorial bird and an intruder of the opposite sex, the male initiating the interaction in 71% of cases and the female in 29%. Also males would threaten and chase away their mate whilst in a territorial dispute with a neighbouring male. Paired birds maintained an average distance of 25–50m between each other, and aggressive interactions within a pair occurred at the rate of 0.6 per 100 minutes in early winter and about 0.3 per 100 minutes in late winter, with the aggression always being initiated by the male (Gwinner *et al.* 1994).

European Stonechat antagonistic display Territory holding male threatening intruder (a). Faces intruder with body held upright on extended legs to display chest to maximum effect and tail is flicked downwards. White neck patches fluffed to create maximum effect and wings partially opened to display white patches. Intruding male crouches low in submissive posture ready to escape (b). (After Glutz & Bauer 1988.)

In the UK, where the population is partially migratory, these territorial interactions occur most widely at the onset of breeding, reaching a peak of almost two per hour in the last ten days of March and the first ten days of April (Greig-Smith 1982b). A similar situation was also recorded in the migratory population in Israel from November to mid-December and to a lesser extent from mid-February to early March (Gwinner *at al.* 1994).

Males also demonstrate aggression to other ecologically similar species. This is usually associated with territorial defence and is almost non-existent outside the breeding season. In the UK European Stonechats have been noted to be particularly aggressive towards Whinchat and Northern Wheatear. On Jersey in spring Northern Wheatears alighting in a European Stonechat territory were flown at and physically attacked by the male, who buffeted them with the breast and pecked them around the head (Johnson 1971b). A study in North Wales suggested that where all three species bred in close association there was a hierarchy in which Northern Wheatears were dominant over European Stonechats which were in turn dominant over Whinchats (Greig-Smith 1982c). In southern Scotland Phillips (1970) also demonstrated that where Whinchat and European Stonechat bred together the latter was dominant. In Germany territorial male European Stonechats in spring have been observed showing aggression towards migrant Black Redstart *Phoenicurus ochruros* and Common Redstart *P. phoenicurus*. Male European Stonechats were seen flying up to 200m to confront these species as well as Whinchat (H. Flinks *et al.* 2001). Little aggression was shown in autumn. The female (but not the male) of a pair of European Stonechat holding a winter territory on the south coast of the UK also showed aggression towards a Black Redstart, flying to wherever it perched and supplanting it (EU pers. obs.).

In the southern Netherlands aggression has been noted towards Common Chiffchaff *Phylloscopus collybita* and Willow Warbler *P. trochilus*, and a stuffed Common Cuckoo *Cuculus canorus* was always attacked by the male (Agatho 1960-1961). A stuffed Common Cuckoo placed in a territory in England was attacked by both the male and the female of a pair with young. The female became so frenzied that she rounded on her own mate and attacked him also and in the space of 15 minutes there were three aggressive interactions between the male and female whilst also attacking the Common Cuckoo. The pair were so enraged by the presence of the cuckoo that they attacked it even whilst it was being removed and continued for minutes afterwards diving at the spot where it had been placed (Hosking & Lane 1970). In Germany, mild aggression by the male towards a cuckoo was seen only once, and only after Meadow Pipit *Anthus pratensis* and Common Whitethroat *Sylvia communis* started mobbing it (H. Flinks *in litt.* 2001). A female nesting in close vicinity to both a pair of Common Linnet *Carduelis cannabina* and Meadow Pipit in southern England showed aggression only towards the latter species (EU pers. obs.). In Germany a pair of European Stonechat, Yellowhammer *Emberiza citrinella* and Tree Pipit *Anthus trivialis* all nested within an area of 3.5m² with no apparent conflict towards each other (Mildenberger 1950).

Although normally one of a pair or solitary, birds can find themselves involuntarily associated with other species. These associations are usually short and initiated by other species. The following species have been recorded in the UK associating with European Stonechat: Dartford Warbler *Sylvia undata*, Common Whitethroat, Lesser Whitethroat *S. curruca*, Willow Warbler, Meadow Pipit, Tree Pipit, Common Linnet, European Goldfinch *Carduelis carduelis*, Lesser Redpoll *C. flammea*, Yellowhammer, Reed Bunting *Emberiza schoeniclus*, Great Tit *Parus major*, Coal Tit *P. ater*, Winter Wren *Troglodytes troglodytes* and Hedge Accentor *Prunella modularis*. These species were generally more tolerant of an intruder's approach, only giving alarm calls when an intruder was 29–41m away and flying away when the intruder was as close as 11–35m, whereas European Stonechats give alarm calls when a predator is 101±26m away and fly from an intruder at 57±26m (Greig Smith 1979, 1981). It would appear that there is no advantage to the European Stonechat from this association and that the associating species are simply profiting from its greater vigilance. Individual Stonechats will actively try to distance themselves from associating species as they have a detrimental effect on feeding activity. Zamora *et al.* (1992) demonstrated that the presence of a Dartford Warbler in a European Stonechat's hunting area interfered with the latter's feeding behaviour, causing it to use more perches without capturing prey and exploiting feeding patches less intensively. This resulted in reducing the latter's prey-catching attempts by 50% during periods when it was followed by the warbler. Similar associations have been observed in Tanzania in southern Africa, most pronounced during the October–January breeding season, involving the Black-lored Cisticola *Cisticola nigrilores* (Harpum 1978) and in Menorca involving Sardinian Warbler *Sylvia melanocephala* (EU pers. obs.).

When perched there is a noticeable wing-flicking action in which the wings are continuously and rapidly flicked outwards from the body and then returned to their normal resting position. This is often accompanied by a similar action with the tail, which is flicked upwards and slightly fanned. Greig-Smith (1982d) studied this and came to the conclusion that it is an advertisement of the bird's arrival on a perch rather than an indication that it is about to fly. Wing-flicking is performed by both sexes, occurs throughout the year, and could possibly assist pairs in maintaining sight of each other. It is also very obvious at the beginning of the breeding season and may bear some relation to the need for individual males to advertise their presence to rivals when establishing or defending a territory. Wing-flicking displays the white inner wing-patches to maximum effect. It may also assist the male in attracting a mate. After the young have fledged both sexes indulge in increased wing-flicking as well as giving distraction calls whenever a potential predator enters their territory. This could suggest that wing-flicking, combined with distraction calls, also forms an anti-predator behaviour, attracting the predator to the adult birds and away from the more vulnerable young. Wing-flicking has possibly evolved because the male and to a lesser extent the female have relatively large conspicuous white patches on the wings formed by the inner greater coverts and these would be exposed to their maximum when the wings are extended. Greig Smith pointed out that, unlike the adjacent European Stonechats, the ecologically similar Whinchat does not indulge in wing-flicking when newly arrived on territories in North Wales, and tentatively attributed this difference in behaviour to the Whinchat having no similar white wing-patches. In fact, however, the male (albeit not the female) Whinchat *does* have similar conspicuous white patches on the inner upperwing and also on the tail.

MOULT

Adult birds in the UK commence a complete post-breeding moult from mid-July to late August, with the first of the ten primary feathers to be shed being the innermost (01) and then they are renewed in sequence on both wings, descendantly up to and including the outermost, much smaller tenth. Moult of the tertials and rectrices usually commences when primary moult has reached primary 04. The 12 tail feathers are usually moulted irregularly or all simultaneously. The six secondaries and all the body feathers will be moulted during this time also. Depending on when the moult commenced it is usually completed by the beginning of September to early October, before either migration or the forming of winter pairs. A migratory population studied in Westfalia, Germany, between 1991 and 1996 commenced moulting at the start of July and (especially those birds with late broods) completed at the end of September or the start of October (H. Flinks *in litt.* 2001). In this population some juveniles from third broods, late in the season, were still in active post-juvenile moult when they left for their wintering areas (Flinks 1999). The complete moult of European Stonechats in the UK has been estimated to take around 50 days (Ginn & Melville 1983). The average duration of moult in retrapped post-juvenile birds in the German study area referred to earlier was 60.1 days with extremes of 45.5–79.2 days. Birds in the rest of Europe apart from in the south moult at a similar time to those in UK, but birds in southern Europe may commence their moult earlier.

The more migratory Siberian Stonechat subspecies *S. m. maura* and *stejnegeri* from Siberia commence their moult earlier, from around late June to mid-July, and complete it by mid-August to early September. A study by Helm & Gwinner (2001) of captive Siberian Stonechats *S. m. maura* between 1997-1999 found that they moulted earlier and faster than both Common and African Stonechat.

European Stonechats, unlike Whinchats, do not undergo a partial pre-breeding moult into breeding plumage in spring but instead the feather fringes of the autumn plumage progressively wear away to reveal the brighter, more contrasted breeding plumage. It is possible that first-winter Siberian Stonechat males of the subspecies *maura* and possibly *stejnegeri*, which show comparatively little dark feathering on the head, may undergo a partial moult in spring in which the pale buff head feathers are replaced by black ones. Svensson (1992) states that the feather bases on the head are grey and therefore reasons that first-year birds must moult these to obtain the black head and throat of spring. This supposition appears to have been confirmed by captive *maura* in Germany which were observed to undergo a partial pre-breeding moult of the head feathers and upper body feathers during the winter months. Captive birds of the European Stonechat subspecies *hibernans*, *rubicola* and African Stonechat subspecies *axillaris* did not moult any head feathers in winter (E. Gwinner *per* B. Helm *in litt.* 2001).

Juvenile birds can be encountered in full juvenile plumage from late March up to mid-August. Birds that fledge later moult more rapidly than those that fledge earlier in the season, owing to photoperiodic control. There seems little evidence that post-juvenile moult ever commences while day length is increasing, as early fledged birds do not commence post-juvenile moult until after the summer solstice (B. Helm pers. comm. 2001). In Westfalia, Germany, from 320 individuals studied between 1991 and 1996 the average earliest start date for post-juvenile moult was 2 July ± 8 days, with the average latest date for finishing being 31 October ± 12 days. Birds from first broods (born between the beginning of April and mid-May) commence post-juvenile moult at an age of 68 ± 11 days; second broods (born between mid-May and end of June) at an age of 46 ± 10 days; and those of third broods (born between the beginning of July and August) at an age of 34 ± 6 days. The average duration of moult for birds from first broods was 71.1 days; second broods 68.2 days; and third broods 57.5 days (Flinks 1999). A similar situation was encountered in the north of England with juveniles only commencing post-juvenile moult in late June/early July (J. Callion *in litt.* 2001). This 'calendar' effect appears to be typical for temperate passerines and in the German study (Flinks 1999) it was found that the termination of moult is advanced by 0.6 days for each day the hatching is later compared to the average.

Captive Siberian Stonechats studied by Helm & Gwinner (2001) commenced post juvenile moult early and finished it quickly compared to European and African Stonechat. The first onset of moult was recorded at the age of 21 days even before the wing feathers were fully grown. Variation in moult timing increased during the course of the moult (difference between earliest and latest moult age: onset 19 days, peak 37.5, completion 51, duration 43 days). It would appear that Siberian Stonechats achieve their moult within the comparatively short time available by having a fairly inflexible onset time for moult and adjusting the moult rate in response to photoperiodic cues. Post-juvenile Siberian Stonechats appear to be unaffected by photoperiodic controls probably due to the short breeding season in their breeding areas which is around midsummer. Photoperiod may not be a useful stimulus for the onset of moult because nestlings are not much subject to days that differ from the maximal midsummer photoperiod. This is in marked contrast to European Stonechat (see above). Photoperiod for Siberian Stonechats does take on increasing emphasis as daylength decreases during moult in late summer. Small differences in hatching dates can result in large daylength differences being experienced in the latter stages of moult. In response to decreasing and short daylength juveniles compensate by reducing the duration of moult through an increased moult rate. This was in contrast to captive European and African Stonechat which did the opposite, advancing the onset of moult in response to shorter daylength but keeping the moult duration virtually unaffected (Helm & Gwinner 1999).

The moult of the body feathers is usually always complete. Post-juvenile moult commences first with the breast, flanks and middle back. It then progresses symmetrically on both sides to the chin, fore-back and upper- and undertail-coverts. After a short pause it commences on the crown, progressing to the forehead and nape. The ear-coverts and some flank feathers are the last body feathers to be moulted. The wing moult commences with the upperwing lesser and then median coverts. The upperwing greater coverts commence moult shortly after the lesser coverts and a short time before or simultaneously with the median coverts. Often there is a visible band of unmoulted median coverts sandwiched between the renewed lesser coverts and the still-growing new greater coverts. The tertials, carpal coverts and the first and possibly second alula feathers are moulted at the same time. The extent of moult in these feathers depends on the individual's age. The earlier it was born the more extensive is the moult in these areas, and none or all feathers from these areas can be replaced depending on age. Late-born individuals replace as a minimum the inner upperwing greater coverts 07–10.

The upperwing primary coverts and primaries are only moulted exceptionally (three birds from 320):

1) Female juvenile 11 November 1997. Upperwing greater coverts new. Active body moult ±60%. Innermost primary covert 01 growing (moult score 10%) on both wings. Similar for innermost primary 01 (moult score 10%). No other primaries being renewed.

2) Female juvenile 11 November 1997. Upperwing greater coverts new. Active body moult ±70%. Primary coverts 01 and 02 almost renewed (moult score 90%) and 03 just commenced renewal (moult score 5%) on both wings. Primary 01 on left wing was half grown (50%). Primary 01 on right wing was old.

   Both females were from a first brood fledged in April.
   Both females were in active moult of the two inner tertials 08 and 09.

3) Male juvenile 13 August 1998. Upperwing greater coverts growing or new (moult score 70%). Active body moult ±40%. Primary covert 01 on right wing just commenced growing (moult score 5%). Primary covert 01 on left wing old. All primaries old.

   This male was considered to have come from a brood fledged in May because no tertials were being moulted (H. Flinks *in litt.* 2002).

Only 17.5% of birds from first broods were found to renew any tail feathers in post-juvenile moult.

In their post-juvenile moult Siberian Stonechats of the subspecies *S. m. maura* moult on average fewer upperwing greater coverts than European Stonechats *S. r. hibernans* and *S. r. rubicola*, and often moult none at all (Svensson 1992).

CONSERVATION

The European Stonechat is classified by Tucker & Heath (1994) under SPEC (Species of European Conservation Concern) Category 3. This incorporates 'species whose global populations are not concentrated in Europe, but which have an Unfavourable Conservation Status in Europe'. Species have an unfavourable conservation status if their European populations are small and non-marginal, or are substantially declining (= European Stonechat), or are highly localised.

Since the 1950s the species has suffered a progressive reduction owing to agricultural intensification in breeding habitats in farmland, notably in north-west and parts of central Europe, with approximately two-thirds of the European population in decline. This trend was first noticed in the UK and western Germany around 1940, and spread over most of north-west Europe during the 1960–1970s. Despite occasional rallies in various populations, the steady decline has continued and is now affecting the large populations of France and Spain. The most important threat is undoubtedly the steady change to more intensive farming practices since the Second World War. The loss of structurally diverse habitat to farming, building or leisure facilities, as well as human disturbance, has contributed to its decline in northern Europe, and throughout the continent an emphasis needs to be placed on preserving or creating suitable habitat by (re-)introducing non-intensive agricultural practices. The preservation of scrub habitat, desisting from covering moorland and fallow land with afforestation, maintaining areas of scrub and rank uncut grass within intensively farmed land, sensitive cutting of grassland areas and controlled and legal burning of moorland would all assist in maintaining populations in Europe (Tucker & Heath 1994).

The Siberian Stonechat and African Stonechat appear to be under no immediate threat and their populations are probably stable. In the case of the former, the fact that they essentially breed at mid- to high-altitudes means they are less affected by changes in lowland agricultural methods or conversion of lowland areas to agriculture, although monitoring is needed to ensure that populations remain healthy. This is especially important for those that winter in lowland areas throughout the Indian subcontinent and where suitable habitat is now under great threat from ever-increasing human pressures to convert it to agriculture, grazing or other unfavourable uses. In the Afrotropical region the species ranges from sea level to mid- and high altitudes; overgrazing and other loss of habitat to human pressure may pose a future potential threat to populations that live or winter at lower altitudes.

Berthold (1993) found increasing evidence that a combination of intensive habitat destruction and use of biocides in breeding and migrant stopover points as well as wintering areas is having a detrimental effect. The resulting reduction in nutritional resources is so great as to impair the forming of fat reserves in preparation for migration.

Populations which migrate through and to the southern Mediterranean face hazards from the increasing human population who with more leisure time and increasing access to guns and sophisticated trapping devices take a considerable toll on small passerine species. The BTO's list of 39 foreign recoveries of UK-ringed individuals shows that 19 (48.7%) were either caught or killed by humans. The birds have to survive despite increasing pressure from the 'traditional' practices of shooting and trapping for sport, the cage bird industry and the thriving trade in pickled birds as a delicacy. This latter is now, in Cyprus and probably other southern Mediterranean countries, no longer simply the occupation of local families taking relatively few birds for their own use but a prosperous and growing commercial business. Several hundred million migrant birds are shot, trapped or sold in the Mediterranean area each year with an apparently virtual total disregard for the consequences; in Italy alone a conservative estimate put the number each year at 175 million (Woldhek 1980). The European Stonechat is one of the various species that make up these huge numbers.

Education in conservation and the value of birds as well as other flora and fauna needs to be introduced in local schools in Mediterranean countries to try to guide younger generations away from the older attitude towards birds. Stronger enforcement of laws by the countries involved, and political dialogue and economic pressure where possible from the EC, should be brought to bear. Many of the southern Mediterranean countries have a thriving tourist trade based on people holidaying from northern Europe where there is a more enlightened approach to bird conservation. It should be made clear that birds are not a limitless resource and many of those killed in southern Mediterranean countries are from populations breeding in northern Europe.

There is also the growing potential threat of severe disturbance to migrant and resident populations from tourism and the increased recreational pursuits associated with it. This is becoming ever more serious around the Mediterranean and to a certain extent in northern European countries.

EUROPEAN STONECHAT
Saxicola rubicola

Plate 5

(*Motacilla*) *rubicola* Linnaeus, 1766, *Syst. Nat.* ed. 12, p.332—Europae [= France]; restricted to Seine Inférieure by Meinertzhagen, 1940, *Ibis*, p.215

Pratincola torquata hibernans Hartert, 1910, *J. Orn.* 58, p.173—Tring, England

Etymology *rubicola* derived from Latin *ruber* meaning red

Alternative names Stonechat, Common Stonechat

TAXONOMY
Polytypic. See discussion on page 131.

IDENTIFICATION
Two subspecies, both in the western Palearctic, *S. r. rubicola* and *S. r. hibernans*

In general terms the overall plumage of the two western Palearctic races compared to the six from the eastern Palearctic are the darkest when fresh, with *S. m. przewalskii* (the easternmost Siberian Stonechat subspecies, found in China and Indochina), approaching the colour tones of darkest *S. r. hibernans*. The two western Palearctic races are similar in appearance with subtle plumage differences generally accepted to be chiefly apparent in fresh plumage, although examples of both sexes of *S. r. rubicola* from more southerly areas of the range can also appear quite different in summer plumage. Indeed males with extensive white neck- and rump-patches are sometimes more similar to one of the eastern races in summer plumage.

There is a clinal variation in plumage for both these races, with individuals from the northern and north-western parts of their breeding range being darker than those from the south and south-east. Thus birds from southern Norway and north and north-west Scotland are slightly darker in tone both above and below than those from southern England, Brittany and Portugal, all of which constitute the race *S. r. hibernans*, and likewise there is a similar clinal distinction between birds from northern mainland Europe and southern Europe/northern Africa, which constitute the race *S. r. rubicola*. Birds of the latter race are also generally slightly paler overall than birds of the race *S. r. hibernans*. It is probable that there is no valid racial distinction between *S. r. hibernans* and *S. r. rubicola*, and individuals from north to south of the inclusive ranges form one continous cline. Meinertzhagen (1934, 1953) assigned individuals from the Hebrides and north-western Scotland to another race, *S. t. theresae*, based on the fact that the females especially were even darker than birds from other areas of Scotland. At the same time he also suggested that only two races should be recognised, *S. t. theresae* and *S. r. rubicola*, with populations in the rest of the range of *S. r. hibernans* being assigned to *S. r. rubicola* owing to the minimal differences in plumage. The race *S. t. theresae* was discounted by Vaurie (1959) as the differences did not appear constant and individuals from the claimed range of *theresae* are now considered part of a cline. The differences in plumage tones between *S. r. hibernans* and *S. r. rubicola* are very subtle, with *S. r. hibernans* being variably darker than *S. r. rubicola*. No specimen of *S. r. rubicola* has been specifically identified in any part of the range of *hibernans* but it is probable that examples do occur (see below) and could well intergrade with *hibernans*. To identify a specimen of *hibernans* from the southern part of its range from a specimen of *rubicola* from the northern part of its range would prove extremely difficult. Fresh-plumaged autumn birds in coastal parts of the Netherlands, Belgium and north to Denmark and south to north-west France were found to be very similar to *S. r. hibernans* (Cramp *et al.* 1988). In a recent examination of 50+ skins of both *S. r. hibernans* and *S. r. rubicola* in the BMNH, I could find little discernible difference between them except that early autumn examples of *S. r. hibernans* had darker fringes to the feathers of the upperparts in fresh plumage, and southern European examples of male *S. r. rubicola* appeared to show more white on the rump and darker axillaries and underwing-coverts. There was, however, considerable individual variation amongst specimens collected at the same time from the same geographical area. Robertson (1977) conducted a similar exercise with the same skins and could find no difference in the races at all, whereas Svensson (1992) detected from skins from other sources that *S. r. hibernans* was somewhat darker in fresh plumage than *S. r. rubicola*. As *S. r. rubicola* also shows a cline of darker birds in the north and paler in the south, it could be that paler specimens from the southern parts of the range of *rubicola* could be discernible if they occurred in parts of the range of *hibernans*, such as when wintering or overshooting on spring migration. That they have not been positively identified up to now is probably due to birders not giving attention to what would be a very tricky and time-consuming examination, and in the majority of cases confirmation may only be achievable in the hand. It is worth noting, however, that individuals considered too pale to be *S. r. hibernans* have been observed recently in southern areas of the United Kingdom in autumn, late winter and spring (Dally 2001, Shepherd 2001, Walker 2001).

In fresh plumage, male *S. r. hibernans* have the feather fringes of the upper parts and head dark rufous-brown and the breast and flanks dark rufous-chestnut (Cramp 1988). The feather centres on the female's upperparts are a deeper black and in both sexes the underparts are darker with the breast and flanks of the male a darker rufous-chestnut than in *S. r. rubicola*. The contrast between the upperparts and underparts is the least obvious and the white areas on the neck, rump, uppertail-coverts and vent are the most restricted of all races. Male *S. r. rubicola* has slightly paler buff-brown to sandy olive-grey fringes to the head and upperparts but not as pale or as extensive as the Siberian Stonechat subspecies *S. m. maura* and *stejnegeri*. The rump and uppertail-coverts of males often show more white than *S. r. hibernans*, sometimes extending more onto the sides of the rump, but again not as much as to give the wrapped-around impression found on Siberian Stonechat subspecies. Resident adult males in fresh plumage on Menorca in mid-August showed prominent white unstreaked upper rumps, with dark streaking only apparent on the rufous-orange uppertail-coverts. The white of the rump also extended slightly onto the sides of the rump, and when the bird flew the rump and uppertail-coverts appeared much paler and more extensive than in *S. r. hibernans* (E.U. pers. obs.). The underparts from breast to undertail-coverts are slightly paler rufous-chestnut. The contrast between the upperparts and underparts is also greater than in *S. r. hibernans*. It has generally been considered that individuals are only racially discernible in autumn when in fresh plumage, and as feather fringes wear they become subspecifically inseparable, but two noticeably pale individuals, showing large amounts of white, especially on the wings and rump, which arrived with other, darker migrant European Stonechats on the south coast of the UK in March 2001, differed so markedly that they were considered possibly to be *S. r. rubicola* (Walker 2001).

Main differences between *S. r. hibernans* and *S. r. rubicola*

Much caution should be used when using the criteria listed below. Probably the best that can be said is that potentially identifiable *rubicola* may emanate from more southerly populations than the majority of individuals found breeding in the UK, although *S. r. hibernans*, at least in southern parts of its range, can show characteristics similar to *S. r. rubicola*. Many are probably virtually indistinguishable. Males in spring plumage are easier to distinguish than males in autumn plumage, and females are virtually identical at all times of the year.

Rump/uppertail-coverts *S. r. rubicola* often shows white even in fresh autumn plumage on the upper rump. The pale white/rufous area of the rump and uppertail-coverts in autumn is usually more extensive and sometimes can appear as if extending onto the sides of the rump. However, it is still never as extensive as on eastern races and only very exceptionally lacks dark streaks, although the streaks can often be sparse and confined to the uppertail-coverts only. In spring the rump can appear very white, increasing in extent as the season progresses, with little streaking evident apart from on the uppertail-coverts.

S. r. hibernans rarely shows any white on the rump in fresh plumage, and the rump and uppertail-covert area is often markedly smaller and darker than on *S. r. rubicola*. Often both the rump and uppertail-coverts are heavily marked with small dark brown/black streaks and blotches. In spring the lower rump and uppertail-coverts gradually become white but not usually as extensive as *S. r. hibernans* nor as early in the year, and often the dark streaks and blotches are present on both rump and uppertail-coverts.

Neck-patches In *S. r. rubicola* these can appear whiter and less obscured by buff fringes in fresh plumage, and in spring as the feather fringes abrade the white neck-patch can be extensive. In *S. r. hibernans* the neck-patch in fresh plumage is usually only visible as an ill-defined white line mainly obscured by buff feather fringes. In spring it becomes white but is usually not as extensive as *S. r. rubicola*, extending less onto the sides of the neck and not quite so broad.

Underpart colouring *S. r. rubicola* is usually buff-orange from breast to undertail-coverts in fresh plumage, with pale feather fringes creating a subtly paler impression than *S. r. hibernans*, abrading in some individuals to only buff-orange on the breast and flanks in spring, with the rest of the underparts becoming white. *S. r. hibernans* is the same as *S. r. rubicola* in autumn although a shade darker in tone owing to less pale feather fringes. In spring it shows a weaker demarcation between the orange-buff breast and flanks and remaining underparts, which often are pale buff rather than white.

Upperpart (head, mantle and scapulars) colouring *S. r. rubicola* is marginally paler in fresh plumage owing to slightly paler brown feather fringes. These areas are indistinguishable in breeding plumage from *S. r. hibernans*, which is darker in fresh plumage with dark olive-brown fringes to the upperparts.

Underwing-coverts Male *S. r. rubicola* shows dark grey, almost sooty underwing-coverts and axillaries, with variable white fringes in spring plumage. Male *S. r. hibernans* shows paler buff-grey underwing-coverts and axillaries, again with variable white fringes. Females are racially virtually indistinguishable. Some examples of *S. r. rubicola* appear slightly paler on both upper- and underparts, although the simultaneous presence of an example of *S. r. hibernans* would probably be necessary to discern the difference. Some individuals of *S. r. rubicola* can also show quite a strong and extensive buff supercilium in both fresh and worn plumage, usually more noticeable from the eye to the rear of the ear-coverts. *S. r. hibernans* can also show a supercilium but when present it is ill-defined and rarely as extensive as in *S. r. rubicola*. However, there is much variation in the supercilium on both races.

DESCRIPTION Based on *S. r. rubicola*

Adult male fresh plumage, September–February The upperparts from the forehead and crown to the back are black, with the feathers broadly fringed grey-brown almost concealing the black so that only the black centres are visible and appear as dark longitudinal streaks. On autumn specimens of *S. r. hibernans* (BMNH) the fringes on the head and upperparts are small, indistinct and rufous-brown but are grey-brown, slightly wider, paler and more distinctive on autumn-plumaged *S. r. rubicola*.

The feathers of the rump and uppertail-coverts are white at the base but partly obscured by extensive rufous-brown tips with occasional white spots and irregular black streaks and blotches. The rumps of some male *S. r. hibernans*, usually from the northern part of the range, can appear completely dark rufous, again with black streaks and blotches and with the white bases to the feathers concealed. The rump-patch is always small and less extensive than is found in any of the eastern Palearctic races. The sides of the head (lores, malar region, cheeks and ear-coverts) down to and including the chin and throat are black with only narrow sandy-buff fringes to the black feathering. The black of the throat sometimes marginally extends onto the upper breast. The predominantly black sides of the head can contrast with the paler buff-brown forehead and crown, although adult males in fresh plumage from southern areas such as Menorca can show little contrast, being predominantly black over the entire head with only very narrow pale buff fringes to the forehead and crown (EU pers. obs.). The sides of the neck to the sides of the breast are white but the visible white is often reduced to a narrow patch by broad black or orange-buff tips to the feathers. Some individuals can show a very thin line of white below the throat, joining the white neck-patches and separating the black of the throat from the rufous-brown upper breast. Others have the black of the throat marginally extending onto the upper breast, separating the white neck-patches. The breast and upper flanks are rufous-brown with a pinkish tinge fading to a paler rufous-buff on the belly, rear flanks and undertail-coverts. The ventral area is buff-white. The rectrices are completely black, showing no white at all at their base, and have narrow, pale buff fringes to the outer webs and tips in fresh plumage. The remiges are mainly black/brown, slightly glossy on the outer webs with off-white crescentic tips. The secondaries are narrowly fringed with pale buff along the outer webs, forming a pale panel on the closed wing. The tertials are black with broad rufous-buff fringes. The upperwing lesser, median and greater coverts are black with chestnut-buff fringes and tips, and there is no contrast between on the one hand unmoulted and browner outer upperwing greater coverts and primary coverts and on the other blacker moulted upperwing inner greater, and all median and lesser coverts. There is a small white patch on the inner upperwing, formed by the white, innermost upperwing greater coverts 08–10 and sometimes 07, with some white also occurring at the base of the outer webs of the tertials and occasionally the innermost (06) secondary. This white patch is often partially hidden by the scapulars. The upperwing primary coverts are black with prominent narrow white fringes to the outer webs and tips which contrast with the predominantly black alula. (Some birds from Germany also show white marks on the inner webs of the upperwing primary coverts 02–04, but this is considered to be an aberration rather than a specific age character; birds from Germany also showed narrower, whitish-brown fringes to the alula feathers when fresh, but these had worn away by the breeding season: Flinks 1994.) The axillaries and underwing-coverts in both winter and summer plumage are dark grey or occasionally dull black with white tips in fresh plumage. The primary projection for both sexes is short, being only about half the length of the overlying tertials. The bill, legs and feet are black and the irides dark brown.

Adult males in fresh plumage have narrower feather fringes to the head and mantle and consequently appear darker than first-year males directly after the partial post-juvenile and complete adult post-breeding moult.

Adult male worn plumage, March–August From around mid-February summer plumage is gradually assumed as the fringes to the feathers wear away. Progressively the head and upperparts become evenly black, large white patches appear on the neck- and breast-sides and contrast both with the black head and rufous-chestnut breast. The rufous-chestnut on the breast is often more restricted than on *S. r. hibernans* with the rest of the underparts fading progressively from rufous-orange to pale buff or almost white. The lower rump and uppertail-coverts become white but retain some black streaks on the longer tail-coverts and the occasional chestnut-buff spot. Both Ullman (1986) and Svensson (1992) mention that some *S. r. rubicola* males can show large white unstreaked rump-patches in very worn plumage. Svensson adds that these birds are usually from the more southern populations but in most cases the white rump-patch is still smaller than is found on Siberian Stonechat. Resident males in Sicily can show a large area of unmarked white on the rump in summer plumage, a large neck-collar sometimes almost meeting on the hindneck, large areas of white on the wings and a richer shade of rufous-chestnut on the breast (Corso 2001).

Males breeding in the southern UK, of the race *S. r. hibernans,* can also show large white rumps, but careful examination reveals that they have dark streaks and or/spots although these may be minimal. The centre of the upper breast becomes rufous-chestnut, noticeably stronger in colour than the pale rufous-orange to rufous-buff of the lower breast and flanks. The belly and undertail-coverts become almost pure white and the white patch on the inner wing becomes more contrasted, as the wing is now mainly black owing to the loss of the pale buff fringes to the coverts. The pale fringes to the remiges and rectrices have worn off leaving them brownish-black. In very worn plumage, from late June/July onwards, all the buff fringes have gone and the upperparts appear a more uniform black, although this is broken up to a certain extent by the irregular appearance of grey feather bases. Occasionally, the white of the lower rump and uppertail-coverts wears away completely leaving the uppertail area dark. The breast and flanks fade even paler with the rest of the underparts becoming a scruffy white, often with areas of grey feather bases showing through. Some adult males on Menorca which had not commenced post-breeding moult in mid-August showed considerable black streaking on the belly as the result of feathers wearing through to the black bases (EU pers. obs.).

First-year male, July–November Very similar to adult male but during the post-juvenile moult the upperwing lesser and median coverts are moulted as are the greater coverts and/or tertials. The upperwing greater coverts are partially or completely moulted with greater coverts 07–09 always moulted. The remiges, rectrices, sometimes the tertials, the majority of the upperwing primary coverts and alula are unmoulted and appear browner. There is a contrast of the outer, browner, unmoulted upperwing greater coverts with the newer black upperwing median and inner greater coverts. Some individuals retain the pale buffish-white droplet-like marks at the tips of the unmoulted juvenile upperwing primary coverts. If the tertials have been moulted they are more black than brown and contrast with the unmoulted and browner inner secondaries.

In fresh plumage the feather fringes on the sides of the head, i.e. lores, malar region, cheeks, ear-coverts, chin and throat, are often slightly broader than in adult birds, obscuring more of the black feather centres and thus causing the head to appear paler than in the adult with a less obvious contrast between the blacker sides of the head and paler brown forehead and crown. However, this is not considered to be a reliable feature, as there can be pale adult males and dark first-year males, with some first-year birds showing a distinct black mask on the sides of the head. The pale buff fringes to the outer webs of the rectrices as well as the tips are slightly broader and less well defined, and the tips of the rectrices are more pointed and less rounded in shape – the opposite of adult. The pale buff-white crescentic tips to the remiges are larger, paler and less well defined than in the adult (Cramp 1988, Flinks 1994).

First-year male, March–July The contrast between the brown outer unmoulted greater coverts and black inner greater coverts becomes even more marked. There are signs of wear to the tips of the primaries, especially 05–08, which can be obvious on individuals as early as March. As the breeding season progresses the fringes to the upperwing-coverts become increasingly indistinct and narrow and may in some cases wear away altogether, especially on the outer upperwing primary coverts 04–08 (Flinks 1994).

Adult female fresh plumage, September–February The female lacks the overall sharply defined plumage of the male, and in comparison the plumage appears drab and insipid. The head and upperparts are dull olive-brown with a greyish cast formed by the extensive grey-brown fringes to the feathers. On the upperparts, females of *S. r. rubicola* show grey fringes whereas *S. r. hibernans* have slightly browner and darker fringes. These fringes when fresh often have a hint of pinkish-brown. The dark brown/black centres to the feathers partially show through, creating an indistinct streaking on the crown, nape, mantle and scapulars. The rump and uppertail-coverts contrast only slightly with the rest of the upperparts, being buff-brown narrowly streaked with black on the uppertail-coverts. There is no white on the rump or uppertail-coverts. The sides of the head, i.e. lores, malar region, cheeks and ear-coverts, are grey or olive-brown similar to the rest of the upperparts.The presence of a supercilium can vary. Often it is only an ill-defined and indistinct greyish-buff supercilium and some individuals do not show this characteristic at all. Others, such as the resident population on Menorca in the south of the range, show prominent pale buff supercilia extending from the bill to the rear of the ear-coverts broadening behind the eye (EU pers. obs.). The chin and throat are buff, mainly concealing the black feather bases, although often there is a hint of the dark feather bases showing through. The lower throat is fractionally paler buff which extends laterally onto the foreneck below the ear-coverts and cheeks. When seen head-on there is a distinct pale buff line of varying thickness separating the marginally darker buff upper throat from the chestnut-brown breast. The sides of the neck are also sometimes marginally paler, and occasionally a narrow buffish-white area appears where the buff-white bases to the feathers are exposed. The breast and flanks are pale chestnut-brown fading to paler chestnut-buff on the belly, ventral area and undertail-coverts. The remiges and rectrices are similar to the adult male. When fresh the remiges can show a weak gloss (Suter 1988). The upperwing lesser, median, greater and primary coverts are uniformly dark brown/black with prominent pale buff fringes and tips. The fringes of the greater coverts are light brown and those on the primary coverts are buff to white (Flinks 1994). Only the innermost two (09–10) upperwing greater coverts show white on them compared to the greater extent on the male, and consequently are less obvious until the bird flies. The underwing-coverts and axillaries are grey at the base broadly edged buff or white. Bill, legs and feet are black. Irides are dark brown.

Adult female worn plumage, March–August As with the male there is a gradual abrasion of the feather fringes, although the changes to the appearance are never as great as in the male. The upperparts become darker owing to the olive-grey or brown fringes partly wearing away to expose more of the dark brown/black feather centres, thereby creating a more prominent dull black or brown streaking on the mantle and scapulars. The supercilium, if present, becomes paler buff and consequently slightly more distinct, especially above and behind the eye. The rump and uppertail-coverts remain streaked brown much as in winter plumage. The throat feathers, through abrasion of the fringes, become increasingly black, while the chin remains buff. The breast and flanks fade to an even paler chestnut version of the autumn plumage, although the upper breast retains a stronger chestnut tone. The belly, ventral area and undertail-coverts become buff-white. By late summer (June–July) with increasing wear the throat is almost black, finely mottled with buff, and the head and upperparts excluding the rump but including the uppertail-coverts are extensively black-brown. The sides of the neck are an indistinct pale, buff-white although occasionally a female in well-worn plumage will show a much larger and distinct area of pure white. The upper breast and flanks fade to a dirty tawny-brown with the belly, ventral area and undertail-coverts off-white, often with darker grey feather bases showing through owing to extensive wear. The remiges and rectrices are similar to adult male. In contrast to first-year birds, the fringes to the upperwing primary coverts remain evenly broad up to the end of May and then show signs of asymmetric abrasion (Flinks 1994). The grey underwing-coverts and axillaries still retain some buff fringes. Females can show considerable variation in plumage tones, especially on the head. The majority slightly resemble fresh-plumaged first-year males, but others can show less colouring and appear quite grey, and there are intermediates between these extremes (Flinks 1994, H. Flinks *in litt.* 2001).

First-year female Similar to adult female but the same juvenile feathers are retained as in first-year male, although it is considerably more difficult to discern the contrast between retained and new feathers. The newly moulted upperwing greater coverts are darker brown and evenly fringed with light brown at the tips. The unmoulted greater coverts have paler buff to white fringes. The upperwing primary coverts are the same colour as the unmoulted upperwing greater coverts. Some females show pale whitish-buff droplet marks at the tips of the primary coverts similar to the first-year male. Any individual showing these is definitely a first-year bird. The primary coverts 05–08 have narrow, distinctly worn, buffish-white fringes, but 01–03 (occasionally 04) are less abraded and broadly and distinctly tipped white (Flinks 1994). As the year progresses the difference between unmoulted and moulted upperwing greater and primary coverts is hardly detectable, although there may be discernible differences in the remiges and also the alula feathers if some of these have been moulted (Flinks 1994).

Juvenile The feathers of the forehead, crown, nape, mantle and scapulars are dark brown or black. The feathers on the forehead and crown have narrow pale buff to off-white central streaks, giving a closely streaked appearance, whilst the scapulars and mantle have more prominent and larger, triangular buff tips usually with a narrow black fringe. The rump and uppertail-coverts are rufous-brown with black spots and streaks. The malar region, cheeks and ear-coverts are mottled black and buff. The lores are buff and there is an indistinct buff supercilium usually extending from the eye to above the rear ear-coverts, although occasionally it can extend from in front of the eye joining up with the lores. The sides of the neck, chin and throat are pale greyish-buff with some darker brown tips. The breast is rufous-buff, stronger in tone than the flanks, belly and undertail-coverts, which are buff, and there is irregular dark brown/black spotting to the upper breast and (marginally less so and greyer) to the flanks. The remiges are similar to the first-year male, with the outer webs of the secondaries and inner primaries narrowly fringed buff and with greyish-white tips. The upperwing lesser and median coverts are dark grey with prominent buff tips; the upperwing greater coverts are black with large rufous-buff tips. The upperwing primary coverts are dark grey with indistinct greyish-white fringes. The four innermost upperwing greater coverts (07–10) show a variable amount of white on males, some all white and others only c.50%, but females have no white on the inner upperwing greater coverts until their post-juvenile moult. This feature is a reliable way of telling the sex of nestlings from c.7 days old (H. Flinks *in litt.* 2001). The rectrices are similar to the first-year male, with prominent buff fringes and tips. The bill is greyish-pink with a darker grey line running down the culmen to the tip. Legs and feet vary from pale brown to dark grey. Irides are dark brown (Cramp 1988). In transitional plumage from juvenile to first adult, individuals can appear in a variety of confusing variations but are distinguishable either by retained juvenile plumage characters or by the parts of the plumage showing adult characters. The latter will also, with reasonable care, make it possible to sex such birds.

Measurements

		Male *S. r. rubicola*	Female *S. r. rubicola*
Wing	(1)	64.0–68.0 (mean 66.4)	63.0–68.0 (mean 65.4)
	(2)	66.0–70.0 (mean 67.7)	65.0–68.0 (mean 67.2)
	(3)	63.0–69.0 (mean 64.8)	62.0–66.0 (mean 63.9)
Tail		43.0–48.0 (mean 45.2)	42.0–48.0 (mean 44.8)
Bill	(1)	13.7–15.6 (mean 14.9)	14.0–15.8 (mean 15.1)
	(2)	15.1–16.0 (mean 15.6)	15.2–16.4 (mean 16.0)
	(3)	14.1–16.2 (mean 15.0)	14.3–14.9 (mean 14.7)

1 = Netherlands, Belgium, central France and northern Italy
2 = north-west Africa
3 = southern Yugoslavia

		Male *S. r. hibernans*	Female *S. r. hibernans*
Wing	(1)	65.0–67.0 (mean 67.4)	64.0–68.0 (mean 66.2)
	(2)	65.0–69.0 (mean 66.9)	64.0–67.0 (mean 65.4)
Tail		44.0–49.0 (mean 46.5)	43.0–47.0 (mean 45.1)
Bill	(1)	14.0–15.3 (mean 14.6)	14.2–15.6 (mean 14.9)
	(2)	15.0–16.4 (mean 15.8)	15.3–16.2 (mean 15.6)

1 = Britain
2 = western Portugal (Cramp 1988)

The bill in northern populations of *S. r. rubicola* is comparatively short (average 14.1–14.5) but slightly longer (15.6–16.0) in southern populations from Iberia, north-west Africa and the south-east Mediterranean. This criterion has been used to propose other subspecies such as *S. t. desfontanei* (Blanchet 1925) from north-west Africa and *S. t. graecorum* (Laubmann 1927) from Greece, but has proved to be unacceptable (Cramp 1988).

DISTRIBUTION

S. r. hibernans

Breeds in western and possibly southern Norway, the UK excluding Fair Isle and the Shetlands, south to France (western Brittany), the Channel Islands and the west coast of Portugal. In the 1970s both Norway (1974) and Shetlands (1975) (after two isolated breeding records in 1961 and 1962) were colonised possibly by overshooting migrants from the Orkney Islands (Robertson 1975). Breeding was last recorded in Shetland in 1977, but it has possibly occurred (though not recorded) in most years in Norway since the initial colonisation. Ree (1977) stated that it was a rare straggler to Norway, only being recorded 12–14 times before 1970, but since then sightings have increased on the west coast. From 1973 it was suspected that European Stonechats attempted to breed in Norway and in 1974 definite proof was obtained at Hordaland and possibly at More and Romsdal. In 1975 20–30 pairs bred between Rogaland and Romsdal but by 1977 this number had declined to 11 pairs breeding in Rogaland with possible breeding in Oppland in 1977 and 1978. Up to 1980 there were possibly 50–100 pairs breeding, although numbers were probably not this high during the hard winters of 1977–1978 and 1978–1979. After 1980 the species disappeared as a breeder in Norway until 1989 when, following a succession of mild winters, numbers had presumably sufficiently increased to enable it to recolonise, again mainly on the west coast. The number of confirmed breeding pairs up to 1992 was much smaller than before 1980, never exceeding 3–4 pairs (Gjershaug *et al.* 1994). The last confirmed breeding records were of 2–3 pairs breeding in 1992, and up to 1996 there have been no further breeding records. Owing to a scarcity of observers and consequent under-recording it is probable that 10–20 pairs have bred each year in Norway between 1990 and 1997 (Runar R. Jabekk *per* A.

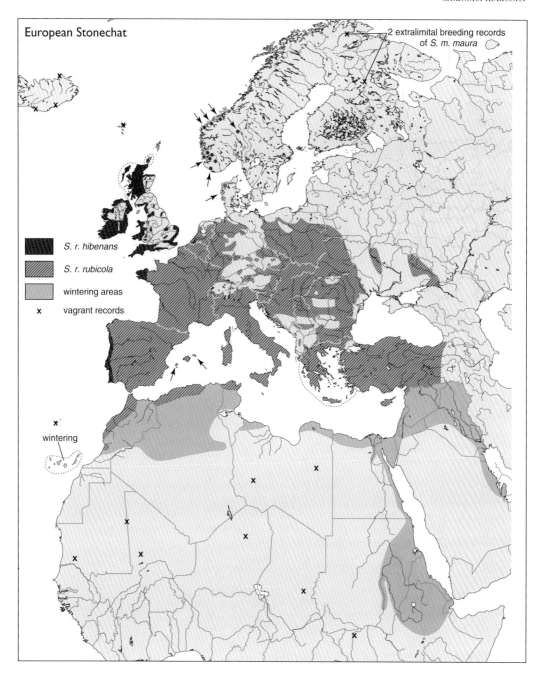

European Stonechat

2 extralimital breeding records
of *S. m. maura*

- **S. r. hibenans**
- **S. r. rubicola**
- wintering areas
- **x** vagrant records

x wintering

W. Clarke *in litt.* 1997). There are now increasing reports of either this subspecies or *S. r. rubicola* from eastern and southern Norway, mainly in spring (Runar R. Jabekk pers. comm. 1999). All records of European Stonechat in Norway prior to 1970 had been referred to the subspecies *S. r. rubicola* from mainland Europe (Haftorn 1971), but Robertson (1975) speculated that birds colonising western Norway from 1974 onwards were more likely to be of the subspecies *hibernans* coming from the northern isles of the UK, namely Shetland and Fair Isle, rather than birds of the subspecies *rubicola* which would, if they had moved up from Denmark, surely have colonised the south coast of Norway and not, as happened, the west coast. Munkejord (1981) tested Robertson's hypothesis by comparing the migratory activity from western Norway with that from Fair Isle over ten day periods in the months February–May for the years 1973–1979: this corresponded significantly, and further evidence was provided by Munkejord (1981) by comparing the dates of spring migration peaks in the years 1976 and 1977, when birds were seen in both Fair Isle and western Norway. In 1976 the peak on Fair Isle was 5–6 March, with six birds present, and on 6–7 March three were present in western Norway. In 1977 12 birds were seen on Fair Isle on 12 March, with 11 in western Norway on 12–13 March. Munkejord suggested that these figures gave a strong indication that European Stonechats observed in western Norway during spring shared a common source area, namely the UK, with those observed on Fair Isle.

Strangely in view of its colonisation and subsequent recolonistaion of Norway the species has not bred on Shetland since the last attempt in 1977. The first breeding attempt was a pair in 1961 and then a single pair in 1962. Following the hard winter of 1962–1963 no more breeding was recorded until a pair was found feeding a fledged juvenile at Dales Voe on 11 September 1975, with other juveniles being found at Fetlar, Sandness and Toft, all in early July 1975, suggestive of breeding. In 1976 four pairs bred with the suggestion that one of these had bred annually at Cunningsburgh since 1972. Finally two pairs bred in 1977 (*Shetland Bird Reports* 1975–1977).

S. r. rubicola

The northern boundary of this subspecies borders the North Sea stretching along the coasts of France (excluding western Brittany), Belgium, Netherlands and Germany to southern Denmark. The range then extends east through southern Poland, Ukraine, Moldova and southern Russia as far as the Podkumka River and the upper reaches of the Kuma River. The range reaches south to Kherson and the Crimea on the north shore of the Black Sea. The northern limits of its range are on the northern edge of the Volyno-Podol'sk Upland, running east through the region of Kiev, Kharkov, lower Don River, and possibly reaching the north western edge of the Stavropol' Upland (Stepanyan 1990). The eastern limits are reached in Georgia, Azerbaijan and northern Armenia, ceasing in the western Caucasus at a line drawn from Grozny to Tbilisi at approximately the 44th meridian, where it comes into contact with the two Caucasian Siberian Stonechat subspecies *S. m. variegata* and *S. m. armenica*. It is present throughout Turkey in all but the eastern mountains. The western limits of its range extend southwards down the Atlantic coast of Europe to the Iberian Peninsula (apart from western Brittany and Portugal). Its range includes the southern European countries bordering the Mediterranean: Spain, the Balearic Islands, France, Italy, Greece and the islands of Corsica, Sardinia, Sicily, Crete and Rhodes but excluding Malta and Cyprus. In central and eastern Europe it is found in Switzerland, Luxembourg, Austria, Slovenia, Slovakia, the Czech Republic, Hungary, Croatia, former Jugoslavia, Albania, Bulgaria and Romania.

It inhabits North Africa from Morocco through northern Algeria and northern Tunisia. It reaches as far south in Morocco as the Middle Atlas Mountains (c.30° on the coast). In northern Algeria and Tunisia it breeds up to the southern foothills of the Tell-Atlas at the c.37th parallel in eastern Algeria and in Tunisia on the central high plateaus south to Lekef and east to Cap Bon (Keith *et al.* 1992). In Denmark it is an extremely scarce breeding bird, being first recorded as breeding in 1942 in south Jutland (Olsen 1992).

During the 1990s the number of pairs rose from one in 1991 to a maximum of 10–11 pairs in 1995, only to fall back to 5–6 pairs in 1996, the majority of breeding attempts being along the west coast of Jutland. A breeding census in 1999 recorded 24–25 pairs (Grell 2000). In parallel with this increase in breeding records, numbers of migrants in Denmark have also been increasing in recent years, with maxima of 50–69 individuals per year in the best years (B. Rasmussen *in litt.* 2000).

STATUS

The European Stonechat populations in western Europe are declining in numbers and the breeding ranges generally contracting, with certain exceptions. In Germany expansion into new areas has been noticed in Schleswig-Holstein, where in the late 1980s it was a scarce breeding bird with from 0–2 pairs; from around 1989 a continuous population increase has been observed until by 1998 there were 120–140 pairs. Similar expansions have occurred in most of the other states of the Federal Republic of Germany and it has also expanded its range north in Denmark, east in Poland and into north-east Ukraine (Pfeifer 2000). Contrary to a general overall decline in the Netherlands, the population in the south-west increased from 41–65 pairs in 1975 to 241–271 by 1993 (Castelijns & van Westrienen 1994).

It has been estimated that up to two-thirds of the European population declined in the two decades 1970–1990 (Tucker & Heath 1994) and this trend continues to the present. The decline has been evident in the UK since the beginning of the twentieth century and has accelerated since the 1940s, together with the populations in western Germany. The decline spread over most of north-west Europe during the 1960–1970s and now includes virtually all of western Europe including the large and important populations in France and Spain. There are, however, areas where populations have remained stable and even increased as stated above (also see below).

The population in the UK is partially migratory and those birds remaining to winter periodically suffer considerable mortality during hard winters. However, numbers are normally restored in 3–4 years provided the subsequent winters are mild. Despite this capacity for quickly recovering from losses, the breeding range in the UK has continually contracted to the traditional strongholds of the southern and western maritime counties, with a marked retreat from inland areas and the east coast. All other northern European populations are migratory except part of those in Belgium, central Germany and possibly in Switzerland, as well as those in southern France, Portugal, Spain and North Africa. Apart from in Portugal (where numbers are stable) these are also in decline. A continuous decline in the amount of suitable habitat, owing primarily to the intensification of agriculture, with afforestation of fallow and marginal areas and excessive disturbance, are considered the main factors contributing to the decline in populations (Hagemeijer & Blair 1997).

Estimates of total breeding pairs for each European country are as follows, and are taken from Tucker & Heath (1994), Hagemeijer & Blair (1997), and Heath *et al.* (2000). Dates in brackets are the year(s) to which the population estimate refers and in which data were collected.

Countries with stable populations 1970–1990

Albania (1991) 1,500–3,000; Andorra (1997) 40–80; Austria (post-1992) 3,000–5,000; Bulgaria (1990– 1997) 10,000–100,000; Croatia (post-1992) 10,000–20,000; Czech Republic (1985–1995) 2,500–5,000; Greece (post-1992) 50,000–100,000; Moldova (1988) 4,500–6,000; Portugal (1989) 10,000–100,000; Romania (post-1992) 50,000–100,000; Russia (post-1992) 10,000–100,000; Turkey (post-1992) 10,000– 100,000; Ukraine (1986) 2,000–3,500.

Countries with declining populations 1970–1990

Belgium (1981–1990) 1,150–1,400 (1); Denmark (1993–1996) 6–11(3); Finland (1990–1995) 0–5(3); France (1997) 100,000–1,000,000 (1); Germany (1985–1994) 1,800–2,300 (2); Luxembourg (post-1992) 120–180 (1); Netherlands (1982) 1,800–2,300 (2); Norway (1990) 0–100 (3); Rep. of Ireland (1998) 13,000–18,000 (1); Spain (post-1992) 300,000–700,000 (1); Switzerland (1993–1996) 500–500 (3); United Kingdom (1988– 1991) 9,000– 23,000 (2); Guernsey (Channel Islands) (post-1992)15–30(3); Jersey (Channel Islands) (post- 1992) 5–10 (2); Isle of Man (post-1992) 90–180 (3).

1 = small decline of at least 20% but less than 50%
2 = large decline of at least 50%
3 = fluctuating with changes of at least 20% but no clear trend

Countries with increasing populations 1970–1990

Hungary (1998) 200,000–400,000 (1); Italy (1988–1997) 200,000–300,000 (1); Liechtenstein (1989) 25– 25 (2); Poland (post-1992) 3,000–6,000 (1); Slovakia (post-1992) 22,000–45,000 (1); Slovenia (post-1992) 8,000–12,000 (1).

1= small increase between 20–49%
2= increase of at least 50%

The North African populations of European Stonechat are also little researched. Anecdotal evidence indicates that in Algeria the species breeds in small numbers; in Morocco it is uncommon; in Tunisia locally common.

MOVEMENTS

S. r. hibernans

Birds emigrating from the UK leave comparatively late in autumn, usually from mid-September to late October, with some stragglers lingering until early November. Concentrations of birds occur along the southern coast of England, notably in October. For example, in coastal southern England (Sussex), concentrations of 28–65 have been recorded at suitable locations on any one day throughout October, usually disappearing by the next day. Similar but smaller concentrations can also be found in southern inland areas. The return movement of birds to their breeding territories that have wintered within the UK commences very early, often from February onwards. Immigrants that have wintered outside of the UK also arrive comparatively early, from late February onwards, reaching a peak in March and continuing on into April, with stragglers into May. Greig-Smith (1979) found a concentration of birds arriving in early March at their breeding areas in southern England (East Sussex). Migrants on Skomer Island off the coast of Wales are most evident in the first 14 days of March, with only occasional records after that and into April. The spring migration is not so marked as in autumn, with very little evidence of the concentration of numbers that is a feature of autumn. Bannerman (1954), although not giving precise figures, states that "large numbers" occurred at the South Foreland Light on the Kent coast of England on 24–25 February; and ten on the southern English coast (Hampshire) on 21 February were considered exceptional (Clark & Eyre 1993). There is only one record of a foreign-ringed individual being recovered in the UK: a male ringed at Tardienta, Huesca, Spain, on 27 October 1979 was retrapped at Surrey Docks, London, on 7 March 1982. This may well have been a British-bred individual returning to its breeding area, although the date it was ringed in Spain is comparatively early for a British emigrant and may indicate an 'overshoot' by an individual from a continental *S. r. rubicola* population. Many birds even in the northernmost limits of their breeding range have returned by March. In the 1970s, when they bred on Shetland and colonised Norway, they had returned to these locations by early to mid-March (Robertson 1976, Munkejord 1981). Vagrants were recorded in Iceland 16 times, involving 19 birds, in the years 1960–1998, all in spring, with records falling between 26 February (three individuals) and 2 April 1994 (one individual). No birds were recorded between 1995 and 1998. The majority (15) came from the south-east of the country, with three from the south-west and one from the north-east. Of the 16 records, seven were between 26 and 28 February, 11 between 9 and 21 March and one on 2 April. Thirteen birds were recorded between 26 February and 10 March, giving an indication of how early they return in spring even to the north-western extremes of their range (G. Petursson *in litt.* 2001). Birds have also occurred on the Faeroe Islands, on seven occasions between 1877 and 1988, although strangely never in the same years as the Iceland birds, and only two records from the Faeroes have been in the last 50 years, singles on 12 March 1954 and 3–4 May 1988 (S. Sorensen *in litt.* 2001). All the birds involved in both countries were considered to be *S. r. hibernans* and presumably were overshooting migrants drifting north-westwards over the Atlantic. The run of occurrences in Iceland between 1972 and 1977 (when they were only not recorded in 1973) correlate with the start of breeding in Norway and Shetland.

Birds from Norway and Sweden migrate south, departing in the autumn and returning in spring, although some are now overwintering (these may be of this subspecies or *rubicola*). In the UK, western Brittany and the Channel Islands, the species is a partial migrant with its winter distribution being roughly similar to its breeding range. In the UK a large proportion of the population remains to winter, often – with others from northern parts of the range – moving south or westwards towards the more temperate coastal areas. Many inland breeding areas are vacated during the winter and some winter territories are often in areas where no breeding occurs, whilst other territories that have been vacated by breeding birds are occupied by different wintering birds. That part of the UK population which migrates usually leaves from late September to early November, with the majority leaving in mid-October. Most of these migrants are first-year birds and they go to southern Europe and North Africa, with the majority of records coming from Spain. Lack (1943–1944) demonstrated that for certain small passerine species a greater proportion of first-year birds migrate than adults. Dungeness Bird Observatory on the south coast of England records European Stonechat as a migrant from mid-September to November, and adults were not thought to figure greatly in this migration (Riddiford 1981). Johnson (1961) considered that autumn migrants on Jersey were invariably first-year birds.

Up to the end of 1996 the BTO had 191 recoveries reported of British-ringed birds. Of these 154 were within the UK, with 57 of them showing movement of less than 10km, 79 between 10km and 100km and 18 in excess of 100km. The remaining 37 were from other countries: Spain 25, France 6, Algeria 3, Morocco, Belgium and Portugal 1 each (BTO 1998).

Since 1996 there have been two more foreign recoveries, one from Morocco (January 1997) and one from Algeria (November 1997). Always accepting that the data may be biased by the varying intensity of observer activity in different countries, the foreign recoveries suggest that the majority of UK-bred European Stonechats that leave the UK winter around the northern, eastern and southern coasts of Spain and possibly on the Balearic Islands, with smaller numbers reaching the North African coast. It also appears that some individuals winter further north, as recoveries from northern France between mid-November and mid-February appear to be of birds in winter territories. The longest-recorded movement of a UK-ringed European Stonechat is of a nestling ringed at Frensham, Surrey, southern England, on 30 April 1988 that was belatedly reported from Casablanca, Morocco, on 3 August 1990, a movement of 2,022km. This record also constitutes the southernmost recovery of a UK-ringed individual to date.

In the UK young birds from first and second broods appear to adopt one of two strategies after they become independent. They may only move a short way out of the territory they were born in, such as in southern England where the distance covered was often only 500–1,000m in the first three months (Greig-Smith 1979); or they may wander considerably further, with two nestlings in the north of England being recovered 340km north-east and 160km south-west respectively from their birthplace, three months after they left the nest. A colour-ringing study of juvenile birds from broods in northern England (Cumbria) has highlighted the existence of what can only be termed juvenile moulting flocks. These are located away from existing territories and are always on the coast, although the individuals comprising them may have been born well inland. They comprise 6–10 individuals, all unrelated, and there are never any adults present. These flocks are only in evidence at the end of the breeding season. Why they only consist of unrelated individuals is unknown but it has been speculated that it could be a means of maintaining a strong gene pool, as presumably some of these birds might pair with another member of the flock (J. Callion pers. comm. 2001).

S. r. rubicola

The majority of the European population of *rubicola* is migratory, with only a small number possibly remaining to winter in central Europe. Birds resident in the extreme south, south-west and south-east of their range around the Mediterranean tend to be mainly sedentary, as for example in Spain, Greece and Crete, where they are widespread and common residents. Possibly some are altitudinal migrants and make local movements to lower elevations in winter, such as in Greece. Birds from the more northerly parts of their range move south and west to winter in the southern part of their range, joining the resident birds. Together they form significant concentrations in Spain, the Balearic Islands and the central and eastern Mediterranean basin. On Malta, although not breeding, it is a common autumn and spring migrant with smaller numbers wintering (J. Sultana *in litt.* 1999), whilst on Cyprus it is a very common and widespread winter visitor mainly below 700m (Flint & Stewart 1992). Winter visitors also augment the resident birds on Greece and Crete. The origin of many of these migrants is western, central and eastern Europe.

In North Africa birds from more northerly European populations join resident birds in northern Morocco, Algeria and Tunisia (Thomsen & Jacobsen 1979). In Libya it is found wintering around the coast and inland at Tripoli, where it is common north of about 32°N in coastal and steppe zones between October and April; in the Cyrenaica provinces of northern Libya and at Al Jabal Al Akhdar (Bundy 1976). Bundy also quotes single records from well inland in the Libyan desert at Sarir on 21 November 1967 (J. Houston), from Sabha in Fezzan province on 7 April 1966 (Erard & Larigauderie in Bundy 1976) and in the Libyan desert at Al Jaghbub between October and March for two successive years (Moltoni 1928).

Recoveries of birds ringed in north and western Europe (Belgium, France, Germany, Hungary, Italy, Luxembourg, Netherlands and Switzerland) indicate a similar wintering area to that of *hibernans*, although recoveries in North Africa showed a slightly more easterly bias than *hibernans* (van Hecke 1965). There also appears to be a tendency for birds originating from eastern Europe to move more eastwards, e.g. a bird ringed in Hungary was recovered wintering in the Peloponnese. Small numbers have also been found wintering as far west as the Canary Islands (B. Small pers. comm. 2001) and also exceptionally as a vagrant to Madeira (Sarmento 1936, Zino *et al.* 1995).

In Algeria *rubicola* has been found to winter regularly along the northern limits of the Sahara and in the oases surrounding the Grand Erg Occidental and also to the west, representing a penetration of up to 500km into the Sahara Desert (Johnson 1971c). An individual ringed at Maastricht in the Netherlands on 30 June 1952 was found in the Algerian Sahara on 16 November 1952 at Beaupetre, Les Oasis (31° 54′N, 3° 41′E). Johnson (1971c) speculated that it would be reasonable to expect to find this species wintering in other intervening oases within the 500km band and possibly in a belt of suitable habitat which exists still further south between Adrar (27° 52′N) and Reggane (26° 43′N), although in the small area he sampled they were not found. The majority of birds wintering in Algeria are presumed to be of this subspecies (although both *rubicola* and *hibernans* have been recovered in Algeria), as there are more recoveries from North Africa of birds ringed in this subspecies range than for *hibernans*. Vagrants possibly of this race have been recorded very rarely south of the Sahara from coastal Mauretania, northern Mali, northern Niger and Chad (Keith *et al.* 1992). In Egypt *rubicola* is locally common in winter along the north coast and in the Nile Delta and Lower Valley, the Faiyum, the Suez Canal and throughout the Sinai areas, as well as around the Western Desert oases. It is uncommon along the Red Sea coast, and the southernmost record in Egypt is of one at Abu Ramad on 18 February 1985 (Goodman & Meininger 1989).

S. r. *rubicola* occurs in all areas of Israel but mostly in the areas of Mediterranean climate in the north and centre (Shirihai 1995). In Jordan it is a common winter visitor from early October to early March in the Northern Highlands, Jordan Valley and Azraq areas, becoming less common in the Southern Highlands and at Aqaba (Andrews 1995). It is similarly regular in Lebanon (Vere Benson 1970) and probably also occurs in Syria. In Saudi Arabia it is an uncommon winter visitor (Meinertzhagen 1954, Jennings 1981a,b) and in Bahrain it is a winter visitor in small numbers (Hirschfeld 1995). In Iraq it has been recorded as common around Mosul and Baghdad from November to mid-February (Allouse 1953), in southern Kurdestan in December and at Nasiriyeh in January (Meinertzhagen 1924) and it winters in coastal Turkey (Cramp 1988). There is some doubt about whether it occurs in the neighbouring Gulf States, although it possibly turns up in the United Arab Emirates and Kuwait in small numbers.

Increasingly, birds of either this subspecies or *hibernans* are being recorded in Sweden and Finland, mainly in the spring and summer periods but also in autumn and now overwintering in Sweden. These records are probably overshooting migrants of the subspecies *rubicola* from mainland Europe, although they could possibly be birds moving east from the Norwegian population. The autumn records are harder to explain unless they are birds dispersing from the Norwegian population or ones which have remained undetected throughout the summer. No breeding of either of these subspecies has been recorded in Finland but a 'pure' pair of either *rubicola* or *hibernans* nested for the first time at Varhallarna, Scania, Sweden, in June 2000, hatching two broods and fledging a total of approximately six young (N. Kjellen *in litt.* 2001). This followed the first record of an overwintering male at Ottenby in Sweden in 1997/1998. The return movement of *rubicola* back to its breeding areas commences at the same time as *hibernans*. A return movement has been noted at Gibraltar, beginning on 17 February and continuing until 20 March (Stenhouse 1921). [See also under breeding for return dates.]

SIBERIAN STONECHAT
Saxicola maura

Muscicapa maura Pallas, 1773, Reise versch. Russ. Reichs, 2, p.428—Karassum, [Ishim River, western Siberia]

Etymology *maura* from Latin *maurus* meaning Moorish, African = black

Alternative names Collared Stonechat, Collared Bush Chat, Collared Indian Bush Chat, Black-headed Chat

TAXONOMY
Polytypic. See discussion on page 131.

IDENTIFICATION
There are distinct plumage characteristics attributable to the subspecies comprising Siberian Stonechat (listed below) that allow them to be identified from the two western races comprising European Stonechat. The most important is the tone and extent of the colouring on the rump and uppertail-coverts. Whilst subtly varying in these parameters amongst the eastern subspecies there is a commonality in that, compared to the two western races, rump and uppertail-coverts are always paler rufous-buff and totally unmarked. The rump-patch is also considerably larger than is normally found in either of the western races and gives in many cases a 'wrapped-around' impression extending onto the sides of the rump, which is not found in European Stonechat. The general overall colour of the upperparts and underparts of this group in autumn and winter is also paler than in European Stonechat.

Main identification criteria of Siberian Stonechat compared to European Stonechat

1. Rump and uppertail-coverts are always a paler orange-buff or rufous-buff and diagnostically without any dark streaking or spots. Male rump shows increasingly white owing to abrasion of the orange-buff tips from very early in the year, often January, and is pure white by the time breeding commences. Female rump is always unmarked and paler, being orange-buff rather than the darker buff-brown spotted and streaked with black of females of European Stonechat. The longest tail coverts of female have thin pale brown shaft-streaks but these are not visible in the field. Some of the shorter tail-coverts often become white as feathers wear.

2. The pale area of the rump and uppertail-coverts is always more extensive in both sexes extending over all the rump and tail-coverts and, in some males, marginally onto the lower back. In males it often gives a 'wrapped-around' impression extending onto the sides of the rump. On Siberian Stonechat the pale area of the rump on both sexes extends up the body to level with or above the tip of the innermost tertial (09). On European Stonechat it usually only reaches to level with longest outermost tertial (07) or falls between (07) and the middle tertial (08).

3. The underwing-coverts and axillaries of adult males are diagnostically black, and some first-year males can also have black feathers as early as September.

4. The tail is marginally (although not invariably, and not visibly in the field) white at the base in male *S. m. maura, indica* and a small proportion of *stejnegeri*. It is more extensively white at the base of the tail and visible on some males of *S. m. armenica*, and extends over a large part of the tail and is highly visible in all male *S. m. variegata*. It is buff at the base and visible, but not extending over such a large area, in female *S. m. variegata*. The only other female with buff at the tail-base is *S. m. armenica* but this is variable, small and not visible in the field.

5. The upperparts appear much paler in fresh plumage due to paler and more extensive fringes to the upperpart feathering and the pale, almost white outer edges and tips of the tertials and inner remiges. This often creates the impression of a pale panel on the inner closed wing and accentuates the black of the remiges and the black centres of the tertials. The tail in fresh plumage is almost black with prominent white fringes to the outer webs as well as tips.

6. The primary coverts, owing to the extensive white outer edges and tips, form a noticeable pale area on the closed wing. The whiteness is accentuated by the largest feather (03) of the alula being mainly black. This contrast is not nearly so apparent in European Stonechat.

7. Rufous on the male's underparts, apart from *S. m. przewalskii*, is paler and less extensive, and abrades to leave a smaller rufous patch only on the breast. The rest of the underparts are white.

8. The white on the neck, sides of breast and inner upperwing-coverts of the male is more extensive.

9. Females and first-winter males of subspecies *S. m. maura* and *stejnegeri* usually show distinct supercilia which meet on the forehead immediately above the base of the upper mandible.

10. The upper breast and flanks of females and first-winter males are paler, more rufous- or tawny-buff than chestnut-brown.

11. The upperparts of females and first-year males from forehead to mantle and scapulars are paler buff-grey or just buff.
12. Females do not show any dark feathering on the chin and throat; these areas remain white or pale throughout the year.
13. First-year males in autumn can show only a little dark feathering on the head, chin and throat and in extreme cases are not separable from females.
14. The primary projection is longer. It is about two-thirds that of the overlying tertials.

Siberian Stonechat
S. maura maura

European Stonechat
S. rubicola rubicola

Siberian Stonechat
S. maura variegata

Wings of European Stonechat *Saxicola rubicola rubicola* (b) and Siberian Stonechat *Saxicola maura maura* (a) and *Saxicola maura variegata* (c) Note the difference in primary projection between the partial or short-distance migrant European Stonechat and the long-distance Siberian Stonechat. European Stonechat has short rounded wing with short wing point reaching just to uppertail-coverts and primary projection extending about half the length of overlying tertials. Siberian wing is more attenuated with wing point reaching as far as half way down tail and primary projection two-thirds the length of overlying tertials. Note also difference in length of P10 (After Glutz & Bauer 1988.)

Rarely, individuals of European Stonechat either *hibernans* or *rubicola* can appear very pale with much of the pigmentation considerably reduced in tone and consequently they superficially show many characteristics of Siberian Stonechat. One such individual, a male, was discovered wintering in Essex in southern England from October 2001–March 2002 (Mike Buckland *in litt.* 2002). However, with careful attention to all the above criteria it should be possible to identify the majority of such individuals. This particular individual showed prominent streaking on the rump and uppertail-coverts and was therefore obviously not a Siberian Stonechat. The possibility of hybrids should be considered but records of hybridisation between European and Siberian Stonechat are very rare. Another female individual found wintering in Kent in southern England also 2001/2002 (Mike Buckland *in litt.* 2002) was considered by some either a hybrid or an abnormally pale European Stonechat, although it appeared to show all the characterisitics of a female Siberian Stonechat. Its true identity at the time of publishing is still not established and may never be, but if it was not a Siberian Stonechat then its very close similarity to a female of that species should serve as a warning for extra vigilance when encountering supposed female or first-winter Siberian Stonechat and the acceptance that in some cases the true identity may never be established.

Male characteristics In autumn and winter plumage the rump is generally dull rufous or orange-buff, and this slowly abrades to white although the speed of the abrasion varies considerably amongst individuals of all eastern races, so that some birds may have virtually white rumps by late autumn or early winter whilst others still show a rufous- or orange-buff rump as late as spring. Abrasion is not uniform, and as it progresses the rump can take on a blotchy appearance, and some rump and uppertail-covert feathers retain orange- or rufous-buff tips.

The upperparts of adult males are similar to those of the western races except that in fresh autumn plumage the fringes to the black feathers are noticeably paler, almost sandy-buff in colour, and slightly longer. This gives individuals of these races a very pale appearance, superficially the tone of a Whinchat, obscuring much of the black feather centres. In breeding plumage the extent of white showing on the inner wing and around the neck and sides of breast is usually more extensive, although it can be variable. In extreme cases some males show a white neck-collar almost meeting on the hindneck, being separated only by buff and grey speckling; in a few, very extreme cases the white actually does meet on the hindneck.

In fresh plumage there is a more noticeable pale panel on the closed wing formed by the pale outer fringes to the secondaries and tertials. The upperwing primary coverts are often strikingly fringed and tipped with white, almost concealing their black centres on the closed wing and contrasting with the predominantly all-black largest feather (03) of the alula. The tail is virtually black with whitish fringes to the outer webs of the tail feathers and prominent white tips. The underparts are generally lighter in tone and not so obviously rufous-brown as in European Stonechat. In breeding plumage there is often a strong demarcation between the bright rufous breast and the white belly, with the rufous on the breast being restricted to a relatively small area in the centre, fading on the flanks. Throughout the year the axillaries and underwing-coverts in adult males and some first-year males (after September) are black with very fine white tips. Males of most of the six eastern races show a varying amount of white at the base of the tail feathers, but this is only truly visible in the field on the race *S. m. variegata* and marginally on some specimens of *S. m. armenica*.

Female characteristics The overall plumage is paler than European Stonechat. The upperparts appear pale buff, streaked with darker brown caused by the darker centres to the feathers. The rump and uppertail-coverts are rufous-buff in autumn, brighter and paler than the western races, fading to a creamy-white in spring and summer. There are no dark streaks or spots and this area is also more extensive than in European Stonechat.

Females of the Siberian Stonechat subspecies *S. m. maura* and *stejnegeri* show distinct pale buff supercilia which meet on the forehead and have a pale buff or white chin and throat contrasting with the darker rufous or tawny-buff breast and flanks, which fades to paler pinkish-buff on the belly, ventral area and undertail-coverts. There are also noticeable pale fringes to the outer webs of the secondaries and tertials which form a distinctive pale panel on the closed wing. First-year males of Siberian Stonechat subspecies-*S. m. maura* and *stejnegeri* can look very similar to females (see below). The pale chin and throat remain throughout the year in females of *S. m. maura* and *stejnegeri* whereas females of the other four eastern races usually always show some dark feathering on the throat which gets progressively darker as the feathers wear. The axillaries and underwing-coverts of all six races are grey fringed with buff. The tail is black or dark brown, and in fresh plumage it is prominently fringed and tipped with pale buff, more so than in the western races. Females do not have any white at the base of the tail feathers, apart from those of the subspecies *S. m. variegata* and *armenica*, and even here this feature is often restricted and never appears pure white but either creamy-white or pale buff. The primary projection in birds of the subspecies *maura*, *stejnegeri* and *indica* is longer than in the European Stonechat, being about two-thirds the length of the overlying tertials. In the subspecies *S. m. armenica*, *S. m. variegata* and *S. m. przewalskii* it is marginally longer still.

Juvenile plumage is very similar to that of the western races but the rump and uppertail-coverts are paler rufous-buff, unstreaked and more extensive. Juvenile males can often show a hint of white at the base of the tail where that is a character of the race, even before they have moulted into first-adult plumage.

S. m. maura

Muscicapa maura Pallas, 1773, *Reise versch. Russ. Reichs* 2, p.428—Karrasum, [Ishim River, western Siberia]

Adult male autumn/winter Slightly smaller and paler than adult male *S. r. rubicola* and *hibernans*. The feathers of the upperparts have much paler sandy fringes which, being slightly more extensive, obscure the darker feather centres more and thus give the bird a noticeably paler appearance. The black feathering on the chin and throat is also more obscured although usually still visible to a varying degree. The rump and uppertail-coverts are rufous- or orange-buff and usually show no dark streaks or blotches. Jannes (1990) and Stoddart (1992) both drew attention to the fact that a few individuals can show thin, brownish, hardly visible shaft-streaks on the longest uppertail-coverts, and at least two specimens of *S. m. maura* in BMNH show this characteristic. The underparts of *maura* are paler rufous than in European Stonechat, with the central breast being distinctly brighter rufous than the surrounding feathers, which are paler orange or pinkish-buff.

The rectrices are dark brown to black, prominently fringed and tipped with pale buff, which also accentuates the overall impression of paleness. The base of the tail feathers can either be all black or show a very small amount of white often confined to the inner web of the feather. The white on *S. m. maura* is given as less than 5mm by Dement'ev & Gladkov (1968), and Svensson (1992) gives a measurement of less than 8mm at the base of the outermost (06) tail feather. Cramp (1988) states that some birds from Turkmenistan and Uzbekistan in the former USSR and the Tien Shan and Altai mountain ranges in north-west Mongolia show up to 10mm of white at the base of tail feathers 02–05, whilst other specimens from western Siberia had between 11–17mm of white in the base of the tail (Ticehurst 1938). On a typical *maura* in the field the white at the tail-base is invisible, being totally obscured by the uppertail-coverts. The remiges are dark brown/black with the secondaries showing prominent pale buff fringes to the outer webs, creating a very distinct pale wing-panel. The upperwing lesser, median and greater coverts are dark brown/black with pale buff fringes to the outer webs and large buff-white tips. The tertials are black with broad pale buff fringes and tips. The underwing-coverts and axillaries are black with narrow white fringes. Bill, legs and feet are black and the irides dark brown.

First-winter male See under *S. m. stejnegeri*.

Adult female autumn/winter Compared to female *S. t. hibernans/rubicola* it shows paler upperparts and underparts owing to the longer, paler sandy-buff fringes to the feathers. Forehead, crown, nape, mantle, scapulars and back are sandy-grey to buff-brown showing indistinct and largely obscured black feather centres. The rump and uppertail-coverts are a more extensive and paler rufous-buff, with some longer uppertail coverts occasionally showing narrow brown shaft-streaks but never broad and black as in European Stonechat. Some of the shorter uppertail coverts show occasional white. The rectrices are black/brown with no pale base but have prominent buff-white fringes to the outer webs as well as tips. The lores are pale buff and the cheeks and ear-coverts speckled black and buff. Prominent buff supercilia which meet on the forehead extend from the top of the bill over the eye to the rear of the ear-coverts. The chin and throat are buff-white and show no dark feather-bases, contrasting with the upper breast and flanks which can vary from a pale rufous or yellowish-brown to tawny-buff. The underwing-coverts and axillaries are dark grey with extensive buff fringes. The remiges are brownish-black with very narrow buff-white fringes to the outer webs. The secondaries and tertials have wider buff fringes to the outer webs which form a noticeable pale panel on the closed wing. The tertials are black with broad pale buff fringes and tips.

First-winter female Similar to adult female. The remiges and rectrices are unmoulted as with the western races during the post-juvenile moult, and therefore slightly more worn and can appear slightly browner with a marginally greater contrast between the moulted upperwing-coverts. The buff fringes to the upperwing primary coverts are broader at the tip than along the edges. In adults they are the same width (Cramp 1988).

Measurements

	Male	Female
Wing	68.0–71.0 (mean 69.1)	68.5–70.5 (mean 69.5)
Tail	46.0–51.5 (mean 49.6)	48.0–51.5 (mean 49.4)
Bill	13.5–15.0 (mean 13.8)	13.0–14.3 (mean 13.8)

[Own measurements BMNH, 2001]

S. m. stejnegeri

Pr.(atincola) rubicola stejnegeri Parrot, 1908, *Verh. Orn. Ges. Bayern* 8 (1907), p.124—Iterup (Etorofu) and Jesso (Hakodate), northern Japan.

This subspecies is very similar in plumage detail and size to *S. m. maura*, so much so that many vagrants that arrive in western Europe in autumn are not specifically identified, being only recorded as *S. m. maura/stejnegeri*, as often it is impossible to separate them racially in the field.

Svensson (1992) noted that museum specimens differed in that *stejnegeri* had a wider base to the bill at the proximal edge of the nostrils than *maura* (4.7–5.7mm, n=39, mean 5.23, against 4.0–4.9 mm, n=44, mean 4.55), but otherwise there was much similarity in plumage characteristics owing to extensive individual variation. Male *stejnegeri* also differ in usually having the tail wholly black, but a small minority can have up to 10mm at the base white although invisible in the field. It is likely that *stejnegeri* intergrades with *maura* over the extensive area where their ranges meet in central and eastern Siberia and Mongolia, which could give rise to individuals with white bases to the tail. In fresh autumn plumage *stejnegeri* from eastern parts of the range (China) had feather fringes both above and below a darker rufous than *maura*, but with abrasion the rufous on the underparts is restricted to the breast and flanks, although the area is slightly more extensive than on *maura*, with the rest of the underparts fading to pale rufous-orange or buff (Cramp 1988). In the tone and extent of rufous on the underparts *stejnegeri* is closely similar to European Stonechat although not quite as dark. Adult male *stejnegeri* in worn plumage appear to show less extensive white on the rump than *maura*. First-year birds have slightly darker remiges and rectrices than *maura* and apparently moult the wing-coverts more extensively, similar to *S. r. rubicola/hibernans*, since ageing in the hand is less easy than for *maura* (Svensson 1992). The axillaries and underwing-coverts of adult and some first-year males after September are black with very narrow white fringes. Bill, legs and feet are black and irides dark brown.

First-winter male *S. m. maura* and *S. m. stejnegeri* Both differ from European Stonechat and to a lesser degree from the other four eastern subspecies in that they appear very pale with some showing hardly any evidence of black or dark feather markings on the head or upperparts. The feathers appear sandy-buff owing to the extensive fringes concealing most of the darker feather centres, and there are usually light buff supercilia which meet on the forehead and extend from the bill to above and to the rear of the ear-coverts. There is a variable amount of dark grey or black feather bases on the forehead, lores, cheeks and ear-coverts, with some showing reasonably extensive darker feathering while, at the other extreme, there is no dark feathering visible at all on the head, making it very difficult to sex these individuals.

The dark feathers of the chin and throat are obscured to a greater or lesser extent by pale tips and fringes and appear buff-white, usually showing little or no dark feathering and consequently contrasting with the pale rufous breast and flanks. The white feathers of the neck are mostly obscured by the extensive buff feather fringes, and the white on the rump and uppertail-coverts is largely obscured by extensive orange-buff tips. Some first-winter males, as with adult males, can show a predominantly white rump as early as October, although the uppertail-coverts usually always show broad chestnut-buff tips. The inner upperwing-coverts show slightly less white than in the adult male, although the distinction is marginal. The primary coverts are prominently fringed with white, which obscures a lot of the black, and they form a contrast with the largest (03) predominantly black feather of the alula. The upperwing greater coverts have large pale chestnut-buff tips, which form a noticeable bar across the wing. There are pale buff fringes along the outer edges of the secondaries and tertials which form a distinct pale panel when the wing is closed again, contributing to the overall paleness of the bird. Possibly because of the more extensive pale fringes the feathers do not appear to wear as quickly as in adult males, which can commence assuming summer plumage from late February. First-years assume the summer plumage later, and there can still be fairly extensive buff fringes to especially the mantle, chin and throat into early summer.

The axillaries and underwing-coverts are again variable, with the majority showing grey feathers with broad buff fringes. Some, however, have assumed jet-black axillaries and underwing-coverts as early as September or show a mixture of grey and black feathering.

Adult male spring/summer Similar to European Stonechat, but it has the rufous confined to the breast with the rest of the underparts paler, rufous-buff or orange, eventually wearing to pure white. The white neck and wing-patches are usually more extensive than the western races, whilst the rest of the upperparts are similar to western races apart from the extensive unstreaked white rump and uppertail-coverts.

Adult female spring/summer Differs from the European Stonechat in being paler and without the dark chin and throat. It can often show noticeable whitish neck-patches and the area formed by the rump and uppertail-coverts is always paler, being orange-buff, more extensive and without any dark streaks.

Adult males seen in western Palearctic Great care should be taken when attempting to identify suspected male Siberian Stonechats of eastern subspecies *maura* and *stejnegeri* that occur in the western Palearctic in late winter and spring when presumably returning to their breeding areas.

The main criteria by which to identify such individuals is the more extensive, paler orange-buff and white rump and uppertail-covert area, which shows no dark streaks or blotches. The rump and uppertail-coverts begin to abrade as early as January so that virtually all males, which from records appear to return comparatively later through western Europe (from late April and mostly May to June), will either show a mixture of orange-buff and white, almost completely white with only a few remnants of orange-buff tips on the uppertail-coverts, or completely white. At the time vagrants are returning through Europe most European Stonechat males will show comparatively less white on the darker rufous-brown rump and uppertail-coverts, which will also show noticeable dark streaks and blotches and be smaller in area.

However, it is becoming apparent that individual males of *S. r. rubicola* from the southern parts of their range can appear very similar to a summer-plumaged Siberian Stonechat male, showing large areas of unmarked white on the rump and uppertail-coverts (but still not quite as extensive as Siberian Stonechat males) as well as large areas of white on the neck and inner upperwing-coverts. Some male *S. r. hibernans* can also show comparatively large areas of white on the rump and uppertail-coverts, usually in late summer, but virtually without exception there will be some black streaking or spots, if only one or two, present on the rump or more usually the uppertail-coverts.

Other identification criteria that can be used in conjunction with the above are the underwing-coverts, which will be solidly black in adult males and also in many first-year males (some *S. r. rubicola* males can also show dark on the underwing but never totally black); the longer primary projection; paler buff, often almost white, on the sides of the breast, belly, ventral area and undertail-coverts, with only a very restricted, slightly darker and richer rufous breast-patch and a larger area of white on the sides of the neck.

With the increasing awareness of the subtleties of plumage variation amongst the European Stonechat group more attention is being paid to the plumage of what are presumed to be birds of the race *hibernans*. Individuals are now being discovered in southern areas of the UK that are much paler than normal *hibernans* and possibly are from southern populations of *rubicola* that may have overshot mainland Europe or drifted west on spring migration. Males of southern populations of *rubicola* can appear extremely similar to spring-plumaged males of *S. m. maura* and *stejnegeri* as stated above. However, the white on the neck, wing and rump is always less extensive than on typical *S. m. maura* and *stejnegeri*. Particular attention should be paid to the rump and uppertail-coverts. Although white, they still form a smaller patch than on the eastern races, which show extensive white feathering occasionally with scattered orange-buff tips on these areas. This large white area extends both laterally on the rump (often appearing almost to extend to the extreme side of the tail) and lengthwise, marginally and irregularly, upwards onto the extreme lower back. *S. r. rubicola* usually shows a variable amount of black or dark brown streaking and/or spotting, sometimes only apparent as one or two dark marks on the uppertail-coverts. Individuals from more southerly populations can have a pure white rump and uppertail-covert patch, although it usually will not be as extensive as an eastern race individual. The white neck-patches usually do not extend so far around in collar fashion onto the hindneck, although some individuals from more southerly populations of *rubicola* such as Sicily (Corso 2001). can have the collar virtually joining on the hindneck. The fringes to the upperparts of *S. m. maura* and *stejnegeri* are slightly paler, and in spring such individuals appear to have these fringes less worn than in *rubicola* possibly owing to their slightly greater length. This usually conveys a paler impression owing to the black/brown of the feather centres being less apparent than on *S. t. rubicola*. However, this criterion should only be used in conjunction with other more distinctive identification criteria. The axillaries and underwing-coverts are deep black, sometimes still with narrow white fringes and tips in *S. m. maura* and *stejnegeri* which contrast with the pale grey to white on the inner webs of the undersides of the remiges, whilst in *rubicola* they are a variably grey to dull blackish-grey often with broader white fringes and tips. The undersides of the remiges are greyer on both webs with no white, so consequently there is less contrast between the axillaries and underwing-coverts and remiges than is apparent on *S. m. maura* and *stejnegeri*.

Measurements

	Male	Female
Wing	68.5–70.0 (mean 69.6)	66.0–67.0 (mean 66.7)
Tail	49.5–51.3 (mean 50.4)	48.5–50.0 (mean 49.3)
Bill	14.3–15.0 (mean 14.8)	14.0–15.0 (mean 14.4)

[Own measurements BMNH, 2000]

S. m. indica

Pr.(atincola) indica Blyth, 1847, *J. Asiat. Soc. Bengal* 16, p.129—India; restricted to Kashmir by Baker, 1921, *J. Bombay Nat. Hist. Soc.* 27, p.709.

This is the smallest of the Siberian Stonechat subspecies. Basically similar in plumage characters to *S. m. stejnegeri*. However, some males have a small but variable amount of white at the base of the tail. Often it is only on the extreme 'fluffy' base of the feathers and it is rarely on the outer tail feathers (Ticehurst 1922–1924). Of 14 skins examined by Ticehurst only three had white on the central pair of feathers extending up to 9mm from the base, whilst another six had only the smallest amount of white possible on these feathers. The other tail feathers had slightly more white, with 11 birds showing white on the inner webs up to a maximum of 12.0mm. One bird had 15mm and the other two showed no white at all (Ticehurst 1938). The fringes to the upperpart feathers are also not quite as pale, being slightly more rufous-brown in shade than the paler sandy-brown fringes of *stejnegeri*. In fresh autumn plumage the male's underparts are entirely rufous, slightly richer on the upper breast. The uppertail-coverts are orange-buff. The undertail-coverts are white. Occasionally a few undertail-coverts show an asymmetrical black or dark brown sub-terminal spot and tawny-buff tip. The white on the inner wing and neck is prominent even in fresh plumage, and the neck-patches are large, often almost joining on the hindneck. In worn plumage the male has only a rich rufous breast-patch. The sides of the breast and the rest of the underparts fade to mainly white suffused faintly with orange-buff. The rump is pure white and relatively small in extent compared to other eastern races, but still more extensive than *S. r. rubicola* and *S. r. hibernans*. The uppertail-coverts are also pure white and unmarked.

The female in fresh plumage shows a pale buff-white chin and throat with greyish feathers showing through, although some can show no dark feathering at all. As the year progresses the throat becomes progressively darker. The upperparts are dark brown with broad pale buff-brown fringes. There is a small white wing-patch on the inner greater coverts and tertials but no white on the sides of the neck. The underparts are entirely pale rufous-buff with the strongest colouring on the breast fading to paler orange-buff on the rest of the underparts. There is an ill-defined buff supercilium from the base of the bill above and behind the eye, and the pale buff outer edges to the tertials and inner secondaries form a pale panel on the closed wing. In both sexes in fresh plumage there are prominent greyish-white tips to both the primaries and the tail as well as broad orange-buff fringes to the tertials.

Measurements

	Male	Female
Wing	64.5–70.0 (mean 66.2)	63.0–65.5 (mean 64.2)
Tail	43.5–49.0 (mean 46.3)	46.5–48.8 (mean 47.3)
Bill	12.5–14.5 (mean 13.6)	12.0–13.5 (mean 13.3)

[Own measurements BMNH, 2000]

S. m. przewalskii

Pratincola maura var. *Przewalskii* Pleske, 1889, *Wiss. Result. Przewalski Reise, Zool.* 2, Vögel, p.46, pl.4, figs.1, 2, 3—mountains of Kansu and eastern Turkestan [= Gansu Province of China]

The largest of the Siberian Stonechat subspecies, slightly larger than *armenica* and *variegata* and considerably larger than *maura* and *stejnegeri*. The general plumage tone of both sexes on the upperparts and underparts is very close to the darkest *S. r. hibernans* and makes this the darkest of all the six eastern races. Examples of *stejnegeri* from the eastern parts of their range (in China), which are darker than those from the west, are still not as dark as typical *przewalskii*. In fresh autumn plumage the upperparts of the male are fringed dark rufous-brown and the underparts differ from other eastern races in being entirely dark buff-orange from breast to undertail-coverts. The rump and uppertail-coverts are also a slightly darker buff-orange in fresh plumage. One male in BMNH shows a very small amount of white at the base of the innermost pair of tail feathers (less than 5mm) but this is exceptional. By spring (mid-May) the dark rufous-brown is restricted to the breast and belly with the rest of the underparts faded to a paler orange-buff. The rump and uppertail-coverts are pure white and the head and upperparts are entirely black. The underwing-coverts and axillaries are black in adult and some first-year males.

The female in fresh plumage has the entire underparts including undertail-coverts orange-buff, but paler and not as rich in tone as the male. The chin and throat are buff but with dark feathers showing through on the throat. There is a short buff supercilium. No white on the neck is apparent or pale base to any of the tail feathers. The rump and uppertail-coverts are orange-buff. The white on the inner upperwing-coverts is restricted to the innermost greater covert (10), of which the inner web is entirely white and the outer web white only on the basal two-thirds.

Measurements

	Male	Female
Wing	73.0–78.0 (mean 75.4)	71.5–74.0 (mean 65.2)
Tail	53.0–59.5 (mean 56.6)	49.0–54.5 (mean 51.9)
Bill	14.5–15.5 (mean 15.0)	14.8–15.5 (mean 15.0)

[Own measurements BMNH, 2001]

S. m. variegata

Parus Variegatus S.G. Gmelin, 1774, *Reise Russl.*, 3, p.105, pl.20, fig.3—Shemakha [= Azerbaijan]

This race and *S. m. armenica* are sometimes colloquially called the Caucasian or Caspian Stonechat owing to their geographical distribution and, apart from *S. m. przewaslkii*, they are the largest of the races found in the Palearctic. The race *S. m. variegata* is similar in plumage to the races *S. m. maura* and *stejnegeri* but is even paler in fresh autumn plumage owing to the extensive sandy-buff fringes to the feathers on the head and upperparts. However, first-year males, unlike some *S. m. maura* and *stejnegeri*, are readily identifiable from females as they all show dark feathering on the forehead, lores, cheeks and ear-coverts as well as the throat. The major plumage distinction from all other Palearctic races is that both first-year and adult males have a large but variable proportion of the bases of the rectrices pure white, whilst in the females it is creamy-white or buff and not so extensive. Males of the races *armenica* and *maura* also have white at the base of the tail but in the case of *maura* it is marginal or even absent and, being hidden under the uppertail-coverts, cannot be used in field identification, whilst in *armenica* it is far less extensive than *variegata* (albeit more so than *maura*). When visible it can possibly be used as an identification feature. Adult male *variegata* also have the largest and palest rump-patch of all races, even in autumn, when the rump is never wholly orange-buff but usually shows white mixed with orange-buff blotches. The rump and uppertail-coverts progressively fade to white as the feathers wear, although the speed of this can vary considerably in individual birds. Most male specimens examined in the BMNH had pure white rumps and uppertail-coverts from late March onwards, and even the lower backs of some specimens had white speckling amongst the grey. One specimen examined had attained a pure white rump and uppertail-coverts by 27 December. At all times the rump and uppertail-coverts are completely free of any black streaks or blotches. The white upper wing-patch is larger than on any of the other races, with predominantly white on the three (sometimes four) 10–08 (07) innermost upperwing greater coverts, extending onto the inner median coverts. The tail has a white base to all 12 feathers, the white decreasing from the outer feathers to the central pair (01). These latter usually show at least 20mm less than on the penultimate pair (05) of outer feathers, which usually show the maximum amount of white. It is often mentioned (Cramp 1988, Svensson 1992, Beaman & Madge 1998) that the white on the base of the tail extends from half to two-thirds of the tail's length, usually being more extensive on the inner web of the feather. Of 16 specimens examined at the BMNH the maximum amount of white on the base of the feather (measuring the second outermost pair of tail feathers, the fifth, which has the most amount of white), varied between 32.5 and 47.0mm. The average tail length of the 16 specimens was 48.6mm with extremes being 46.5 and 51mm. The white in the tail of all but two specimens exceeded two-thirds, varying from 67% up to two examples where it was 90%. The mean from the 14 specimens exceeding two-thirds was 81.8%. In some cases the white on the tail can be so extensive on the outer feathers as to suggest a tail pattern similar to Northern Wheatear *Oenanthe oenanthe*. Nevertheless, *variegata* individuals in the western parts of its range are stated to have c.50% or less white in the tail than those from more eastern parts of the range which have in excess of 70%. Individuals with the largest amount of white in the rectrices are found in the north-east of the range on the northern shore of the Caspian Sea east of the River Volga delta and around the Ural River delta (Stepanyan 1990).

Males from all areas, examined in fresh autumn plumage, showed white fringes and tips to the outer tail feathers (06–03). The inner two pairs (02–01) are unmarked black. In worn plumage the white neck-patches are also larger than on any of the other subspecies, and in some cases virtually form a collar where they meet on the hindneck. The breast-patch is, apart from *S. m. armenica*, the least extensive of the races, being confined largely to the central upper breast, and is a distinct deep rufous-chestnut in the centre fading to pale buff on the outer edges. The rest of the underparts, from the sides of the breast and flanks to the undertail-coverts, are to a large extent white contrasting markedly with the central breast-patch. The axillaries and underwing-coverts in the adult male are black. Males at all times of the year appear to show a larger amount of white than any of the other races. In fresh plumage this gives the bird a pleasing and distinctive orange, white, black and buff – hence almost tortoiseshell – appearance. The extensive whitish-buff fringes and tips to the tail of both sexes in fresh plumage are the most distinctive of all races but have usually worn away by spring. Females show either a creamy-white or buff base to the tail, never pure white as in the male. The patterning mirrors that of the male with the same tail feathers showing greater or lesser amounts of pale marking at the base, although the central pair on some examples do not have a pale base. Of nine skins examined at the BMNH, six showed creamy-white bases to the tail feathers whilst three were a darker buff. The extent of the pale base varied amongst the specimens from 12 to 23 mm, and was greatest on the inner web. The average area of pale feather base was 47.9% of the tail, less than the male but still extensive. The large pale base of the tail in females of this race is a diagnostic difference from pure females of all other races. The pale base to the tail of female *S. m. armenica* is often but not exclusively restricted to the central pair of feathers, with the amount, if any, in the other feathers being marginal. Caution should, however, be exercised when observing either sex, as intergrades between the two subspecies *armenica* and *variegata* do apparently occur.

Robertson (1977) and Stoddart (1992) mention that female and autumn examples of *S. m. variegata* have the rump and uppertail-coverts usually white with little orange coloration. Female specimens at BMNH in fresh autumn plumage show extensive rufous-orange to rufous-buff rump and uppertail-coverts with little white visible. By December the uppertail-coverts show more extensive white but still with rufous-buff or rufous-orange blotching. The rump remains predominantly rufous-buff or rufous-orange until at least March, but in a few cases shows fairly extensive white patches by January.

Measurements

	Male	**Female**
Wing	68.0–75.0 (mean 70.6)	68.0–72.5 (mean 69.0)
Tail	46.5–51.0 (mean 49.6)	46.5–50.0 (mean 48.1)
Bill	13.5–14.9 (mean 14.0)	13.0–14.3 (mean 13.9)

[Own measurements BMNH, 2000]

S. m. armenica

Saxicola torquata armenica Stegmann, 1935, *Doklady Akad.Nauk. S.S.R.* n.s. 3, p.47—Adshafana, Kurdistan

Males are similar in plumage to *S. m. variegata*, except they lack the extensive white in the tail, the white on the rump is slightly less extensive, and they are slightly larger in size, only exceeded in measurements by *S. m. przewalskii*. There is a slight difference detectable in fresh plumage to the fringes of the upperpart feathers in that male *S. m. armenica* has the fringes more rufous-brown rather than the pale sandy fringes of *S. m. variegata*. The main plumage difference between these two races is the restricted amount of white at the base of the tail of *armenica*. Of ten specimens in BMNH the white base extends 20–29mm and the extent of white in the tail varies from 38.8%–55.2% (mean 42.8% of total length). This is considerably more than the often quoted information (Cramp 1988, Beaman and Madge 1998) that only the basal quarter is white, although this latter may refer to the amount of white visible on the tail in the field. The long white uppertail-coverts obscure a considerable amount of the white tail-base. In worn plumage the breast-patch is deep rufous, contrasting markedly with the extensive white sides of the breast, flanks, belly and undertail-coverts.

Females are generally similar to *S. m. variegata* but marginally paler in fresh plumage, larger in size and with far less extensive pale bases to the tail feathers. The pale base is so small that it is virtually useless as an identification feature in the field. Of five specimens in the BMNH, one shows none at all whilst the other four show a creamy-white or pale buff base extending 12–14mm (mean 13.0). This represents 24.5% of the tail length.

Measurements

	Male	Female
Wing	73.0–76.5 (mean 74.4)	71.0–72.5 (mean 71.8)
Tail	51.5–56.5 (mean 53.7)	52.0–54.5 (mean 53.3)
Bill	13.0–15.0 (mean 14.3)	13.0–14.9 (mean 14.2)

[Own measurements BMNH, 2001]

DISTRIBUTION

S. m. maura

Breeds over a huge area comprising the northern and eastern European parts of the Russia Federation to the south-east shores of the Caspian Sea, extending into Mongolia, China, Kazakhstan, Kirghizstan, Tadzhikistan, Uzbekistan, Turkmenistan, Kashmir, Pakistan, Afghanistan and Iran. Its north-westernmost limits are around the south-western shores of the White Sea, Arkhangelsk, Mezen and Syktvkar. Its range extends east across Siberia to the Pechora River valley and the northern Ural Mountains [Uralski Ykhrebet] continuing to the lower reaches of the River Ob at 66°N and onwards to the Taz and Elogui Rivers around 64°N – in the extreme north of its range beyond the Norilskiye Lakes and source of the Pyasina River it is rare but regular as far north as 71°45´N (Krechmar 1966), but it is common as far north as Potapovo, 68°40´N (Rogacheva *et al.* 1983). Its range then runs south-east from Turukhansk on the Yenesei River to Irkutsk near the western shore of Lake Baykal. Along the easternmost borders of its range it intergrades with *stejnegeri* (Stepanyan 1990). It then extends south into north-west Mongolia including the Khangai Mountains [Khangayn Nuruu] and also into the mountains of the Tien Shan, then southwards to include the Xinjiang Uygur Autonomous Region in China, west to Tadzhikistan in the mountains lying east of Kulyab, and the valleys of the Gunt and Shakh-dara Rivers near Shugnan. It has also been recorded breeding by the Beik River in the Pamir Range. It is uncommon in northern Afghanistan, only definitely breeding in the Hazarajat region (Paludan 1959). It also breeds in Baluchistan, Kashmir and the western Himalayas. In the western Russian Federation it occurs around Gissar, on the Sanzar River in the Turkestanskiy Khrebet Range, the mountains north of Tashkent and in the Kirghizskiy Khrebet Range in Kazakhstan. The boundary runs north just west of the 70th meridian to almost Petropavlosk and then west south of Dzezkagan and north of Chubar-Teniz to almost Aktyubinsk, crossing the Ural River slightly north of the 50th parallel, then turning north again to form the western boundary of its range. It has bred around Belebei, Buzuluk, Bugurusian and Bashkiria and also the former province of Kazan as far west as Kama. Further north it has been found around Perm at 58°01´N 56°10´E (Dement'ev & Gladkov 1968).

In 1992 two pairs bred for the first time in Kuusamo (65°57´N 29°15´E) in north-east Finland well to the west of its normal breeding range and another female and three young were discovered in the same year in the far north at Utsjoki (69°54´N 27°01´E). No further breeding was recorded in Finland until 1997 when a pair again raised young. No breeding was attempted in 1998 (T. Lindroos *in litt.* 2000). In Germany the first mixed-race breeding for central Europe occured on Heligoland when a male of this subspecies was paired with a female of the subspecies *S. r. rubicola* (25 May–22 July 1997). They bred successfully, raising four young which were last seen on 23 August 1997 (Gottschling *et al.* 2000).

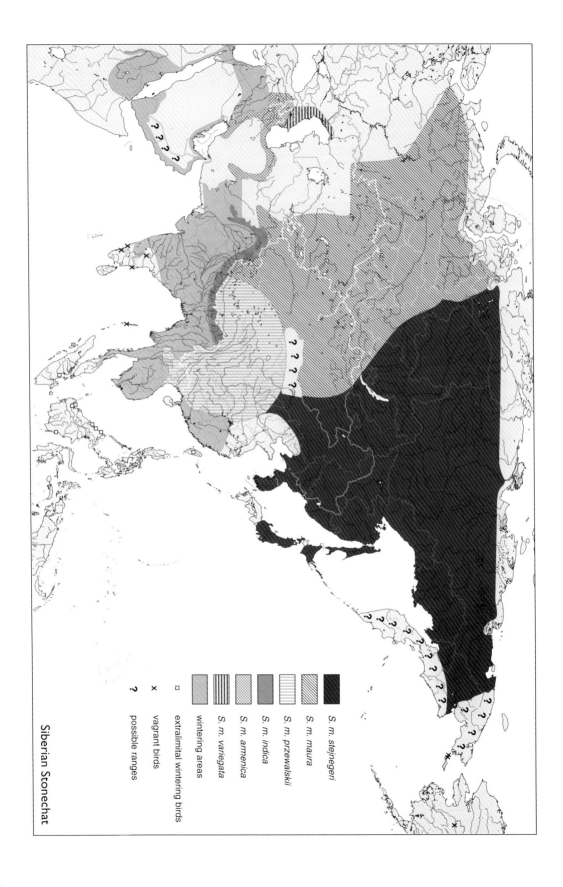

Siberian Stonechat

S. m. stejnegeri

S. m. variegata

S. m. armenica

S. m. indica

S. m. przewalskii

S. m. maura

wintering areas

☐   extralimital wintering birds

×   vagrant birds

?   possible ranges

S. m. stejnegeri

Breeds from the eastern border of the range of *maura* with which it intergrades from, in the north-west, Turukhansk (100th meridian), the middle Yenisey River region and Lake Baykal, north-east around latitude 68°/69°N through Yakutsk. Its range extends north to the mouth of the Lena River, the upper reaches of the Indigirka River and the Kolyma River delta, then south-east to the Anadyr River basin, Penzhina River valley, the Sea of Okhotsk and Sea of Japan. It breeds on the Shantar Islands and Sakhalin as well as on Moneron Island and the Kuril Islands north to Iturup. It reaches as far south as Japan to the Tsuruga-Nagoya line on Honshu Island breeding in the Maritime Territory to the south-eastern boundaries of the Russian Federation. It breeds in North and South Korea (where it is a common summer visitor), Ussuriysk and Manchuria. In China it breeds in the south-eastern part of the Nei Mongol Autonomous Region, the north-east provinces and the northern part of Hebei province. It also breeds in eastern Mongolia, with the western limit of its range running north-west from the upper reaches of the Kerulen River to Irkutsk north of Lake Baykal and on to the upper and middle reaches of the Nizhnyaya Tunguska River (Dement'ev & Gladkov 1968). In Myanmar pairs have twice been suspected of breeding at Sinlum in Bhamo district and in the Hkamti Long plain, but neither was adequately substantiated (Stanford & Ticehurst 1938).

S. m. variegata

Breeds through Transcaucasia. It does not breed in Armenia (V. Ananian per M. Wilson *in litt.* 2002) but extends north from the borders of Armenia, through Azerbaijan and Georgia (westward as far as the Gori region) and is limited to the east by the western shore of the Caspian Sea. It continues north through the Bolshoy Kavkaz Mountains, Chechnya region, Podkumka River valley and the upper reaches of the Kuma River, the Astrakhan steppes, around the lower reaches and delta of the Volga River and north-east to the delta of the Ural River at Guryev on the north-east coast of the Caspian Sea, in Kazakhstan.

S. m. armenica

Breeds as far north as the 42nd parallel and east as far as the 47th meridian, primarily breeding south and east of the range of *variegata,* possibly intergrading with *variegata* where their ranges overlap in Transcaucasia. It inhabits the mountains of eastern and south-eastern Turkey, which are the westernmost limit of its breeding range (Kumerloeve 1969), and extends eastwards across southern and eastern Transcaucasia, with breeding specimens obtained from Shemakha and around Tbilisi in Azerbaijan, and others collected from Zakataly in Georgia (Dement'ev & Gladkov 1968) and across northern Iran to Elburz and in the Elburz Mountains south to Kerman. Dement'ev and Gladkov (1968) state it breeds in the Armenian Highlands in Kurdistan and Urmia (Urmia is now Orumiyeh and is in Iran) and quote"Dal' (1936)" who states it breeds in southern Armenia (this in fact is a mistaken reference in Dement'ev & Gladkov, there is no Dal 1936, the correct ref is Dal 1946). Adamian & Klem (1999) record it as a rare breeding bird in Armenia. In Iran it extends around the southern coast of the Caspian Sea east to include the Elburz Range and then south-east as far as the province of Kerman and east to the south-west province of Fars. Both Vaurie (1959) and Ripley *et al.* (1964) record it as breeding in northern Iraq and the Syrian desert, but there has been no reliable subsequent information to substantiate or refute this.

S. m. indica

Breeds from northern Baluchistan and the North-West Frontier Province in Pakistan and through the Himalayas from Gilgit in eastern Kashmir ranging east to Nepal, then in India through Sikkim, Bhutan, Arunachal Pradesh and western Assam. Roberts (1992) considered most of the Pakistan breeding population to belong to this subspecies or *S. m. maura.*

S. m. przewalskii

Breeds in China in the north-eastern and the southern parts of Qinghai province; in the western, north-western and southern parts of Gansu province; in the north, north-western, north-eastern, central, western and south-western parts of Sichuan province; Shanxi province; the western part of Hubei province; Guangxi Zhuang Autonomous Region; Guizhou province; in the north-western, western, southern and south-eastern parts of Yunnan province; and the western part of the Xizang Autonomous Region (Cheng Tso-hsin 1987). It breeds south and east through Tibet, being found there between mid-April to mid-October (Vaurie 1972) and is also found in eastern Nepal. Smythies (1986) states it also probably breeds in north-eastern Myanmar, where it is considered to be an uncommon resident in the mountains on the border with Yunnan (China). However, Stanford & Ticehurst (1938) could find no proof of its reported breeding in the Kachin Hills and Shan States, and a supposed nest of this race in the Lower Chindwin Valley was not adequately substantiated. There were also reports of its breeding in the hills east of Bhamo near the Chinese border but again these were not substantiated (see above under *S. m. stejnegeri*). Two surveys in the extreme north of Myanmar north-west of Putao in January–February 1998 and November 1999 found it to be uncommon, possibly resident at elevations of 440–1,050m (King *et al.* 2001).

There are also isolated breeding records for the extreme north-west of Thailand (Eve & Guigue 1996). It is stated to breed in north and central Laos and it has also been found breeding in the western and eastern Tonkin region of northern Vietnam (Vaurie 1959). However, in the Dong Nathat Conservation Area in Savannakhet province, northern Laos, it was found on three of four visits during 26 January–2 March but on none of five visits during 4 May–6 July (Evans 2001).

STATUS

There is little information on the status of Siberian Stonechat, but what there is indicates that the populations are stable.

MOVEMENTS

S. m. maura

Birds are recorded as leaving their more northerly breeding areas as early as mid-August in western Siberia. Those from Tomsk leave around early September and from the southern steppes in mid-September. Migration continues until the end of September, with stragglers occurring until 9 October on the upper Irgiz in the Kyrgyz Steppe.

The majority of the population winters in northern India, reaching as far south as Madhya Pradesh (where it is a visitor from October to early March) and Maharashtra. Individuals have been recorded at sea west of Bombay on 15–29 September, 29 October and 1 November 1983 (Simpson 1984). *S. m. maura* also reaches Pakistan and southern Afghanistan in the west and north-western Myanmar [Burma] in the east. In western Siberia birds arrive in the Tomsk area in the first half of May but in the south, such as at Semipalatinsk, as early as mid-April and in the southern Altai at the end of April. The average over 16 years at Tomsk is 13 May and on the Sosva River in the Urals 20 May. In central Siberia they arrive up to a month before the nesting season, between 6 May and 18 May, with a five-year average of 14 May.

It is considered a winter visitor of uncertain status to Nepal (Inskipp & Inskipp 1991). It also winters in Iraq south of Baghdad, being 'not uncommon' around Feluja in November and December, at Hilla in November and abundant at the Hammar Lake in January (Meinertzhagen 1924). In the Eastern Province of Saudi Arabia it is a passage migrant and widespread but never numerous winter visitor (Bundy *et al.* 1989). It is a common winter visitor in Bahrain from September to March (Hirschfeld 1995) and an uncommon passage migrant and occasional winter visitor in Oman (Gallagher & Woodcock 1980). It is an irregular passage migrant in September and April through the United Arab Emirates (Richardson 1990). Goodman & Meininger (1989) produced no evidence of occurrence in Egypt, but in Jordan it or the very similar *stejnegeri* has been recorded in the Northern Highlands, Rift Margins and at Azraq in January, March, April, October and November (Andrews 1995). It is a rare migrant and very irregular winter visitor to south and east Israel (Shirihai 1995). Flint & Stewart (1992), referring to Cyprus, stated under Stonechat *S. m. maura*: "2 records: one trapped Akrotiri, 4 Dec 1971 (NR2), and one found dead in mistnet at Cape Pyla, 1 Jan 1991 (J. Bullock *per* C.J.L. Bennett). Pale birds with large white rumps, presumably *S. m. maura*, *armenica* or *variegata*, are often seen in winter, especially in the bleaker parts of the Mesaoira [One collected spring 1938 was identified as *maura* (Payn), but the skin (in BMNH) does not show characters of that race (P. Colston).]" It is unlikely that these birds were Siberian Stonechats apart from the two definitely identified, as Cyprus is well to the west of the normal wintering range of *S. m. maura*, whilst *S. m. variegata* and *S. m. armenica* winter in the Horn of Africa. It is more likely that birds with large white rumps are from southern populations of *S. r. rubicola*. Since the above a third specimen of *S. m. maura* was definitely identified on 3–4 September 2000 (*Cyprus Annual Report* 47, p.88).

Increasing but variable numbers of vagrant *maura* or *stejnegeri*, mainly in autumn with a few in spring, have been recorded in western Europe (285 in the UK up to and including 2000: Rogers *et al.* 2001). However, in the light of modern information and knowledge about plumage variation in individuals of the European Stonechat subspecies *hibernans* and especially *rubicola*, spring records of 'Siberian' individuals in the UK are to be reviewed by the British Birds Rarities Committee (BBRC) owing to possible confusion with examples of *rubicola*-type individuals, especially males, which are now strongly suspected to occur in the UK and which show extensive white, comparatively unmarked rumps and large white upperwing and neck-patches.

A single example of Siberian Stonechat on 10 October 1913 constituted the first acceptable record for the UK, with a long gap to 26 October 1960 when the next individual was recorded. Since 1974 individuals of either *maura* or *stejnegeri* have been recorded in varying numbers, but often in double figures, in every year in the UK. Usually records involve single birds but there are three records of two birds together, one of three birds and one of a remarkable five birds together on 29 September 1987 on Fair Isle in northern Scotland. All these multiple records were in years when there was a high number of records. The majority of records are in autumn, mainly from late September to early November, with specifically 70 in September, 157 in October and 31 in November. There are three additional records for December and four wintering records. The earliest occurrence was a male on 4 September 1994 in Norfolk, eastern England, and the latest a female/first-winter in Lancashire, northern England, on 26 December 1983. Most records constitute individuals present for 1–5 days with a few individuals remaining for 2–3 weeks. Where these birds move on to is unknown but presumably they may go south into southern Europe although there are relatively few records from this area, with only 15 from France, 3–4 from Spain, two of which were in spring (2 March and 6 April 1997) and three from Portugal. Whether this is a true reflection of the actual numbers occurring in this area is again unknown. It is possible that they are not recorded more often owing to the less comprehensive coverage by smaller numbers of birders in these countries. Spring records total just 24 for the UK with three in April, 18 in May and three in June, and with a distinct pattern of occurrences in May on the east coast. The earliest record was a male in Yorkshire on the east coast of England on 21 April 1990 and the latest a male which held a territory in Aberdeenshire in north-east Scotland from 2 to 24 June 1993.

A similar increase in records can also be traced in Scandinavia, notably Sweden and Finland, from 1970 onwards. Sweden has a total of 423 records of European and Siberian Stonechats up to the end of 1997, 304 of which are either *hibernans/rubicola* or racially unidentified, although a number of unidentified records are thought to refer to these races and 119 are *maura/stejnegeri* (N. Kjellen *in litt.* 1999). Finland has a total of 277 records of European and Siberian Stonechat up to 1997, of which 112 are *maura/ stejnegeri*, 145 racially unidentified although strongly suspected to be *maura/stejnegeri* and 20 *hibernans/ rubicola* (T. Lindroos *in litt.* 1999).

Why there should have been such an increase of records for this and the following race since 1970 is not obvious. Robertson (1977) suggested the increase in the UK was genuine and not just attributable to increased awareness and ability on the part of birders. However, it probably reflects, and has been fuelled by, a combination of these two factors, resulting in a growing awareness of the likelihood of these birds occurring and a better knowledge of their identification criteria. The increase in visitors, if indeed genuine, matches a growth and westward expansion in populations of *S. m. maura*. A pair of *maura* bred for the first time in Finland in 1992 and again in 1997, well to the west of the subspecies' normal range. It is virtually impossible from field observation to specify whether such individuals in western Europe belong to *maura* or *stejnegeri*, so they are often lumped as *maura/stejnegeri*. There is a possibility that most are of the race *maura* participating in the phenomenon of 'reverse migration'. The hypothesis of reverse migration, if correct, would make it unlikely that the vagrants arriving in western Europe are from the race *stejnegeri* (see Cottridge & Vinicombe 1996 for a detailed discussion).

There are also additional records of vagrant Siberian Stonechats presumed *S. m. maura/stejnegeri* from the following countries:

Austria (1997) 01 May 1985
Belarus (1999) 01 no details
Belgium (1996) 05 Oct 93/Apr 95/Oct 95/Oct 96 (2)
Channel Islands (1997) 02 Oct 85/Oct 95;
Denmark (1996) 27 Sept 55/Sept 64/May 78/Oct 78/Oct 80/Nov 80/Sept 81/Sept 82/May 83/
    May 84/Sept 84/Oct 86/Dec 86/Oct 87/Apr 88/Oct 88 (3)/May 91/Oct 91/Oct 93/Sept 94
    (2)/Oct 95/Sept 96/Oct 96/Apr 96
Estonia (1999) 04 June 88/July 88/May 93/May 94
Faeroe Islands (1997) 01 Sept 46
France (1996) 15 Feb 78/Oct 78/Apr 80/Dec 80/Oct 82/Oct 85/Oct 87 (2)/Nov 87/Oct 88/Apr
    89/Oct 91/Oct 92/Apr 94/Oct 94
Germany (1997) 17 Oct 1883 (*first record for Europe*)/Dec 81/Nov 87/Oct 89/Oct 91/Nov 92 (2)/
    Oct 93 (3)/Nov 94/Apr 95 (2) Oct 95/Nov 95/May–July 97 *male paired with female rubicola*/Oct 97
Italy (1997) 02 Oct 88/Nov 92
Latvia (1999) 02 1889/April 1999
Lithuania (1998) 01 no details
Netherlands (1996) 26 Oct 73/Oct 77 (6)/Oct 78(2)/Oct 80/Mar 81/Oct 82 (2)/Nov 86/Nov 89/
    Oct 91/Oct 93 (2)/Oct 94/Oct 95 (4)/Oct 96 (5)
Norway (1995) 12 Nov 77/Oct 78/Oct 79/June 81/Oct 81/Sept 85/Oct 88/Oct 91/May 92/Sept
    92/Oct 94
Poland (1999) 02 Apr 95/Mar 99
Portugal (1998) 03 Nov 93/Nov 95/Oct 97

Spain (1998) 04 Mar 97/Apr 97/Sept 97/Mar 98
Ukraine (1997) 01 Aug 77

Key = Country name/last year of reporting/number of records/() if more than one individual/ month/year

S. m. stejnegeri

In autumn birds from Japan leave mainly in late September, with stragglers into October, and return in late April and early May (Austin & Kuroda 1953). However, the earliest date for a returning bird on Hokkaido, Japan, between 1977 and 1986 was a male on 10 April 1983. Females tend to arrive 1–3 days later, with the first in 1983 being seen on 13 April (Fujimaki *et al.* 1994). The latest record for Korea was a bird recorded on 10 September and the earliest return date 21 March (Austin 1948). In winter a very few remain in the southernmost limits of their breeding range, as shown by winter records from Japan: one at Miyako-jima in January and "in winter" from Kyushi to Fukushima-ken in northern Honshu (Brazil 1991). In the Russian Federation birds leave the Shantar Islands in early September, Yakutia in late August and Transbaykal from late September to early October. Migrants have been noted in mid-September in the Lesser Khirgan Mountains. It has been recorded as returning in spring to Lake Khanka on 24 April, Sakhalin in the last two-thirds of May, and the Baykal area in early May (Dement'ev & Gladkov 1968). The earliest record for autumn arrival in the Malay Peninsula is 12 October and for spring departure 11 April (Medway & Wells 1976).

The majority winter in northern India, Myanmar [Burma], where it is found from mid-August to mid-May (Smythies 1986), Laos, where it occurs over a wide altitudinal range (Duckworth *et al.* 1999) and Thailand, where it is a very common winter visitor to the lowlands of all provinces as far south as the Isthmus of Kra (Lekagul & Round 1991). Deignan (1945) recorded the first autumn migrants in north-east Thailand on 16 September in Chiang Mai province and the latest spring migrant on 16 April in Nan province. Migrants in both autumn and spring have occurred several times on high mountains in Chiang Rai province, ranging from 1,000 to 1,670m. A similar migration involving small numbers has been observed in northern Myanmar [Burma] in the hills of Myitkyina district from 15 March to 21 April (Stanford & Ticehurst 1938). In Vietnam it is a common winter visitor to appropriate habitats such as the Red River in Hanoi, arriving in September (J.W. Duckworth *in litt.* 2001), south-east China including Hunan, Yunnan, Fujian and Guangdong provinces (Cheng Tso-Hsin 1987) and Hong Kong, where it is common and widespread often in large numbers, mainly in the New Territories, from the end of September to late April. Migrants are regular at the Mai Po marshes and there are occasional records from urban areas such as Kowloon Bay reclamation area and Kai Tak Airport. The mean arrival date in the years 1958–1976 was 27 September, and the mean departure date 20 April; extreme dates were 26 August and 5 May (Garland & Melville 1979). Wintering birds in Hong Kong are judged to be *S. m. stejnegeri* based on weight and distribution, but there is the possibility based on wing measurements they could also include some *maura* (Garland & Melville 1979). It is referred to as a straggler to Taiwan by Meyer de Schauensee (1984) but as an annual but rare winter visitor by Chang (1980).

It is reasonably common in the northern Malay Peninsula and has occurred as a vagrant in the south of the peninsula. Smythies (1999) lists it as a rare vagrant to Borneo with the following chronologically arranged records, all involving single birds: Kuching, Sarawak, 31 January 1898; Satang Island, 2 December 1955; Kuala Niah, 23 February 1958; Tanjung Aru, Kalimantan, 4 February 1960; Kuching racecourse, Sarawak, 24 March 1963; Muara (an immature), Brunei, 27 December 1966 (Harrisson 1967); Kg. Nukohan grazing swamp (a female), Kuala Penyu, Sabah, 26 March 1975 (Wells 1976, Medway & Wells 1976, Smythies 1999); Berakas, Brunei, 10 December 1983 (Mann 1987); Tempasuk (immature male), Kota Belud, Sabah, 11–12 December 1984 (Beadle & Whittaker 1985); on an oil rig off the Brunei coast, 6–7 April 1992 (R. Hiscock *per* C.F. Mann in Smythies 1999). There are also two records from Sumatra. The first was of a bird in the central province of Jambi on 26 January 1976 (Harvey & Holmes 1976). The second was on the late date of 4 May 1990 when a female, probably of this race, was found at Lahewa on the western tip of the island of Nias off north-west Sumatra (Dymond 1993). Some older reference books give the Philippines as one of the southern extremes of its range but Dickinson *et al.* (1991) give no record of the species in that country.

Bundy *et al.* (1989) considered that this subspecies and *maura* probably migrated through and in some cases wintered in the Eastern Province of Saudi Arabia, although it is more likely that the more westerly breeding *maura* is predominant. There are also many records from western Europe involving this or the virtually identical *maura* (see above). There are four records of vagrancy to North America (Nearctic region), probably and at least once positively involving this subspecies. The first was an unsubstantiated sight record on 6 June 1978 at Gambell on St Lawrence Island, Alaska, which may have been this species (Roberson 1980); this was followed by a substantiated record of a first-winter female of either the subspecies *stejnegeri* or *maura* on Grand Manan Island, New Brunswick, Canada, on 1 October 1983 (Wilson 1986), and by a male again at Gambell on 5 June 1985; and finally the frozen remains of a bird positively identified as *stejnegeri* were recovered from a hole made by a Bank Martin [Sand Martin] *Riparia riparia* on the Yukon River at Galena, Alaska, on 19 April 1986 (Osborne & Osborne 1987).

Neither *S. m. maura* nor *S. m stejnegeri* has been satisfactorily identified as wintering in Africa. There are a number of old winter records from Africa, particularly for the north-east region, of 'Siberian Stonechats'. These are now considered to refer to the subspecies *S. m variegata* and *S. m. armenica*.

S. m. variegata

In winter some birds only move to south-eastern Transcaucasia, but the majority of the population move south-west through eastern Iraq and south-west Arabia to spend the winter in north-east Africa. Birds have been found wintering in northern and eastern Sudan around Berber and Khartoum as well as further south along the White Nile, with one vagrant being found in south-west Sudan (Keith *et al.* 1992). This subspecies is also found in northern Ethiopia as far south as 8°N and especially in Eritrea, where it is widespread as both a winter visitor and passage migrant. It arrives in September (earliest date 9th) and departs again in late March (Smith 1957, Urban & Brown 1971). A recent series of wildlife surveys of Eritrea, 1997–2001, whilst not completely comprehensive, found it in two ecogeographical zones; the central-eastern escarpment and on the central plateau at 2,200–2,400m (Zinner 2001).

Cheesman & Sclater (1935) found it to be a common passage migrant and winter visitor on the high plateau of Ethiopia, recording it from 19 September to 18 March. There is also an isolated, old record for north-west Somalia of a male and female on Mt Wagar on 22 September 1905, but these birds are more likely to have been displaced migrants than actually wintering. Two other migrants have been collected in the north-west just over the border in Ethiopia (Ash & Miskell 1998). There is a somewhat confusing picture in the Middle East, with differing opinions as to whether it winters in the countries comprising the region. In Iraq and south-west Arabia Ripley *et al.* (1964) state that it winters, whilst Vaurie (1959) says it does not. Allouse (1953) reported that it occurs in small numbers from October to December around Mosul and Kut in Iraq, but that it then disappears only to reappear in March but does not remain to breed.

In Bahrain birds of this subspecies or *armenica* have been seen between 31 August and 5 April and were considered to be late autumn or early spring passage migrants rather than winter visitors (Hirschfeld 1995), although there is a specimen in BMNH collected in Bahrain on 19 February. In the Eastern Province of Saudi Arabia this subspecies and *armenica* occur in March on spring passage, and it has been collected in Jeddah in late February (Bundy *et al.* 1989). It has been found in Oman, where it is probably an uncommon passage migrant and occasional winter visitor from September to April (Gallagher & Woodcock 1980). It has been recorded in late November and December in Yemen but it is unknown if these are wintering birds.

It is a passage migrant in Israel, probably more frequent in the northern part of the Rift Valley than previously thought. It is apparently a regular passage migrant in small numbers in northern Israel, with for example 1–3 individuals being recorded at Kefar Ruppin in the Bet Shean Valley between 8 and 20 October in the 1990s. It probably occurs every year but is not recorded owing to spasmodic coverage of the area. It has also been found on passage in the Hula Valley between the slightly later dates of 25 October and 27 November, with up to four individuals recorded on one day, and it may well be present earlier in October but goes unrecorded (J. Smith pers. comm. 2000).

One or two birds are recorded wintering in the Eilat and Yotvata areas of southern Israel, and it has been noted at Eilat as a passage migrant in varying numbers (3–27) from 1984–1986, mostly 25 October–20 November (Shirihai 1995). There are also single records of presumably passage birds from Mizpe Ramon in the Central Negev on 21 October 1996 and at Kibbutz Lotan in southern Arava on 9 November, but generally it occurs far less frequently than in the North (J. Smith pers. comm. 2001). Return passage at Eilat usually involves an average of five individuals each spring, mainly in February–March. Goodman & Meininger (1989) state it has been collected in Egypt. It has been recorded twice in the UK and five times in the rest of Europe: UK, October 1985 and September 1993; Norway, June 1983; Estonia, May 1990; Cyprus, February 1985 and March 1999; Greece, November 1986.

S. m. armenica

This subspecies migrates south-west and Vaurie (1959) records it as wintering in Iraq, these possibly being breeding birds remaining to winter, although Sage (1960) found none in winter in eastern Iraq. It has been recorded once as a vagrant from Cyprus when a male was seen at the Asprokremmos Dam on 22 March 1997 (A.E. Sadler *in litt.* 1999), a date which suggests that it was on spring migration. The majority move south-west to winter in varying numbers in south-west Arabia, Yemen, possibly Oman, and Egypt, eastern Sudan and north and central Ethiopia. Urban & Brown (1971) record it as an uncommon visitor to the highland grasslands of both the Rift Valley and the Western Highlands of Ethiopia. There is also an isolated record of a male from north-west Somalia.

In Israel it is recorded only on migration in very small numbers, although J. Smith (*in litt.* 2001) considers that this subspecies, as with *variegata*, is probably more frequent in the northern part of the Rift Valley than is apparent from records. Single birds have been recorded from northern Israel at Ginnegar in the Jexreel Valley on 11 October 1991, at Tirat Zevi in the Bet Shean Valley on 26 March 1996 and 14 November 1997, and the Hula Valley on 11 November 1997. At Eilat in southern Israel, it was recorded regularly from 19 October to 2 December between 1982 and 1988, with up to three being seen each autumn; in the spring of these same years there were only two confirmed records, in March and April (Shirihai 1995), with presumably the record from Tirat Zevi in 1996 constituting another. There is also an old specimen in BMNH collected in Jerusalem on 29 December 1917 which could conceivably have been wintering.

There is still much confusion and lack of precise knowledge over which subspecies occur in many Middle Eastern countries, and over the status of each subspecies at migration times and in winter. Many fieldguides still do not mention the subspecies involved, although the situation is improving concerning Israel and Bahrain, but there is still little detailed information for Lebanon, Syria, Iraq, Kuwait, Yemen, Oman, the United Arab Emirates, Qatar and Iran.

S. m. indica

This subspecies migrates through northern India and Pakistan and occurs in Bhutan at 790–2,205m where it is an uncommon passage migrant and winter visitor (Inskipp *et al.* 2000). In India it winters south throughout the subcontinent to Hyderabad and Mysore, occurring as far south as the state of Karnatka and as far east as Jalpaiguri and Assam, as well as central and southern Bhutan and Bangladesh (Ali & Ripley 1968–1998, Inskipp *et al.* 2000). However, some birds wintering in the more northerly areas could be *maura*. In Pakistan a strongly marked passage in spring and autumn draws birds through the Indus plains and a few winter in the Salt Range in northern Pakistan. They also winter in southern Punjab and are noted there in considerable numbers on spring migration. In the province of Sind they often winter by riverine areas and lake margins, being commonest around Upper Sind and the Indus Valley, arriving at the earliest on 1 October and departing at the latest on 16 February. Ticehurst considered it comparatively scarce in lower Sind but mentions Blanford who found it in Thar and Parkar (Ticehurst 1922–1924, Roberts 1992). Vaurie mentions that birds are said to have reached the Andaman Islands although no definite records appear to exist. There is a certain amount of intergradation with *maura* in eastern Kashmir and northern Punjab, and both subspecies can be found wintering together over a considerable area of northern India.

S. m. przewalskii

On autumn migration this subspecies is abundant in the high Himalayas and has been recorded moving in large numbers at up to 5,100m, through the Kharta Valley just east of Mount Everest (*Ibis* 1922). Thousands of birds presumed to be this subspecies passed through the Nepal Valley between 5 and 14 April 1948 but no similar large-scale movement was seen there in the autumn (Proud 1949). Birds from the more northerly areas of their breeding range move south to winter in Nepal, and others winter in the Himalayan foothills in India, from Kangra in Himachal Pradesh east to Arunchal Pradesh and Assam, then south to the River Ganges, Meghalaya and Nagaland (Ali & Ripley 1968–1998). It also occurs in the foothills of northern Myanmar [Burma] but not apparently south of Myitkyina (Stanford & Ticehurst 1938). A specimen was collected near Papun on 13 February (Stanford & Ticehurst 1938). Three specimens in ZMMSU were collected in January and March 1909 from Bhamo on the north-east border of Myanmar [Burma] and China (M. Kalyakin *in litt.* 2001). Occasionally *pzrewalskii* also straggles to Kashmir (Vaurie 1959). It is a winter visitor from September to April to Thailand (Eve & Guigue 1996).

In Vietnam Wildash (1968) states that resident birds make seasonal movements within the country and in winter the population is augmented by winter visitors from further north, all being very common in suitable habitat up to 1,050m. In northern Vietnam the subspecies was collected at Chapa and Pakha (Delacour 1930). In the Red River area in Hanoi winter visitors arrive in September (J.W. Duckworth *in litt.* 2001), whilst up to 20 'Siberian Stonechats' were seen in mid-March frequenting a relatively small area of grass and rice in the Tram Chim area of the Mekong Delta (N. Moores *in litt.* 2000). In central and southern Vietnam it appears to be only a winter visitor, despite Wildash's assertion that it breeds. It has been recorded in central Vietnam on migration from Hah Tinh province on 8–9 September 1997 in grassland at 200m, and in Central Annam apparently wintering from 8–30 January 1990 in artificial grassland at 700m (M. Kalyakin *in litt.* 2001). It was also found to be common in Ha Son Binh province in south-western Tonkin in October–November 1978 and in lowlands alongside roads between Hanoi and Hoshimin

(Stepanyan 1995). It is stated to be only a winter visitor to the Mekong Delta in southern Vietnam (J. Tobias *in litt.* 2001), and Stepanyan (1995) thought it a common wintering species near Buon Luoi village on the Thainguyen Plateau in southern Vietnam. (This was based on four specimens – three males and one female – collected there on 10–19 October 1986.) In 1987 birds were first recorded there slightly later, on 26 October. The race is a common winterer in Dong Nai province in southern Vietnam, being recorded from 28 September to 6 April (M. Kalyakin *in litt.* 2001). It is possible that in winter both this and *stejnegeri* are found in Vietnam. It has also been found in Cambodia around Phnom Penh and further north around Senmonorom in Mondul Kiri province during a survey conducted in January and February 1997 (Duckworth & Hedges 1998).

(*Motacilla*) *torquata* Linnaeus, 1766, *Syst. Nat.* ed. 12, 1, p.328—Cape of Good Hope [South Africa]

Alternative names Stonechat, Common Stonechat

TAXONOMY

Polytypic. See discussion on page 131.

IDENTIFICATION

S. t. torquata

Adult male in fresh plumage The forehead, crown, nape, mantle, scapulars and back are black but apart from the centre of the feathers the black is virtually obscured by the extensive olive brown fringes creating a streaked appearance. The upper mantle has noticeably less extensive brown fringes and appears distinctly blacker than the rest of the upperparts. The sides of the head are black. The lores and malar region are pure black whilst the cheeks and ear-coverts are less pure with very fine pale brown fringes to the feathers, especially to the rear of the ear-coverts and on the lower cheeks. The chin and throat are black but many feathers have very fine white fringes creating a grizzled appearance. The sides of the neck show small narrow white patches partially obscured by a mixture of pale grey, olive and orange buff feather tips. The neck-patches are joined by a narrow and indefinite white line running across the top of the breast. The breast and flanks are a dark brownish chestnut with paler buff fringes. The sides of the breast, belly and ventral area are a slightly paler buff-orange. The undertail-coverts are pure white broadly tipped with black and buff. The rump and uppertail-coverts are white forming an extensive patch (as large as on any Siberian Stonechat) with scattered orange and grey tips especially to the uppertail-coverts. The remiges are dark brown with the inner webs of the feathers fringed white. The upperwing lesser and primary coverts are black with narrow greyish-white fringes. The upperwing median and greater coverts are black with pale buff fringes apart from the inner median and greater coverts which are white. The amount of white on the upperwing greater coverts can vary, being present from the innermost four to eight (03-10) coverts but is always extensive and more so than is found on either European or Siberian Stonechat. The innermost tertial (09) is white for up to 50% from the base, the rest is black with a white edge to the outer web. On some individuals the white can also extend onto the basal part of the outer webs of the innermost secondaries. The remaining two tertials (08 and 07) are black with pale buffish white tips and outer fringes which combine with the buff fringes to the outer webs of the two innermost secondaries to form a distinct but narrow, pale panel on the closed wing. The underwing coverts are black with broad greyish-white fringes. The tail is dark brown/black with no pale fringes or tips. The bill, legs and feet are black. The irides are dark brown.

In worn plumage the head including the chin and throat as well as the rest of the upperparts are completely black and have a slight gloss. The rump and uppertail-coverts are pure white with no streaks or orange buff tips. The breast and flanks become a deep reddish-chestnut contrasting with the pure white sides to the breast, belly, ventral area and undertail-coverts. The tail has a small area of white at the base of the innertail feathers (c11mm) obscured by the upper tail coverts. The neck-patches become pure white and appear more extensive than in fresh plumage extending towards the hindneck and also onto the sides of the breast.

Adult female In fresh plumage the feathers of the forehead, crown, mantle, scapulars and back are dark brown broadly fringed with paler buff-brown creating an overall subdued streaked appearance. There is a faint buff supercilium most noticeable above and behind the eye. The lores and malar region are brown with narrow grey and buff fringes giving a slightly grizzled look. The cheeks and ear-coverts are a slightly paler buff and there is a distinct darker line running from the base of the bill through the eye to the rear of the upper ear-coverts. There is an extremely small area of cream, not white, feathering on the sides of the neck. The chin and throat are a pale creamy buff with a suggestion of darker feathering at the base of the throat feathers. The breast and flanks are a rufous buff usually appearing a richer colour than the rest of the underparts which are slightly paler chestnut or pinkish buff especially around the ventral area and undertail-coverts. The lower rump is predominantly white (a feature of all females of Afrotropical and Malagasy subspecies apart from *S. t. felix*) with a scattering of small orange buff tips.The uppertail-coverts are also white but with larger and more extensive buff-orange tips and some of the outer uppertail-coverts have dark brown/black central shaft streaks. One specimen examined had all the uppertail-coverts black with ginger fringes and only a minimal amount of white. Some feathers on the rump had black shaft streaks. The retrices and remiges are dark brown with fine, pale grey, crescentic tips to the remiges. There is no white at the base of the retrices. The tertials are dark brown with rich tawny-brown tips and outer fringes. The upperwing lesser, median and greater coverts are dark brown, all with buff fringes to the outer webs and tips apart from white present on the inner median and inner three (08-10) upperwing greater coverts, creating a white patch on the inner wing which is more reduced than on the male. The underwing-coverts and axillaries are grey with extensive buff fringes.

As the plumage wears the upperparts become darker brown due to the paler feather fringes wearing away. The neck-patches still remain negligible but become slightly more noticeable and slightly paler although still not white. The chin and throat become much darker as more of the black feather bases become exposed by wear. The upper breast and flanks fade slightly to a paler chestnut-buff while the rest of the underparts become dull white. The lower rump and upper tail coverts become white although a very few outertail-coverts may still retain dark shaft-streaks.

Measurements

	Male	Female
Wing	70.0–75.0 (mean 73.1)	64.5–71.0 (mean 67.2)
Tail	50.5–55.0 (mean 53.5)	48.5–53.5 (mean 50.1)
Bill	14.0–15.5 (mean 15.0)	13.5–15.5 (mean 14.6)

[Own measurements BMNH, 2000]

Geographical variation in the Afrotropical subspecies mainly involves the intensity and extent of the rufous or chestnut on the male's underparts (this tends to be redder in tone than Palearctic subspecies), the extent of white on the rump of both sexes, the coloration of the female's upper and underparts, and size. The main differences of the other subspecies of African Stonechat from *S. torquata torquata* are listed below.

There is, however, one African subspecies, *S. t. albofasciata*, which was suggested by Hall & Moreau (1970) as possibly being an incipient species that differs quite markedly in plumage from the other 14 subspecies, and this has been described in greater detail.

S. t. clanceyi

Saxicola torquata clanceyi Latimer, 1961 (March), in Clancey, *Durban Mus. Novit.* 6 p.90—Wallekraal, western Little Namaqualand, north-western Cape Province, South Africa

Saxicola torquata clanceyi Courtenay-Latimer, 1961 (October), *Bull. Brit. Orn. Club* 81 p.116—Wallekraal, western Little Namaqualand, north-western Cape Province, South Africa

The male is closely similar to *S. t. torquata* but in fresh plumage the fringes to the upperpart feathers are greyer in tone and there is more white on the sides of the breast and along the flanks. In worn breeding plumage differences are more obvious owing to the more extensive white along the sides of the body from the neck to the flanks. The flanks have no obvious chestnut-red extending from the breast. The chestnut-red colouring on the sides of the breast extends on the body about equal to or shorter than the apices of the primary coverts.

The female's upperparts in fresh plumage are darker, also with a greyish tone rather than the brown tone of *S. t. torquata*. The centres to the feathers are blacker and the tips noticeably greyish-olive. The throat is whiter, often with a large amount of black feather base evident. The sides of the neck have prominent white patches. The upper breast and flanks are darker rufous-buff in tone. The rest of the underparts, including the lower breast, belly, rear flanks, ventral area and undertail-coverts, are white, not pinkish-buff. Abrasion results in the upperparts becoming darker and more uniform black/brown, as well as the throat becoming darker. The upper breast-patch becomes more yellowish-chestnut in tone (Clancey 1961).

Measurements

Male	Female
Wing 68.0–73.5 (mean 71.3)	68.0–72.5 (mean 69.7)

[Clancey 1961]

S. t. stonei

Saxicola torquata stonei Bowen, 1932, *Proc. Acad. Nat. Sci. Philadelphia* 83 (1931), p.8—Villa General Machado, Angola

In fresh plumage the male has lighter-coloured buff-brown fringes to the feathers of the upper parts than *S. t. torquata*, giving a slightly paler appearance. The underparts are paler, not such a rich chestnut-red on the upper breast and flanks. The lower breast, belly, ventral area and undertail-coverts are a pale pinkish-buff, not white. In breeding plumage the upperparts are similar to *S. t. torquata* but the upper breast and flanks appear paler and more yellowish in tone and consequently contrast less strongly with the pale pinkish-buff or buff lower breast, belly and ventral area which are never completely pure white as in *S. t. torquata*. It also tends to show more white on the sides of the neck and breast in worn plumage and more white at the base of the rectrices.

Females are very similar to *S. t. torquata* but average darker both on the upperparts and underparts, although they are not always separable (Clancey 1961).

Measurements

Male	Female
Wing 70.0–73.0 (mean 71.0)	67.5–70.0 (mean 68.8)

[Clancey 1988]

S. t. oreobates

Saxicola torquata oreobates Clancey, 1956, *Durban Mus. Novit.* 4, p.281–40 miles east of Maseru on new mountain road, c.8,000ft [2,440m], Basutoland [= Lesotho]

In fresh plumage the fringes to the feathers of the male's upperparts are darker and redder-brown in tone than *S. t. torquata*. The breast and flanks are a darker chestnut-red and the rest of the underparts from belly to ventral area are pale buff rather than white. Females tend to be darker, more vinous-grey on the upperparts, with more rufous feather fringes, and the throat, breast and flanks are also a darker and redder-buff. Slightly larger in size than *S. t. torquata*.

Measurements

Male	Female
Wing 70.5–76.0 (mean 72.7)	69.0–71.0 (mean 70.2)

[Own measurements BMNH, 2001]

S. t. promiscua

Saxicola torquata promiscua Hartert, 1922, *Bull. Brit. Orn. Club* 42, p.51—Uluguru Mountains [Tanzania]

Both male and female are slightly smaller than either *S. t. torquata* or *S. t. salax*. The male's plumage is similar to *torquata* and *axillaris* but has slightly more black on the throat, and the chestnut-red on the upper breast is more restricted than on even *axillaris*. It differs from the neighbouring *stonei* in that the chest is a darker chestnut-red and the belly and flanks are less buff, more white, as in *torquata*. It differs from *salax* in that the feathers of the upperparts, including the uppertail-coverts, have more extensive rufous edges in fresh plumage.

The female differs from *torquata*, *salax* and *orientalis* in being generally paler, especially on the underparts, apart from the breast which is stronger coloured and contrasts with the rest of the underparts. The uppertail-coverts are brownish-buff and not white.

Measurements

Male	Female
Wing 64.0–71.0 (mean 68.4)	61.0–64.0

[Male, own measurements BMNH, 2000]
[Female (no mean given) Hartert 1922]

S. t. altivaga

Saxicola torquata altivaga Clancey, 1988, *Bull. Brit. Orn. Club* 108, p.62–64, Banti Forest Reserve, 1,750m, south of Mutare, Zimbabwe

Very similar to *promiscua* and only comparatively recently distinguished from that subspecies. The male is similar to *stonei* but Clancey felt the population sits between *promiscua* and *stonei* and differs sufficiently from both to warrant being assigned to a separate race. The males differ from *stonei* in having the belly, ventral area and undertail-coverts white rather than pale buff. In breeding plumage the male differs from *promiscua* and *axillaris* in having the chestnut-red of the breast extending down over the sides of the breast onto the flanks.

The female is also similar to *stonei* but the underparts are pale pinkish-buff and it is generally paler on the throat and belly. It differs from *promiscua* in that the upper breast does not have a darker band of stronger colouring across it but is uniform with the rest of the pinkish-buff underparts. Both sexes are smaller than *stonei* with average wing being 67.2 (male) and 65.6 (female) as against 71.0 and 68.8 respectively in *stonei*. In size they are similar to *promiscua* (Clancey 1988).

Measurements

Male	Female
Wing 66.0–69.0 (mean 67.2)	64.0–66.0 (mean 65.6)

[Own measurements BMNH, 2000]

S. t. axillaris

Pratincola axillaris Shelley, 1884, *Proc. Zool. Soc. London* p.556—Kilimanjaro 7,000ft (2,135m) [Kenya]

Adult male in worn plumage has only a narrow band of chestnut-red feathering on the upper breast, much less extensive than on *S. t. torquata* with the rest of the underparts pure white. They are closest in plumage to *salax*. Specimens examined by Hartert (1910) showed only a chestnut-red band 10–17.5mm deep on the upper breast whereas *salax* specimens ranged from 20–30mm deep. Specimens from northern Kenya can show much black on the upper breast with only a narrow band (c6mm deep) of chestnut red formed by the tips to the black feathering on the upper breast. The black feathering sometimes continues irregularly onto the lower breast below the chestnut. In other individuals from the north-east of Kenya the chestnut-red is restricted to just a spot below the black chin and throat and occasionally is virtually absent. Both Hartert (1910) and Meinertzhagen (1922) suggested this demonstrated a link between this subspecies and *albofasciata* from neighbouring Ethiopia.

It also has the most extensive white wing-patch of all African Stonechat subspecies and also can show more extensive white areas on the neck and flanks. Males can show in addition to the normal area of white on the innerwing-coverts, white fringes to the outer webs of the inner secondaries and some tertials. It also differs from the similar *salax* in having black axillaries with narrow white fringes. The rump and uppertail-coverts are pure white, the tail occasionally has a very small amount of white c1–2mm at the base but is normally entirely black.

Females are darker on the upperparts and very similar to *salax*. The chin and throat are comparatively dark even in fresh plumage. In extreme examples the throat is almost black and the black can extend in the form of a bib onto the central upper breast. They also show more extensive white on the wings than any other African Stonechat subspecies and some birds have small pure white neck-patches although neither area is as extensive as on the male. The lower rump is white. The uppertail coverts in fresh plumage have buff tips and dark brown shaft-streaks but abrade to white. It is on average smaller in size than *S. t. torquata*.

In fresh plumage the forehead, crown, mantle, scapulars and back are dark brown broadly fringed with slightly paler buff-brown creating an overall dark and subdued streaked appearance. The overall appearance is dark brown with a greyish tone. There is a faint buff supercilium most noticeable above and behind the eye. The lores and malar region are brown with narrow grey and buff fringes giving a slightly grizzled look. The cheeks and ear-coverts are slightly paler buff and there is a distinct darker line running from the bill through the eye to the rear of the upper ear-coverts. There is variably a very small area of white feathering on the sides of the neck. The retrices and remiges are dark brown/black with narrow paler brown fringes to the outer webs and thin, pale grey, crescentic tips to the remiges. The tertials are dark brown with rich tawny brown tips and outer fringes. The upperwing lesser, median and greater coverts are dark brown, all with buff fringes to the outer webs and tips, apart from white present on the inner median and inner greater upperwing-coverts, creating a white patch on the inner upperwing which is more reduced than on the male. The female shows more extensive white wing-patches than most other African Stonechat subspecies and the extreme base of the innermost secondaries are white. The lower rump is white. The uppertail-coverts in fresh plumage have buff tips and dark brown shaft-streaks which abrade to white although a few outer uppertail-coverts may retain dark shaft-streaks. The chin and throat show comparatively extensive black bases even in fresh plumage with buff and not white tips. In extreme examples as the plumage wears the throat is almost black and the black can extend in the form of a bib onto the central upper breast. The upper breast is rufous buff with a considrable amount of white on the lower breast, flanks, belly, ventral area and undertail-coverts. As the plumage wears the upper breast fades slightly.

Measurements

Male	Female
Wing 71.5–73.0 (mean 71.8)	68.5–71.5 (mean 70.3)

[Own measurements BMNH, 2001]

S. t. salax

Pratincola salax J. & E. Verreaux, 1851, *Rev. Mag. Zool.* [Paris] 3(2), p.307—Gabon

Closely similar to *clanceyi.* The head of the male (including lores, ear-coverts, chin, throat and nape) and upperparts (including mantle and scapulars) are black with only very fine brown fringes to the feathers in fresh plumage, which abrade very quickly leaving the upperparts jet-black. The white neck-patches extend onto the nape and virtually meet, this area being only intermixed with scattered black feathering. The feathers of the lower back are greyish-black with broad white tips. The rump and uppertail-coverts are pure white. The white wing-patch is extensive, with the inner upperwing median and greater coverts white and white bases to the outer webs of the innermost secondaries. The axillaries are not black but greyish-brown with broad white fringes. In fresh plumage the male is similar to *clanceyi* but the chestnut-red on the breast is paler and more restricted to the upper breast in a transverse band some 10mm deep at its central point with no extension onto the sides of the body as in *clanceyi* and *torquata* (Clancey 1961), although more extensive than *axillaris.* The rest of the underparts become pure white.

The upperparts of the female are similar to female *clanceyi*, being dark brown, the feathers fringed with paler rufous-brown on the mantle, scapulars and back. The remiges are dark brown, the primaries with narrow pale brown and the secondaries with broader paler brown fringes to the outer webs. The inner greater coverts and extreme base of the innermost secondaries are white. The underwing-coverts are black mixed with buff. The axillaries are dull black with greyish-white fringes. The rump and uppertail-coverts are white. The underparts differ markedly from *clanceyi.* The chin and throat feathers show more black bases to the feathers and the tips are buff, not white. There is also more extensive white feathering over the lower breast, belly, flanks, ventral area and undertail-coverts. The upper breast is the only area that shows any strong rufous-buff colouring. It is one of the smallest Afrotropical subspecies, with a shorter bill than any of the indigenous races in South Africa (Clancey 1961).

Measurements

Male	Female
Wing 65.0–69.0 (mean 66.4)	63.0–66.0 (mean 64.6)

[Own measurements BMNH, 2000]

S. t. adamauae

Saxicola torquata adamauae Grote, 1922, *J. Orn.* 70, p.486—Genderu Mountains [north and west Cameroon]

Identical to *salax* apart from the adult male having a narrower chestnut breast-band and in many cases 1–2mm of white at the base of the tail. It is also identical in plumage to *pallidigula* but much smaller in size, and the female has a strong russet wash to the belly. Keith *et al.* (1992) do not recognise this subspecies and lump it with *salax.*

Measurements

Male	Female
Wing 67–70	69.0/69.0/71.0

[Rand 1952 from specimens collected by Bates in Chicago NMH]

S. t. pallidigula

Saxicola torquata pallidigula Reichenow, 1892, *J. Orn.* 40, p.194—Kamerun [= Cameroon]

Although treated by Ripley *et al.* (1964) as a valid subspecies, Keith *et al.* (1992) lumped both *pallidigula* and *adamauae* under *S. t. salax.* However, it is markedly larger than *salax* and *adamauae* (and indeed *axillaris*), and this, together with other subtle structural differences such as bill length and plumage differences, suggest that it is a valid subspecies. It is, in fact, the largest of all subspecies of European, Siberian or African Stonechat (see measurements below).

Adult male upperparts are very black at all times. Even in fresh plumage there is little brown fringing to the feathers and the black can show a slight gloss. The rump and uppertail-coverts are pure white and the base of the tail can variably show a tiny fraction of 1–2mm of white or none at all. The chestnut-red breast is similar to *axillaris*, being marginally richer and darker red in tone and does not extend onto the sides of the body or flanks. The lower breast, flanks, belly and undertail-coverts are pure white. The male differs from *torquata* in that the inner edges of the remiges are fringed brown, not white. The female is much darker above than the female of *salax* and is nearer to *albofasciata* in colour. The rump is white and the uppertail-coverts are white with chestnut fringes in fresh plumage. The breast is rich chestnut extending onto the sides of the breast but not the flanks. Progressively as the feathers wear there is a marked demarcation between the rich colouring of the breast and the almost white flanks, belly and undertail-coverts. The throat of the female is also very dark brown/black, being much darker than either *salax* or *axillaris* and nearer to *albofasciata*.

Measurements

	Male	**Female**
Wing	76.5–79.5 (mean 78.0)	76.0/76.5

[Own measurements BMNH, 2001]

S. t. moptana

Saxicola torquata moptana Bates, 1932, *Bull. Brit. Orn. Club* 53, p.8—Mopti, French Sudan [= Mali]

Slightly smaller than *salax* which it most closely resembles and therefore the smallest of all recognised subspecies. Geographically, the respective ranges are still separated by some 2,250km. It differs from all other Afrotropical subspecies in having the underwing-coverts and axillaries in both sexes mainly white. Adult male has a large area of white on the sides of the neck forming an almost complete collar separated by c.10mm of black on the hindneck. Most of the breast and belly are white, leaving only a small, pale chestnut patch (even paler than in *salax*) on the central upper breast. Female is very pale on the underparts, with pale rufous-buff upper breast and flanks and the rest of the underparts very pale buff-white or white. The rump and uppertail-coverts are white with the slightest creamy tinge.

Measurements

	Male	**Female**
Wing	63.0–65.0 (mean 64.0)	61.0/61.5–62.0

[Own measurements BMNH, 2001]

S. t. nebularum

Saxicola torquata nebularum Bates, 1930, *Bull. Brit. Orn. Club* 51, p.51—near Birwa Peak, Kono District, Sierra Leone

Both sexes are rather small and the nearest race with similar plumage is *adamauae* from the Cameroon highlands. They differ from that subspecies and most other Afrotropical subspecies in having deeper colouring especially on the breast. Adult males show a more extensive and uniform area of deeper chestnut-red on the breast which extends far down the breast and onto the flanks, leaving only the belly and sides of the breast white.

Females also have a reddish tinge to the breast. Rump and uppertail-coverts are usually white with a few rufous-buff tips in fresh plumage.

Measurements

	Male	**Female**
Wing	67.0–70.0 (mean 68.6)	66.0–67.5 (mean 67.0)

[Own measurements BMNH, 2001]

S. t. jebelmarrae

Saxicola torquata jebelmarrae Lynes, 1920, *Bull. Brit. Orn. Club* 41, p.17—Jebel Marra, Darfur [= Sudan]

Similar to *sibilla* and *axillaris* but slightly larger and the male has broader brown fringes to the feathers of the upperparts. The rump and uppertail-coverts are pure white. The underwing-coverts and axillaries are black with narrow white fringes. It is also paler chestnut-red on the breast than the nominate race but still darker than any Palearctic race, with a ginger tinge rather than reddish. The area of chestnut is more extensive, reaching from the upper breast to the flanks. The lower breast and belly are white. The female is very similar to *sibilla* but generally paler, being more buff than brown. The lower rump and uppertail-coverts are pure white, but this covers a smaller area than in the nominate race, with extensive buff-orange tips in fresh plumage. Smaller in size than nominate race.

Measurements

	Male	**Female**
Wing	67.0–72.0 (mean 69.4)	66.5–68.0 (mean 67.3)

[Own measurements BMNH, 2001]

S. t. albofasciata

Saxicola albofasciata Rüppell, 1845, *Syst. Uebers. Vog. Nord-ost. Afr.* p.39—Simen Province, Abyssinia [= Ethiopia]

Possibly may prove to be a valid full species, and therefore detailed plumage descriptions are given.

Friedmann (1937) collected ten male specimens from December 1911 to February 1912 and stated that "the male lacks all the rufous-chestnut on the breast and has the black of the throat extending over the breast to the anterior margin of the abdomen. Occasionally there is a rufescent tinge to the black breast, but this disappears with wear". He also stated that two males collected from the Arussi Plateau "have some dull dark brown feathers among the black ones on the crown and occiput. They are otherwise similar to the other specimens and may be in their first adult plumage". Hartert (1910) also alluded to the fact that individuals showing this plumage were "presumed to be younger birds".

Examination (by EU) of 48 skins in BMNH revealed that the black feathers on the lower breast of 28 specimens possessed chestnut-brown tips and fringes of varying extent and in some cases also narrow chestnut tips and fringes to the feathers of the head and upperparts. One exceptional specimen also had prominent chestnut fringes on the white belly and black/white flanks. This would appear to contradict Keith *et al.* (1992). The remaining 20 specimens in the collection just showed a basic black and white pattern with no evidence of chestnut-brown fringes.

At first it was considered that birds with the chestnut-brown breast-band were in fresh plumage and that these chestnut fringes disappeared with wear, as was suggested by Friedmann. However, there are BMNH specimens with this feature collected in all months apart from April/May. Two specimens collected in the same month in Ethiopia showed the extremes of these plumages: a male with a very broad, dense, chestnut-brown breast-band collected on 3 January 1899, and a male collected on 16 January 1901 with not a trace of chestnut-brown. The individual possessing the chestnut fringes had worn, faded brown remiges and rectrices contrasting with darker brown/black, fresher wing-coverts and scapulars. The individual without the chestnut possessed far less worn remiges and rectrices. They were not faded brown but black and did not contrast with the wing-coverts, so presumably were fresher. It is known that the African Stonechat has a partial moult of the body feathers from juvenile to first-year plumage some 2–3 months after its birth but does not shed the remiges or rectrices until its first complete post-breeding moult in the following year.

It could therefore be reasonably assumed that birds showing chestnut on the breast are birds in their first breeding year that have undergone a partial post-juvenile moult the previous autumn (first-year males) and that birds showing no trace of a breast-band are older individuals (adult males) that have undergone at least one full post-breeding moult involving the remiges and rectrices. If this is correct then males can be in one of two different plumages depending on age: (1) first-year male birds, i.e. those that have undergone a partial moult from juvenile to first-year adult, have a highly variable, chestnut-brown breast-band with occasionally isolated chestnut-brown on other parts of the body (this plumage is carried through into the bird's second calendar year and is lost after the first full post-breeding moult); (2) second-year males (following the full post-breeding moult from first-year bird to adult) and older males do not show any chestnut-brown fringes to any feathers, especially on the breast, and are basically black and white.

First-year male Forehead, crown, nape, lores, malar region, cheeks, ear-coverts, chin, throat and upper breast black with some birds showing very fine chestnut fringes to scattered feathers on the forehead and nape. The sides of the neck are pure white extending down onto the sides of the breast and upper flanks. The white also extends considerably onto the hindneck and, in extreme cases, can meet on the hindneck forming a collar. Mantle and scapulars black with a slight gloss but variably some birds also possess fairly broad chestnut-brown fringes to some of these feathers, giving the plumage an irregular appearance. The rump and uppertail-coverts are pure white. Lower breast black with broad, chestnut-brown tips to the feathers. The number of feathers with chestnut-brown tips varies considerably amongst individuals, from a virtually solid band of chestnut c.20mm deep to an irregular band of black and chestnut. Belly, ventral area and undertail-coverts white. Flanks black with many feathers showing broad white tips, creating an uneven black-and-white blotching. The white on the belly and rump of a few individuals shows an irregular, pale yellowish caste. One individual with a chestnut breast-band showed scattered chestnut blotches on the belly and flanks as well as on the upper and undertail-coverts.

Remiges dark brown with buff tips to the secondaries in fresh plumage. The upperwing primary coverts are dark brown with narrow buff fringes to the outer webs and buff tips. Upperwing lesser coverts are dark brown with, variably, some of the innermost white. Upperwing median coverts dark brown with outer ones narrowly tipped with buff. Inner median coverts are white. Upperwing greater coverts dark brown or black narrowly tipped white or buff. Inner two greater coverts (09–10) are white, whilst the next (08) has a white inner web and black on the outer web. Smallest tertial (09) is black with the basal half of the outer web white. Rectrices are black and in some specimens the tail can show a small amount of white at the base. Of five specimens examined at BMNH two show no white while the others show 9, 12 and 15mm at the base respectively. The average tail length of these five specimens was 51.8mm so the white forms only a very insignificant proportion of the tail and would not be visible in the field. The underwing-coverts and axillaries are black with very narrow grey to white tips. Bill, legs and feet black. Irides dark brown.

Adult male As first-year male but without any trace of chestnut-brown, thus just a combination of black and white. The black feathering of the head and upperparts is also slightly glossier. Some birds have a small, white basal area to the tail as in first-year male. One specimen examined also had small white tips to the outer rectrices. The remiges, rectrices and upperwing-coverts are black rather than the brown of first-year males and consequently show little contrast with the black of the mantle and scapulars.

Adult female Feathers of forehead, crown, nape, mantle and scapulars black broadly fringed buff-brown in fresh plumage obscuring all but the dark centres of the feathers, giving the bird a somewhat dark but streaked appearance. Friedmann (1937) found that the colour of the fringes to the upperparts varied from dull, amber-brown to tawny-olive and greyish earth-brown, this last being found on individuals in worn plumage. Upper rump pale buff. Lower rump and uppertail-coverts pure white with orange-buff tips and dark centres to the uppertail-coverts. The amount and extent of white can vary considerably and in some birds in worn plumage the longest uppertail-coverts remain dark brown broadly fringed chestnut and have dark shaft-streaks.

There is an indistinct buff supercilium stretching from the bill to behind the eye. Chin and throat are buff-white in fresh plumage with darker brown/black feather bases on throat showing through. The chin remains buff but the throat becomes progressively darker with wear, contrasting with the paler chestnut-buff breast. Some birds in worn plumage have the dark throat extending as a bib onto the upper breast, contrasting with the chestnut-buff. There are no pale sides to the neck, just a suggestion of a paler buff colour in this area. The lower breast, belly and flanks are pale rufous-buff. The ventral area and undertail-coverts are buff with occasional streaks of rufous.

The remiges are dark brown with narrow buff fringes on the outer webs and buff tips. The tertials are dark brown with the outer webs broadly fringed buff and the tips buff. The upperwing-coverts are dark brown broadly fringed with chestnut-buff apart from the white on the innermost greater and median coverts. The smallest tertial (09) has the basal third of the outer web buff. The underwing-coverts are dark brown with chestnut-buff fringes, and the axillaries are chestnut-buff. Rectrices dark brown with buff tips which disappear as the plumage wears. No pale base to the tail. With wear the upperparts progressively darken. Bill, legs and feet black or very dark brown. Irides dark brown.

Juvenile The feathers of the forehead and crown, mantle, scapulars, back and rump are black at their base but otherwise chestnut-buff with prominent black fringes, giving a scaly appearance. The uppertail-coverts are white with broad buff tips. The chin and throat are pale buff, the breast and flanks slightly darker rufous-buff, giving a more even and paler appearance than in the adult female, and all the feathers have narrow black fringes. The belly and undertail-coverts are a pale chestnut-buff. The remiges are dark brown with prominent whitish-buff tips and fringes to the outer webs. The upperwing lesser, median and outer greater coverts are dark brown with broad chestnut-buff tips. The innermost upperwing greater coverts are white with similar buff tips and the white can extend onto the outer web of the smallest tertial (09). The other tertials are dark brown with prominent chestnut-brown fringes and tips. The rectrices are dark brown with narrow buff fringes to the outer webs and buff tips.

Measurements

	Male	Female
Wing	69.5–73.5 (mean 71.2)	66.0–68.5 (mean 67.2)
Bill	12.6–15.5 (mean 14.3)	13.1–15.2 (mean 14.3)
Tail	46.5–55.0 (mean 51.6)	45.0–51.5 (mean 48.1)

[Own measurements BMNH, 2000]

S. t. felix

Saxicola torquata felix Bates, 1936, *Bull. Brit. Orn. Club* 57, p.20—Menacha [= Manakha] Yemen

Distinctly smaller than *axillaris*. The general colour of the male upperparts including the tail is always black, as it only has very narrow buff fringes to the feathers in comparatively fresh plumage. The axillaries and underwing-coverts are black with white fringes. The uppertail-coverts are white with black shaft-streaks similar to the European Stonechat *S. rubicola* but not so wide. In breeding plumage the adult male differs

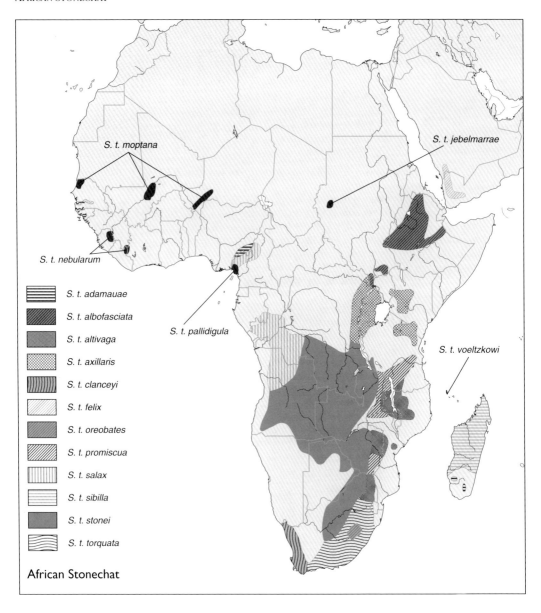

African Stonechat

S. t. moptana

S. t. jebelmarrae

S. t. nebularum

	S. t. adamauae
	S. t. albofasciata
	S. t. altivaga
	S. t. axillaris
	S. t. clanceyi
	S. t. felix
	S. t. oreobates
	S. t. promiscua
	S. t. salax
	S. t. sibilla
	S. t. stonei
	S. t. torquata

S. t. pallidigula

S. t. voeltzkowi

from *torquata* in having paler ginger chestnut colouring only on the breast. The sides of the breast and belly are pure white. The female lacks a white rump and uppertail-coverts (these areas are chestnut-brown).

Measurements

Male

Wing 63.0–67.0 (mean 65.1)

[Own measurements BMNH, 2000]

S. t. sibilla

Motacilla Sibilla Linnaeus, 1766, *Syst. Nat.* ed. 12, 1, p.337—Madagascar

The male is similar to *torquata* and also *axillaris* but smaller and with almost pure white underwing-coverts and axillaries. It has a considerable amount of white in the wing but not as extensive as *torquata* with white being present only on the inner 50% of the greater and median upperwing-coverts and basal half of the inner web of the smallest tertial (09). The inner webs of the remiges have broad, pure white fringes. The rump and uppertail-coverts form a smaller area of white than on *axillaris*. In fresh plumage the upperparts are mainly black but with prominent chestnut fringes to the scapulars and lower mantle. The underparts also have more chestnut-red than *axillaris* with this colour extending irregularly onto the lower breast and flanks but less extensive than *salax*. In worn plumage the chestnut-red is restricted to a small crescentic patch on the lower breast, with the black of the throat extending to form a bib on the upper breast. The rest of the underparts are pure white including the undertail-coverts with some black feather bases showing through on the flanks in worn plumage.

The female has a very small white rump in worn plumage. In fresh plumage the white is virtually obscured and the rump and uppertail-coverts are pale rufous-buff with some of the rump and longer uppertail-coverts having broad black centres and the tail-coverts additionally having black and chestnut-buff tips. The upper breast shows a strong rufous-buff colouring contrasting with the buff throat and pale buff belly and flanks. There are pale grey-white markings to the sides of the neck in worn plumage and extensive white on the inner greater and median upperwing-coverts. Some of the lesser coverts also have white tips.

Two other subspecies have been proposed for the population on Madagascar: *S. t. ankaratrae* which is said to be local to mountains near Ankaratra in central Madagascar and areas to the south and west of Antananarivo, and differs from *sibilla* by its larger size and *S. t. tsaratananae* which is confined to the Tsaratanana massif in the north and differs from *sibilla* by its darker upperparts and by a largely black breast with only the tips of the lowest breast feathers coloured rufous-chestnut. Neither race was considered valid by Ripley *et al.* (1964) or Keith *et al.* (1992).

Measurements

Male	Female
66.0/68.0	66.0

[Own measurements BMNH, 2001]

S. t. voeltzkowi

Saxicola torquata voeltzkowi Grote, 1926, *Orn. Monatsb.* 34, p.146—La Convalescence, 1,800m, Grand Comoro Island

Similar in size and plumage to *torquata*. Chestnut-red possibly extends slightly further down the breast and flanks. The belly is buff. Some older males have the white neck-collar meeting on hindneck. Female has possibly the smallest area of white on the rump and uppertail-coverts of all Afrotropical and Malagasy races.

DISTRIBUTION

S. t. torquata

South Africa: from the winter rainfall area of south-western Cape Province [Western Cape] and coastal districts of the southern and eastern Cape [Western and Eastern Cape], north-east to KwaZulu-Natal (not breeding in the north-eastern coastal belt), western Swaziland, eastern Orange Free State [Free State] and the highveld of the Transvaal [Mpumalanga]. In the south-western Cape [Western Cape] it intergrades with *clanceyi* to the north of the Berg River (Clancey 1961).

S. t. clanceyi

South Africa: inhabits the coastal sand-dunes and adjacent areas of north-western Cape Province [Northern Cape] from approximately the mouth of the Orange River (Alexander Bay) south to the area between the mouths of the Berg and Olifants Rivers (Clancey 1961).

S. t. stonei

South Africa: the dry interior of the eastern Cape, northwards through the western Orange Free State [Free State], and northern and western Transvaal [Northwest Province]. Northern and eastern Botswana, north-east Namibia and the Zimbabwe plateau (excluding the eastern mountains). Southern and eastern Angola north to the Cuanza River, southern parts of the Democratic Republic of Congo, Zambia. Some birds occur as winter visitors in north-eastern KwaZulu-Natal (Clancey 1964). In south-west Tanzania it occurs between 800 and 2,000m on the narrow strip of grassland that lies between Lakes Tanganyika and Rukwa north to c.6°S and east to Tuduma (Britton 1980).

S. t. oreobates

The Highlands of Lesotho, breeding at elevations often over 3,200m, and peripheral areas in the eastern Cape Province [Eastern Cape], KwaZulu-Natal and Orange Free State [Free State]. The Lesotho populations winter down to lower altitudes from May to September in KwaZulu-Natal, Swaziland, eastern Transvaal [Mpumalanga] and southern Mozambique.

S. t. altivaga

The southern and central highlands of Malawi and adjacent parts of northern Mozambique. South of the Zambezi River in the eastern highlands of Zimbabwe from Inyanga to the Chimanimani Range and the Melsetter district. South of the Limpopo River in the northern highlands of the Transvaal [Limpopo Province]. Also found on Mt Gorongosa in southern Mozambique (Clancey 1988).

S. t. promiscua

Parts of the eastern Tanzanian Highlands at 500–1,600m, between Mpwapwa and Kilosa to Mikumi NP, the foothills of the Ulugurus and northern Iringa (Britton 1980).

S. t. axillaris

In Tanzania it is found from Songea in the south-west to Kibondo in the north-west and in all highland areas and the north-east including the Lake Victoria basin to the Crater Highlands, Arusha NP and Mt Kilimanjaro. In Kenya in the Chyulu and Taita Hills, above 1,800m in the western and central highlands from Kisii and Sotik in the south-west east through the Mau Escarpment, Mt Suswa to Ngong and north to Mt Elgon and Trans Nzoia district, then south-east through Cherngis, Laikipia district, to Mt Kenya and Mt Uraguess. The breeding populations of Tanzania and Kenya are about 100km apart and it is not certain if there is any intergradation between them (Scheuerlein 2000).

It also occurs in south and west Uganda north to Masindi and West Nile extending east to Jinja (Britton 1980). Also Rwanda, Burundi and eastern parts of the Democratic Republic of Congo (Mackworth-Praed & Grant 1960, Keith *et al.* 1992).

S. t. albofasciata

The western and south-eastern highlands of Ethiopia and higher elevations of the Rift Valley; occurs at 2,440–3,050 m, locally at and rarely below 2,135m (Cheesman & Sclater 1935, Friedmann 1937), also in south-east Sudan and north-east Uganda.

This subspecies has been considered by some (Hall & Moreau 1970, Keith *et al.* 1992) as an incipient species and provisionally named "Ethiopian Stonechat"; Sibley and Monroe (1993) also intimated that it may be worthy of consideration as a valid species, but did not promote it to that level.

S. t. salax

North-west Angola, the lower Congo, Gabon, south-eastern Nigeria (where only resident on the montane Obudu Plateau =>1,525m), Cameroon at lower levels such as grasslands near the Nyong river at Akonolinga and at Efufut (Louette 1981).

S. t. adamauae

The highlands of northern and western Cameroon at 1,372–2,745m (Genderu Mountains) and as far south as the Mbo Mountains, which are approximately 200km north of Mount Cameroon.

S. t. pallidigula

Cameroon Mountain from 1,760m and common from 2,745m, being seen up to 3,500m (Boulton & Rand 1952). Mountains of Bioko in Equatorial Guinea.

S. t. moptana

The inner Niger delta, Mali, northern parts of Senegal as well as the Senegal delta.

S. t. nebularum

The Highlands of Sierra Leone above 1,220m, Guinea, and the western Ivory Coast. It is a common breeder in Guinean and Ivoirean parts of Mt Nimba but is rare and local in Liberia. It was observed once on the Liberian part of Mt Nimba in 1967 or 1968 and a few pairs expanded into Liberia after extended fires on the summits (Gatter 1997).

S. t. jebelmarrae

Western Sudan.

S. t. sibilla

Madagascar. Common in the north, east and west but rare in the south of the island where it is only found around rivers and lakes. Found from sea level up to 2,400m (Langrand 1990).

S. t. voeltzkowi

Grand Comoro Island.

S. t. felix

Mountains of south-western Arabia and Yemen.

STATUS

In Africa it is widespread at higher altitudes usually above 1,000m (Keith *et al.* 1992). In Kenya it is a common resident, being widespread in the west and central highlands, the Chyulu and Taita Hills.

Similarly it is common in Tanzania's Crater and Mbulu Highlands, Arusha National Park (NP), Mt Meru, Kilimanjaro, North and South Pares and the Usambara Mountains (Zimmerman *et al.* 1996). The population of *S. t. axillaris* in the Arusha Region of Tanzania is estimated at a minimum of c.2,000 breeding pairs (Scheuerlein *et al.* in prep.). In Zimbabwe it is also considered widespread on the central plateau and eastern highlands with the close proximity of water a prerequisite, and it may be increasing in developed areas although most farming activities, especially grazing, cause it to disappear (Irwin 1987). In southern Africa it is not considered under threat and probably has expanded its range into farming areas, although overgrazing may be a negative factor. The highest reporting rates for the *Atlas of southern African birds* came from the grassland habitat of eastern and east-central South Africa. It is common in the winter rainfall areas of the western and south-western Cape Province [Western Cape] and in the wet Okavango Delta and Caprivi Strip (Harrison *et al.* 1997).

MOVEMENTS

In Sierra Leone, West Africa, there is apparently some altitudinal movement with some and possibly the majority of birds at higher elevations moving lower. On Mt Bintimani on 22 November at 1,370m a pair of African Stonechats were observed but on 17–18 April many more pairs were found breeding from the 1,370m contour to the summit (Serle 1949). In southern Africa, there is also some seasonal movement, with birds making local altitudinal movements in the southern hemisphere winter c.January–June and returning in spring, such as from the highlands of eastern South Africa to lower altitudes, some reaching southern Mozambique and birds from Lesotho reaching eastern Zimbabwe. Other movements take place to the west and east of the Stormsberg/Drakensberg/Transvaal [Eastern Cape – Mpumalanga] escarpment ridge. For example, to the east some move to north-eastern KwaZulu-Natal, and to the west the species is mainly a winter visitor to eastern Botswana. In June in the Katse Basin, Lesotho, it was virtually absent above 2,400m, but only 40% less common in fields between 2,000–2,400m than in summer months (Tarboton *et al.* 1993). In KwaZulu-Natal there is evidence of a drop in sightings at higher altitudes in winter and a corresponding rise in sightings at lower altitudes. There is also evidence of winter influxes in south-east Zimbabwe. In the Swaziland lowveld the adjoining Lebombo range and southern Mozambique it is only known as a non-breeding winter visitor. Birds from Malawi descend from breeding areas at 1,000–2,000m to a minimum elevation of 450m (Harrison *et al.* 1997).

(*Muscicapa*) *tectes* Gmelin, 1789, *Syst. Nat.*, 1 (2), 940 *in insula* Bourbon, *ex* Brisson, 1760, Ornith., 2, p.360

Etymology *tectes* derived from the local Réunion name for this species "tec-tec" which is based on its call

TAXONOMY

Monotypic. Endemic to Réunion Island in the Indian Ocean. Ripley *et al.* (1964) classified it as a subspecies of African Stonechat *Saxicola torquata tectes* but the majority of authors now consider it a full species. Hall & Moreau (1970) suggest it is a species and Sibley & Monroe (1993) classify it as a separate species.

Collins (1984) drew attention to the fact that *S. tectes* was very similar in plumage to the Canary Island Stonechat (see Taxonomy under *S. d. dacotiae* for more detail). Réunion Stonechat also appears to be very close to African Stonechat *S. torquata* but differs in that the male always has a white, as opposed to black, chin and throat and usually, but not invariably, a white supercilium. The range of habitat used by *S. tectes* is also greater and more variable than that used by *S. torquata*.

IDENTIFICATION

Size 12.5cm/4.9 inches. Sexually dimorphic although some males can resemble females (see below). A short, rounded species which perches prominently flicking its wings and tail. It is confiding, allowing approach to within a few metres, and will often come towards an intruder.

A typical male has a predominantly black head with a prominent buff to white supercilium, white chin and throat. The rest of the upperparts are black/brown including the tail, relieved only by a white patch on the rump and uppertail-coverts. There are prominent white neck- and upperwing-patches. The breast is chestnut-buff and the rest of the underparts are buff-white. Various plumage morphs in males result in much individual variation (see below).

Females are dull greyish-brown on the head with a thin buff supercilium. The rest of the upperparts are also greyish-brown with darker brown/black wings and tail. There is no white on the neck and rump but a variable white upperwing-patch usually smaller than on the male. The uppertail-coverts are chestnut-brown. The underparts are pale buff, often with a deeper chestnut-buff tone on the breast but not as strong as in the male.

Confusion species None. No other *Saxicola* species occurs on Réunion Island.

DESCRIPTION

Male in fresh plumage In fresh plumage the forehead, crown, nape, mantle and scapulars are black with extensive rufous-brown fringes virtually obscuring the black. The fringes steadily wear away to expose the black. The lores, cheeks and ear-coverts are black with some brown streaking contrasting with the more extensively brown-fringed feathers of the forehead, crown and nape. The supercilium is buff-white, becoming whiter with wear, and extends from the bill over the eye to the rear of the ear-coverts. The back is dark grey grading into white on the lower rump and uppertail-coverts, although the white can be largely obscured by orange-buff fringes. The longest uppertail-coverts are also white but with extensive black and cinnamon-brown tips. The central chin, throat and centre of the upper breast are pure white. The sides of the neck and upper breast are mottled black, chestnut-buff and white, and the breast is a rich chestnut-buff fading to paler on the flanks. The mottling on the sides of the neck and upper breast disappears gradually with wear to leave the sides of the neck white and the upper breast chestnut-buff. The belly and ventral area are buff-white with irregular orange-buff blotches, the undertail-coverts buff-white. The tail is dark brown with narrow pale buff tips and fringes to the outerwebs. The remiges are dark brown with the inner secondaries narrowly fringed buff on the outerwebs and broadly fringed white (up to 50%) on the innerwebs. The tips of the primaries and secondaries show very narrow off-white crescentic tips. The underwing-coverts and axillaries are greyish-white. The majority of the upperwing greater coverts are black but at least the three innermost greater coverts (08–10) are pure white with the outerweb of the third innermost (08) being black. The upperwing median and lesser coverts are black with the two innermost median coverts being white on the innerwebs. The smallest tertial also has white on the proximal two-thirds of the outerweb, the rest of the feather being dark brown to black. The other two tertials are predominantly black-brown with a small white base to the outerwebs. The bill, legs and feet are black. The irides are dark brown.

Whilst studying this species in 1964 A.S. Cheke noticed apparent females singing and acting territorially and it became apparent that these 'females' were in fact males. This species is unique in its genus in that there exists amongst the males a wide range of plumages varying from female-type through varying gradations to the full black and white of the typical male. Even in the typical black and white plumage there appear to be several variations (see plate 4). Cheke's investigations led him to conclude that there are two main types of variation. The first is in the dominant colour of the head and back, which can vary from dull grey-brown (female-type) to black (male-type). The second is in the amount of white around the eye, on the wing and on the rump. The presence, absence and extent of white in these parts varies independently so that birds can be found with all possible combinations. In addition to a larger or smaller area of white or none at all, the rump may be greyish and show no pure white. The chestnut-buff breast-patch can also vary in size and strength of colour. Although lacking conclusive evidence Cheke suggested that the grey-brown to black plumage variation in males may be related to age, but that the amount of white in the final plumage may be polymorphic (Cheke 1987).

Female in fresh plumage Forehead, crown, nape, mantle, scapulars, back and rump are dark brown with slightly paler broad rufous-brown fringes which mainly obscure the dark brown centres of the feathers, creating a mainly uniform appearance. As the feather fringes abrade, more of the dark centres are revealed creating a more streaked appearance. The base of the forehead and lores is buff. The malar region and ear-coverts are dark brown with paler, narrow streaking giving a grizzled appearance. A buff-white supercilium (narrower in front of the eye, broader above and behind the eye) extends from the bill over the eye to half-way along the top of the ear-coverts. The rump and uppertail-coverts contrast only slightly with the rest of the upperparts and are a slightly paler chestnut-brown with narrow, darker brown shaft-streaks. The feathers on the sides of the neck have small white bases but are mainly medium brown streaked buff and broadly fringed pale cinnamon brown, giving this area a distinct pale appearance. The chin and throat are buffish-white contrasting with the stronger orange-buff tone of the upper and lower breast and flanks. As the feathers of the chin and throat wear, the darker feather bases start to show through. The belly and ventral area are a slightly paler buff-white than the chin and throat. The undertail-coverts are slightly deeper buff. The tail is dark brown tipped with buff-white and with the outerwebs of the rectrices narrowly fringed buff-white. The remiges are also dark brown narrowly fringed with buff on the outerwebs. The fringes of the innerwebs of the underside of the remiges show increasingly broad buff fringes from the 05–01 primaries. The upperwing lesser coverts and all but the innermost upperwing greater coverts and innermost upperwing median coverts are dark brown narrowly fringed and tipped with grey-buff. The upperwing primary coverts are dark brown with buff-white tips and fringes to the outerwebs. There is a noticeable white outer edge to the base of the outer primary covert and smallest feather of the alula which shows on the bend of the wing. There is a small amount of white on the innermost upperwing greater and median upperwing-coverts which varies amongst individuals possibly owing to age. Of two females both collected in September, one had the innermost three (08–10) upperwing greater coverts broadly fringed whitish-buff on the outerwebs, paler than the remaining greater coverts, and the two innermost upper median coverts broadly tipped white. The innermost upperwing greater covert (10) also had a white shaft and a broad dull white fringe to the innerweb. The other individual collected in the same month had the inner two upperwing greater coverts largely white: the innermost (10) was completely white with only a subterminal brown spot on the outerweb, 09 was dark brown on the outerweb and the innerweb was white with a brown subterminal spot, 08–07 were dark brown with a small white spot at the base of the innerweb. Another female collected in June had no white at all in the wing.

   Underwing-coverts and axillaries are grey-buff to white. The bill, legs and feet are black. The irides are dark brown. As the plumage wears the supercilium becomes whiter, the central upper breast white, the flanks and belly whiter; flanks and belly begin to show black streaks where the darker bases of feathers show through. The sides of the neck become paler with the white bases to the feathers showing as the cinnamon-brown fringes wear away. The pale fringes and tips to the remiges and rectrices also wear off but some pale tips remain on the outer secondaries. The pale tips to the upperwing-coverts wear off, with a bird collected in September retaining buff tips only to the outer upperwing greater coverts.

Juvenile The feathers of the upperparts are a slightly darker brown than on the female with a faint chestnut tone. The feathers of the forehead, crown, nape and neck have pale buff central streaks. The feathers of the mantle have triangular buff tips not as pale as the streaks on the head. There is a pale buff supercilium extending from the base of the bill, above the eye to half-way along the upperside of the ear-coverts. The supercilium is not as distinct or broad as in the female and the feathers have fine brown tips giving it a grizzled appearance. The lores, malar region and ear-coverts are brown with narrow buff central streaks. The rump and uppertail-coverts are slightly more chestnut-brown contrasting slightly with the rest of the upperparts. The chin and throat are a dull greyish-white. The breast and flanks are chestnut-buff with some birds showing dark brown centres to the feathers. The belly and undertail-coverts are pale buff-white.

The remiges and rectrices are dark brown with pale buff fringes to the outerwebs and tips. The underwing-coverts are white with a faint buff tinge. The upperwing greater coverts have broad pale tips which form an indistinct pale bar on the wing. In one specimen examined the innermost greater upperwing-covert (10) showed the slightest hint of white on the innerweb. The legs and feet are brownish-black, the bill black apart from the basal half of the lower mandible which is pale horn. The irides are dark brown.

Mesasurements

	Male	**Female**
Wing	66.0–68.0 (mean 66.9)	63.0–66.0 (mean 64.9)
Tail	49.0–53.0 (mean 50.7)	45.5–52.0 (mean 48.6)
Bill	15.0–15.3 (mean 15.1)	12.8–15.5 (mean 14.6)

[Own measurements BMNH & CMNH 2000]

As much care as possible was taken in examining the specimens available to make sure they were correctly sexed, particularly as some males appear very similar to females.

DISTRIBUTION AND STATUS

Endemic to Réunion Island. It is described by Barré *et al.* (1996) as very common, being typically a species of higher elevations, extending from the lower limits of forest (300–800m) upwards to the upper limits of heathland. It is more commonly found above 1,200m; this was evident as long ago as at least 1868 (Schlegel & Pollen 1868) although it was also found 'sparsely' at sea level at that time. Pollen (1868) found it along the St Denis–St Marie road where it would never be found now, and Régnaud (1878 [1984]) also found it at sea level as well as on the highest parts of the island. It is now very unusual at very low altitudes although birds occasionally turn up at sea level especially outside the breeding season. One individual perching on papyrus *Cyperus papyrus* was seen in just such circumstances, hawking insects over water at Etang de St Paul on 11 May 1974. Barré & Barau (1982) gave two records of individual birds: from canefield tracks above Bras Panon at 40m above sea level in April 1980; and wooded grassland at La Saline at 130m above sea level in January 1980. Cheke found a singing male on the east coast at La Vièrge au Parasol (Grand Brûlé) on 11 October 1978.

There is no apparent reason for this retreat to higher altitudes but it has been paralleled by the Réunion Olive White-eye *Zosterops olivaceus*.

Its general lower limits are 800–900m in the north and north-east of the island, but reaching down to 300m at Mare Longue (St Philippe) and the Rivière des Remparts in the south. In places further north it occurs at low altitudes in secluded places such as Ilet à Guillaume (700m) and Grand Etang (500m). The fact that it occupies lower elevations in secluded areas suggests that its upwards retreat is due to disturbance or changes to its habitat caused by man. In the west, although information is limited, it would appear that north of St.-Pierre it is very scarce below 950m, except in the beds of major rivers such as Bras de la Plaine and Rivière St Etienne.

There appears to be no upper altitude limit, with birds being encountered at the highest elevations on the island. This species has been recorded at the summit of the island on the Piton des Neiges (3,069m) by both Cheke (in May) and Barré, although Cheke doubted they bred at such a height. In November 1974 Cheke counted nests in an area of tamarins with little undergrowth at Plaine des Chicots. In six 1ha grid squares he found eight nests and suspected the existence of three more – an average of nearly two per hectare. He judged this normal and thought the same situation applied throughout the Plaines d'Affouches and des

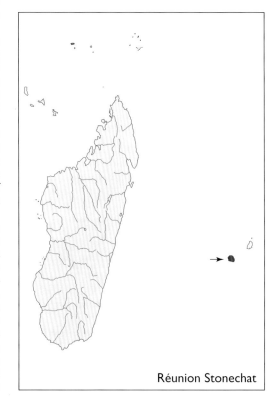

Réunion Stonechat

Chicots, Bebour, the forest up to the Petit Matarum at Cilaos and elsewhere. The densities in cloud forest were considerably lower (see under Food for possible causes). Barré (1983) estimated a population of 180,000. Cheke estimated a population in excess of c.100,000 pairs.

BREEDING

The breeding season lasts from mid-October to late January. A female was seen carrying nest material on 17 October 1971 (Barré & Barau 1982). Cheke in 1973 and 1974 at the beginning of November found that the most advanced nests had hatched on 31 October with therefore the first egg being laid around 15 October (Plaine des Chicots in 1974). Another nest had a bird incubating on 12 October 1978. Last nests were on very similar dates in 1974 and 1975, with a nest at Cilaos with three four-day-old young being found on 21 January 1974 and one or two nests with large young being found at the Plaine des Chicots on 22 January 1975. Cheke revisited the area on 14 February and found no active nests but this may have been influenced by a cyclone that had struck in the meantime. Older records also suggest a similar situation, with eggs in November and January (Carie in Berlioz 1946) and eggs and young in December (Milon 1951). Régnaud (1878 [1984]) reported birds laying in September and Cheke suggests that birds at lower altitudes may have commenced breeding earlier.

There is little evidence of pairs synchronising their breeding. In 1979 there was at least 3.5 weeks' difference between the first eggs in the earliest and latest nests from a sample of eight nests discovered at the Plaine des Chicots. Between 3 and 15 December Milon (1951) found one nest containing three young eight days old and another containing two young two days old.

Although there would be time for early nesters to raise two broods, Cheke suspects that this species is single-brooded. However, if the first nest is predated pairs will attempt a second. The little information available suggests that, after fledging, family groups become nomadic, moving away from their breeding territories.

Nest are generally either located on the ground under a tussock in a grassy area or in open understorey. Another common site is a vegetated bank where a path has been cut out of a slope. Birds frequently breed in the banks of forest tracks, where nests can be found every 200–300m (Milon 1951). Nests are usually well concealed although some on banks can be relatively exposed. Occasionally they can be found on a low branch or in a cavity in a tree trunk 1–2m above ground (Barré et al. 1996).

Nests are constructed of moss, especially on the lip of the nest cup, with coarse grass and dead leaves at the base. The nest cup is lined with finer grasses, small feathers and hair. One nest contained a large piece of moulted reptile skin. Dimensions of six nests examined were as follows: average external dimension 130 x 130mm with a height of 85 x 110mm. The average diameter of the nest cup was 50–55mm with a depth of 39–55mm (Milon 1951).

The female builds the nest alone and this part of the breeding cycle is similar to African Stonechat. Cheke records the normal clutch as comprising 2–3 eggs, although others have reported four (Barré & Barau 1982). From 12 clutches Milon (1951) found 11 comprised three eggs and one two eggs, whereas Cheke had a ratio of 8:6 (1973 and 1974 combined). Cheke states that the average clutch size probably varies from year to year and possibly also with date, altitude and locality.

The eggs are generally a pale dull blue-green finely spotted with reddish-brown mainly at the larger end (Berlioz 1946, Barré & Barau 1982); rarely they are cream with similar spotting. Eggs with both ground colours have been observed in the same clutch (Cheke 1987).

The incubation period is approximately 14 days. Cheke found four nests with complete clutches which hatched in 12, 13, 13 and 14 days respectively. The time between hatching to fledging is probably also around 13–15 days. This again corresponds closely with African Stonechat.

Only the female incubates the eggs and probably only she broods the young. The male assists her in feeding the young both in the nest and after fledging. A nest containing three four-day-old young was watched for 75 minutes on 21 January 1974 and during that time the male brought food five times and the female six. The female also brooded the young for four periods during that time (for 1.5, 2.5, 4.0 and 7.25 minutes). There is no information on the period of post-fledging juvenile dependency but young can remain with the parents for up to two months in family parties.

The success of nests is high even though according to Cheke they are easy to find. This may be due to the scarcity of ground predators. Of 11 nests followed to beyond the stage when the nestlings were over half-grown, six remained successful when last examined, two were flattened by mules and/or a bull, one was destroyed by human interference, one lost eggs to an unknown predator and one may have fledged (Cheke 1987).

HABITAT

The Réunion Stonechat can be found in a wide range of habitats although it is not equally common in each. In addition to typical *Saxicola* habitat, i.e. open scrub, it also frequents open ground as favoured by wheatears *Oenanthe* and forest as favoured by robins *Erithacus*, and is the one species which takes advantage of all the small thrush habitat niches available to it. Barré (1983) found it commonest (25% of population) in the clear open environment under tamarins *Acacia heterophylla* where there were 2.1 individuals per hectare.

It was also common along tracks in *mesotherme* (mixed mid-altitude evergreen forest) and in *brandes* (heath forest) with openings and clearings. In this latter habitat it was only exceeded in numbers by Mascarene White-eye *Zosterops borbonicus*. Amongst these ericaceous shrubs the limiting factor seems to be the percentage vegetation cover. It becomes scarcer towards the summits of the island where the clumps of heath vegetation are scrawnier and too scattered to afford suitable vantage points and heath gives way to grass. The sparse vegetation around the Volcan had only a small population widely spread, and gorse scrub *Ulex europaeus* also attracted few birds. At about 500m at Grand Etang birds were very scarce and also in the cloud forest along the east side of the island. In apparently suitable habitat at the Bois Bon Accueil (Plain des Makes 970–1,200m) there were very few birds present. While it has, remarkably for a *Saxicola*, been able to benefit from and consequently extend its range into the forest habitat, it only exceptionally penetrates *savannes* (open grassy areas) where the edges of roads and tracks, burnt areas, deforested tracts or farmed plots offer much apparently suitable habitat for a *Saxicola*. Although it avoids these man-made areas it does adapt to and quickly utilise man-made clearings in forest where it can be very abundant along the edges (4.7 individuals per hectare: Barré 1983).

It is also present in good numbers under closed canopy woodland in excess of 20m high such as in the Forêt de Mare Longue. It also occurs in any kind of secondary vegetation at the right altitude and was the commonest species in tamarin plantations but was only present in low densities in *Cryptomeria*.

In *Philippia* heath it was common but less so than in mixed forest. In mixed forest where open ground could suit it, it is probable that it is limited by the shade which hinders its ability to catch insects (Barré 1983). The very dense vegetation in *Pandanus* (screw-pine) thickets makes this habitat unsuitable.

It also occurs in meadows and fields of crops grown at higher elevations on the island and even in gardens around houses in the upper parts of the island such as at the Plaine des Palmistes and at Cilaos. Barré (1983) thought that it initially colonised lava flows during the phase when grassy vegetation was becoming established under tamarins (*Acacia heterophylla*) and heaths were becoming established on alpine grassland.

Barré considered it significant that this chat is the only small endemic passerine that has no counterpart on Mauritius, where volcanic activity ceased long ago and where the less extreme altitudes have not permitted the development of these last two vegetation types mentioned above.

The breadth of this species' habitat and its extension into forested zones is unusual for a typical *Saxicola* species. However, Rand (1936) and Milon *et al.* (1973) both point out that the African Stonechat on Madagascar does not have a very different ecology to *S. tectes*. Both authors met with the former frequently in the high plateaux at 500–2,400m by the edges of roads, clearings in forest, along forest tracks and in open scrub. It was also rare at low altitudes and absent from grassland.

VOICE

The species' scientific name reflects its local onomatopoeic name "Tec-Tec", derived from its call note *tec tec*. This note is uttered by both sexes and can vary in form and function. Barré *et al.* (1996) describe it as metallic and harsh. It may be given singly or as a double note or preceded by a plaintive *hweet*. Both the *tec* and *hweet* notes are similar to those of African Stonechat and are given in similar situations to that species. When the *hweet* note is used in conjunction with the *tec* note, the bird slowly raises and lowers its tail. This vocalisation is often used when there is an intruder in the bird's territory. Pairs also use the *tec* note for contact, calling frequently from perches or on the ground often accompanied by a bobbing motion, wing-flicking and tail-flirting. It is also used by males when they are interacting aggressively and Cheke once heard it between two interacting females.

The song according to Cheke is a series of discrete phrases with variable inter-figure intervals delivered from a prominent perch or during a display-flight. Display-flights are closely similar to that of African Stonechat with the male dancing in the air, alternately rising and falling a few feet. These flights may be prolonged, reaching a height of over 30m, and are apparently given more readily than in African Stonechat. Shorter display-flights are also made, from tree to tree within the forest, across a clearing in the forest or on the open mountainside. These shorter displays are often accompanied by frequent short, sharp notes delivered rapidly and which are similar to a series of fast *tec* calls. In mid-September at high altitudes no song was given by perched birds and only occasionally in display-flight. Later in the year song was heard throughout the day with main peaks of activity at dawn and dusk. According to Cheke this species is one of the earliest to sing in the morning, beginning before light, mainly from perches. Later in the morning it would sing in display-flight. Birds would continue singing and displaying at intervals throughout the day, even when their habitat was covered in thick mist.

Recently fledged birds have a modified version of the *tec* note combined with a buzzy sound which serves as a contact call with their parents and a demand for food.

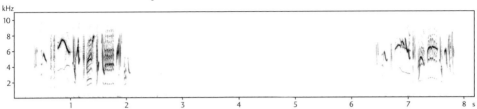

Réunion Stonechat *Saxicola tectes* NSA 26632. Song. Plaine de Chicots Réunion Island, 13 December 1974. *J.F.M. Horne*

FOOD

The relatively little information points to a similar diet to congeners, consisting almost entirely of insects and other invertebrates. Old records mention Diptera caught by flycatching (Schlegel & Pollen 1868) and "grasshoppers, larvae, ants and flies picked up from the surface of the ground" (Gúerin 1940–1953).

The majority of prey is usually too small to be identified by observation. Larger prey identified includes caterpillars up to 4.5cm long of unidentified moths. Birds also take advantage of unexpected opportunities to capture prey such as when stumps of dead wood were broken open to expose large 5–7cm cerambycid larvae. A bird that spent 20 minutes picking small items from gravel on a wet road was thought to be catching tiny dipteran larvae. On occasion birds have taken crumbs of bread thrown to them by hikers in the forest. Two nestlings which were fully fed when found dead contained a range of insects and some vegetable matter.

Adult birds invariably feed singly. The preferred method is to perch on an exposed vantage point such as a rock, low branch or top of a heather bush and survey the surrounding area until a prey item is seen. Birds locate prey up to 3m from their perch. They then descend to the ground to seize it, mostly returning to a different perch to consume it. However, if there are a number of prey items together, such as ants, it may remain on the ground to capture and eat them. If the item is large the bird often lands beside it to assess it before dealing with it. Larger insects are beaten on branches before being consumed. Food is also taken whilst the bird is in flight, being snatched from foliage, walls and rocks. In vegetation, feeding occasionally turns into leap-snatching or search-gleaning, and birds also catch flies by sallying up from a perch. Birds often feed from the ground in a fashion similar to a robin (*Erithacus*), hopping or flying to seize prey when they detected some movement. Cheke suggested that the need to feed largely by capturing prey on the ground may limit their numbers in cloud forest. This habitat has a dense rampant undergrowth of *Machaerina* and ferns, and the thick moss and ground litter make normal feeding methods impractical. Consequently the birds are restricted to foraging on the vegetation, which, being dense, restricts them from surveying for prey at any distance. The optimum habitat for feeding was considered to be open fields with sparse ground vegetation.

MOVEMENTS

The species is sedentary apart from some possible altitudinal movements to both higher and lower locations. This may not involve adult birds but dispersing juveniles.

BEHAVIOUR

This species is conspicuous, tame and inquisitive (Cheke 1987). In the breeding season pairs are strictly territorial but Cheke did not know if they remain paired and within the territory all year. Where there is a high density of pairs there is frequent interaction between adjacent territorial males. Males and females on territory remain solitary apart from brief encounters.

MOULT

No information. Probably similar to African Stonechat. Young birds were widely in evidence throughout the island in January and February but all had undergone a post-juvenile moult by April and were then indistinguishable from adults (Cheke 1987).

CONSERVATION

There appears to be little threat to this species, although its population at lower elevations may have declined owing to the activities of man. A Ministerial Decree issued on 17 February 1989 established it as a specially protected species and it is strictly forbidden to hunt it, keep it in captivity or disturb it in any way. Consequently, the population appears to be under no threat and is left alone by collectors and hunters of birds on the island. Its adaptability and readiness to occupy both the wildest habitat as well as habitat degraded or cleared by man or his animals, or such as by deer on the Plain des Chicots, allows it to maintain its population.

There are records of possible predation by Réunion Harrier *Circus maillardi*.

Pratincola leucura Blyth, 1847, *Journ. Asiat. Soc. Bengal* 16, p.474—Upper Sind [Pakistan]

Etymology *leucura* derived from Greek *leukouros* meaning 'white-tailed'

Alternative names White-tailed Bushchat, Black Stonechat

TAXONOMY
Monotypic.

IDENTIFICATION
Size 12.5cm/4.9 inches. Sexes dimorphic. The male in both fresh and breeding plumage is similar to Siberian Stonechat *S. maura* apart from its tail pattern. The head, including the chin and throat, and mantle are black, and there are distinctive white neck-patches, white on the inner upperwing greater coverts and an unmarked white rump and uppertail-coverts. The tail is distinctive with a large amount of white extending from the base. All the tail feathers show almost completely white inner webs apart from the central pair which are all black. The rufous on the underparts in worn plumage is very restricted and is only present on the central upper breast with the rest of the underparts pure white. The colour of the breast-patch is darker and richer chestnut-brown than in Siberian Stonechat – more red than orange. In fresh autumn plumage the male is similar to Siberian Stonechat, being pale grey-brown with dark streaks on the upperparts with extensive pale fringes to the head, mantle and scapular feathers. The underparts are buff-orange.

Females in fresh plumage are pale greyish-brown above with indistinct brown streaking and darker brown remiges and rectrices. The underparts are pale tawny-buff and the breast only shows a slightly stronger orange-buff tone. In worn plumage the female becomes almost white below with an indistinct orange-buff breast-patch. The upperparts also appear pale greyish-brown with slightly stronger, more prominent brown streaking.

The tail is similar to the male but the inner webs are grey-buff rather than white and do not extend quite so far down the feathers or form such a contrast with the outer webs as in the male and the central pair of tail feathers are dark brown rather than black.

Confusion species Male White-tailed Stonechat can be told from male Siberian Stonechat as follows: *S. leucura* has extensive white on the inner webs of all tail feathers, apart from the central pair which are very noticeable in flight or when the tail is being fanned, whereas *S. maura* has no white in the tail or occasionally a very small white base to the tail (completely hidden by the uppertail-coverts); the breast-patch in worn *leucura* is a rich darker reddish-chestnut in tone and restricted to the centre of the upper breast, but in *maura* it is less red and more orange in tone and extends slightly more onto the lower breast.

Females of the two species can be told as follows. The tail of *S. leucura* shows noticeable pale brown inner webs contrasting with darker outer webs, whereas in *S. maura* it is uniform dark brown; *leucura* is pale grey-brown on the head and upperparts with indistinct streaking, while *maura* has slightly darker upperparts owing to browner, less grey feather fringes, and it has bolder, darker streaking on both head and upperparts; below, *leucura* is pale tawny-buff with a slightly stronger and hence marginally contrasting ornage-buff tone to the breast, while *maura* is stronger chestnut-buff with noticeably stronger colouring to the breast and thus greater contrast with the rest of the underparts.

Female *S. leucura* can appear superficially similar to female Stoliczka's Bushchat *S. macrorhyncha* but differs as follows: *S. leucura* is smaller and structurally much more compact, with a short bill, tail and wings in proportion to the body, *S. macrorhyncha* is larger (by 2cm) and more attenuated with a proportionately longer bill, tail and wings; the tail in *leucura* does not show such a marked contrast between the paler inner webs and darker outer webs, whereas in *macrorhyncha* it shows a clear contrast between the pale buff inner webs and the outer darker brown webs; *leucura* has paler underparts, almost white in worn plumage, *macrorhynhca* is more evenly and deeper buff with a noticeably stronger tone to the breast; in *leucura* the buff supercilium is indistinct, but in *macrorhyncha* it is broad, long and striking; in *leucura* the chin and throat usually show some greyish feather bases, while *macrorhyncha* has a pure white chin and throat at all times.

DESCRIPTION
Adult male in fresh plumage Forehead, crown, neck, mantle and scapular feathers are black or very dark brown, virtually entirely obscured apart from their centres by extensive pale greyish-brown fringes. The

dark centres create the appearance of slight streaking on the head and upper mantle. The lores, malar region and ear-coverts are black with occasional narrow pale buff fringes, and contrast markedly with the paler grey-brown forehead and crown. The chin and throat are black but have extensive white fringes and tips partially obscuring the black especially on the throat. The sides of the neck are white but this is mainly obscured by extensive buff-chestnut tips. The breast, belly, flanks, ventral area and undertail-coverts are pale buff-chestnut with a markedly stronger tone on the breast. The rump is white with extensive buff-chestnut fringes and tips. The uppertail-coverts are long and white with extensive pale chestnut tips. The rectrices are dark brown-black. The outerweb of each tail feather is brown-black with narrow white fringes. The brown-black fades into extensive pale milky-brown tips on the outerweb which extend around onto the innerweb and then merge into the white, extending as a darker brown and narrowing wedge up the shaft of the feather. The inner webs of all feathers (06–02) apart from the central pair (01) have extensive white, reaching almost to the tip on 03–02. The central pair (01) are completely brown-black with narrow pale buff fringes and tips.

Tail Feather	Length	White
6	46.0	31.0
5	47.0	40.5
4	48.0	40.8
3	49.0	48.0
2	49.5	47.5
1	47.0	none present

The remiges are brown-black with pale buff fringes to the outer webs and crescentic buff tips. The tertials are black with consequent greater contrast with the pale outer fringes and tips. The inner secondaries and tertials have slightly darker and broader buff fringes to their outer webs and greyish-white tips. The pale fringes on the tertials and inner secondaries form a distinct pale panel on the closed wing. The lesser, median and greater coverts of the inner upperwing are white. The outer ones are black with long greyish-buff fringes and tips, the fringes being more grey than the tips. The upperwing primary coverts are black with greyish-buff fringes. The underwing-coverts are black. The axillaries are dark grey. The legs, feet and bill are black. The irides are dark brown.

Adult male worn plumage The chin and throat become entirely black extending as a slight bib onto the upper breast. The dark reddish-chestnut of the breast is confined to the upper central breast with the sides of the breast, belly, flanks and undertail-coverts becoming pure white and in extremely worn plumage the black bases to the feathers of the belly often show through. The sides of the neck are pure white merging with the white on the sides of the breast. The rump and uppertail-coverts are pure white with no streaking or chestnut tips. The head and upper mantle become progressively blacker as the buff fringes wear away, with the lower scapulars the last to lose the buff fringes. The pale tips to the rectrices wear away leaving the tail feathers brown-black on the outer webs and almost pure white on the inner webs with a slight subterminal brown smudge on the white of the innerweb. The pale fringes to the remiges and upperwing-coverts wear away to leave them brown-black and black respectively.

First-year male Similar to adult male apart from browner remiges, tertials and rectrices, which become progressively more faded and worn until the first post-breeding moult. The upperwing greater coverts are retained with only the innermost moulted in the post-juvenile moult. This creates a contrast between the unmoulted, browner outer greater coverts and the black inner greater and median coverts.

The primary coverts are also retained and consequently are brown rather than black. The feathers on the ear-coverts are paler and not so black as in the adult male, owing to more extensive pale greyish-buff fringes, and contrast less, than in the adult male, with the similar pale-fringed black feathers on the forehead and crown.

Adult female fresh non-breeding plumage Forehead, crown, nape, mantle and scapulars are dark brown with similar extensive pale buff fringes and tips to that of the male, leaving only the dark centres of the feathers visible, giving an indistinct streaked appearance. There is a pale buff, indistinct supercilium extending from the bill over the eye to the rear of the ear-coverts. The lores, malar region and ear-coverts are pale brown with slightly darker centres to the feathers, creating a grizzled appearance. The lower rump is tawny-buff. The uppertail-coverts are pale buff with whitish-buff fringes and faintly discernible narrow dark shaft-streaks.

The chin and throat are white with the dark grey bases of especially the throat feathers just visible. The breast, flanks and belly are tawny-buff, slightly stronger orange-buff tone on the breast and flanks and contrasting with the white throat. The undertail-coverts are buff-white. The closed tail appears dark brown with a pale buff outer edge. The rectrices, apart from the central pair (01), are mid-brown on the proximal two-thirds to half of the outer webs. The basal third to half of the outer webs are pale buff. On the proximal two-thirds of the tail feathers the pale buff of the base narrows as a wedge towards and then along the fringes of the outer webs to the tips of the tail feathers. The inner webs are paler than the brown outer webs, being grey-buff darkening slightly towards the tips. The tips of the inner webs are prominently pale buff. The outermost pair (06) have a narrow buff-white fringe to the outerweb, and the central pair (01) are entirely dark brown with narrow buff fringes and tips. The remiges are dark brown with narrow buff-white fringes to the outer webs. The secondaries have pale grey-white crescentic tips and the primaries also have similar tips but are far more indistinct. The tertials are dark brown almost black with broad buff fringes and grey-white tips to the outer webs. The buff fringes merge with the outer fringes of the inner secondaries to form a pale panel on the closed wing. The upperwing primary coverts are grey-brown with indistinct buff fringes and tips. The alula is dark brown with very narrow buff fringes to the outer webs. The upperwing lesser and median coverts have heart-shaped black-brown centres with extensive buff fringes. The upperwing greater coverts are dark brown with large pale buff tips and slightly darker buff fringes. The innermost greater covert is white. The underwing-coverts and axillaries are buff. The legs and feet are black. The bill is black-brown. The irides are dark brown.

Adult female breeding worn plumage The head and upperparts become darker grey-brown and not so greyish-buff as the pale fringes wear away but still remain paler than Siberian Stonechat with some slightly darker brown streaking evident. The chin and throat show some darker grey feather bases through the white. The underparts progressively fade from tawny buff to buff then almost white apart from the breast which remains orange-buff. The supercilium becomes slightly more defined but is still indistinct.

First-year female Very like the adult female. The same feathers are retained as in the first-year male but it is much harder to discern the difference between first-years and adults owing to the difficulty in differentiating between newer moulted and older unmoulted feathers.

Juvenile Virtually identical to the juvenile Siberian Stonechat apart from the tail pattern, which is similar to the adult of the respective sex.

Measurements

	Male	Female
Wing	65.0–70.0 (mean 67.8)	65.0–68.0 (mean 66.5)
Tail	45.0–49.0 (mean 47.6)	43.5–50.0 (mean 47.3)
Bill	14.1–15.9 (mean 14.8)	14.2–15.9 (mean 14.9)

[Own measurements BMNH 2001]

DISTRIBUTION AND STATUS

It occurs along the Indus river system in Pakistan extending eastwards through the Punjab and the watershed of the Ganges and Brahmaputra Rivers in India through Nepal to Assam in north-east India, south as far as northern Orissa and possibly Bangladesh, then extending into most of Myanmar.

In Pakistan the White-tailed Stonechat is endemic to the Indus River system, being found locally but in 'adequate' numbers along the main tributaries in the Punjab and throughout the Indus riverine plains of northern and central Sind. It has not been recorded in lower Sind and is now scarce with a very restricted range in the country (Roberts 1992), but formerly was probably commoner although always local. Ticehurst (1922–1924) refers to Hume, who found it abundant but local in the 'jheels' of Upper Sind. Ticehurst did not find it in Lower Sind and never found it in the eastern Narra district, even though the habitat appeared suitable. He collected a male in breeding condition once by the Manchar Lake on 9 March 1918 or 1919 and breeding birds have been noted from Khairpur, Sukkur (several pairs in the Keti Shah Forest April 1904 and many pairs March 1906), Larkhana [Larkana] and Jacobabad districts and at Dalipota in the northern Hyderabad district, all in Sind (T.R. Bell in Ticehurst 1922–1924). The distribution of this species would appear to be not only very localised but also subject to changes in local conditions. When Ticehurst revisited the areas in Sukkur in December 1918 where Bell located his pairs he found none. This was attributed to the area being very dry and consequently without crops owing to the low level of the Indus.

It has been recorded as far north as Mianwali on the R. Indus and it had spread to Rawal lake with several pairs present in the winter of 1986/7 (M. Mallalieu in Roberts 1992). Its range extends south down the R. Indus through Dera Ismail Khan district (being described as a locally common breeding resident: Kylanpaa 2000) and further south on the Indus through Dera Ghazi Khan and Mianwali districts. It is also found along the rivers Ravi, Jhelum and Chenab and has been recorded around Alipur at the confluence of the Chenab and Sutlej rivers and Panjnad headworks at the confluence of the Indus and Chenab rivers.

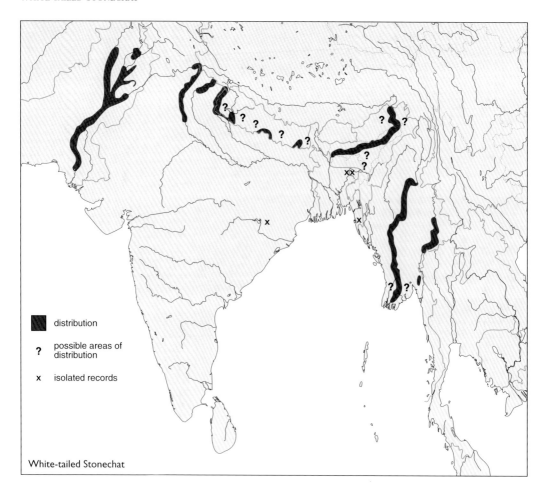

distribution

? possible areas of
distribution

x isolated records

White-tailed Stonechat

It has been seen around Trimmu headworks on the Chenab and also breeding along the Sidhnai spill channel in Multan district (Roberts 1992). Around 1913 at Multan on the Chenab River it was breeding in considerable numbers (Currie in Baker 1924). Slightly further north it was stated to be resident in Jhang district with five birds being collected by Ticehurst from Dab Kalan district on 24 and 25 December 1918, a male at Ahmadpur on the Chenab River on 1 January 1919 and small numbers being seen further north at the Nurpur escape again by the Chenab River during January and February 1919 (Whistler 1922).

In Pakistan it is dependent upon areas of extensive *Saccharum spontaneum* grass and *Typha* reedbeds, however much of this habitat has been lost to agriculture, land-levelling and flood controls. It appears to be less adaptable to man-made ecological changes than Sind Sparrow *Passer pyrrhonotus* or Eurasian Starling *Sturnus vulgaris* but more so than for example Jerdon's Babbler *Chrysomma altirostre* (Roberts 1992).

In northern India it is patchily distributed (Ali & Ripley 1968–1998), endemic to the watershed of the Ganges and Brahmaputra Rivers in the Himalayan terai from Firozpur on the Pakistan–Indian border across Punjab, Kumaun division of Uttar Pradesh and the Yamuna River area, Bihar, north-west Bengal, Assam and Manipur. Baker (1924) recorded that it had been found south to Dehra Dun. It has also been recorded from as far south as Delhi, where it was found to be a common and resident breeding species (Vyas 1996). W.G. Harvey (*in litt.* 2001) only knew of it from the Yamuna reedbeds in Delhi where it has been recorded, probably breeding annually, for many years – it was first recorded on Okhla Island, within Yamuma River, in 1978 (N.J. Redman *in litt.* 2002). It has been recorded further south wintering in northern Orissa (Ali & Ripley 1968–1998).

In Nepal Baker (1924) reported that "Mr Stevens obtained them breeding in the Mai Valley in East Nepal", but Inskipp & Inskipp (1991) indicate that the species was first recorded in the country by F.M. Bailey at Bilauri, at an elevation of 275m on 28 January 1937. It is a local resident of the lowlands below 275m, although it has been recorded up to 915m at Pokhara in central Nepal (unpublished record post-

1990: H.S. Baral *in litt.* 2001), whereas throughout the rest of its entire range from Pakistan to Myanmar it has not been recorded above 700m. It is fairly common and has been proved to breed at Sukla Phanta Wildlife Reserve, Royal Chitwan National Park, and north of Kosi Barrage (Inskipp & Inskipp 1991). Although currently unconfirmed it might also breed in Royal Bardia National Park and Kosi Tappu Wildlife Reserve (H.S. Baral *in litt.* 2001). There are two records of birds found below Tokha Sanitarium in April and at Taudha Lake in May in the Kathmandu Valley (Fleming *et al.* 1984), considerably above the normal altitudinal range; however, these records are doubtful according to Inskipp & Inskipp (1991). It is fairly common in grasslands along larger rivers such as the Narayani, Karnali, Rapti, Mahakali and Kosi (H.S. Baral *in litt.* 2001).

Its status in Bangladesh is uncertain. It was first recorded in the nineteenth century from the Garo Hills in what is now the central north-east part of the country (Godwin-Austen 1870) but the only recent record is of a single male on 20 April 1990 in paddyfields by the road to Banderban, which is in the south-east (Thompson *et al.* 1993).

It occurs in the lower hills of south, east and north-east Myanmar, being recorded from Bhamo and Minbu district, the Karen Hills (Papun), the Shan States, the plains of southern Myanmar and Karenni and described as locally common in suitable areas (Roseveare 1949, 1952, Ripley *et al.* 1964, Smythies 1986, Sibley & Monroe 1990). It was not found in northern Myanmar in the restricted areas of river-island '*kaing*' crops, nor was it found in the large areas of thatching grass growing in the northern parts of the Irrawaddy and Mogaung valleys (Stanford & Ticehurst 1938).

Baker (1924) considered it commoner than supposed throughout its range suggesting that it was often overlooked owing to its similarity to Siberian Stonechat.

BREEDING

Monogamous. It has adapted to the annual monsoon cycle of the major river systems throughout the Indian subcontinent. In Pakistan it is local in occurrence and breeds close to areas of seasonal inundation along the Indus. The nest is often situated in the dried-out bed of a swamp (Roberts 1992). In Assam in India, it bred in tracts of thatching grassland which ran for miles interspersed with swamps and patches of coarse *ekra* and reeds (Baker 1924). In Myanmar nests were found to be located in swamps of '*kaing*' grass or '*thetke*'. Ticehurst (1922–1924) quotes nesting notes by T.R. Bell, who found four nests in the Keti Shah Forest near Sukkur in 1906. The breeding birds were frequenting open ground (destined for vetch cultivation but at that time vegetated with grass tussocks and low tamarisks) in the immediate vicinity of backwaters of the Indus River. The four nests were found within an area of 80–120ha although other pairs were considered to be breeding in this area also.

The species commences breeding from February and continues until May. However, nests have been found at Sukla Phanta in Nepal in both December and May (H.S. Baral *in litt.* 2001), which may indicate two breeding seasons or possibly that it has a single, more extended breeding season than elsewhere. In India pairs form in February and by the last week in March some were nest building whilst a few others were feeding young in the nest (Ali & Ripley 1968–1998, Vyas 1996). For example, on 28 March one nest held three well-incubated eggs and another a single newly hatched nestling, while two other nests with two and three eggs respectively were found a few days later (T.R. Bell in Ticehurst 1922–1924). A nest was discovered near Delhi with nestlings on 3 April, which would suggest that first clutches would be laid from early to mid-March (W.G. Harvey *in litt.* 2001). In Myanmar a nest with well-incubated eggs was found on 20 February and another was found with young on 1 March. A pair considered to be of this species were seen with 3–4 fledglings on a river island in Myanmar on the 5 June 1936 (Roseveare 1952). In Pakistan nesting commences in early March with peak breeding in April and no further nests after mid-May (Roberts 1992).

Nests are built by the female only. They are well concealed and difficult to locate, sited (e.g.) under a clod of earth or in a depression amongst the roots of grass. In Pakistan they were hidden in dead leaf-litter of lotus lilies *Nelumbium* or in the roots of *Tamarix diocia*. One nest found at Kairo Deiro on 14 March 1905 was in a depression completely concealed by leaves and stems of vetches, and another on 28 March 1906 at Sukkur was under a little heap of dead tamarisk twigs left after clearing a field for sowing (T.R. Bell in Ticehurst 1922–1924). In Garwhal they were sited in a tangled mass of stranded grass brought down by floods. One nest was fully two feet inside one such mass (Baker 1924). One nest in Myanmar was at the end of a tunnel at least one foot long in a heap of straw located on an island in the Irrawaddy River (Smythies 1986). A nest near Delhi on 3 April 2001 was a deep cup of fine grasses, deep in the centre of a cut over clump of *Typha*, partly covered by bent-over dead *Typha* leaves and surrounded by a relatively open reedbed. The female approached the nest from about a metre away, running under the bent over leaves; but she flew directly from the nest site (W.G. Harvey *in litt.* 2001).

Nests in Myanmar are usually built of grasses and leaves lined with hair and/or fur. Four nests found in riverine forest north of Sukkur, Pakistan, were described as small neat cups well hidden in natural depressions, with one hidden under a pile of brushwood. The outer rim consisted of tamarisk leaves and the inner cup was lined with dried grasses, with most nests having three or four Black Partridge *Francolinus francolinus* feathers in the cup. The nest was 9.6cm in external diameter with an internal diameter of 5.7cm and 4.5cm deep (T.R. Bell in Ticehurst 1922–1924).

The normal clutch is 3–5 eggs. Different nests observed in the same area up to early May revealed that only the female incubated with the male remaining close by but very secretive. The period of incubation is not known but is likely to be 13–14 days, similar to Siberian Stonechat.

The colour of the eggs is pale blue or blue-green, paler and less blue than Siberian Stonechat with variable reddish-brown freckling and spotting often concentrated into a ring or cap at the larger end (Smythies 1986). Mean measurements of 24 eggs were 18.0 x 14.0mm (maxima 19.1 x 14.1 and 16.8 x 14.6mm, minima 16.4 x 14.4 and 17.5 x 13.6mm) (Baker 1924).

The male assists in feeding the young, the adults dividing the work evenly between them. During a 37-minute period of observation the male and the female both visited the nest with food three times (Roberts 1992). Roberts considered that owing to the annual flooding, which usually occurs in the monsoon months in their nesting habitat, birds are probably adapted to rear only one brood per year.

HABITAT

It is always found near water although it will inhabit drier micro-habitats alongside main river channels (Roberts 1992). It has been found in early March in north Hyderabad district probably breeding in dry cultivation surrounded by dry canals with high grass along them (T.R. Bell in Ticehurst 1922–1924). In winter it often shares the same habitat with Siberian Stonechat and throughout the year with Pied Bushchat *S. caprata* (Roberts 1992). Ticehurst (1922–1924) quotes Hume's description of its habitat in the jheels of Upper Sind as

"Where the water, as it were, was paved with the leaves of the lotus and 'singhara' *Trapa bispinosa* and dotted over with tiny clumps or single stems of reeds and flowering grasses, the White-tailed Chat might be seen perched sideways on one of these wind-swayed reeds, every now and then darting down on to one of the lotus leaves, seizing some insect there and returning to its previous perch, instantly recognisable when on the wing by the great amount of white in the tail. Outside high-water mark I never saw a single specimen".

Ticehurst also quoted W.E. Brooks, who found it near Sukkur on a backwater of the Indus "where blue vetches and small tamarisks were growing". In Jhang district Ticehurst collected birds from a patch of tamarisk and pampas grass between cultivation and a pool of water in one of the channel beds of the river. Another was collected in tamarisk scrub bordering a cultivated field of vetch and wheat (Whistler 1922). The distribution of this species is very local and this can be caused not only by man-made changes to its environment but also natural ones such as low water levels not allowing crops to be grown (see also Ticehurst 1922–1924 under Distribution).

In India it is found in grassland, reedbeds and stretches of elephant grass, scrub and cultivated areas in lowlands, frequently adjacent to swampy or moist areas and often along rivers. In the vicinity of Okhla and Madanpur in south Delhi it is a common resident and frequents marshes, reedbeds and wet cultivation (Vyas 1996). W.G. Harvey (*in litt.* 2001) found that around Delhi it seems to prefer open reedbeds which had been 80% cut over for fodder, grazed by buffalo or burned.

Of Garhwal in Uttar Pradesh Whymper wrote "I never saw them in our parts except in the Terais and Bhabers, so that 1500 (457m) or, at the outside 2000 feet (610m) is their limit, though, doubtless if there was swampy ground and heavy grass I can imagine their following it up hill considerably higher" (Baker 1924).

In Nepal it has been reported from bushes on dry open slopes (Fleming *et al.* 1984). However, Baral *in litt.* (2001) states it is an obligate grassland specialist restricted to riverine or large phantas of short to medium grassland (minimum 0.5m tall) and in 14 years of observations he has never seen this species utilising habitat that consists entirely of bushes.

In Myanmar it is a typical species of extensive areas of '*kaing*' grass but is also found in crops of maize, peas, tomatoes and tobacco grown along the banks and on islands in the Irrawaddy in southern Myanmar during the low-water season (Smythies 1986).

VOICE

Vocalisations of the White-tailed Stonechat are apparently similar to Siberian Stonechat (Smythies 1986).

The song, given only by the male, was described by T.R. Bell (in Ticehurst 1922–1924) as short and repetitive with notes similar to a lark but quite different from Pied Bushchat. In India at Delhi, song commenced in late January with males giving song flights in March. These flights consisted of males flying up to 5m in the air, then fluttering down whilst singing and the tail spread open (Vyas 1996).

Bell (in Ticehurst 1922–1924) also described the alarm note of both sexes as a *peep-chaaa*. However, Roberts (1992) heard pairs at Kandhkot, Pakistan, utter a hard dry *kek-kek-kek* warning call, somewhat similar to Siberian Stonechat. He speculated that the call heard by Bell might have been a more intense alarm call. Alarm calls of a pair recorded by N. Gardner in 1996 reveal vocalisations very similar to those of Siberian Stonechat: as in that species, two notes are combined, with the *wheet* note slightly more musical and the *trrack* note having a slightly buzzier sound. Presumably the individual and combination uses of these notes have the same functions as in Siberian Stonechat.

FOOD

Little detailed information. Diet in Pakistan is presumed to consist of spiders and small molluscs owing to the species marshy habitat. In late February at Kandhkot in Jacobabad district of Pakistan birds were observed to feed extensively on flying insects of the families Culicidae and Chironomidae in the evenings, making aerial sallies from reed stems to snatch the insects from a swarm (Roberts 1992). A pair in Minbu district in Myanmar were observed feeding green caterpillars to newly hatched young on 1 March 1936. A pair south of Delhi were seen to feed their young on large orange-coloured flies, a white moth and a green caterpillar (W.G. Harvey *in litt.* 2001).

MOVEMENTS

Mainly sedentary and resident. Possibly some seasonal movements occur to lower elevations during the winter, and other movements may take place when habitat becomes unsuitable owing to unfavourable weather or ground conditions.

BEHAVIOUR

Little detailed information. It appears to be similar in behaviour to Siberian Stonechat, and in Pakistan at least often shares the same habitat with both that species and Pied Bushchat (Roberts 1992). In Nepal at Royal Sukla Phanta Reserve it is found in winter in association with Siberian Stonechat and Hodgson's Bushchat *S. insignis*. It shares the same feeding behaviour as Siberian Stonechat, perching on reeds and bushes to survey the ground and flying down to seize prey and then returning to the same or a similar perch. It also makes aerial sallies to catch airborne prey from these perches. When perched it moves its tail slowly up and down, fanning it and exposing the white on the tail feathers. In Pakistan it is stated to be relatively confiding in the presence of humans but in India it is shy (Ali & Ripley 1968–1998, Roberts 1992). In India it is found outside the breeding season singly or in loose groups of 4–5 individuals (Ali & Ripley 1968–1998).

MOULT

No information. Probably similar to Siberian Stonechat. A female in BMNH collected in Myanmar on 21 August 1933 had renewed primaries 01–02 and almost completed renewing primary 03. Primaries 04–10 were old. There was no evident tail moult.

CONSERVATION

Little or no information. In Pakistan drainage, flood control, conversion of grasslands and reedbeds to agriculture, and the cultivation and levelling of land have contributed to a great decrease in available suitable habitat. The species appears to be only partly adaptable to man-made changes in its habitat (Roberts 1992).

Similarly in Nepal it is possibly threatened because of the loss of tall riverine grasslands (H.S. Baral *in litt.* 2001). In Nepal and probably in other countries it was previously abundant but the loss of tall grassland habitat has apparently now restricted it to isolated areas of suitable habitat.

Motacilla Caprata Linnaeus, 1766, *Syst. Nat.* ed. 12, 1, p.335—Luzon

Etymology *caprata* is derived from the local Spanish name (Philippines) of *Maria-caprata* for the Pied Bushchat

Alternative names Pied Stonechat, Pied Chat, Ceylon Pied Bushchat

TAXONOMY

Polytypic. Current taxonomic classification recognises a considerable number of subspecies in this complex species. Ripley *et al.* (1964) list no fewer than 16 subspecies discontinuously spread from Transcaspia in the west to New Guinea and New Ireland in the east. Authors vary widely over the validity of subspecies, perhaps because there is (or appears to be) such variation in plumage within supposed subspecies as well as much intergradation where some subspecies come into contact. Some of the criteria used to accord subspecific status for certain populations appears weak by current standards, *S. c. burmanica, nilgiriensis randi* and *anderseni*, for instance, and the populations in New Guinea may be just one subspecies rather than the current three.

Ticehurst (1926–1927) stated that his examination of specimens of *S. c. bicolor* taken from different areas of its supposed range were indistinguishable from *S. c. rossorum* breeding to the west, and he considered that *bicolor* was invalid. Parkes (1960), whilst himself proposing a new subspecies, *S. c. randi*, stated that a female specimen from Panay, Philippines, which is one of the islands supposedly inhabited by *S. c. randi* was too pale to be of that subspecies whilst another from Mindoro inhabited by *S. c. caprata* was too grey to be of that subspecies. Other specimens from islands south of Luzon (inhabited by *S. c. caprata*) and north of Negros and Bohol (inhabited by *S. c. randi*) prompted Parkes to suggest that there might be justification for yet another subspecies.

There are three currently recognised subspecies throughout New Guinea – *S. c. belensis, S. c. wahgiensis* and *S. c. aethiops* – and Rand & Gilliard (1967) viewed an isolated population in the Telefomin Valley in New Guinea as possibly yet another separate subspecies, although if it is it remains to date unnamed and officially unrecognised. This unnamed population occurs in the mountains between the two other montane subspecies *S. c. belensis* and *S. c. wahgiensis* and could belong to either of these two montane forms. Gilliard & LeCroy (1967) had earlier suggested that this population may belong to *wahgiensis*, as females appeared very similar in coloration. Mees (1964) considered it imprudent to recognise more than one subspecies in the New Guinea Highlands, thereby rendering *wahgiensis* invalid and assigning birds from the central mountains of Papua New Guinea to *belensis*.

Sibley & Monroe (1990) suggested that possibly the subspecies *S. c. aethiops* of lowland northern New Guinea and the Bismarck Archipelago is a distinct species and that the other two subspecies currently recognised from New Guinea, *S. c. wahgiensis* and *S. c. belensis*, should be included with it. They proposed that if *S. c. aethiops* is a separate species it be called Black Bushchat *Saxicola aethiops*. In their subsequent revision (Sibley & Monroe 1993) they confirmed their original 1990 classification. Undoubtedly this species would benefit from mtDNA analysis to establish a more precise indication of the relationships between the various isolated populations throughout its range.

Subspecies of Pied Bushchat

Saxicola caprata rossorum
Saxicola caprata bicolor
Saxicola caprata burmanica
Saxicola caprata nilgiriensis
Saxicola caprata atrata
Saxicola caprata caprata
Saxicola caprata randi
Saxicola caprata anderseni
Saxicola caprata fruticola
Saxicola caprata pyrrhonota
Saxicola caprata francki
Saxicola caprata albonotata
Saxicola caprata cognata
Saxicola caprata aethiops
Saxicola caprata belensis
Saxicola caprata wahgiensis

IDENTIFICATION

Size 13.5–15cm/5.5–5.9 inches with variation in size amongst subspecies. Sexes dimorphic. Stocky, exhibiting typical *Saxicola* behaviour such as perching conspicuously, flicking tail and wings, dropping to the ground to seize prey and returning to a prominent perch. Both male and female have mainly dark plumage. The male in breeding plumage is predominantly black, only relieved by a large white upperwing-patch, and with variable amounts of white depending on the subspecies, on the rump, uppertail-coverts, belly, ventral area and undertail-coverts. Males in non-breeding plumage have a variable amount of brown fringes to the black feathers of the upperparts and underparts, less so on the head. The white on the rump and upper- and undertail-coverts is broadly tipped chestnut-buff in fresh plumage.

The female in breeding plumage is predominantly dark brown on the upperparts with darker streaking but showing less contrast than in Siberian Stonechat *S. maura*. The underparts are greyish-brown also with darker brown streaking but not so prominent as on the upperparts. Females of the majority of subspecies lack a white upperwing-patch and generally have a chestnut-brown rump and uppertail-coverts, although subspecies from the Sunda Islands show varying amounts of white in the wing and have white rumps and uppertail-coverts. Females of the various subspecies from New Guinea and New Ireland also have white rumps. The lores, malar region, chin and throat are buff and the vent and undertail-coverts are pale chestnut-buff. Females in non-breeding plumage are similar to breeding but appear plainer and less streaked owing to the greyish-brown fringes of feathers obscuring most of the darker centres. The wing-coverts and inner secondaries have pale buff fringes to the outerwebs. Legs, feet and bill are black in the male and dark brown in female. Irides are dark brown in both sexes.

Differentiation between subspecies is not greatly marked for a species with such a wide range and generally involves size, proportion of black and white in the plumage of males, and, in females, size, colour of rump and uppertail-coverts, presence of white on the inner upperwing, and general plumage tone. There also appears to be a bewildering variety of subtle plumage variations as well as size differences between individuals of the same subspecies, possibly owing to intergradation.

Confusion species Where the five subspecies *S. c. rossorum, bicolor, burmanica, nilgiriensis* and *atrata* come in to contact with the Siberian Stonechat subspecies *S. m. maura* and *stejnegeri*, females and immature Pied Bushchats could possibly be confused. However, adult female *S. caprata* of the subspecies concerned have no white on the inner upperwing, whereas *S. maura* always show some white on the inner upperwing although often obscured until it flies; *caprata* has a less extensive patch of rufous on the rump and uppertail-coverts (usually only the lower half of the rump and uppertail-coverts are this colour and usually slightly darker in tone), while *maura* has a paler chestnut-buff patch (occasionally in worn plumage showing some white) which covers the entire rump and uppertail-coverts; *caprata* tertials are dark brown only narrowly fringed greyish-buff, *maura* tertials are almost black with broad almost white fringes which create a noticeable contrast with the black centres; *caprata* the overall strength of colour on the body is uniformly darker and browner and in fresh plumage it has variable but only faint streaking both above and below, becoming slightly more noticeable as the plumage wears, while in *maura* the overall colour is far paler at all times with a greater contrast between the darker upperparts and paler underparts with prominent dark streaking on the brown upperparts and paler unstreaked buff-chestnut rather than brown below; fresh-plumaged *caprata* has very narrow, pale buff edges to the outer fringes of the inner secondaries and consequently does not show a prominent pale panel on the closed wing, while fresh-plumaged *maura* has more prominent pale fringes to the outerwebs and consequently shows a more prominent pale wing-panel; *caprata* shows a greater contrast between the brown flanks and the buff undertail-coverts, *maura* far less owing to the paler tone of the flanks; *caprata* has only a faint suggestion of a supercilium, while *maura* shows a more definite and extensive supercilium. *S. caprata* can be told from *S. m. variegata/armenica* by a combination of the above plus (*variegata* only) the lack of pale buff at the base of the tail.

Vagrant *S. caprata* to the western Palearctic require more care in identification as the females of European Stonechat *S. rubicola* are darker in plumage tone than the eastern subspecies; however, much of the above applies in these cases also. European Stonechat females also show a darker chin and throat than *caprata*, and the rump and uppertail-coverts are darker chestnut-brown and streaked with black whereas in *caprata* it is paler unstreaked chestnut.

S. leucura is much paler, grey-brown above and almost white below. It also has buff innerwebs to the rectrices and a white patch on the inner upperwing.

DESCRIPTION Based on nominate *S. c. caprata*

Adult male autumn/winter Entire upperparts and underparts including the head are a deep glossy black, apart from the lower rump and upper- and undertail-coverts, which are white with rufous-buff tips. The longer outer uppertail-coverts are also tipped black. The feathers of the head, neck, mantle and scapulars have very narrow, indistinct, pale buff-brown fringes whilst those from the chin to the lower breast, flanks and belly have broader and more distinct buff fringes. Remiges, rectrices and tertials are also black with narrow pale buff fringes to the outerwebs and tips, showing little contrast with the black upperwing-coverts, mantle and scapulars. The inner secondaries have narrow buff fringes to the outerwebs as well as tips. The tertials have slightly broader pale buff fringes to the outerwebs. The upperwing primary and lesser coverts are black with narrow pale brown fringes with a variable amount of white on the innermost lesser coverts. The alula is black. The upperwing inner median and inner greater coverts as well as the base of the outerwebs of the innermost secondaries are white, forming a distinct elongated patch on the otherwise black wing. The outer upperwing median and greater coverts are black with pale brown fringes. The underwing-coverts and axillaries are black. Legs, feet and bill black. Irides dark brown.

Adult male spring/summer Similar to adult male in winter except that the buff and brown fringes and tips to the black feathers wear away leaving a pure glossy black and white plumage. Some pale buff fringes to the feathers of the lower breast occasionally do not wear away completely. The pale fringes and tips to the remiges, rectrices and tertials also wear away to leave these pure black. The upperwing primary coverts retain their narrow brown fringes. The rufous-buff tips to the white undertail-coverts and rump and black tips to the long outer uppertail-coverts wear away to leave these areas pure white.

First-year male Similar to adult male but not so bright, the black appearing duller and not glossy, with a faint brown tone. The upperpart feathers all have broad greyish-brown fringes which wear away to leave only thin fringes in worn plumage. Chin, throat, upper breast, sides of breast and upper flanks also have broad pale buff fringes to the feathers which slowly wear away, apart from those on the sides of the breast and upper flanks. There is less of a distinct demarcation between the black of the underparts and white of the undertail-coverts than in the adult. The white upperwing-patch is smaller with the inner upperwing lesser coverts dull black with pale whitish-buff rather than pure white markings; the upperwing median and greater coverts are as in adult male but with no white on the inner secondaries. The underwing-coverts and axillaries are black with prominent buff fringes. There is a more marked contrast between (a) the more worn, unmoulted, faded brown remiges, rectrices, upperwing primary coverts, outer upperwing greater coverts and usually tertials and (b) the fresher, blacker plumage of the mantle and scapulars. The remiges and tertials retain narrow buff-white crescentic tips, slightly more noticeable on the secondaries.

Adult female autumn/winter Forehead, crown, nape, hindneck, mantle, scapulars, back and upper rump are grey-brown with darker brown centres mainly concealed by extensive grey-brown fringes. The lower rump is rufous-brown contrasting with the grey-brown of the rest of the upperparts, and the longest uppertail-coverts are a slightly richer rufous than the lower rump. The lores, periorbital and malar regions, chin and throat are pale greyish-buff. The cheeks and ear-coverts are darker grey-brown, similar to the crown. Central breast, sides of breast, upper flanks, belly and ventral area are pale greyish-brown with a rufous wash (wash strongest on the lower breast, rear flanks and belly). All the feathers below have black-brown centres mainly concealed by the extensive grey-brown fringes but variably showing as faint streaking. The undertail-coverts are pale rufous or off-white. The rectrices are deep black-brown with paler rufous to buff fringes to the outerwebs. The remiges are blackish-brown with narrow pale rufous to whitish-grey fringes to the outerwebs and tips. The tertials are black with pale buff fringes on both webs and buff tips. The upperwing primary, lesser, median and greater coverts are greyish-brown with buff fringes to the outerwebs and tips. The upperwing greater coverts have slightly broader buff fringes to the outerwebs than the other coverts. Some of the inner upperwing lesser coverts and innermost upperwing greater coverts are paler, almost white in some individuals, giving the suggestion of a white wing-patch. The underwing-coverts and axillaries are pale buff. Legs, feet and bill black. Irides dark brown.

Adult female spring/summer Similar to fresh-plumaged female but appears darker and browner on both upper- and underparts, with most of the grey-buff fringes to the body feathers and buff fringes to the remiges and rectrices progressively wearing away leaving the wing dark brown/black. The rufous coloration below becomes less pronounced and the flanks can show darker shaft-streaks. The lores, malar region, chin and ear-coverts are flecked with buff and brown.

First-year female Very similar to adult female although the remiges, rectrices and some outer upperwing greater coverts remain unmoulted and can appear much more worn than in adult although not much difference in colour to adult. Some individuals have large buff triangular spots on the retained juvenile outer upperwing greater coverts and the upperwing primary coverts can sometimes show more pointed tips and have wider buff fringes than in the adult.

Juvenile The male is blackish-brown on the upperparts whilst the female is dark brown with narrow grey-brown fringes on the upperparts. The feathers of crown and nape have tiny, pale buff spots in their centres, those on the mantle, scapulars and upperwing lesser coverts having larger pale buff centres. The sides of the head have numerous narrow, pale buff shaft-streaks on greyish-brown feathers. The lower rump and uppertail-coverts are uniform unstreaked pale rufous or yellowish-buff. The underparts from chin to breast, sides of breast and fore-flanks are pale yellowish- to rufous-buff with narrow dark brown fringes (these fringes become more marked and extensive on the breast and fore-flanks, giving a scaly appearance). The belly and ventral area are whitish-grey tinged brownish-yellow. The undertail-coverts are buff-white. The rectrices are dark brown/black with narrow chestnut-buff fringes and tips. The remiges are also dark brown/black and the secondaries have broad whitish-grey tips and fringes to the outerwebs. The tertials are black in males with broad greyish-buff fringes. The upperwing primary coverts and alula are black with pale buff fringes to the outerwebs and tips. The upperwing median coverts are black with thin pale buff shaft-streaks and broad chestnut-buff tips. The upperwing greater coverts are black with broad rufous-buff tips or spots at the tip. In females all these preceding feather tracts substitute brown for black; the underwing-coverts and axillaries are buff. Males often but not invariably show the beginnings of a white wing-patch on the innermost lesser and/or median coverts, although the white is suffused with buff and can be indistinct.

Measurements

	Male	Female
Wing	64.0–67.0 (mean 65.5)	61.5–66.0 (mean 63.9)
Tail	47.0–55.0 (mean 49.3)	44.0–49.0 (mean 46.9)
Bill	14.0–15.2 (mean 14.7)	14.4–15.1 (mean 14.7)

[Own measurements BMNH 2001]

	Male	Female
Wing	64.0–70.0 (mean 65.9)	61.5–68.5 (mean 64.9)

[Stresemann 1912]

S. c. rossorum

Pratincola caprata rossorum Hartert, 1910, *J. Orn.* 58, p.180—Merv, Transcaspia [= Turkmenistan]

Larger than other subspecies apart from *S. c. atrata*, *wahgiensis* and *belensis*. The male differs from the closely similar *S. c. bicolor* in having a large amount of white on the belly often extending up to the middle of the breast so that the only areas of the underparts that are completely black are the chin, throat, upper breast, sides of breast and flanks. The black of the male is also said to have less gloss than *S. c. bicolor* or *S. c. caprata*, appearing brownish or dull black when in worn plumage (Stresemann 1912). Males supposedly differ from nominate *caprata* in having marginally less extensive white on the upperwing, although on BMNH specimens this is highly variable and not a consistent character. It has also been stated that *rossorum* does not show white on the outerwebs of the innermost secondaries but again this is variable and inconsistent on specimens.

Females differ from *S. c. bicolor* in all plumages by appearing lighter in colour both above and below and in having a reduced rufous tone to the feathers. Stresemann (1912) found two specimens which he judged paler than any female from the other subspecies known at the time, being almost sandy-brown above. In breeding plumage the upperparts are greyer in tone, the rump and uppertail-coverts are rufous (slightly darker than in nominate *caprata*) with some white appearing in very worn plumage, and the belly and undertail-coverts are white. Generally the underparts lack the longitudinal dark brown streaks of *S. c. bicolor* although there can be some faint streaking especially to the sides of the breast (V.M. Loskot *in litt.* 2000).

Measurements

	Male	Female
Wing	73.0–79.0 (mean 76.5)	74.0–77.0 (mean 75.4)

[Cramp *et al.* 1988: Turkmenistan and Afghanistan]

	Male	Female
Wing	71.0–76.5 (mean 72.5)	68.1–75.1 (mean 71.5)

[Loskot *in litt.* 2000: Turkmenistan]

	Male	Female
Wing	70.0–76.0 (mean 73.4)	67.0–74.0 (mean 71.0)

[Stresemann 1912]

S. c. bicolor

Saxicola bicolor Sykes, 1832, *Proc. Zool. Soc. London* p.92—Dukhun [= Deccan]

Slightly smaller than *S. c. rossorum*, larger than nominate *caprata* and intermediate in size between *S. c. burmanica* and *S. c. atrata*, with a slimmer, smaller bill. The male has duller black plumage than *S. c. caprata* and white around the ventral area as well as the undertail-coverts (Hartert 1910). Differs from very similar *S. c. rossorum* with which it intergrades in not showing white on the belly or central breast. The female is on average darker brown and has darker rufous uppertail-coverts (Vaurie 1959). However, owing to intergradation with *S. c. rossorum* individuals showing characters to varying degrees of both subspecies are not uncommon and may be widespread. Baker (1924) could only find consistent differences in plumage between males of the two subspecies when using specimens of *rossorum* from the extreme western parts of its range in Iran and Afghanistan.

Measurements

Male	**Female**
Wing 64.0–72.0 (mean 68.5)	64.0–69.0 (mean 66.5)

[Stresemann 1912]

Wing 67.0–72.5 (mean 70.3)	66.5–71.0 (mean 68.5)

[Own measurements BMNH 2001]

S. c. burmanica

Saxicola caprata burmanica Baker, 1923, *Bull. Brit. Orn. Club* 43, p.19—Pegu

There is some contention as to whether this is a valid subspecies. It was originally separated from *S. c. caprata* on the male's alleged slightly larger wings and bill: *burmanica* wings 67–72mm generally under 70mm, bill 11.0–11.5mm rarely 11.0mm, *caprata* wings 63–65mm, bill 10–10.5 (Baker 1923, 1924). Ticehurst (1933) originally supported this subspecies but suggested its subspecific status was weak. Based on subsequent examination of skins Stanford & Ticehurst (1938) stated it was inseparable from *S. c. caprata*. Their wing and bill measurements of both subspecies, *burmanica* and *caprata* were considerably different from those originally given by Baker. *Burmanica* wings 66.0–73.0mm, bill 13.5–14.5 mm; *caprata* wings 68.0–74.0mm, bill 14.5–15.0mm. They further commented that some *burmanica* were shorter in the bill but there was a 60% overlap. My measurements of wings in the BNMH from an admittedly small sample showed a disparity between the two subspecies. *Burmanica* male wing was 69.5–71.0mm (mean 70.3) whilst *caprata* male wing was 64.0–70.0mm (mean 65.9). Males were also found by Stanford & Ticehurst to be indistinguishable from *S. c. caprata* in plumage detail. However, Baker found in a few exceptional males the white on the undertail-coverts extends onto the tips of the longest feathers on the rear of the flanks but never extends onto the belly as in *S. c. rossorum* and some *S. c. rossorum/bicolor* intergrades (Baker 1923).

Adult female *burmanica* is said to be separable from adult female *caprata*. It has the crown and mantle dark grey-brown with the feathers showing darker centres but paler than *caprata*. The lores, forehead, chin and throat are greyish-brown, gradually darkening on the breast and increasingly becoming suffused with reddish-brown or tawny, stronger than on *caprata*, especially on the belly and rear flanks. The breast and fore-flanks are streaked to varying degrees with brown. The streaks are narrower and less distinct than on *caprata*, although sometimes streaking can be entirely absent. The lower rump and uppertail-coverts are rufous-chestnut and the undertail-coverts are paler rufous-chestnut. The rectrices and remiges are black/brown narrowly fringed pale reddish-brown.

Measurements

Male	**Female**
Wing 69.5.0–71.0 (mean 70.3)	64.0–69.5 (mean 66.8)

[Own measurements BMNH 2001]

S. c. nilgiriensis

Saxicola caprata nilgiriensis Whistler, 1940, *Bull. Brit. Orn. Club* 60, p.90—Ootacamund, Madras

This subspecies was split from *S. c. atrata* on the basis of its smaller bill and restricted distribution and was considered by Whistler (1940) to be the intermediate between *atrata* from Ceylon [Sri Lanka] and nominate *caprata* from the Philippines, which has an even smaller, more delicate bill "13.5–15mm" in length. He argued for recognition of this subspecies, stating

> "I think the intermediate merits recognition, as we have not here an ordinary case of intergrading
> in size from south to north of a generally distributed species e.g. *Corvus macrorhynchus*. In Ceylon

[Sri Lanka] *S. c. atrata* is confined to a limited area of the central hill mass above 900m. It is not found in the rest of the hills nor in the plains, so its insularity is unusually emphasised. *S. c. nilgiriensis* is not found in the plains of South India, but is confined to the hill ranges of the south-west corner which are remarkable for other peculiar forms, subspecific and specific. *S. c. caprata* [now the subspecies *S. c. bicolor*] on the other hand is found in the eastern hill ranges and in the plains of South India."

The male's upperparts only show white on the rump and innermost greater and median upperwing-coverts, much less extensive than on *S. c. caprata*. The underparts are entirely black apart from the ventral area and undertail-coverts, which are white.

Measurements

Male	Female
Wing 72.0–77.5 (mean 74.6)	71.0–77.0 (mean 74.2)

[Own measurements BMNH 2001 and CMNH 2000]

S. c. atrata

Pratincola atrata Kelaart, 1851, in Blyth, *J. Asiat. Soc. Bengal* 20 p.177—Newera Elia, Ceylon

The largest subspecies apart from the two New Guinea subspecies *S. c. wahgiensis* and *S. c. belensis* and with a longer bill than nominate *S. c. caprata*. The male differs from *S. c. caprata* in having a generally duller black plumage and white around the ventral area as well as the undertail-coverts.

Measurements

Male	Female
Wing 75.5–80.5 (mean 78.2)	72.0–77.0 (mean 75.3)

[Stresemann 1912]

Male	Female
Wing 78.0–82.0 (mean 80.2)	74.0–80.0 (mean 76.4)

[Own measurements BMNH 2001]

S. c. caprata

Motacilla Caprata Linnaeus, 1766, *Syst. Nat.*, ed. 12, 1, p.335—Luzon, Philippines

See description above. The adult male has a very deep glossy black plumage. Smaller than *S. c. rossorum* and *S. c. bicolor* with the white areas in the male's plumage restricted to the wing-patch, rump, upper- and undertail-coverts.

Measurements

Male	Female
Wing 64.0–70.0 (mean 65.9)	61.5–68.5 (mean 64.9)

[Stresemann 1912]

Male	Female
Wing 64.0–67.0 (mean 65.5)	61.5–66.0 (mean 63.9)

[Own measurements BMNH 2001]

S. c. randi

Saxicola caprata randi Parkes, 1960, *Proc. Biol. Soc. Washington* 73, p.59—Bondo, Siaton, Negros, Philippines

The male is similar to, and not with certainty distinguishable from, *S. c. caprata* which is found to the north and *S. c. anderseni* to the south of its range but usually has white tips to the black axillaries similar to *S. c. anderseni* whilst *S. c. caprata* usually has all-black axillaries (Parkes 1960).

The female differs from *S. c. caprata* in being much darker on the upperparts. The throat is paler, being grey or white rather than cinnamon-buff. The underparts have heavy and distinct black shaft-streaks especially in worn plumage and the feathering on the tibia is distinctly spotted. The undertail-coverts are on average paler buff and contrast more with the belly. There is a small, partially concealed white wing-patch formed by the white innerwebs of the smaller tertials and inner upperwing greater coverts, although this feature is variable and on some birds is absent altogether.

The female's cold plumage tones and presence of white wing-patch is similar to *S. c. anderseni* but the latter is paler, more grey in tone, and lacks the distinct streaking on the underparts.

No specimens were available for measurement.

S. c. anderseni

Saxicola caprata anderseni, Vidensk. Medd. Dansk naturhist. Foren. 115 p.260—Del Monte, Bukidnon province, central Mindanao, Philippines

Similar to *S. c. caprata* in both plumage and size, possibly slightly larger. The main difference is that adult females are distinctly paler, especially on the underparts, which are greyish-tawny with very slightly darker shaft-streaking; there is a small white wing-patch on the upperwing; and the throat is a paler grey. The upperparts are greyer and lack the brownish tinge of *S. c. caprata*. Adult males are indistinguishable from *S. c. caprata* (Salomonsen 1953).

Measurements

	Male	Female
Wing	68.5–72.0 (mean 70.2)	66.0–67.0 (mean 66.8)

[Salomonsen 1953]

S. c. fruticola

Saxicola fruticola Horsfield, 1821, *Trans. Linn. Soc. London* 13, p.157—Java

Similar to *S. c. pyrrhonota*. Adult males are indistinguishable from *S. c. pyrrhonota*. Rensch (1931) considered that birds from Lombok to Alor did not differ consistently from *S. c. pyrrhonota*, but Mayr (1944) recognised them as *S. c. fruticola* stating that adult females were distinctly greyer and the undertail-coverts were usually whitish and not rufous in 12 of the 14 specimens examined. The rump is pale rufous-brown or light tawny, although one female from south Java had a whitish rump only faintly washed rufous (Stresemann 1912). There is also no white at the base of the inner greater upperwing-coverts. Salomonsen (1953) considered birds of this subspecies variable and stated that females are darker then *S. c. caprata* "with the dark shaft-streaks on the underparts strongly developed" and also larger.

The wing of the adult male is usually 72.0–77.0mm although occasionally only 70.0mm. Birds collected from Mt Tosari on Java at 1,525m had a wing length for the male of 77.0mm and female 70.0–74.0mm, which was much larger than a series collected in the lowlands in which the male wing was 71.0–72.0 and female 69.0mm. Three females collected from Bali had a rufous tone to their plumage whilst four females from Sumbawa were very grey with hardly a trace of rufous in their plumage except on the rump; one bird also had notably brownish-rufous underparts. A single female collected from Flores was very dark with a grey caste to the plumage, and two females from Lomblen were also quite dark but with a brownish-rufous wash below (Mayr 1944). Mees (1975) stated that females from Java are colder in tone, less rufous-brown on the undersides than *S. c. pyrrhonota* from Timor and often, but not invariably, more or less spotted (=streaked).

Measurements

		Male	Female
Wing	Java	70.0–74.0 (mean 71.5)	68.0–74.0 (mean 70.3)
Wing	Bali	69.5–71.5 (mean 70.9)	68.5–70.0 (mean 69.2)
Wing	Lombok	70.0–74.0 (mean 72.4)	69.0–70.0 (mean 70.0)
Wing	Sumbawa	70.0–73.5 (mean 71.3)	68.0–69.0 (mean 68.7)
Wing	Alor	70.0–71.0 (mean 70.5)	
Wing	Flores	71.0/72.0 (2 specimens)	
Wing	Lomblen	69.5/70.0 (2 specimens)	

[Stresemann 1912]

S. c. pyrrhonota

Oenanthe pyrrhonota Vieillot, 1818, *Nouv. Dict. Hist. Nat.*, nouv. ed., 21, p. 428—New Holland [*errore* = Timor]

Salomonsen (1953) considered this subspecies to be nearest in plumage to *S. c. anderseni*, although males are also closely similar to *S. c. fruticola* (see above).

Adult females are rather pale compared to *S. c. cognata* and *S. c. fruticola* and are more rufous in tone. Mees (1975) states they are rufous-brown below without spots (=streaks). From ten females the undertail-coverts were rufous apart from two from Savu and Kisar which were white. The base of the inner upperwing greater coverts is white in females from Savu but not in the five females examined from Timor. The rump is rather deep rufous in all the females apart from the one from Savu which was pale yellowish-brown. A specimen in BMNH from Savu has white bases to the feathers of the rump with extensive pale chestnut-buff tips. The overall size is small compared to *S. c. cognata* and *S. c. fruticola* except for examples from Wetar and the mountains of Timor (Mayr 1944).

Measurements

Wing		Male	Female
Wing	Savu	69.0	66.5
Wing	Timor	67.0/68.5/69.0/70.5	67.0/68.0/70.0/73.0

(The two large females from Timor were collected on Mt Mutis)

Wing	Wetar	72.0/74.0/74.0/76.0	70.0/70.0
Wing	Kisar	70.0/70.0/72.0	68.0–69.0

[Mayr 1944]

Wing	Wetar	71.5–74.0 (mean 72.6)	69.0
Wing	Timor	66.0–71.0 (mean 69.3)	65.0–71.0 (mean 67.6)
Wing	Kisar	68.0–70.0 (mean 69.5)	67.0–72.0 (mean 68.8)
Wing	Savu	68.5 (one specimen)	65.0/67.0

[Stresemann 1912]

Wing	Timor	69.0–73.0 mean (70.4)	66.5–70.0 mean (68.5)
Wing	Savu	69.0 (one specimen)	67.0 (one specimen)

[Own measurements BMNH 2000 and LMNH 2000]

S. c. francki

Saxicola caprata francki Rensch, 1931, *Treubia* 13, p.380—Laora

Females from Sumba differ from *S. c. pyrrhonota* in having white or creamy-white rumps, upper- and undertail-coverts, and a more even and lighter tone of brown to the plumage. This latter feature also separates them from *S. c. aethiops*, which also has a white rump (Rensch 1931).

Measurements

Male	**Female**
Wing 70.0–75.0 (mean 73.0)	68.0–72.0 (mean 70.0)

[Rensch 1931]

S. c. albonotata

Pratincola caprata albonotata Stresemann, 1912, *Novit. Zool.* 19, p.321—Indrulaman, Celebes

Males have narrow black fringes and tips to the white upperwing-coverts. Females differ from all other subspecies in that the inner upperwing greater coverts are not dark brown but mainly pure white with varying broad blackish-brown fringes. The centres to the inner upperwing median coverts are also white. On the closed wing the white is never completely hidden by the overlying scapulars. The female also has a pure white rump and uppertail-coverts with the rest of the upperparts a dark ashy-grey and the underparts whitish-grey with darker brown feather centres giving a streaked appearance and lacking any rufous wash. The undertail-coverts are white. The underwing-coverts and axillaries are usually white with a buff to yellowish tinge, not rufous- or yellowish-grey as in the other subspecies (Stresemann 1912).

Measurements

Male	**Female**
Wing 67.0–69.0 (mean 68.1)	64.0–67.0 (mean 65.7)

[Stresemann 1912]

S. c. cognata

Saxicola caprata cognata Mayr, 1944, *Bull. Amer. Mus. Nat. Hist.* 83, p.156—Tepa, Babar Island

Similar to *S. c. francki* from Sumba but marginally smaller. The rump and uppertail-coverts of females are white but the rest of the body colour is very dark, with a dusky brown rather than greyish caste. The shaft-streaks on the upperpart feathers are very prominent even in worn plumage. It is also slightly smaller than *S. c. aethiops* and the upperparts of the female are darker (Mayr 1944).

Measurements

Male	**Female**
Wing 69.0/72.5	66.5/64.5/66.0

[Stresemann 1912]

S. c. aethiops

Poecilodryas aethiops Sclater, 1880, *Proc. Zool. Soc. London* p.66, pl. 7, fig. 1—Kabakadai, New Britain

Both sexes very similar to *S. c. albonotata*. The black feathering of the male appears slightly glossier and deeper in tone. The female has white, not rufous, on the lower rump and uppertail-coverts; the undertail-coverts are also white. She also has white or very pale buff on the inner upperwing-coverts but not as extensive as *albonotata*, the white or pale buff being present only on the inner median and not on the greater upperwing-coverts. Smaller than *S. c. belensis* and some females from the Huon Peninsula are slightly paler overall, especially below (Rand 1940).

Measurements

Male	**Female**
Wing 69.0–77.0 (mean 73.4)	70.0–75.0 (mean 72.25)

[Rand 1940]

Wing 75.0–78.0 (mean 77.0)	73.0–74.0 (mean 73.7)

(An aberrantly small male from Hubertushohe had a wing length of 69.0)

[Stresemann 1912]

S. c. belensis

Saxicola caprata belensis Rand, 1940, *Amer. Mus. Novit.* 1072, p. 4—Balim River, 1,600m, Snow Mountains, New Guinea

Females are very dark with obscure streaking on the underparts. They have the lower rump and uppertail-coverts white, similar to *S. c. francki, albonotata, aethiops* and *wahgiensis*. There is no concealed white or buff feather-patch on the inner upperwing-coverts, unlike *S. c. albonotata* and *S. c. aethiops* and they are also larger than *S. c. aethiops*. Rand lacked any specimens in fresh plumage and considered size the only criterion to be safely used to separate this subspecies from *S. c. aethiops*. Individuals from the Snow Mountains [Maoke Mountain range] appear to be slightly larger than those from the rest of the range (Rand 1940).

Measurements

Male	**Female**
Wing 79.0–84.0 (mean 82.4)	79.0–82.0 (mean 80.8)

[Rand 1940]

S. c. wahgiensis

Saxicola caprata wahgiensis Mayr & Gilliard, 1951, *Amer. Mus. Novit.* 1524, p.8—Mafulu, Central Division, Papua New Guinea

Possibly not a valid subspecies (see Mees 1964) and hence synonymous with *S. c. belensis*. Mayr & Gilliard (1951) thought the female was nearest in plumage to *S. c. aethiops* but larger in size from wing and tail measurements. Both sexes are slightly smaller than *belensis*; *S. c. belensis* and *S. c. wahgiensis* males are indistinguishable on plumage, but females appear to differ from *belensis* by having much lighter, greyer plumage particularly on the underparts, upper rump and sides of neck.

Males (both adult and first-year) are deep glossy black. First-year males after the post-juvenile moult show a contrast between unmoulted brown remiges and the black of moulted outer lesser and median upperwing-coverts, mantle and scapulars. First-years also have variable amounts of white at the tips of the mantle feathers. Adults do not show this. White is also present on the inner upperwing lesser, median and greater coverts, rump, uppertail-coverts, ventral area and undertail-coverts.

Females in fresh plumage show obscure streaking owing to the black-brown feathers having extensive greyish-brown fringes and tips which are possibly less evident on the other New Guinea subspecies. The belly is slightly richer buff. The upperparts, especially the back and lower mantle, which contrast with the white lower rump and uppertail-coverts, are grey-buff with a brownish tinge caused by extensive fringes. There is no white on the inner upperwing-coverts. In fresh plumage the rump and uppertail-coverts also have buff tips but these only partially obscure the white. The female in worn plumage is darker in tone than the female of *S. c. caprata*.

Measurements

Male	**Female**
Wing 79.0–81.5 (3 specimens)	72.0 (1 specimen)

[Rand & Gilliard 1967]

Wing 77.5–80.0 (mean 78.8)	75.0–78.5 (mean 76.8)

[Own measurements BMNH 2001]

DISTRIBUTION AND STATUS

The Pied Bushchat inhabits the southern Palearctic and Oriental regions. The majority of its subspecies are found in the Oriental region. Only one subspecies, *S. c. rossorum*, is found exclusively in the Palearctic, with two others, *S. c. bicolor* and *S. c. burmanica*, inhabiting both.

It occurs discontinuously over a wide area from the Aral Sea, southern Kazakhstan, Uzbekistan to southern Turkmenistan and eastern and southern Iran eastwards through Afghanistan, Tadzhikistan, Pakistan, India, Nepal, Bhutan and Sri Lanka to Bangladesh, Myanmar [Burma], southern Sichuan and Yunnan provinces in south-western China, the north-west, central and north-east parts of Thailand, Laos, Cambodia and southern Annam and Cochinchina in Vietnam. It is absent from the Malay Peninsula and Borneo but reappears further east in Java, the Lesser Sunda Islands, Sulawesi and the Philippines. It has spread east to New Guinea (both political halves) and to New Britain and New Ireland in the Bismarck Archipelago. It is evident that this species, especially in the eastern parts of its range, is composed of what are in effect a large number of more or less isolated populations reflecting the irregular areas of suitable grassland habitat that occur within its range.

Mayr (1944) found the historical distribution of this species puzzling. He quotes Stresemann, who judged that the species must have arrived in the Lesser Sunda Islands via the Philippines and Celebes but who could not account for its presence in eastern New Guinea and New Britain. If the species had used Australia or southern New Guinea as a bridge it would be expected still to occur in these areas, but in fact it has only comparatively recently extended its range (1960) to south-eastern New Guinea (Bell & Swainson 1985). Colonisation from the Philippines would entail a single jump of almost 2,000km, since all intervening country is unsuitable; but this would appear to be the most likely explanation.

Bell & Swainson (1985) argued that the Pied Bushchat is a continental Asian species which has only recently colonised the tropics. They supported this by the fact that in New Guinea, as in other similar tropical areas, cup-shaped nesters have very small clutches (c1–4 eggs Rand & Gilliard 1967), whereas the Pied Bushchat lays almost as many eggs as it does in its Palearctic distribution. Also few insectivores in New Guinea (as in other tropical areas) lay second clutches if the first was successful, whereas the Pied Bushchat does. Response to increasing day length seems to be the proximate trigger to its breeding, even where such breeding is completely out of phase with all other insectivores, such as in Flores. Its breeding seasons in the tropics, despite multiple broods, are more circumscribed than those of true tropical species. Lastly, throughout its tropical range it is more abundant in the cool highlands than the hot lowlands, and in some countries such as southern India, Sri Lanka and Vietnam it appears to be confined to highlands.

From many areas of its range this species is described as common, and no particular population for which there is information appears to be threatened. Its range in the east in New Guinea is still expanding, and it continues to take advantage of new suitable habitat created by man's local clearing of forest to make way for indigenous agriculture. However, colonisation of suitable areas can be quite random, and suitable habitat was unoccupied at Efogi (1,000m) close to existing populations of *S. c. wahgiensis* and *S. c. aethiops* (Bell & Swainson 1985). Similarly, the Malay Peninsula, Borneo, Sumatra and the Moluccas remain unoccupied although all have areas and climates apparently similar to those of adjacent occupied areas.

S. c. rossorum

Migratory. It is found breeding as far west as Bam in eastern Iran, also in south-eastern Turkmenistan where it is stated to be a common breeder in the Murgab, Tedzhen and Kushka valleys (Vorob'ev 1955) and along the Amudar'ya valley on the northern border with Uzbekistan. In Uzbekistan it occurs in suitable places in the Kyzlkum Desert, Zeravsham and Tashkent Oasis, reaching its north-eastern limits at the Syrdar'ya valley and Karatau foothills in southern Kazakhstan, where it is considered a rare breeding species (Dement'ev & Gladkov 1968, Gubin 1994). Between 1980 and 1993 it was found on the eastern outskirts of the Chimkent region in Kazakhstan, single males being seen on 10 May 1987 and 23 June 1989 and a pair on 5 June 1989. Single males were also seen near the district capital Chardara and on the edge of the main Kyzylkum desert 45km south-west of Baymakhan Well on 12 and 23 May 1988, and pairs were found twice in rice settlements in the agricultural zone near Ak-Altyn on 8 September 1988 and 3 September 1990. There is an isolated instance from considerably further north of single migrant birds on 10 and 15 May 1991 in association with Siberian Stonechat on the southern shores of Lake Biylikol in the Maly (Little) Karatau foothills in the Dzhambul region. Breeding pairs were found on the outskirts of Kyzyl-Orda on 23 June 1984 and 9–10 pairs were dispersed on cultivated farmfields on the left bank of the Syr-Darya River in Chimkent region on 25–26 June 1993. Apart from the Lake Biylikol records, it would appear that the species' range and rare breeding status in Kazakhstan have not changed in the last 100 years (Gubin 1994). It also occurs in northern and western Afghanistan where it is common at lower altitudes but avoids the central highlands and is not found in the extreme north-east (Paludan 1959). In Pakistan it is found in the Makran districts of southern Baluchistan, and Quetta in the northern highlands

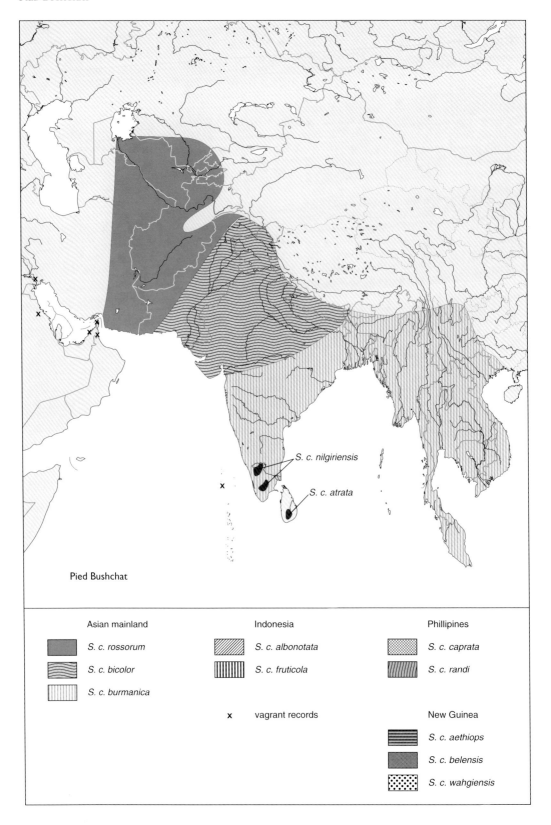

S. c. nilgiriensis

S. c. atrata

Pied Bushchat

Asian mainland	Indonesia	Phillipines
S. c. rossorum	S. c. albonotata	S. c. caprata
S. c. bicolor	S. c. fruticola	S. c. randi
S. c. burmanica		

x   vagrant records

New Guinea

S. c. aethiops

S. c. belensis

S. c. wahgiensis

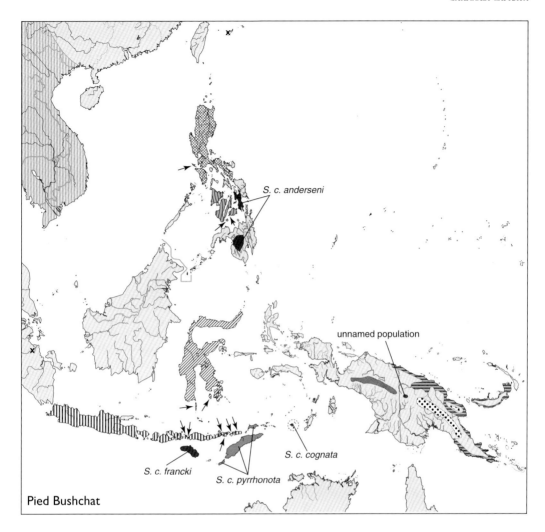

S. c. anderseni

unnamed population

S. c. cognata

S. c. francki

S. c. pyrrhonota

Pied Bushchat

of Baluchistan, from 1,525m to 3,050m (Meinertzhagen 1920), the Pamirs and northern Kashmir. It intergrades with *S. c. bicolor* in northern Baluchistan, the Makran and northern Kashmir, and also apparently from the north-west Himalayas east to the Punjab (Vaurie 1959). It winters in southern Iran as far west as Fars, southern Afghanistan and southern Baluchistan and the plains of north-west Pakistan as far south as Sind and eastwards to the western United Provinces. It occasionally occurs well to the west of its normal range, reaching the Mediterranean Sea (see Movements).

S. c. bicolor

Partial migrant. It breeds in western Pakistan, in the north from North-West Frontier Province, where it is a common summer visitor, to Dera Ismail Khan District, Kashmir, and northern Baluchistan (where it intergrades with *S. c. rossorum*), then south through Chagai, where it is a common passage migrant and summer visitor (Christison 1941) to Sind. In Pakistan it occurs up to 1,800m, more often only up to 1,500m, and locally up to 2,400m in summer. In northern Baluchistan it breeds up to 1,525m, but smaller numbers reach 3,050m (Ticehurst 1927). A survey between 1988–1998 found birds wintering on four occasions in Dera Ismail Khan District in North West Frontier Province (Kylanpaa 2000).

In India, Whistler (1941) stated that it occurred only locally above 1,700m, from Punjab and Himachal Pradesh in the north to Delhi in the south, then east to northern Bengal. It has been recorded in the Kumaon Himalaya in Uttar Pradesh at 1,800–2,200m (Sultana & Khan 2000). Birds at least as far north in India as Khaddar in Dehra Dun are fairly common lower-altitude (610m) residents, and in the neighbouring area of Dholkhand are found at 500–730m (Singh 2000). It has been found as high as 2,450m in Kashmir in summer, but usually remains in the foothills up to 1,525m (Bates & Lowther 1952); there is also a record of it occurring in winter at Gilgit in Kashmir (Scully in Ali & Ripley 1968–1998).

Around Jodphur in October and November it was found to be very common and generally distributed both in desert and on the hill-top at Sunda (Whistler 1938). In Nepal it is common and very widespread from the terai up to 915m, fairly common up to 1,400m, sometimes summers up to 2,400m and has been noted as high as 2,665m at Marpha in March. Most birds breeding above 1,400m descend to the foothills in winter (Grimmett *et al.* 1998). Proud (1955) did not often encounter it in the Nepal Valley but in 1953 saw several birds on eroded cliffs at the base of Sheopuri; they were very common along the new road below 915m. It winters mainly in India, southwards in Rajasthan and Gujarat including the Rann of Kutch and Kathiawar, east to Madhya Pradesh, where it is both a regular but never common resident and a migrant (Hewitson 1955), then south to Maharashtra, northern Andhra Pradesh, northern Karnataka to around 15°N and uncommonly as far south as northern Mysore (12.5°N). There is one isolated record from the Middle East well to the west of its normal range, in Oman (see Movements).

S. c. burmanica

Mainly resident with some birds subject to small seasonal movements (Ali & Ripley 1968–1998). Breeds south and east of *S. c. bicolor* and is common southwards into eastern and central India, found through Orissa, Hyderabad, Andhra Pradesh, Madras and Mysore. It is said to intergrade with *S. c. nilgiriensis* in western Mysore (Ripley *et al.* 1964). In India it breeds up to 2,100m in Nagaland and 1,200m in the Eastern Ghats (Ali & Ripley 1968–1998). It may also be the subspecies found in Bhutan, where it is a rare and very local resident, the first published record being of one in subtropical farmland at Punakha (c.1,280 m) on 3 November 1991 (Inskipp & Inskipp 1993); single males have since been seen annually in terraced farmland at 1,600m below Mongar from 27 April 1997 to May 2001 (K.D. Bishop *in litt.* 2001). It is also found in Bangladesh and in most parts of northern Myanmar [Burma] up to 1,525m, although its current status in the latter country is unknown; from Myitkyina in Kachin State southwards through Chin State and Shan State it was regarded as a common breeding resident (Baker 1923, Stanford & Ticehurst 1938), its range extending as far south as the southern part of Tenasserim. It is a common resident in the grasslands, scrub and cultivated areas from the plains up to 1,600m in north and north-east Thailand (Lekagul & Round 1991). Deignan (1945) found it a common or locally abundant resident on the open plains of Mae Hong Son, Chiang Mai and Chiang Rai provinces, recording it mainly in the lowlands but on Dong Ang Ka up to 135m. It is resident and possibly common in Laos (Duckworth *et al.* 1999) and is also found in Vietnam, where it is very common up to 1,068m (Wildash 1968). A survey conducted in January and February 1997 in Cambodia found birds present around Phnom Penh and Senmonorom (Duckworth & Hedges 1998). In southern China, Cheng Tso-hsin (1987) describes it as a rare resident in south-west Sichuan and in the north-west, west, south and south-eastern Yunnan. However, MacKinnon & Phillipps (2000) call it a common resident in south-west China and south-east Xizang, occurring from lowlands up to 3,300m.

S. c. nilgiriensis

Resident in southern India. It is not found on the plains but inhabits the hilly areas in the south-west corner of India in western Tamil Nadu and Kerala south of the range of *S. t. bicolor*. It occurs mainly in the Nilgiri, Palni and Travancore hill ranges which separate it from lowland *S. t. burmanica*, although they may intergrade where they meet.

S. c. atrata

Resident in Sri Lanka where it is rarely found below 870m, being almost confined to the drier eastern side of the central hill mass in Uva province but ascending higher to Nuwara Eliya (c.2,500m) and the Horton Plains. It is not found in the rest of the central hill mass or on the plains (Whistler 1940, Henry 1998).

S. c. caprata

Resident, northern Philippines: Lubang, Luzon, Mindoro.

S. c. randi

Resident, central Philippines: Bantayan, Bohol, Camotes, Cebu, Masbate, Marinduque, Negros, Panay, Siquijor and Ticao Islands.

S. c. anderseni

Resident, southern and eastern Philippines: Central area of Biliran, Camiguin Sur, Leyte and Mindanao (Dickinson *et al.* 1991, Kennedy *et al.* 2000).

S. c. fruticola

Resident. Java, Bali, Lombok, Sumbawa, Sangeang, Komodo, Rinca, Flores, Paloe, Lomblen and Alor islands, Indonesia (White & Bruce 1986, MacKinnon & Phillipps 1993, Coates & Bishop 1997, Verhoeye & Holmes 1999). Common resident in Java and Bali especially in drier eastern parts (MacKinnon & Phillipps 1993). On Java it is present from sea level up to the intermontane plateaus such as the Ijen (Holmes & Nash 1989). Very common from sea level to 1,600m on Flores (Verhoeye & Holmes 1999). On Lombok it has been recorded at 1,200–2,400m and on Sumbawa it is found from the lowlands up to 800m (Coates & Bishop 1997). A male or two males thought to have come from Java and therefore presumably of this subspecies were recorded at the same location in Jambi province, Sumatra, on 1 April 1991 and 3 February 1992 (Rusila 1992).

S. c. pyrrhonota

Resident. Roti, Dao, Doo, Semau, Sawu, Timor, Kisar and Wetar islands, Indonesia. On Timor found from sea level (near Kupang) to around 2,000m (Gn Mutis in West Timor) (Coates & Bishop 1997). Also recorded near Dili in East Timor (Mayr 1944).

S. c. francki

Resident. Sumba Island, Indonesia. Sea level to c.950m (Coates & Bishop 1997).

S. c. albonotata

Resident. Sulawesi, Butung, Salayar Islands, Indonesia. Inhabits lowlands to 1,100m, mainly above 600m in Sulawesi and locally in southern Sulawesi to 1,890m. It is widespread on Sulawesi apart from the northern peninsula where it appears to be absent (Coates & Bishop 1997).

S. c. cognata

Resident. Babar Island, Indonesia.

The three following subspecies *aethiops, belensis* and *wahgiensis*, plus an unlikely and unrecognised possible fourth subspecies in the Telefomin valley, have probably only comparatively recently colonised New Guinea. This species appears to be continuing to expand its range in this area in response to the creation of suitable habitat through local clearance of forest.

S. c. aethiops

Resident. Lowlands of northern New Guinea up to 1,500m. Occurs from Jayapura, Humboldt Bay and Sentani Lake in extreme north-east Irian Jaya, eastwards to the middle Sepik region, Saidor, the foothills of the Huon Peninsula (below 1,500m) in Madang and Morobe Province – in Papua New Guinea, the northeastern foothills (below 1,500m) of the Owen Stanley range in Northern Province through Popondetta, Safia and Tufi eastwards into Milne Bay Province around the coast and foothills.

It appears to have recently expanded its range to include the area of savanna around Port Moresby, being first discovered there in 1960 (Watson *et al.* 1961–1962). It may have been overlooked earlier, but owing to human developments it is now much more abundant and widely distributed than it was in 1960. Other areas around Port Moresby where it has been reported are Sogeri Plateau in 1970 (Coates 1990) and Fisherman's Island in November 1985 (Hicks 1985). It has also been been recorded on the south east coast from Cape Rodney, Maragarida and Amazon Bay (Coates 1990).

Watson *et al.* (1961–1962) state that it occurs from c.90–1,830m in the Port Moresby and surrounding areas. Coates (1990), upon which the above account is largely based, states that birds from the Port Moresby area are "provisionally" assigned to this subspecies.

It also extends further east into the Bismarck Archipelago. It was first reported from New Ireland in January 1985 (Finch 1985), although this may not represent initial colonisation as the species is known to have been established on the eastern part of neighbouring New Britain for some time prior to this record, and it has also occurred on Watom Island which forms a link between the two (Coates 1990). Bishop & Jones (in press *Emu*) state "Coultas collected four specimens, including a juvenile female at c.1,200m elevation near Lobi in the Nakani Mountains. Coultas noted this species as uncommon in native gardens. Neither we, Gilliard nor Diamond found this species in the mountains and, to our knowledge, there are no other records of the Pied Chat in West New Britain. Presumably this paucity of records reflects the almost total lack of suitable habitat – open scrubby areas – available in the region in addition to the lack of observers".

S. c. belensis

Resident. From Lakes Paniai and Tigi east throughout the Maoke Mountain range where it has been recorded up to 2,400m (in the Nassau, Oranje and Snow Mountains) of central Irian Jaya in western New Guinea, to approximately the border with Papua New Guinea. Possibly synonymous with *S. c. aethiops* (see Taxonomy).

S. c. wahgiensis

Resident. Found in the central mountains of Papua New Guinea extending from Enga province and Southern Highlands province east through Western Highlands province, Chimbu province, Eastern Highlands province, above 1,600m in Madang Province, continuing south-east onto the Huon Peninsula through the mountains of Morobe province and south-east into the Owen Stanley Range of mountains in Northern and Central Provinces. Possibly synonymous with *S. c. belensis* and thus *S. c. aethiops* (see Taxonomy). The birds found in and around the Telefomin valley and suggested by Rand & Gilliard (1967) to be a separate subspecies are possibly this subspecies or *belensis*. It has also expanded its range from Telefomin, being found certainly south and west on the southern slopes of the central mountains in the Tabubil Valley in Papua New Guinea. Its expansion may have been facilitated by the advent of the Ok Tedi mine near Tabubil (K.D. Bishop *in litt.* 2001). It has also been found nearby on Mt Fubilan up to c.1,900m (Gregory 1995). It has been recorded annually in the Tari Valley since 1985, and also around Moro annually since 1994, on the southern slopes of the central ranges of Southern Highlands province. It also occurs commonly throughout most other highland valleys in the central ranges including the Wahgi Valley, but it is still unclear exactly how far east it extends (K.D. Bishop *in litt.* 2001).

In the north-east of its range in Morobe, and south-east in Central Province, it is said to occur within 100km of the lowland-dwelling *S. c. aethiops*, but it is only found from 1,600m upwards (Bell & Swainson 1985). Four specimens in BMNH were collected at 2,225m on Mount Giluwe in Southern Highlands province. The maximum height it has been recorded was at 3,660m near the summit on Mt Albert Edward (3,991m), Central Province. Others have been recorded in the mountains as high as 2,850m, although it is not certain if these latter heights are exceptional or normal (Beehler *et al.* 1986).

BREEDING

In north-eastern Iran and neighbouring countries the Pied Bushchat commences breeding from April and continues until late July. Birds in Tadzhikistan do not arrive on their breeding grounds until late April (earliest record 22 April) or early May but in southern Turkmenistan birds arrive in the first third of April. In the Kushka River area, by 10 April migration was well under way and local birds were already occupying territories. The first nest containing a complete but unincubated clutch was found on 30 April with others found on 1 and 2 May and the last on 21 May. Laying therefore takes place over a period of three weeks and only one clutch is laid (Vorob'ev 1955, Chunikin & Drozdov 1968) although pairs losing their first clutch early in the season may possibly make another breeding attempt.

In southern Kazakhstan arrival appears to be later with, exceptionally, birds still on spring migration on 10 and 15 May at Dzhambul (see under *S. c. rossorum*). A pair observed at Kyzyl-Orda on 3 June were feeding a fledgling there on 23 June.

In Pakistan birds in the Sind area commenced breeding from early March continuing through to late July and August when a nest with eggs was found (Baker 1924). In northern Sind two nests with four eggs each were found on 26 and 31 March, and near Karachi a nest with three fresh eggs was located on 22 March (Ticehurst 1922–1924). Birds in Baluchistan did not commence breeding before the end of April or early May. However, in the south-eastern Iranian province of Baluchestan va Sistan, which borders Baluchistan, it is said to arrive in early March to breed (Scott in Colston & Gallagher 1984), whilst in Baluchistan the first spring arrivals were seen on 4 March although nests with eggs were only found between 26 April to 2 June (Meinertzhagen 1920).

In India the breeding season of *S. c. bicolor* and *S. c. burmanica* commences in March. A bird on the coast was 'excavating' a nest hole on 9 March (Ticehurst 1926). The season is extensive, with birds breeding into August. Specimens from Thailand of *burmanica* in full juvenile plumage have been collected at Chiang Mai on 1 July and at Chiang Rai on 1 August (Deignan 1945).

In northern India it does not breed before April. In Kashmir it usually starts at the end of May or early June, continuing at least until August (Bates & Lowther 1952). However, in 1981, at Chitwan in southern Nepal, nest building was observed as early as 1 February (Inskipp & Inskipp 1991). In southern India *S. c. nilgiriensis* and in Sri Lanka *S. c. atrata* commence breeding at the end of February and cease in May (Ali and Ripley 1968–1998). Colston & Gallagher (1984) suggest that breeding in both *S. c. rossorum* and *S. c. bicolor* may be earlier than noted in the literature based on the fact that there is a juvenile from Kandahar (Afghanistan) in BMNH collected on 29 March indicating start of breeding in February.

In Indonesia birds have been seen in breeding condition in April on Lombok; on Flores they breed from July to November, and in Sulawesi eggs have been found in June and October (White & Bruce 1986) with an occupied nest at Palu in December 1980 (Watling 1983). In the savannas of Port Moresby, New Guinea, breeding begins with males singing in late July and eggs being laid mainly from late August to January, peaking in September. There is one record of an exceptionally early nest in June. Breeding starts in the extreme dry season when food would be assumed to be at its scarcest but second or third broods were commenced in December and January in the rainy season (Bell & Swainson 1985). In the highland provinces it starts laying eggs from March to November at least, while in the mountains of the south-east breeding extends from August to November at least (Coates 1990). In eastern New Britain males sing from late August with breeding commencing in September and lasting until January (Dahl 1899).

The pair-bond is monogamous and birds breed when they are a year old. A single observation of a pair in July 1975 at Port Moresby, New Guinea, recorded a male fluttering in front of suitable crevices. The female flew to and perched near the male and followed him to a crevice. The male disappeared inside, then re-emerged. The female then went inside. Both went in and out twice more. This site had a completed nest in mid-September and eggs were laid in October (Bell & Swainson 1985). From observations in the Hari district of Papua New Guinea, Hadden (1975) reported both male and female carrying nest material. In India Ali & Ripley (1968–1998) also state both sexes build. However, Bell & Swainson (1985) observed a pair in which the female enlarged and excavated a cavity in a vertical bank of earth unassisted by the male. Lumps of earth were carried out in the bill and dropped at least 20–30m away. The male remained on his song post throughout. The cavity and nest were completed in three days but the male did not participate at any stage during the observation period. In Turkmenistan ready-made holes and crevices are used, with the bird enlarging a hollow in which to build the nest. The nest holes are usually very small with a width of 90–110mm, height of 65–90mm and depth of 150–330mm; the nest is invariably placed right by the entrance but in such a way as to avoid direct sunlight (Chunikin & Drozdov 1968).

In Pakistan, only the female was observed nest building with the male in close attendance but not contributing. Nest sites are usually in a small natural cavity in a bank, slope or erosion gully, sometimes in a mound of vegetation in a grassy area. Two nests were concealed in the bottom of grass clumps in tamarisk jungle (Ticehurst 1922–1924, Roberts 1992). In India nests have been found in holes in dead or fallen trees, walls of houses and wells, and in railway cuttings (Baker 1924). Other favourite sites are crevices in rocks or under large stones, whilst others are sited in a depression on level ground hidden underneath a grass tussock. In the highlands of Papua New Guinea three nests were situated under roofs and one in the side of a ditch (Hadden 1975); nesting has also been recorded in ditches along garden borders (Mayr & Rand 1937). In Myanmar [Burma] a popular site is a hole made by cattle hooves. Unusual sites include an old upturned petrol tin and the drain pipes of houses in Sulawesi (Watling 1983); 23cm above ground in the base of a thick shrub with grass growing all around (Campbell 1975); and a hollow in a discarded bamboo pole in Myanmar [Burma] (Smythies 1986). In the former Soviet Union nests are frequently built at ground level in the base of a bush (Dement'ev & Gladkov 1968) In Kashmir they were located in hollowed grass tufts at level ground (Bates & Lowther 1952).

In Turkmenistan steep banks by watercourses appear to be a favoured area in which to build nests. Dry cliffs or banks as little as 200–300m from watercourses are not occupied. Of 23 nests found, 19 were in steep riverbanks or the walls of irrigation canals, two in wells, and one each in an uninhabited building and in a clay wall (Chunikin & Drozdov 1968). In Kazakhstan nests were in similar situations built into the spoil alongside cleared canals and two were built into the sides of pools or gullies formed by water running out of the canals to irrigate fields (Gubin 1994).

Males (Turkmenistan) defend territories within a radius of 80–100m of the nest site, chasing off conspecific species as well as members of its own species. Near Bairkum nine pairs were discovered on a 4km transect and four nests located. They were separated by 60, 100, 110 and 1,550m respectively (Gubin 1994). Where it is abundant, aggressive conflicts between males are frequent.

In Port Moresby virtually all nest sites were close to human activity and this species seems to be remarkably tolerant of human presence both in the savanna and in the highlands. A nest with young that collapsed was reconstructed, with the young successfully fledging. Two recent man-made holes were quickly occupied and nests built into them. In Port Moresby freshly turned earth such as at building sites seemed to be attractive to nesting birds and nests constructed in drainage ditches would often be destroyed when they were filled in. Birds in Turkmenistan breed in villages (Chunikin & Drozdov 1968).

Nests are similar to those of other *Saxicola*. The nest is a neat, deep, compact cup of coarse dead grass, rootlets, plant debris or similar material lined with finer grass stems, fibres, hair or fur. Nests in Pakistan are often lined with plant down, from the seeds of *Callatropis* or *Saccharum munja* (Roberts 1992). One nest in Pakistan was built entirely of grass (Ticehurst 1922–1924). Nests in Turkmenistan consist of three basic layers: an outer layer of coarse rootlets and grasses, a middle layer of finer grasses and a lining of cow hairs and/or sheep's wool. Only one nest in 23 lacked a wool lining. The dimensions of the nests in Turkmenistan were: outer diameter 110–130mm, inner diameter (cup) 60–75mm, depth of cup 30–43mm, and height 45–70mm (Chunikin & Drozdov 1968). Dimensions from Kazakhstan were similar. A nest in Kazakhstan was described as having flimsy walls made from half-rotten fragments of reed stems, and the cup was lined with reed panicles (Gubin 1994).

There is no information on laying sequence and little on clutch size. Of 31 clutches in Port Moresby one contained two, 29 had three and one had four eggs. Ali & Ripley give clutch size in India as 3–5 eggs. In Pakistan from "over 100 nests" about 30% contained three eggs and 70% four eggs (Roberts 1992). Of 14 nests in Turkmenistan with full clutches or nestlings, ten contained five eggs or nestlings, three contained four, and one contained three well-incubated eggs (Chunikin & Drozdov 1968). Clutches in Kazakhstan normally contain 4–5 eggs (Gubin 1994).

Incubation lasted for 14 days in New Guinea and is given as 12–13 days in India. As with other *Saxicola* it is probably only done by the female. On 22 occasions on which sitting birds were flushed from nests in Port Moresby, all were females; and in Kashmir males were never found incubating (Bates & Lowther 1952). Similarly in Turkmenistan all incubating birds observed in 1952 were females (Vorob'ev 1955).

The eggs are short, broad and oval in shape and only slightly glossy. Their normal ground colour in India is pale bluish-white, less frequently pale stone colour or pinkish-white, and rarely darker blue. The markings are light reddish-brown consisting of freckles, specks and small blotches somewhat indistinct and numerous all over the surface, occasionally bolder and well defined (Baker 1924). They are almost always more numerous at the larger end where they form a ring or cap. Eggs in New Guinea and from Pakistan are similar. Sometimes the markings are missing altogether. In Turkmenistan, eggs vary from pale dove-grey to intense sky-blue heavily spotted with red and brown of differing intensities; some have the entire surface covered with red-brown spotting (Chunikin & Drozdov 1968).

The mean size of 23 eggs of *S. c. rossorum* from Turkmenistan was 18.1 x 14.3mm (Chunikin & Drozdov 1968); 100 eggs of *S. c. bicolor* measured 17.6 x 13.9mm [maxima 19.2 x 14.5 and 18.2 x 15.0, minima 16.2 x 13.4 and 17.0 x 12.9mm]; 62 eggs of *S. c. burmanica* were 16.8 x 13.9mm; 50 eggs of *S. c. atrata* 19.5 x 15.2mm [maxima 21.0 x 15.2 and 20.0 x 16.2, minima 17.5 x 14.6 and 17.7 x 14.1] (Baker 1924).

Nestlings take 13–15 days to fledge. On hatching they are naked with an orange-brown skin tone, and some individuals have tiny tufts of fine grey down on the head and dorsal surfaces. After 13 days they are fully feathered and can be sexed by plumage. If one of the parents disappears the other can successfully raise a brood by itself. A male managed to raise two out of three nestlings to fledging when his mate disappeared, but the young did not fledge until 18 days old. Observations at Port Moresby suggested that females do most of the feeding of the young and also most removing of faecal sacs, with the male only occasionally assisting. Females removing faecal sacs were accompanied by the male but if she left the territory the male stopped at its boundary. However, males were found to be brooding young on two occasions at Port Moresby and it is not safe to assume that they do not share a good proportion of the effort of raising the young (Bell & Swainson 1985). A pair observed in the Margalla hills in Pakistan both shared parental feeding duties; in Kazakhstan both parents fed young in the nest; and Baker stated that in India both sexes take part in all nesting activities.

The species is normally double-brooded in New Guinea. Reports from the entire range of the species suggest that two broods are normal or at least attempted, with three broods possible. However, Chunikin & Drozdov state it is single-brooded in Turkmenistan. One pair at Port Moresby successfully raised three broods of three young each, all in the same nest. The first clutch was commenced about 28 August, with the young fledging on 27 September. The second clutch was started about 24 October, with the young fledging on 23 November. The third clutch was started on 7/8 December and the young fledged on 4/5 January. Two were subsequently seen to be fed by the adults on 16 January but thereafter disappeared. The observers suggest that this is exceptional and was probably due to broods being lost soon after fledging, which enabled the adults to commence a new breeding cycle. In territories where young survived after fledging there was no such rapid resumption of nesting. In two cases where juveniles were present 8–9 weeks after fledging the adults made no second attempt at breeding. In another case a single ringed female fledged around 29 November was still present in the territory on 26 December. The adults started a second clutch about 3 January from which three ringed young fledged around 31 January. One of these young, together with the juvenile from the first brood, was seen with the adults in the territory in mid-March. Success rates for nests in Port Moresby were as follows: success in hatching from 69 eggs laid 58%; success in rearing nestlings from 33 eggs hatched 69.7%; and total success from eggs to fledging 40.4%.

In New Guinea there was little evidence to determine whether young merely disperse from the territory they were reared in or are evicted by their parents. Young from second broods or final breeding attempts appear to remain on the territory with the parents for some time after breeding finishes. In New Guinea there is some evidence that dispersal of young to "new localities" takes place around March and April (Bell & Swainson 1985).

In Pakistan, India and Myanmar [Burma] the species is often parasitised by Common Cuckoo *Cuculus canorus* (Ali & Ripley 1968–1998, Smythies 1986). Of 31 nests observed in the Port Moresby area of Papua New Guinea none were parasitised by the abundant Brush Cuckoo *Cacomantis variolosus* (a common brood-parasite of the species in Indonesia), which may suggest that it had not yet responded to the comparatively recent arrival (1960) of *S. c. caprata* in the Port Moresby area (Bell & Swainson 1985). From 129 nests on Java and Flores 10% were parasitised by Brush Cuckoo (Hellebrekers & Hoogerwerf 1967, Ottow & Verheijen 1969). In Pakistan eggs are frequently taken by lizards *Calotes versicolor* (K. Eates in Roberts 1992). In Vietnam nestlings are often taken for the live bird trade (Craik 1998).

Adults and their fledglings habitually roost in 2m high cane grass in Port Moresby, with the fledglings remaining there during the day (Bell & Swainson 1985).

HABITAT

Throughout its range, the Pied Bushchat is typically found in open areas with few trees, on plains or in the foothills of mountain ranges but usually not above 2,500m, often near to human dwellings. The areas it frequents can vary from stony waste ground with scrub, interspersed with cultivation, to heavily cultivated areas and orchards. In Pakistan it is described by Roberts (1992) as typically a bird of open, rather treeless tracts of cultivation, with patches of waste ground containing clumps of *Saccharum* grass. It avoids forests and much human disturbance and is not found around villages, although in India it is said to inhabit cultivated fields around villages (Ali & Ripley 1968–1998). In Sind, Pakistan, Ticehurst (1922–1924) also found it around cultivation, and open thickish jungle of tamarisk and acacia such as are found on the edges of jheels and along the banks of rivers. In Myanmar [Burma] it frequents open country, avoiding heavily forested areas but inhabiting grasslands and all types of scrub in both cultivated and semi-cultivated areas. It avoids open paddy plains (Baker 1924, Smythies 1986). It is found in a wide variety of habitats from, in Pakistan, juniper forest up to 2,400m, zones of subtropical pine and on saline flats that are subject to seasonal flooding along the Indus River. In India it inhabits bare or sparsely vegetated hillsides, tamarisk growth, reeds and grass near tanks and canals used for irrigation. In Sri Lanka it is commonest around villages, cultivated areas, grasslands and light scrub jungle (Baker 1924). In Russia it is said by Dement'ev & Gladkov (1968) to inhabit damp meadows and cultivated areas with abundant water. It is also found along river and canal banks overgrown with high grasses, as well as on the edges of human habitation. In Turkmenistan it favours river valleys for both breeding and migration, with nests being found in tamarisk thickets or in groves of "variable-leaved" poplar (Chunikin & Drozdov 1968). In Kazkhstan it has been found around canals irrigating fields of rice, maize and clover (Gubin 1994). It would appear to show a preference in the west of its range for areas associated with water, certainly so in Turkmenistan and Kazakhstan, but this preference is not so evident in other parts of its range such as Sri Lanka, Annam and New Guinea (Bell & Swainson 1985). Throughout Laos it is found mainly in the lowlands in areas of secondary growth and cultivation, with natural habitat being dry dipterocarp forest and scrub on river islands (Duckworth *et al.* 1999). In northern Thailand it is found usually in pairs on roadside hedges and fences, in areas of abandoned cultivation and after harvest on bunds and bushes in ricefields (Deignan 1945). In Wallacea (Sulawesi, the Moluccas and Lesser Sunda Islands of Indonesia) it inhabits grassland, scrub, wooded savanna and cultivated areas with scattered trees and shrubs. It is also occasionally found in irrigated ricefields, degraded woodland, swampy areas and towns (Wardill *et al.* 1992, Coates & Bishop 1997, Verhoeye & Holmes 1999).

Throughout most of its range it appears indifferent to the close proximity of man, and indeed it would appear to be a species that has benefited from landscape changes wrought by man. It shows a marked preference for areas that have suffered the attentions of man doubtless because these create habitat suitable for its needs. It occupies all anthropogenic grasslands in the highlands of New Guinea, including gardens, small patches of secondary vegetation and large tracts of grasses such as airfields. In many areas the ground is temporarily disturbed from digging drainage ditches and few trees are left apart from isolated dead ones. In the lowlands such habitat is less available and more fragmented (Bell & Swainson 1985). As with its congeners, widely scattered elevated perches located in otherwise open ground appear to be essential for both territorial singing and locating prey.

In New Guinea much use is made of artificial perches such as overhead wires, radio masts, flagpoles, roofs and fences as well as any natural perches available such as dead trees, canegrass stems and low shrubs. Territories are rarely far from roads. A sample of habitat based on 9ha quadrats demonstrated that quadrats with nests had significantly less tree cover but more stony ground than quadrats without nests. No quadrat with nests lacked bare ground whereas 15 of the 26 quadrats without nests lacked any bare ground. Nesting quadrats had highly significantly more stony embankments than those without. Only one nesting quadrat lacked an embankment but had 110m of deep ditches. Of the 13 quadrats with nests seven were located at quarries, four at gravel pits, one at a deep road cutting and another at a construction site. Almost all sites had powerlines which males utilised as song posts. One nesting site in a quarry lacked powerlines but several dead trees were used as song posts. In the highlands suitable habitat has probably only become available with the onset of agriculture.

Bell & Swainson (1985) thought Mayr & Rand (1937) mistaken in considering that natural phenomena such as landslides could have created suitable habitat in New Guinea. They point out that the species is absent from intervening areas of similar terrain and climate in Peninsular Malaysia, Borneo, Sumatra and the Moluccas. Suitable habitats probably became available with the onset of agriculture in the highlands with extensive clearings and creation of drainage ditches. The absence of this species until comparatively recently from the savanna of Port Moresby and its present absence from the Trans-Fly and northern Australia is probably related to the lack of any agriculture and, in the latter two areas, flat terrain and absence of nest sites. Bell & Swainson referred to Moreau (1972), who suggested that there may have been no suitable original habitat for the species in its current Russian and Himalayan ranges. It may have been restricted to the Indian subcontinent where burning and later agriculture could have created more suitable habitat, particularly in monsoonal areas. The subsequent spread into wetter areas of South-East Asia and Malesia probably followed agriculture, but only where human agency could effectively modify the environment. They point out that the areas where the species now exists are those where man could have most easily modified the environment, either those with monsoonal climates (Lesser Sundas, Timor, parts of coastal New Guinea, parts of Sulawesi) or those with highly fertile soils capable of supporting dense human populations such as parts of Java and the highlands of New Guinea. Areas from which the species is absent are those of year-round high rainfall and/or low soil fertility such as in Malaysia, Borneo, parts of Sumatra and the Moluccas, where until machinery was introduced man had extreme difficulty in restricting regrowth of forest.

MOVEMENTS

One subspecies – *S. c. rossorum* – is migratory and another – *S. c. bicolor* – is a partial migrant; both inhabit the southern Palearctic, *S. c. rossorum* exclusively and *S. c. bicolor* partially. The other 14 subspecies inhabit the Oriental and Papuasian regions and are chiefly sedentary, with some making local altitudinal movements. Only those subspecies which have been documented exhibiting some movements are treated below.

Most migration would appear to take place during the night although single birds and small parties have been observed moving by day (Paludan 1959). There is an interesting record of a male (race unknown) arriving on a ship at 11:00hrs and remaining until well after dark on 6 October, and another male passing over the same ship together with a female that briefly landed on board, both on 30 October. The ship's position at the time was near the Laccadive Islands, 10° 17′N, 71 °26′E, off the west coast of southern India (Simpson 1984).

The records listed below are only presumed to refer to the subspecies under which they are listed as these are the subspecies nearest to where the records came from. Little is known about movements of this species apart from those of subspecies on the Indian subcontinent and whether such movements that have been recorded are regular or just isolated vagrancy.

S. c. rossorum

In Turkmenistan it arrives to breed in early April (9–11th earliest dates), whilst in Tadzhikistan it arrives in late April (22 April earliest date), sometimes later in early May. Autumn departures from the Gissar valley in the mountains of Tadzhikistan have ceased by 20–22 September (Dement'ev & Gladkov 1968). In Kazakhstan it has been recorded on 10 and 15 May in the region around Dzhambul and then not seen again until the start of June (Gubin 1994). Birds are still present in Kazakhstan in early September, e.g. a male and female present on ricefields near Ak-Altyn on 8 September 1988 and 3 September 1990 (Gubin 1994). It also intergrades as a migrant breeding bird with *S. c. bicolor* in the Makran, northern Baluchistan and north-west Kashmir (Ripley *et al.* 1964). It was recorded at Chitral in the far north of India at 1,830m in February and then not again until September when large numbers arrived at Drosh just south of Chitral evidently migrating south (Perreau 1910). In western Afghanistan around Farah it was very common in early April (2–6th) but numbers had declined by the end of June (27th) presumably because some of the April birds were migrants moving further north. Similarly in southern Afghanistan it was common from Kandahar northwards to Kabul in early May (4–7th) but numbers had declined by the end of June (24–25th) with none found north of Kandahar. Small numbers of autumn migrants have been observed in northern Afghanistan in the area of Bamian between 7 September and 6 October with a single bird on 15 October. A female on migration in this area was recorded at 3,050m (Paludan 1959).

It winters in southern Iran, southern Afghanistan and southern Baluchistan as well as the adjacent plains around the Indus River in north-west Pakistan where it mixes with *S. c. bicolor.*

There are a number of vagrancy records for this species, presumably of this subspecies, west of its normal range. A male was seen at the Al-Khobar corniche in the Eastern Province of Saudi Arabia on 17 October 1993 (Ramsay 1994). Nine birds have occurred in the United Arab Emirates of which four could be assigned to *S. c. rossorum*. These were single males at the Emirates Golf Course, Dubai, on the west coast of UAE on 6 May 1994 and 22–23 March 1996, at Fujairah National Dairy Farm, Dibba (on the northern point of UAE's east coast bordering Oman/Musandam), on 3 September 1999, and (apparently wintering there) from 17 November 2000 to at least late February 2001. The five others (included here as they are most likely to be of this subspecies although it should be noted that *S. c. bicolor* has occurred once in Oman: see below) were: one (presumed) male, 4 April 1996, Al Wathba camel track 30km west of Dubai; one female, 22 August 1997, Fujairah National Dairy Farm; one male, 26 March 1999, Emirates Golf Course; one male, 30–31 March 1999, Fujairah National Dairy Farm; one male, 31 March 1999, Al Ain camel track, Al Ain, in eastern UAE (C. Richardson *in litt.* 2001).

In Iraq there are two very old records from Fao in March and November 1886 (Allouse 1953) and it was listed as an accidental straggler to that country by Sarudny in 1911. It has been recorded from Cyprus twice; a male in Larnaca, 3–11 November 1986 (Flint & Stewart 1992) and a female at Paphos on 23 November 1997 (*Birding World* 1998). There are five records for Israel up to the end of 2000: a male that had probably overwintered at Eilat, January 1979 (J.P. Smith *in litt.* 2001); a first-winter male at Beeroyatim, north-west Negev, 28 October 1994 (Shirihai 1995); a male at Eilat, 4–7 November 1996 (S. Brand *et al.* per J.P. Smith *in litt.* 2001); a (probable first-winter) female at Kibbutz Lotan, 4 November 1997 (J.P. Smith *in litt.* 2001); and a male at Kibbutz Shizzafon, 18–22 October 2000 (J.P. Smith *in litt.* 2001). An adult female overwintered in the parking lot of the International Birding and Research Center in Eilat from early autumn 2001 to at least 29 March 2002 (R. Yosef & M. Rydberg-Hedaen *in litt.* 2002).

S. c. bicolor

Birds in the south of their range are described by Roberts (1992) as widespread and resident in Pakistan throughout the Indus plains and in southern Baluchistan along the Makran. They are also resident and widely distributed in the Jhang district in Punjab (Whistler 1922). These residents are augmented by more northerly breeding birds in winter. In summer the migratory population moves north into warmer and drier regions in the mountains and ascends to elevations of 1,500m in northern Pakistan and India and up to 2,100m in Nepal. This subspecies is a rare visitor to Bhutan.

It is also a summer migrant in Pakistan to the Chagai region on the borders of Afghanistan, the central Makran, central and northern Baluchistan and the Jhang district in Punjab, arriving in mid-February to early March and occupying the broader lower valleys and plains regions up to 1,525m. Smaller numbers ascend to 3,050m. In the more northerly parts of its range and at higher elevations it arrives in late February or March, leaving again in September and October. In the south-eastern part of the North-West Frontier Province it is a common summer visitor with males first arriving 13–18 February and both sexes generally common by March (Kylänpää 2000). It penetrates the main valleys of Dir and Chitral in northern Pakistan in summer but only up to elevations of around 1,800m (Perreau 1910). In the Kurram valley it arrives to breed in the second week of March but only reaches elevations of 900m (Whitehead 1911). Roberts (1992) saw it in the main valley of the Indus in June as far up as the Chilas district of Gilgit in Kashmir but it is rare around the town of Gilgit with only one record of a vagrant being recorded in December (Scully 1881). Bates & Lowther (1952) state that it is uncommon as far north as the Kishenganga Valley, reaching elevations of 825m at the end of April. In the Murree Range it reaches 1,800m at Ghora Gali and can be commonly found in the lower reaches of the Neelum Valley in Azad Kashmir up to c.1,500m (Roberts 1992). It is a migrant to the foothills of Kashmir extending through the Jhelum Valley to within five miles of Baramula, although only found commonly as far as Chenari.

Birds generally leave the northern breeding areas again from mid-September. However, Ticehurst quotes an unsubstantiated report saying they leave in October, the latest date being 11 November (Ticehurst 1926). In the southern part of the North-West Frontier Province at Dera Ismail Khan district the last birds left for the south by 20 November. It mainly winters in western India in the Rann of Kutch and Gujarat north to Rajasthan, then south and east to Madhya Pradesh, Maharashtra, Andhra Pradesh and northern Karnataka. Roberts saw a bird at Zangi Nawar lake in Nushki, Baluchistan, on 18 January but considered that most birds from this and other similar areas migrate down to the plains to winter. Wintering birds have been found as high as 1,400 m.

This subspecies has been recorded once as a vagrant in Oman. A male was collected at Khasab (26° 11′ N, 56° 15′ E), the capital of the Musandam region, on 10 April 1983 (Colston & Gallagher 1984).

S. c. burmanica

Ali & Ripley (1968–1998) state that it is subject to small seasonal movements. In Myanmar [Burma] Smythies (1986) noted a great influx into the tea estate at Thadaung in April, suggesting that many birds winter on

243

the plains and ascend to the hills to breed in spring. In Shwebo district in northern Myanmar [Burma] it is absent in March, scarce in April and uncommon in May, whilst in Minbu district in east-central Myanmar [Burma] it is common in all months except March and April, suggesting birds moving to breeding areas (Roseveare 1949, 1952). Two birding expeditions to northern Myanmar [Burma] in January–February 1998 and November 1999 found it to be rare, with birds only seen up to 980m, suggesting that the majority of birds may move south and to lower altitudes than in the breeding season (King *et al.* 2001).

There is one record of vagrancy presumably involving this subspecies: a single bird was on Yonaguni-jima, Japan, on 24 January 1989 (Brazil 1991).

S. c. caprata

All vagrant records are from Borneo. It should be stated unequivocally that all are controversial. The origins and subspecific identity of any individuals that may genuinely have been found there remain speculative, but the range of *S. c. caprata* would seem the most likely source.

Ripley *et al.* (1964) list Borneo as within the range of this species based on one record, although they are uncertain of the subspecies involved. Their assumption was based on a record of two specimens, a male and female obtained from Maison Verreaux in Paris and presented to the Braunschweig Museum (Blasius 1883). They were said to have come from Borneo but there was no substantiating evidence as to where (probably in Kalimantan: Smythies 1999) and by whom they were collected. This record has subsequently been rejected by Andrew (1992).

Smythies (1999) lists four other records:

A female was seen at Kuala Belait on 23 December 1970 (Vowles & Vowles 1985) but again was not accepted (Mann in prep. in Smythies 1999).
Another possible sighting of an adult male in May 1975 was made at Batu Niah Estate, Sarawak (Duckett 1987).
A male was described by Counsell (MS in Smythies 1999) at Sg. Batu Apoi, Temburong, Brunei on 17 January 1984 but the record has been rejected (Mann in prep. in Smythies 1999).
Finally, another male was reported at Kinabalu Park HQ at c.1,550m on 2 May 1998 (C. Gonner & S. Schwarz in *Oriental Bird Club Bull.* 28 [1998]: 45).

S. c. fruticola

Two records exist of single adult males found at Simpang Malaka in the Berbak Game Reserve in Jambi province, Sumatra, 104° 00´E, 1° 24´N. The first record was on 1 April 1991 and the same or another male was found at the exact same location on 3 February 1992 (Rusila 1992). The origin of this bird or these birds was considered to be Java. This may possibly point to some movements of not only this subspecies but of others that have previously gone unrecorded.

VOICE

Only the male sings. "The song is typically a short, high-pitched, musical, warbled phrase of variable pattern repeated at intervals of a few seconds. On Sumba the song was noted as a clear, very fast series of c.15 somewhat stilted, medium-pitched whistled notes (duration 5.5 sec), irregular in rhythm; this same song, or slight variations, are repeated at variable intervals" (Coates & Bishop 1997). Other descriptions of the song have been given as a soft *preep-pretty-seeeer; pree-pretty lessup-chur-rip* (Fleming *et al.* 1984); *Erithacus* robin-like warbles, quite emphatic with the last part rising and falling in cadence and starting with 3–4 short piercing whistles with brief pauses in between, e.g. *whit-whit-tit-wheee-tyeear-tiyeear-tuh* (Roberts 1992); short and whistling, lasting approximately two seconds and beginning with a double *chick-chick*, and transcribable as *we are tea for two* (the highest note being the tea) (Ali & Ripley 1968–1998); a weak, somewhat hoarse but musical, whistled song of 4–8 notes in an irregular rhythm, each pattern being repeated several times before another commences (Beehler *et al.* 1986); a delightful warbled tune reminiscent of European Blackbird *Turdus merula* but weaker and higher in pitch, consisting of a short phrase of several notes repeated at intervals of several seconds, then switching to another tune also repeated several times (Coates 1990). Individual birds have a repertoire of several tunes. Watson *et al.* (1961–1962) found song was most obvious first thing in the morning and last thing at night. It is sometimes delivered at night. A bird was heard at 22:00 hrs in New Guinea four hours after sunset.

In Kashmir and Nepal birds start territorial singing in February (Fleming *et al.* 1984). In the southern and central parts of Pakistan (Sind and Punjab) they begin singing in mid- to late February, continuing to early June (Roberts 1992), while in Jhang district they begin in March (Whistler 1922). Birds moving north to breed in Turkmenistan commence in late March or early April and continue until the end of June, when the song becomes monosyllabic and very short (Chunikin & Drozdov 1968). In Tadzhikistan they start in late April or May (Dement'ev & Gladkov 1968).

Around Port Moresby, Papua New Guinea, males start singing vigorously in July although no nests were found until late August (Bell & Swainson 1985), and as breeding continues until January presumably so does singing. In eastern New Britain males commence singing in late August with breeding only starting in September but again lasting until January (Dahl 1899).

The song is delivered from a number of exposed and prominent perches within the territory. Whilst singing the male depresses his tail and partly droops and quivers his wings, raising the scapulars to expose the white wing-patches which are everted or fluffed up and displayed prominently, and simultaneously raising the white feathers on the rump (Baker 1924). When intensely excited the singing male occasionally takes exaggerated leaps c.1m into the air, hovering like a butterfly before returning to the same perch (Roberts 1992). Bates & Lowther (1952) describe a similar behaviour with "the bird flying a few feet upwards from its perch and then sinking slowly to the ground with wings spread and white axillaries and rump feathers conspicuously fluffed out, singing as it falls to posture beside its mate". E.N. Panov *in litt.* (2001) states that song-flights are very characteristic of the early part of the breeding season, birds rising 2–4m above the ground with strong, even beats of the fully spread wings. They do not, however, hover like the Common Stonechat. Whistler (1922) describes singing males as flying up into the air with tail fully spread, wings flapping slowly and deliberately in an exaggerated action and held high above the head. When they descend they sail down in an arc to another perch with wings and tail fully spread, prominently displaying the white rump and wing-patches (Dement'ev & Gladkov 1968). Males also sing in threat display (see Behaviour below).

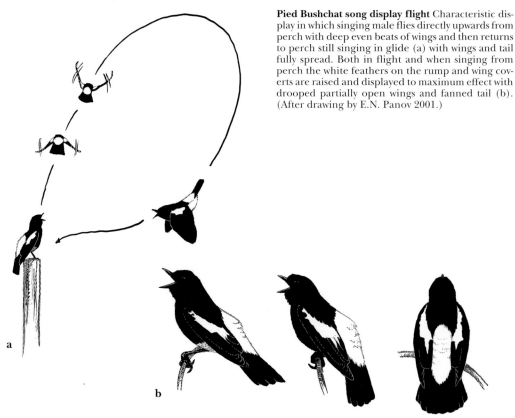

Pied Bushchat song display flight Characteristic display in which singing male flies directly upwards from perch with deep even beats of wings and then returns to perch still singing in glide (a) with wings and tail fully spread. Both in flight and when singing from perch the white feathers on the rump and wing coverts are raised and displayed to maximum effect with drooped partially open wings and fanned tail (b). (After drawing by E.N. Panov 2001.)

a

b

Other vocalisations Adults of both sexes have a short staccato warning call of either one or two distinct notes similar to Siberian Stonechat. Variously described as a hard *tsak tsak* alternated with a musical plaintive *hweet* (King *et al.* 1975) or a muffled *chshk...chshk...chshk* alternating with a whistling *eeoo...eeoo* sound (E.N. Panov *in litt.* 2001). Similar calls have been noted from Pakistan (Roberts 1992) and Thailand (Lekagul & Round 1991).

Newly fledged young also utter a rather grating, soliciting call similar to the alarm call of the adults but it is a more continuous and uninterrupted *churr-churr-churr* (Roberts 1992). Almost independent young utter a rasping chirp *creek creek* (Henry in Ali & Ripley 1968–1998).

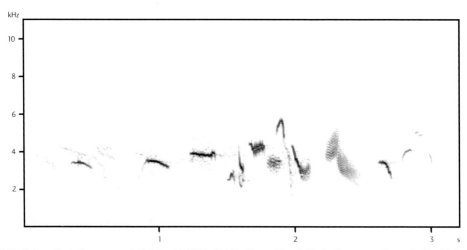

Pied Bushchat *Saxicola caprata* (*nilgiriensis*) **NSA 65440. Song. Tamil Nadu State, southern India 25 January 1996.** *P. Holt.*

FOOD

Little detailed information. Invertebrates are the main prey. In India and Pakistan birds have been recorded taking small orthoptera (grasshoppers and crickets), various larvae, beetles, ants and some vegetable matter, also other insects and spiders (Ali & Ripley 1968–1998). In New Guinea identified prey includes caterpillars, beetles, moths, midges, ants, larvae and earthworms (Bell & Swainson 1985, Coates 1990). A pair in the Margalla hills, Pakistan, consistently brought their young small caterpillars (Roberts 1992).

The main method of feeding is by locating prey from prominent perches, flying down to seize it on the ground and then returning to the original perch or another nearby. In Pakistan birds also seize prey in aerial sallies and this seems especially prevalent in late afternoon and evening, possibly owing to increased insect activity and the air becoming calm (Roberts 1992). In New Guinea they also make insectivorous aerial sallies, almost exclusively at 17:00–18:00 hrs (Bell & Swainson 1985). One bird perched on a fence a few feet from a large pig and would drop to the ground to seize prey as the pig rooted up the soil. Birds usually perch singly or in pairs, with males perching more prominently than females (Coates 1990). A vagrant wintering female at Eilat, Israel, was observed to walk on the ground taking terrestrial insects (R. Yosef & M. Rydberg-Hedaen *in litt.* 2002).

BEHAVIOUR

Birds are usually seen singly or in pairs, occasionally in family groups, and apart from the migratory *S. t. rossorum* and *S. t. bicolor* appear to be mainly sedentary and strongly territorial all year round. In Pakistan they form long-lasting pair-bonds and show territorial attachment outside of the breeding season (Roberts 1992). In New Guinea they remain in their breeding territory all year, being most obvious in the spring and becoming secretive when with young. In cases where territories adjoined, both males and females were active in territorial defence and interactions (Bell & Swainson 1985). In the Indian subcontinent pairs show territorial aggression throughout the year and defend feeding areas as much as breeding areas, chasing off other *Saxicola* and even larger *Oenanthe* spp. in winter months (Ali & Ripley 1968–1998, Roberts 1992). A vagrant wintering female at Eilat, Israel, defended a territory c.35 x 20m. It was involved in territorial disputes with Bluethroat *Luscinia svecica* and White Wagtail *Motacilla alba*. A male European Stonechat *Saxicola rubicola* holding an adjacent territory regularly courted it (R. Yosef & M. Rydberg-Hedaen *in litt.* 2002). There are several observations from India of "strong and sustained" attacks on Common Cuckoos when they are in the act of laying an egg in a nest (Baker 1942). In a threat display the male droops his wings and displays the white wing-patches in a menacing manner, the tail is depressed and spread, the white rump fluffed out and the neck stiffly craned forward, all accompanied by excited bursts of song.

Both sexes have the habit common to most *Saxicola* of flicking their wings and rapidly half-opening and closing their tails when nervous or excited.

MOULT

Adults have a complete post-breeding moult whilst juveniles have a partial post-juvenile moult.

In Turkmenistan and Tadzhikistan adults moult over a prolonged period. The general moult occurs in the second half of July or August. However, birds collected at Chardzhou in Turkmenistan were in the early stages of moult in mid-June whilst those from Kerki, further south, had not commenced moulting by 7 July; but birds from both locations had nearly finished moulting by early August (Dement'ev & Gladkov 1968). In Afghanistan moult begins around early July and is completed by late August (Cramp 1988).

Juveniles in Turkmenistan were in heavy moult by the beginning of August, whilst in Tadzhikistan it was slightly later, in mid-August (Dement'ev & Gladkov 1968). In Afghanistan and Pakistan juvenile moult commences around mid-July (Cramp 1988).

Post-juvenile moult involves the head, body, lesser and median upperwing-coverts and inner greater upperwing-coverts and occasionally some tertials. The juvenile remiges and rectrices, together with the greater upper primary coverts and 01–06 outer greater upperwing-coverts, are retained.

Fledglings in Papua New Guinea acquire first adult female plumage 6–8 weeks after leaving the nest. Of two males one acquired the adult-type black feathering six weeks after fledging, while the other had 'adult type' remiges and rectrices after nine weeks but still retained the dark grey juvenile body plumage apart from a patch of black feathers on the upper breast (Bell & Swainson 1985).

CONSERVATION

Although there is little detailed information available the Pied Bushchat does not appear to be threatened anywhere in its range and indeed it seems to be expanding in the eastern parts of its range in Indonesia and New Guinea as man-made changes to the landscape, such as clearance of forest, create suitable habitat. Local threats which may take on increasing significance include shooting and capture for the live bird trade, for which it is one of the most sought-after species in Vietnam (Craik 1998) and possibly other neighbouring countries. In lowlands around Port Moresby, Papua New Guinea, where it inhabits areas close to human development such as roads, it is reported as being killed by passers-by and its survival is surprising (Bell & Swainson 1985). In highland areas, however, it is regarded as a sacred bird (Majnep & Bulmer 1977). Although there are no apparent threats little is known about the size of the populations of the different racial groups, which may be important in the case of those that are restricted to just a few islands.

Oreicola jerdoni Blyth, 1867, *Ibis*, p.14, new name for *Rhodophila melanoleuca* Jerdon, 1863, *Birds India*, 2, p.128—Purneah [= India], *nec Oenanthe melanoleuca = Saxicola gutturalis* Viellot, 1818, *Nouv. Dict. Hist. Nat.*, nouv. éd., 21, p.435

Etymology *jerdoni* in honour of Major Thomas Claverhill Jerdon (1811–1872), Scottish field ornithologist, collector and author

Other names Jerdon's Chat, Rufous-breasted Bushchat

TAXONOMY
Monotypic.

IDENTIFICATION
Size 15cm/5.9 inches. Sexes dimorphic. Similar in shape and size to Grey Bushchat *Saxicola ferrea* with longish tail in proportion to the body, but the tail is slightly longer and more rounded than *S. ferrea* with the outer pair (06) of rectrices noticeably shorter than the others. The wing is comparatively short and rounded with the primary projection c.50% of the length of the overlying tertials. The breeding male is very distinctive, being entirely uniform glossy bluish-black above and pure white below, with a sharp demarcation between the gleaming white chin and throat and the blue-black lores, malar region and ear-coverts. The female is entirely rufous-brown and unstreaked above, with richer chestnut-brown on the rump and uppertail-coverts; the underparts are pale brownish-buff shading to white or buff-white on the belly and undertail-coverts; chin and throat, as in the male, are gleaming white, and the ear-coverts are uniform with the forehead and crown (not forming a darker patch on the side of the head as they do in female *S. ferrea*). The majority of females lack any form of supercilium but a minority may show a slight narrow buff supercilium in front of the eye. The tail lacks any of the chestnut fringing found in female *S. ferrea*. Juvenile males are similar to the female but slightly darker brown in tone with prominent black-brown fringes to the feathers of the upperparts and breast.

Confusion species Adult males are unlikely to be confused with any other *Saxicola*. Females and juvenile males are superficially similar to female Grey Bushchat but differ as follows: in *S. jerdoni* the tail feathers show no rufous-brown fringes and the dark brown tail contrasts strikingly with the rich chestnut uppertail-coverts and rump, while *S. ferrea* has prominent rufous-brown fringes to the tail feathers (even when closed) merging into the concolorous uppertail-coverts and rump; in *S. jerdoni* the tail is slightly longer in proportion to the body and more rounded, creating a subtly different, more attenuated profile, while in *S. ferrea* it is less rounded and slightly shorter in proportion to the body; *S. jerdoni* has no supercilium although an occasional female can show a faint, narrow buff supercilum which at most only extends from bill to eye; *S. ferrea* has a long broad buff supercilium running from the bill to the rear of the ear-coverts; in *S. jerdoni* the ear-coverts are a similar rufous-brown to the rest of the head, while in *S. ferrea* they are darker brown than the rest of the head forming a distinct darker patch accentuated by the broad pale super-cilium. A frequently claimed difference is that the belly and undertail-coverts are white or buff-white in *S. jerdoni* and darker, usually buff with little white, in *S. ferrea*, but on BMNH specimens there is much variation in females of both species and it would be unsafe to use this criterion alone to separate the two species.

DESCRIPTION
Adult male in fresh plumage Forehead, crown, nape, neck, lores, malar region, ear-coverts, mantle, scapulars, back, rump and uppertail-coverts are a uniform glossy black with a noticeable blue sheen. The chin and throat are silky white. The breast and belly are also silky white but suffused with buff. Some specimens, presumably in very fresh plumage, show extensive grey-buff tips to scattered feathers on the lower breast. The flanks are predominantly white with a variable amount of grey tips to some feathers. The undertail-coverts are silky white. The rectrices are dull black with a faint blue gloss to the fringes of the outerwebs. The remiges are dull black. The alula and upperwing primary, lesser, median and greater coverts are black with glossy bluish-black fringes on the outerwebs and tips. The innermost median coverts show a fractional amount of white at their bases. The inner secondaries and tertials also show a dull blue-black gloss to the fringes of the outerwebs. The underwing-coverts are glossy blue-black and the axillaries are black with narrow white fringes and tips. As the plumage wears the breast, belly and flanks become increasingly white and in very worn plumage the black feather bases to these areas increasingly show through. The legs, feet and bill are black. The irides are dark brown.

First-year male Similar to adult male but the upperpart plumage is considerably duller with only a faint gloss, although still retaining a bluish tinge. The feathers of the forehead, crown, lores, malar region, ear-coverts, mantle, scapulars, rump and back have prominent brownish fringes and tips. The rump feathers can also show buff-white fringes. The uppertail-coverts are bluish-black with brown tips.

The underparts from chin to undertail-coverts are similar to adult male except that they are suffused with buff and no part of the plumage is obviously white. The chin and throat are slightly paler than the breast but the demarcation is less obvious between chin and throat and the sides of the head and rest of the underparts, especially the breast, as in the adult male.

The remiges and rectrices, together with the alula, upperwing primary coverts and greater coverts, are unmoulted and dark brown, but show a faint gloss on the fringes of the outerwebs contrasting with the blacker, fresher-looking moulted feathers on the mantle and scapulars and the upperwing lesser and median coverts, which also have narrow brown fringes. The alula has pale buff-white tips and the primary coverts have buff-white fringes to the outerwebs and tips. The outermost upperwing greater coverts can show pale buff tips; the innermost merely have a tiny amount of white at their base. The secondaries show narrow greyish-white crescentic tips. The two outermost tertials show narrow white fringes to the outerwebs. The rectrices are slightly darker blackish-brown than the remiges. The outermost three pairs 06–04 also have buff-white tips of variable extent. One first-year male examined had the right-hand outermost tail feather (06) showing an almost completely white outerweb. The brown fringes to the feathers gradually wear away so that the plumage becomes increasingly similar to, but duller than, the adult male apart from the browner unmoulted flight feathers. Birds can still show some faint brown fringes close to the breeding season. A specimen collected in Myanmar [Burma] on 22 February (breeding April–May) still had brown fringes to the lower mantle and scapulars. The legs and feet are brown-black. The bill is black and the irides are dark brown.

Adult female in fresh plumage Forehead and crown are black with extensive rufous-brown fringes which obscure all but the centre of the feathers giving only a faint streaked appearance on the head. The darker centres become slightly more obvious as the plumage wears. The lores, malar region and ear-coverts are rufous-brown, contrasting with the white chin and throat, but are not darker than the crown. There is usually no supercilium. The mantle and scapulars are a warmer, marginally brighter brown faintly streaked with darker brown and with a slightly more chestnut tinge, especially on the lower mantle and scapulars, merging into the rich chestnut-brown of the back, rump and uppertail-coverts. The chin and throat are silky white, contrasting markedly with the greyish-buff breast and slightly paler belly. The flanks are also greyish-buff, but with a slightly more rufous tone. Some individuals can show a variable amount of bright chestnut on the rear flanks and thighs, almost merging with the uppertail-coverts. The undertail-coverts are buff-white. The tail is long, graduated and entirely dark brown. The outer pair of tail feathers (06) have indistinct narrow pale buff fringes to the outerwebs and tips. The remiges are dark brown and the outerwebs of the secondaries are narrowly fringed with dull chestnut but not sufficient to form a panel on the closed wing. The upperwing lesser, median and greater coverts are dark brown with chestnut-brown fringes and tips. The upperwing primary coverts are brown with pale buff fringes to the outerwebs and tips. The alula is slightly darker brown with chestnut fringes. The tertials are dark brown with broad chestnut fringes to the outerwebs and tips. One specimen examined had the largest tertial on the left wing entirely dull bluish-black on the outerweb and for 50% from the base of the innerweb. The underwing-coverts are grey–brown with paler buff fringes and the axillaries pale cinnamon-buff. The legs and feet are brown-black. The bill is black, the irides dark brown.

Juvenile Forehead, crown, mantle and scapulars are mid-brown. The forehead and crown have prominent narrow buff streaks in the centre of each feather. The mantle and scapulars have larger triangular buff tips. The overall impression is of mid-brown upperparts with much buff streaking and spotting. There is no supercilium and the ear-coverts are the same mid-brown as the crown, so there is no contrast between sides of head and crown. The ear-coverts have very fine buff streaks. The rump and uppertail-coverts are chestnut-brown contrasting with the dark brown tail. The chin and throat are buff, the rest of the underparts greyish-buff with no narrow darker brown fringes. The remiges are dark brown with buff fringes to the outerwebs. The upperwing lesser, median and greater coverts are brown with rufous-buff fringes and tips.

Measurements

	Male	Female
Wing	65.5–69.5 (mean 67.4)	65.0–67.5 (mean 66.2)
Tail	62.5–67.5 (mean 64.6)	61.0–65.0 (mean 62.9)
Bill	15.0–17.0 (mean 15.9)	15.0–16.5 (mean 15.5)

[Own measurements BMNH 2001]

DISTRIBUTION AND STATUS

Its range is given by Collar *et al.* (1994) as India, Bangladesh, Myanmar, Laos, Thailand, Vietnam and China. Its range has contracted greatly due to loss of habitat. Research of latest records show it is now found only in the extreme north-east of India, in Bangladesh where it has only been seen three times in the last 15 years and in Nepal most recent records come from the west of the country. In Laos and Thailand it is found in the north, principally along the Mekong River and tributaries. It is also still present in north and central Myanmar and in south-western China. There are no contemporary records for Vietnam or Cambodia.

The following is largely based on Duckworth (1997), who made a summary of published information – both historical and contemporary – relevant to population, distribution and habitat use. Other more contemporary records since Duckworth's review have also been included in this section.

In India it used to be common all over the Brahmaputra basin in thick vegetation (particularly grass hedges) along streams and wet ditches, and one of the commonest birds in Manipur, including the suburbs of the capital Imphal, although not seen in the hills (Hume 1888). It was very common in North Cachar in cold weather, with a few remaining to breed on the higher hills (Baker 1894–1901) and a common resident in the Khasia Hills and common in adjacent plains in cold weather, ascending above 900m in the breeding season from March onwards (Baker 1907). It was resident in parts of Upper Assam, occurring throughout the plains in the cold season (October–February) and confined to reed and grass adjacent to rivers (Stevens 1914–1915). It was described as an abundant breeder, laying eggs in April–May over vast plains of Sun or Thatch grass *Imperata arundinacea* on the north bank of the Brahmaputra in Lakhimpur district and also occurring right under the foothills in this district and in smaller numbers as far west as the grass plains in the north of Kamrup district and in some of the upland grass plains of the Chin Hills (Baker 1924).

It was particularly common in Assam, breeding in many places in Sibsagar and North Lakhimpur from February–April in grasslands and grassy riverine sandbanks flooded by Himalayan meltwater.

Today there are few records from the Indian subcontinent and most areas of long wet grassland in which the species was found have suffered continued degradation and modification (D. Allen *in litt.* 2000). More recently Duckworth states singles have been recorded over a period of several years in November, March and May in grass and reeds along river or channel banks in the Dibru-Saikhowa Wildlife Sanctuary (DSWS 27° 40´N 95° 24´E) in north-east Assam. Choudhury (1995, 1997) states it is an uncommon resident in the DSWS. This area is located on the flat floodplains of the Brahmaputra, Lohit and Dibru Rivers north-east of an area where Stevens (1914–1915) recorded it regularly. Kazmierczak & Allen (1997) found one in the Kolomi area of DSWS in 1996. In 1998 two pairs were present near Kolomi on 13 March (Hornbuckle *et al.* 1998). D. Allen (*in litt.* 2001) comments he saw "at least 6 males, probably many more" in March 1998, and adds that

> "we barely saw it at Kolomi in 1996 probably because our approach route from the south to the Kolomi lodge and then back south along the river missed the main area for it there, which seems to be just north of the lodge, along a river bank past where we had visited in 1996. At Kolomi in 1998 I would say they averaged every 100m along a reed-lined (probably *Phragmites*) river/ditch about 10m wide with low woodland backing the reeds. They didn't seem to be around in the forest itself or in shorter grassland areas. I conclude it is rather local at Kolomi and almost certainly prefers a distinct habitat".

Allen (1998) also visited the Amarpur area between 17–21 March 1998 well to the north of Kolomi and not part of DSWS but instead part of the wider Dibru-Saikhowa Biosphere Reserve (DSBR). Here he found "many" birds but not evenly distributed over the area. They were in similar habitat to Kolomi including "in clearings with reeds in woodland not apparently adjacent to open water, though not so far from it" (D. Allen *in litt.* 2001). It was also found to be "common in tall grass especially along watercourses". Allen noted that there appeared to be a male holding territory every hundred metres or so, just as in Kolomi. On 8 March 2001 K.D. Bishop encountered "similar numbers, mostly singing males, within 2–3m tall 'elephant grass' in the margin between river channels and low woodland at DSWS, both above and below Kolomi at an elevation of 96m a.s.l." (Bishop *in litt.* 2001).

There are only a few records from Kaziranga National Park (26° 32´N, 93° 00´E) in Assam and Barua & Sharma (1999) report it as being an occasional resident, being seen in small numbers in suitable habitats on only a few visits. This is despite the habitat still retaining extensive grassland which would appear to remain ideal for the species. In Bangladesh it is a rare winter visitor, with a single nineteenth-century record (Godwin-Austen 1870) followed by just three recent published records, all from the north-east – a male at Baroorah Tea Estate at Srimangal, February 1985; a female at exactly the same site, February 1986; and a male in extensive grassland at Bara Haor, 4 December 1992 (Thompson *et al.* 1993) – and one unpublished record of one in February 1992 in the wetland of Bara Beel close to the Sylhet–Tambil highway,

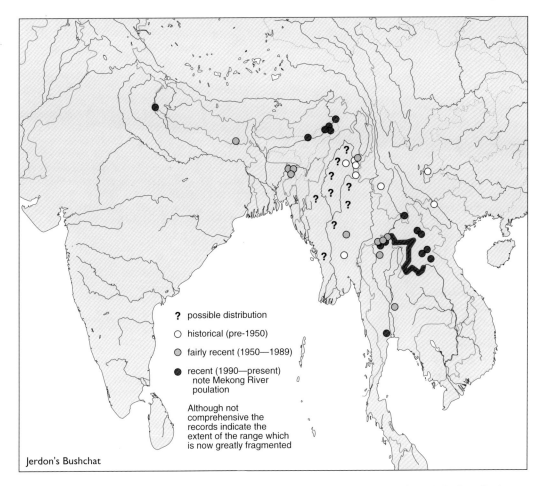

? possible distribution

○ historical (pre-1950)

◑ fairly recent (1950—1989)

● recent (1990—present)
   note Mekong River
   poulation

Although not
comprehensive the
records indicate the
extent of the range which
is now greatly fragmented

Jerdon's Bushchat

also in the north-east (Rashid *in litt.* 2001). The only records from Nepal, where it is described as a threatened species and a very rare and local breeding resident, come from areas of extensive grassland. In the east, birds were seen in May 1975 and June 1976 at Kosi Barrage (75m a.s.l.) (Inskipp & Inskipp 1991). All the most recent sightings are from Sukla Phanta (200m a.s.l.) in western Nepal. In May 1996 some singing males were discovered, with the largest number recorded in a day from this location being "less than a dozen" comprising both males and females. A male and female were also trapped there in May 1998. It is stated to be a resident breeding species at Sukla Phanta (Baral 1998).

In Laos it is only found in the north, the southernmost record to date being at Ban Thanasanghin between Vientiane and Sangthong in 1998. In uplands where its current status is uncertain it was found to be a common resident above 1,400m in Tranninh, especially at Ban Nonghet which is a high valley (1,500 m) dominated by rocks and tall herbs in place of the original forest and subject to frequent fires, frosts and fog (Delacour & Jabouille 1927, David-Beaulieu 1944). A specimen was obtained at 1,600m on Phou Khoum, a deforested mountain on the borders of Louangphabang [Luang Prabang] and Tranninh in 1943 (David-Beaulieu 1944). A breeding female was taken on 12 May 1929 at Ban Muangyo in the extreme north of Laos at 750m in an area of ricefields surrounded by good forest (Bangs & van Tyne 1931). More recent records from mid-altitude, deforested uplands (up to 28 February 1999) come from Nam Et National Biodiversity Conservation Area (NBCA); Phou Louey NBCA; Sangthong District and Nam Theun Extension (Duckworth *et al.* 1999).

In March 1996 Duckworth located a large, previously unknown lowland breeding population of 100–200 pairs in a complex of scrub-dominated islands in the channel of the mainstream Mekong River which separates Laos and Thailand, at Paksang, 60km upstream from Vientiane. A further discovery came from an island in the Mekong 2km downstream from the mouth of the Nam Ou where a male was found in low bushes on 1 April 1996 (W.G. Robichaud in Duckworth 1997). Despite thorough searches none was found in 1992–1996 on Don Chuan, a large island in the Mekong near Vientiane (Thewlis *et al.* 1998) or in an area of extensive sand with patches of bushland around Thadua some 25km downstream of Vientiane, despite a specific search for it on 10 April 1996 (R.J. Tizard & R.J. Timmins verbally to Duckworth 1997) Duckworth observes that the species is so conspicuous in this river channel habitat during the breeding season that if it is present it is certain to be noticed. D. Allen (*in litt.* 2001) suggests it can be very local and is easily missed at distances of 100m or so from the right area. This happened in Thailand, where surveys of the banks of the Mekong without covering the actual river channel gave a false impression of its scarcity (J.W. Duckworth *in litt.* 2001).

A combined boat and land-based survey of the Upper Lao Mekong, Xiangkhouang province, and the Mekong in Vientiane municipality, in November–January and April from 1998–2000 (Duckworth *et al.* unpublished 2001) confirmed that observers had been looking for this species in the wrong places and at the wrong times, and rather than being a scarce species it was abundant in the right habitat, which was right in the river channel itself rather than on the associated floodplains. In northern Laos on the Upper Lao Mekong it is locally abundant wherever channel habitat is suitable in the Mekong upstream of Vientiane to beyond the Burma [Myanmar]–Thai border, and is present in good numbers in both the winter and non-breeding months as well as April and the rest of the breeding season, although more difficult to detect in the former. The areas supporting the highest numbers appeared to be where there were wide stands (not simply narrow bands) of rocky bushland.

The following is the list of records from ground-based observations in Laos 1998–2000 (Duckworth *et al.* Unpublished 2001). Note the increased observation of birds in April as they become less skulking and perch more prominently.

Upper Lao Mekong
(River channel habitat)
30 December 1999 Ban Namgniou (20° 22´N, 100° 22´E): four single males, one in bushland and three in tall grass growing beside the channel.
9 April 2000 Ban Namgniou: 24 males minimum with up to five males and one female visible at one time.
1 January 2000 Ban Khonkeo (20° 1´N, 100° 24´E): two single males and two unsexed individuals calling in response to a male in view.
6 April 2000 Ban Khonkeo: seven males (some singing).
2 January 2000 Ban Namgon-Kao (20° 25´N, 100° 20´E): one male.
29 January 1999 between Louangphabang and Pak Ou (19° 03´N, 102° 13´E): four males.
21–22 April 2000 Pakchom sandbar (18° 02´N, 101° 52´E): between Ban Vang (18° 03´N, 101° 51´E) and Don Chan (18° 11´N, 102° 03´E): c.ten pairs, some with fledged young in *Homonoia* scrub.

Vientiane
15 November 1998: Ban Thanasanghin (18° 05´N, 102° 18´E): one male in *Homonoia riparia* (this represents the furthest downstream evidence of its presence).

In other habitat apart from river channel

Xaisomboun
13 November 1999: Muang Xaisomboun (18° 54´N, 103° 06´E): one male in a dry, scrubby valley just north of the town with extensive hill grassland rising up to 1,250m.

Xiangkhouang Province
19 April 2000 on Phou Gnouan (c.1,700m) (19° 25´N, 103° 18´E): one male in *hai* (areas left fallow after a few years of growing dryland rice).

The Upper Lao Mekong was counted in 15 stretches by a combination of boat and land-based observations between Ban Xiangkhok and Louangphabang, and boat-based observations from Paklay to Vientiane ranging from 17.5km to 103.5km. From observations made from two boat trips in winter (27 December–8 January 2000) and in spring (April 7–11 2000) it was apparent that many individuals were being overlooked from the boat surveys, as shown by only two individuals being counted from the major population known to exist at Sangthong. If it is assumed that similar proportions of birds are present throughout the length of river surveyed, the population in the Paklay to Sangthong stretch and in some parts of the far north can be assumed to be very large (Duckworth 1997). There is also some suitable habitat downstream between Sangthong and Vientiane, and the southernmost record in Laos is of an individual found before the breeding season at Ban Thanasanghin (see above).

Vietnam has only two old records, both from hilly areas of Tonkin in the north, the first at Lao Kay (Kuroda 1917) and the second at 1,300m in a mainly deforested area at Pakha (Delacour 1930). There are no records from Cambodia and recent surveys in the breeding season of typical rocky bushland habitat, for example in the Mekong channel in the north, did not find the species. Hill scrub in Cambodia has not been surveyed for it, however, so it is not known whether it occurs in such areas although this seems unlikely if it is not found in its favoured river channel habitat.

Its skulking nature outside the breeding season, and the fact that it was being sought in the wrong areas and at the wrong times, undoubtedly created a false impression of scarcity in Thailand, where it was considered to occur only in the north, possibly extending down to some central areas, and was judged to be very scarce, inhabiting tall grass in riverine floodplains. It is now known to be much more abundant than was previously thought.

Two very encouraging discoveries of populations of this species have been made in Thailand. The first is the Mekong mainstream channel population discovered by Duckworth on the Laos side but extending into Thailand, and the second concerns a few birds in the uplands in Nan province. A record already existed of a single bird from Doi Ang Khang in Fang district on 6 February 1985 (J.R. Howes per P.D. Round *in litt.* 2000), but at the time this was discounted by Round as he was unaware of upland records from elsewhere. He is now of the opinion that it is probably a valid record even though the species has not been recorded in that locality again, since elsewhere in the uplands of Nan province there are records of a male from Doi Phu Kha on 2 January 1994 (Suthee Supparatvikorn *et al.* per P.D. Round *in litt.* 2000) and a male on 27–28 December 1997 at Pu Chee Fa, on the border with Chiang Rai province (Kampol Sukhumalind *et al.* per P.D. Round *in litt.* 2000). More recently, on 21 April 2000 several pairs including one with fledged young were discovered on the Mekong River sandbanks of Loei province, which marks an extension of its known range into the north-western part of north-east Thailand. This record is the same as the Pakchom sandbar record quoted above for Laos (Duckworth *et al.* 2001).

In the 1960s two males and two females on 23–25 January 1965, as well as two other females on 23 and 24 January 1965, were trapped in "tall grass and secondary growth" by B. King at 400m, 30km south-east of Chiang Saen, virtually on the banks of the Mekong in Chiang Rai province. In Chiang Mai near the Myanmar [Burma] border, 4km north-east of Fang, two males and one unsexed individual were collected on 18 and 24 December 1965, 500m or so from the Fang River, which is a tributary of the Kok River (P.D. Round *in litt.* 2001). There have also been a lot of sightings over the years around Tha Ton and Chiang Saen in the far north of Thailand but never more than two males at Tha Ton and two males and one female at Chiang Saen. J.N. Dymond (*in litt.* to Duckworth 1997) saw the species at Chiang Saen where a maximum of three at any one time were present. All the birds recorded in these areas were in a narrow belt of tall riverside grass containing a few thorny bushes or in similar habitat around the margins of cultivation such as tobacco. This was probably less favoured habitat because the channel bushland in this area has few rocks; but as this was one of the areas on the Thai side of the Mekong favoured for observations it also resulted in a false impression of scarcity.

P.D. Round considered that there could be birds inhabiting the mainstream Mekong River downstream of Chiang Saen, between Chiang Saen and Chiang Khong and probably elsewhere, and so it has proved with the surveys of 1996 and 1998–2000 (Duckworth 1997, Duckworth *et al.* 2001). A single male was observed at Mae Chan on 5 November 1981 (R.S.E. Swanqvist per P.D. Round *in litt.* 2000). Round also considered, despite a lack of any definite records, that this species would have occurred south of Chiang Mai along the floodplain of the Ping River south to at least where it passes by the foot of Doi Inthanon. The localities known to Round in 1990–1991 were all located in the floodplains: Chiang Saen on the Mekong River in Chiang Rai province near the common border with Laos and Myanmar [Burma]; Tha Ton, in the north of Chiang Mai province, on the Kok River (a tributary of the Mekong) and nearby at Fang district on the border with Myanmar [Burma] (see below). There is a record of a single male from Mae Taeng, where the Mae Taeng River flows into the Ping about 39km north of Chiang Mai, on 18 October 1981 but no birds have been seen at this locality since (P.D. Round *in litt.* 2000). There is also an exceptional record of a single bird which was also found in reeds at Bung Boraphet, Nakhon Sawan province, central Thailand, on 28 August 1984 and was still present on 30 September, 12 December and 13 January 1985 (D. Ogle *in litt.* to Round). The species has also recently been recorded in early May 2001 from Kaeng Krachan National Park south-west of Bangkok (T. Tarrant *in litt.* 2001).

Populations in Thailand are considered to have declined owing to drainage, clearance and burning of reedbeds for agricultural purposes (Round 1988). Conversion of suitable habitat to grazing could also be a factor (D. Allen *in litt.* 2000). Round considered that owing to agricultural intensification Thailand would be likely to lose the populations on the floodplains and on cultivable river margins, as cultivators follow the retreating riverwater down and plant vegetables and tobacco on the banks. However, these judgements were made before the populations were found in the Mekong channel. Round's concern over the loss of floodplain grassland populations may be unwarranted if the records in question prove to represent marginal usage by the nearby river channel breeders rather than relics of floodplain populations (J.W. Duckworth *in litt.* 2001). The spread of *Mimosa pudica* could also be a problem for this species as it readily invades these disturbed habitats and also the favoured river channel habitat, preventing any other plant species becoming established. Although many species of bird frequent *Mimosa* neither Round nor Duckworth has seen Jerdon's Bushchat utilising it.

The main hope for this species in South-East Asia, according to Round, has to be the *Homonoia* scrub on the rocky uncultivated areas in the mid-channel of the Mekong River. Duckworth (*in litt.* 2001) makes the observation that so long as the river is wide enough to allow the habitat to be two-dimensional – i.e. rocks and bushland – then this species can also occur quite close to the banks. It is important to note that because of the rocks the habitat is probably uncultivable and thus less liable to disturbance.

Round was unable to say, owing to lack of evidence, whether in Thailand there are really significant numbers in the deforested uplands. Duckworth *in litt.* (2001) considers it reasonable to assume there are, as he considers there are significant upland populations in Laos and there are still vast areas of northern Laos and northern Thailand that are virtually ornithologically untouched.

In Myanmar, Smythies (1986) found it a local bird of the plains from Myitkyina and the Upper Chindwin through central to southern Myanmar. In lower (southern) Myanmar Stanford & Ticehurst (1935) collected only one in three years. This specimen was inhabiting *kaing* grass in Leikchuang and they agreed with Oates that it was extremely rare in that part of the country. It has been found in the north in high *kaing* grass at Sahmaw and Ayeindama, at Sinbo and Mogaung on the Irrawaddy River and on the western edge of the Indawgyi Lake where about a dozen males were seen in early February (Stanford & Ticehurst 1938). It bred in long grass and briars in Bhamo in the Irrawaddy Valley in the north during April–May (Harington 1905, 1909). Historically there has been controversy over its status in the country. Stanford & Ticehurst (1938) noted that the *Fauna* gave its distribution as the majority of the Chin Hills, Kachin Hills and the lower hills of central Myanmar to Prome but stating that this contradicted the records which showed it only occurred in vast grass plains at low altitudes. Blanford (1870) found it in elephant grass in the Irrawaddy Valley and Wickham (1929–1930) found it nowhere else. Oates (1883) considered it a rare resident. From 1973 to 1982 three January–February visits recorded up to nine in the reeds surrounding Inle Lake (King 1983). It still appears to be relatively common in this location (ten birds seen in one day) inhabiting 3–4m high reeds at the lake's edge and in the huge floating mass of reeds on the lake. Birds were observed feeding in areas of aquatic crops and floating vegetable gardens in this mass (F.R. Lambert in Duckworth 1997).

In China it is a rare resident (Cheng Tso-hsin 1987). There are a few records from Yunnan province where it is stated to be resident in the west (Meyer de Schauensee 1984). A male was seen along the Namting River in February 1917 (Rothschild 1926), four specimens were collected in Luxi and Gengma counties during the 1960s, and a few sightings were made in Menglun, Xishuangbanna, in April 1994 (Han Lianxian in Duckworth 1997).

In general, records from throughout its range indicate that Jerdon's Bushchat is irregular and somewhat localised in occurrence. There are areas where it is locally abundant separated by extensive tracts where it is scarce or absent. Its skulking habits outside the breeding season, and the lack of detailed ornithological surveys in many areas of the countries it is known to inhabit, suggest that there may be considerably more populations waiting to be discovered. The surveys of the Mekong River and its eastern tributaries have revealed larger-than-thought populations and significant populations are probably due to be found in mid-altitude and upland scrub habitat.

HABITAT

Baker (1933) gave information for Assam stating it bred in many places from Sibsagar and North Lakimpur from February–April extending onto upland grass plains and foothills to 700m.

In Laos the situation is still confused since several different sorts of habitat appear to be used with little in common between them. Jerdon's Bushchat not only utilises primary river channel scrub along the lowland Mekong River but also nests in mid- and high-altitude secondary scrub and tall grassland (especially stands of *Imperata* and *Saccharum*) subject to annual burning (Duckworth *et al.* 1999 & unpublished 2001). Historical records indicate that in the breeding season at least it was found at higher elevations (1,650 m) on grassland plains and fallow ricefields (*hai*), and there is at least one contemporary record from Laos in this habitat: one bird was located in an area of *hai* in a vegetated gully at 1,700m in 1999 (see above). It may be that more birds frequent this habitat, which is extensive throughout Laos, as this record was only from a casual survey and little other investigation has been done. A similar situation may also apply to northern Thailand (J.W. Duckworth *in litt.* 2001). Generally most contemporary and historical records appear to indicate a preference for areas of tall grass, reeds, scrub and low bushes, often near, or almost surrounded by, water of various sorts such as large rivers, lakes, ricefields, wet ditches, irrigation channels and other watercourses.

A large population breeds in river island scrub on the upper reaches of the Mekong River in Laos when the river was at its annual low flow and further surveys in 1999–2000 (Duckworth *et al.* 2001 unpublished) revealed it to be particularly abundant in this habitat on the upper reaches of the Mekong. This is of great importance given the current paucity of contemporary records from the rest of the species' range and known habitats. The habitat described by Duckworth was a rich mosaic comprising a variety of sedimentary islands and bars of mainly sand, silt and gravel extending from the banks amid extensive rocky outcrops from the riverbed. Much of this sedimentary plain exposed in the channel by the low water levels during the dry season supports a dense willow-like scrubland, composed of a few woody species (identified through P.D. Round and T. Evans as predominantly *Homonoia riparia* [Euphorbiaciae]) growing no higher than 2–3m. These bushes are submerged by high flows of water from mid-July to mid-October, after which the water levels drop, being at their lowest in April. Two main islands remain at the peak flow of water, Don Nou, which has extensive scrubland, and Don Sadok, which also has extensive areas of rank grassland but also in places groups of mature trees on its downstream half which lie above all but the most exceptionally high water levels. Jerdon's Bushchats were found breeding abundantly in the dense scrubland in March and April when the water levels were lowest whilst in June–July when habitat was much more restricted owing to rising water levels, smaller numbers of birds were still present in the island's scrubland with one bird in grassland. No birds were seen in the extensive areas of trees, bare rock or sediment on the islands, up the Nam Sang River, or in the dryland habitats adjacent to the Mekong channel.

In Nepal the species is stated to be partial to *Phragmites* and *Saccharum arundinaceum* marshes (H.S. Baral *in litt.* 2000). In Bangladesh one was seen in grassland associated with freshwater wetlands (S.M.A. Rashid *in litt.* 2001). In southern Myanmar Smythies (1986) describes it as a bird of the high *kaing* grass (land in a riverbed exposed in the dry season and often cultivated during the dry season) and *thetke* areas of the plains, especially of the drainage area of the Myitmaka. In the north, it also showed a distinct preference for *yezi* (wild briar *Rosa bracteata* or now possibly known as River Sandbar Rose *Rosa tonkinensis*) found growing on sandy islands in the larger river valleys, and could almost be guaranteed to be found in such habitat (Stanford & Ticehurst 1938). A female was observed by Roseveare (1950) perching on rushes on 4 August 1935 at Paunglin Lake in Minbu district in north-eastern Myanmar.

BREEDING

The breeding season is March–May in Thailand, April–May in Myanmar (one nest discovered in Myanmar on 21 May), and February–May in India. However, Baker (1924) thought that it did not commence laying eggs in India until early April and continued to the end of May, with most eggs being laid in the last week of April. In Laos, as in Thailand, it breeds from March to May on the Mekong River (low river-flow season) with some evidence that more extreme northern populations commence establishing territories later than those further south. In winter birds were perching prominently downstream of Paklay throughout the day but at Bokeo none was seen from boat surveys. On land it was also apparent that males were not singing or perching prominently. The breeding season would also appear to be the same for individual breeding in mid-altitude scrubland (J.W. Duckworth *in litt.* 2001).

The nest is usually on the ground among the roots of a grass tuft or in a hollow in a bank or ditch. It is a compact, well-built and stout little structure made up of rootlets, grasses and other fibrous materials, with the cup lined with finer grasses or feathers (Smythies 1986). Baker states "the nest is very hard to find being tucked away amongst the roots of the grass and quite invisible until these are torn apart." Incubation is only by the female. The incubation period is unknown but is likely to be around 13–14 days. The number of eggs in a clutch is usually four, sometimes three (Baker 1924). Smythies (1986) states the clutch is usually 3–4, rarely two. The eggs are slightly glossed and are a deep turquoise, similar to Hedge Accentor *Prunella modularis* and usually unmarked. Very occasionally they have a very faint ring of brownish-red freckling around the larger end. Mean size of 30 eggs was 16.2 x 13.2mm (maximum 18.0 x 13.6mm, minimum 15.2 x 12.4mm) (Baker 1924).

There is no information on nestlings, how long they remain in the nest, their behaviour once they leave the nest or the relationship with their parents. It is also not known if this species rears more than one brood per year, although in the Mekong River channel this would be unlikely (J.W. Duckworth *in litt.* 2001).

VOICE

Males in north-east India were described as singing a clear thrush-like song of two or three syllables followed by a trill rendered as *swee swoo swoo* (rapid trill) (Allen 1998). Duckworth (1997) described the song of birds heard in March in Laos as a thin warble similar to that of a *Sylvia* warbler but without any harsh or churring notes. Song recorded by Round at Paksang on the Mekong in northern Thailand was a short, slightly energetic warble *swee sweedle-ee*, again somewhat reminiscent of *Sylvia* warbler but purer and less throaty. It is delivered in a slightly hurried fashion on a descending scale with a rising inflection at the end. It consisted of around six thin but clear notes usually without any slurring, with the first two being particularly clear, although there was some variation in the song, presumably from different males (three were present), and some of the later notes in some songs were slightly slurred or trilled. Occasionally the pure and slurred notes were varied in sequence. This short song was repeated over and over. In northern Thailand (Chiang Saen) from December to February (outside of the breeding season) no song was heard from birds present in the area, although many pre-roosting calls were heard (J.N. Dymond in Duckworth 1997). Upstream of Paksang on the Thai side of the Mekong River on 21 April 2000 (in the breeding season) at least three males were singing from exposed perches at around 18:00hrs (P.D. Round *in litt.* 2000). Singing can continue all day, even in the searing heat of midday (J.W. Duckworth *in litt.* 2001).

The most frequent call is a plaintive, loud, single *heeeeew*. This call is also given pre-roosting outside of the breeding season (J.W. Duckworth *in litt.* 2001). Lekagul & Round (1991) describe this call and add that it is higher-pitched than other chats. A single, swearing rasp note, similar to fingers being run rapidly over the teeth of a comb, is also given. Recordings on 21 April 2000 in northern Thailand showed males giving a two-note alarm call. The first note was the rasping swearing note, *tchzzt*, followed immediately by a short pure single whistle *psweeeh* rising at the end. These notes were repeated over and over alternately *tchzzt psweeeh, tchzzt psweeeh, tchzzt psweeeh*. Females also give these calls and juveniles were heard to give the rasping *tchzzt* call (P.D. Round *in litt.* 2000). Outside the breeding season Jerdon's Bushchat is described as generally silent but the male sometimes utters a low *chit-churr chit-churr* and a *chirr* alarm note, at the same time usually flirting its expanded tail (Baker 1924, Smythies 1986); these notes are evidently the same as those described above from breeding birds.

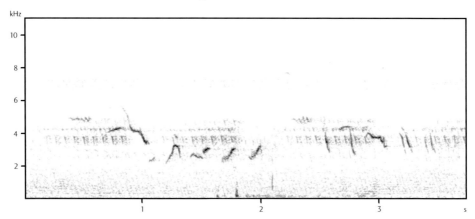

Jerdon's Bushchat *Saxicola jerdoni* NSA 100524. Song. Assam, India, 2000. *C. Robson.*

FOOD

There is no information beyond "insects" (Ali & Ripley 1968–1998).

MOVEMENTS

In Bangladesh Jerdon's Bushchat is described as a rare winter visitor and in Nepal as a very rare and local breeding visitor, but for most parts of both its lowland and upland range it is not known for sure what its movements are, as the majority of records are incidental, with no year-round checking for the species. It was, however, historically recorded to be subject to local altitudinal movements in India, moving down to the plains in winter but ascending above 900m in the breeding season, and it was also reported to make similar altitudinal movements in Myanmar. It may also make local movements owing to temporary but regular changes to its habitat such as flooding. In Laos when the Mekong River floods each year, it was not found in adjacent dry vegetation at Paksang and it is not really known where the populations of birds found along the Mekong go in the time of high water flow. Duckworth (1997) speculated that they might make short local movements to some other natural scrubland habitat or possibly just become more skulking.

BEHAVIOUR

At Amarpur in north-east India a survey in 17–21 March 1998 found singing males perched 2–3m up near the top of *Phragmites* stems. Females were far more skulking and rarely seen (Allen 1998). At Paksang in Laos on 13 March males were found singing from sprays of vegetation projecting above the general bushland cover. They also spent much time on similar perches in complete silence. After a bout of singing they frequently dived to the base of an adjacent bush. During a five-hour (08:00–13:00hrs) visit on 13 March, song continued intermittently but at high levels throughout. The closest singing males were 30m apart. Follow-up visits on 22 June and 15 July found no males singing. Males were observed as close as 6m apart without any sign of aggression and they continued to spend much time perched prominently at the tip of projecting twigs and grasses (Duckworth 1997). Although males were highly visible females were much harder to observe on all visits and are perhaps more skulking in behaviour both inside and outside the breeding season. It is also possible that males become more skulking outside the breeding season from July to February. In northern Thailand in late April males were only observed singing from exposed perches. Occasionally they would fly c.4m up into the air and return to their perch in between each song, but it was thought this was not part of a song-display but more likely a feeding manoeuvre. Birds observed in January–February were very skulking (P.D. Round *in litt.* 2000).

Ali & Ripley (1968–1998) mention that it is found singly or in pairs and is usually very shy. They describe it as perching on reed stems or bushes and then darting to the ground to seize insects, sometimes foraging at the base of clumps of grass and reeds. Baker (1924) states that it is not so agile on the wing as other members of its genus but is relatively more agile when searching for food on the ground. Most of its prey is taken by short flights from a perch on top of a bush or a tall reed, sometimes clinging to the lower parts of reeds before flying to the ground to seize prey. It also regularly hunts prey at ground level amongst the bottoms of reeds and grasses similar to babblers Timaliinae and unlike other *Saxicola*. The tail is constantly expanded and flirted. It is stated to be less active on the wing than Siberian Stonechat *S. maura* (Grimmett *et al.* 1998). Its flight is described as direct and strong, but usually it does not fly far (Baker 1924).

MOULT

Little information. An examination of specimens in BMNH suggest that this species has a moult sequence similar to Siberian Stonechat, with a juvenile plumage which is partially moulted into first-adult after a few months. This plumage is then retained until after the following breeding season, when the bird undergoes its first complete post-breeding moult. Breeding adults also undergo a full post-breeding moult and breeding plumage is acquired by wear to the feathers and not by a pre-breeding moult as in Whinchat *S. rubetra*. There is no information on timing of moult and length of time taken to complete it. Presumably it would occur on or shortly after the cessation of breeding as with other members of the genus.

CONSERVATION

Under IUCN criteria Jerdon's Bushchat is listed as Near-Threatened (Collar *et al.* 1994). The discoveries of large populations on the Laos–Thailand border along the Mekong River by Duckworth *et al.* (2001) suggest that its conservation status, in Laos at least, should now be revised to Not at Risk (Duckworth *et al.* 1999).

In Laos it is not considered under immediate threat as it is locally present in large numbers and is found in two different habitats, although changes in the sediment-flow dynamics of the Mekong River could be detrimental, as the scrubland frequented by this species in the Mekong grows on river-borne sediment. If substantial quantities of sediment are removed from the river or trapped by barriers, water with an unnaturally low sediment load will just wash away, without replenishment, the sand and silt deposits downstream. Intensive extraction of sediment by the human population since 1994 has caused a major shrinkage of one large island downstream from Vientiane and similar extraction has taken place upstream of Vientiane, half-way to Paksang, where this species was discovered breeding in 1996. Actual extraction at Paksang is unlikely owing to the rocky outcrops. However, if extraction occurred upstream of Paksang it would have a detrimental effect on the important and recently discovered population breeding in the Paksang region. Further potential threat comes from a plan for a chain of cross-Mekong hydropower dams which would seriously disrupt the ecology of the entire basin as well as the sediment flow (Duckworth 1997). Similar points apply to the whole stretch upstream from Sangthong to beyond the Myanmar–Thailand border. Duckworth *in litt.* (2001) is less worried about these threats now that he has established how extensive the population of this species is and knowing how much sediment is present in the long stretch of river referred to above. He considers it inconceivable that a significant proportion of the species could be wiped out by extraction, especially if the increased sediment burden in the Mekong caused by rampant deforestation in its upper catchment area is taken into account.

GREY BUSHCHAT
Saxicola ferrea

Plate 13

Saxicola ferrea Gray, 1846, *Cat. Mamm. Birds Nepal, Thibet*, pp.71,153—Nepal

Oreicola ferrea haringtoni [= *Saxicola ferrea haringtoni*] Hartert, 1910, *Vög. pal. Fauna*, p. 711—Lien-kiang, near Fu-tschau [Foochow], China.

Etymology *ferrea* derived from Latin *ferreus* meaning iron grey

Alternative name Dark-grey Bushchat

TAXONOMY

Monotypic. Despite Hartert's description of an eastern subspecies *S. f. haringtoni* and its acceptance by Baker (1924) and Vaurie (1959), most taxonomists and ornithologists have considered the Grey Bushchat monotypic. Kinnear (1934), Stresemann (1940), Mayr (1941), Ripley *et al.* (1964) and Ali & Ripley (1968–1998) all rejected Hartert's subspecies, and Stanford & Ticehurst (1938) and MacKinnon & Phillipps (2000) regarded it as doubtful.

Indeed, the justification for *S. f. haringtoni* is weak and, despite his acceptance of it, Vaurie (1959) observed that the species is strongly clinal. Hartert's chief character for *haringtoni* was the difference in the length of the tail, but Baker (1924) pointed out that the tails of *S. f. ferrea* and *S. f. haringtoni* measured 55–60mm and 51–63mm respectively! However, Baker found that male *S. f. haringtoni* had whiter underparts in worn plumage. According to Vaurie (1959) male *S. f. haringtoni* differs from the nominate in fresh plumage by being darker below and less grey/more ferruginous above. In worn plumage males are not so white below. Females are more rufous-brown above, generally darker (distinctly so on the breast, flanks, thighs, belly and undertail-coverts), and on average very slightly smaller than the nominate.

Female specimens in BMNH display these differences in the underparts, with the breast of *S. f. haringtoni* showing a marginally darker shade of grey and the flanks, thighs, belly and undertail-coverts having a definite chestnut tinge to the overall buff colouring; but they do not support the view that female *S. f. haringtoni* is more rufous-brown above. Additionally, worn male specimens in BMNH support the view of Baker (1924), who said worn male *S. f. haringtoni* were whiter below, rather than Vaurie (1959), who said they are not so white. Vaurie was however correct in stating that male *S. f. haringtoni* in fresh plumage had darker underparts, although the differences between specimens of the two races in BMNH were marginal and not consistent. Saha & Datta (1979) examined recently taken specimens from Kashmir, Bhutan and Assam and strongly asserted the validity of *S. f. haringtoni*. In addition to the criteria mentioned above they noted that males of nominate *ferrea* had the outer web of the outermost tail feather (06), including the basal two-thirds of the shaft, white, contrasting with *haringtoni* in which the same area (apart from the extreme tip) was sepia and on its outer web a "brownish-grey line runs between the shaft and the marginal white". They also stated that the rufous-brown of the female's uppertail-coverts and the outer fringe of the basal 50% of the tail feathers is a deeper (almost cinnamon-) brown in *haringtoni*.

IDENTIFICATION

Size 15cm/5.9 inches. Sexually dimorphic. Larger and with longer tail than Siberian Stonechat *Saxicola maura*. Structurally very similar to Jerdon's Bushchat *S. jerdoni* but with a tail less graduated and slightly shorter in proportion to the body. The adult male in fresh plumage is ash-grey on the head and upperparts with indistinct black streaking. It has a long broad white supercilium and white chin and throat which contrast with the black ear-coverts. The underparts are predominantly white to buff-white with a distinct grey suffusion on the breast and flanks. The wings and tail are dark brown/black with a small white patch on the inner upperwing and white fringes to the outer webs of the outer tail feathers. The female is rufous-brown on the head and mantle, slightly streaked with darker brownish-black. There is a prominent long buff supercilium and white chin and throat which contrast with the dark rufous ear-coverts. The dark ear-coverts contrast with the paler brown on the rest of the head (in *S. jerdoni* they are uniform with the rest of the head). The rump, uppertail-coverts and outer webs of the tail feathers are bright chestnut-brown. The underparts are mainly buff-white with a greyish-white breast and slightly rufous undertail-coverts. Birds in juvenile plumage can be sexed on plumage differences.

Confusion species See under Jerdon's Bushchat.

DESCRIPTION

Adult male In fresh plumage the feathers of the forehead, crown and nape are black with long ash-grey fringes which obscure all but the black centres of the feathers, creating a streaked effect on the head. The neck, mantle and scapulars are similar but the ash-grey fringes are even longer, thus obscuring most of the black and making the black streaking indistinct. The back is predominantly grey with virtually no black markings. The rump is unmarked ash-grey and the uppertail-coverts black with pale grey fringes and tips. In very fresh plumage the extreme tips of the uppertail-coverts are occasionally brownish-olive and the ash-grey of the upperparts is suffused with a distinct olive caste caused by narrow olive-brown fringes to the extreme ends of the feathers. The lores, malar region, ear-coverts and foreneck are glossy black. There is a prominent white supercilium extending from the bill over the eye to the rear of the ear-coverts and slightly onto the nape. The supercilia do not meet on the nape but almost meet on the forehead. The chin and throat are pure white. The breast and flanks are pale grey. The belly, ventral area and undertail-coverts are buff-white. In very fresh plumage the grey on the underparts is sometimes suffused with cinnamon. The tail is black but with very narrow bluish-grey fringes to the white outer edges. There are prominent white edges to the outer webs of all the rectrices apart from the central pair (01). The white on the outer webs extends the whole length of all the tail feathers apart from the innermost two pairs (01–02) where it does not reach the tip. The outer web of the outermost feather (06) is entirely white. The outermost three pairs of tail feathers (06–04) also have white tips which extend marginally as a fringe onto the extreme distal part of the inner web. The remiges are black with pale buff to grey-white fringes on the outer webs, especially on the secondaries. The pale fringes to the inner secondaries combine with similar fringes on the tertials to form a pale panel on the closed wing. The secondaries and primaries have pale buff-white crescentic tips in fresh plumage. The innermost tertial is black with the basal c.25% white, and the outer web has a greyish-white fringe and tip. The remaining two tertials are black with the outer fringes and tips grey-buff. The upperwing lesser coverts are black with pale blue-grey fringes to the outer webs. The outer upperwing median coverts are black with pale blue-grey fringes and the inner ones are white with narrow indistinct pale grey fringes. The upperwing greater coverts are black with indistinct pale grey fringes. The innermost upperwing greater covert is all white apart from a narrow indistinct grey fringe to the outer web. The alula is dark blue-grey with greyish-white fringes to the outer webs and slightly buff tips. The upperwing primary coverts are blue-grey with crescentic white tips. The underwing-coverts are dark grey with extensive buff-white tips. The axillaries are dark grey with extensive white fringes.

In worn plumage a large proportion of the grey fringes are lost, leaving the bird predominantly black on the head and the remaining upperparts with only variable but small grey tips to the feathers. The supercilium extends to the sides of the nape and is slightly more defined and prominent. The mantle and scapulars tend to retain more grey tips to the feathers and be less pure black than the head, appearing distinctly more streaked. The rump becomes purer grey and the grey tips to the uppertail-coverts wear away to leave these black. The pale fringes to the tertials also disappear. The pale tips to the primaries and secondaries wear away to leave these dull black. The tail is black losing the blue-grey fringes but retains the white edges to the outer webs. The upperwing-coverts become entirely black apart from the lesser coverts, primary coverts and alula, which retain small grey tips. The underparts also become whiter although the grey suffusion on the breast remains but to a lesser and variable extent than in fresh plumage.

The legs, feet and bill are black. The irides are dark brown.

First-year male Very similar to adult male. The supercilium is not so extensive and usually does not reach onto the sides of the nape. In worn plumage before its first post-breeding moult the head and upper mantle are usually more extensively grey and do not show so much black. The retained and therefore more worn and browner remiges, upperwing primary coverts, alula and outer greater coverts usually contrast with those upperwing lesser, median and inner greater coverts which have been moulted and are blacker. There is a very small amount of white on the inner web of the innermost upperwing median covert and also on the inner web of the innermost upperwing greater covert. The rectrices are also a dull brown, showing more contrast with the black uppertail-coverts, and the white edges to the outer webs of the rectrices are narrower and less distinct than in the adult male.

Adult female Forehead, crown, nape, mantle and scapulars are rufous-brown with faint dark brown triangular feather centres giving a slightly streaked appearance on the head and upper mantle. In very fresh plumage there is a greyish wash to the brown upperparts caused by the extreme tips of the feathers being pale grey (these gradually wear away). The lower mantle does not become brighter nearer the rump as in *S. jerdoni*. The rump and uppertail-coverts are a rich unstreaked chestnut with this colouring extending onto the outer webs of the rectrices.

The lores, malar region and ear-coverts are rufous-brown with the ear-coverts a darker, richer rufous contrasting with the paler brown forehead, crown and nape. There is a long, prominent buff to greyish-white supercilium extending from the bill to the rear of the ear-coverts. The chin and throat are white with a slight buff tinge extending slightly onto the foreneck. The breast is distinctly greyish-buff contrasting with the belly, ventral area and undertail-coverts, which are yellowish-buff. The flanks are buff with a definite chestnut tint on the rear flanks similar to, but not as strong in tone, as that in *S. jerdoni*.

The central pair of tail feathers (01) are dark brown with a narrow chestnut fringe to the outer webs. The remaining feathers (02–06) are entirely chestnut on the outer web and pale brown on the inner web apart from the outermost pair (06) which have the outer web entirely pale buff and the inner web pale brown. When the tail is closed it appears dark brown with prominent rich chestnut edging. The tips of the tail feathers are marginally paler brown. The remiges are dark brown with very narrow pale buff fringes to the outer webs and crescentic off-white tips. The tertials are dark brown with broad rufous-brown fringes to the outer webs and pale buff tips. The upperwing primary coverts are dark brown with narrow greyish-white fringes to the outer webs and pale buff tips. The alula is dark brown with grey-white fringes to the outer webs. The upperwing lesser, median and greater coverts are black-brown with large pale rufous-brown tips and narrower pale rufous fringes to the outer webs. The innermost upperwing median and greater coverts show slightly paler buff tips. The underwing-coverts are greyish-white with extensive buff fringes and tips. The axillaries are buff. The legs, feet and bill are black-brown. The irides are dark brown.

There is a leucistic female specimen in BMNH collected at Myitkyina in north-east Myanmar on 21 December 1934. The entire plumage is an overall creamy-white apart from the head, mantle, back and upperwing-coverts, which are pale greyish-buff. The rump, uppertail-coverts and outer webs of the tail feathers are very pale chestnut. The breast and rest of the underparts, together with the remiges and rectrices, are creamy-white. The bill, legs and feet are dark brown.

Females of the race *S. f. haringtoni* are marginally separable from *S. f. ferrea* but not under field conditions. Males of the race *S. f. haringtoni* are marginally separable on the colour of the underparts in both fresh and worn plumage but not under field conditions. (For differences on male and female of *S. f. ferrea* and *S. f. haringtoni* see under Taxonomy.)

Juvenile Forehead and crown are dark brown with prominent pale buff shaft-streaks extending into an inverted pale buff triangle at the tips of the feathers. The mantle and scapulars are black largely obscured by dark brown fringes and paler buff-white tips. The pale streaks on the head and black streaks on the mantle and scapulars, combined with the triangular spots and buff-white feather tips, create a streaky, spotted appearance. There is a buff supercilium but not as well defined as on the adult and less extensive, barely reaching the rear of the ear-coverts. The lores, malar region and ear-coverts are dark brown with faint chestnut streaks. The ear-coverts contrast with the rest of the head as they are darker brown and do not have pale shaft-streaks. The chin and throat are pale buffish-white and the breast is greyish-buff, but with faint brown streaks and fringes to many of the feathers creating a mottled appearance. The flanks are buff-white with scattered grey tips and fringes. The undertail-coverts are buff. The rectrices have white edges on the outer webs but also have prominent pale chestnut-buff fringes and tips extending round onto the inner web, divided by a darker brown shaft-streak. This colouring is most extensive on the outermost three pairs of tail feathers (06–04) and least present on the central pair (01). The remiges are dark brown with narrow chestnut-buff fringes to the outer webs and greyish-white crescentic tips. The tertials are almost black and in common with the inner secondaries have broad chestnut-buff fringes to their outer webs and tips. The upperwing greater coverts are black-brown with pale chestnut fringes and large buff-white tips which form a noticeable wing-bar. The innermost upperwing greater covert has an all-white outer web. The upperwing lesser and median coverts are black-brown with buff fringes and tips. The inner upperwing median coverts have a small amount of white at their base.

Measurements

	Male *S. f. ferrea*	Female *S. f. ferrea*
Wing	68.0–70.0 (mean 69.2)	62.5–67.0 (mean 65.1)
Tail	63.0–67.0 (mean 65.2)	58.0–64.0 (mean 61.4)
Bill	13.2–15.4 (mean 14.3)	14.1–15.0 (mean 14.4)

	Male *S. f. haringtoni*	Female *S. f. haringtoni*
Wing	66.0–69.5 (mean 67.4)	63.0–68.5 (mean 64.7)
Tail	60.5–67.0 (mean 63.5)	61.0–65.5 (mean 62.2)
Bill	14.0–15.2 (mean 14.7)	14.2–15.5 (mean 14.9)

[Own measurements BMNH 2001]

DISTRIBUTION AND STATUS

The Grey Bushchat is primarily a species breeding in the higher altitudes of southern Asia and Indochina. It is found from the border of Afghanistan and Pakistan, in Kashmir, east along the southern edge of the Himalayas through northern India, Nepal, Bhutan, south-east Tibet to China, the northern parts of Myanmar, north-west Thailand, northern Laos, Cambodia and Vietnam. Baker (1924) states it breeds throughout its range between 1,220 and 2,745m, possibly even higher to 3,050m.

In Pakistan it is a common, largely sedentary breeding species with a rather restricted range in the outer Himalayas (Roberts 1992). It inhabits the North-West Frontier Province (NWFP) and eastwards along the outer ranges of the lower Himalayas at 1,980–2,900m. Roberts (1992) states it does not extend westwards into Afghanistan nor south down to the Safed Koh range in NWFP and it is not found as far south as Chitral. He found it breeding in summer in Swat Kohistan up to 2,700m. It also occurs in Indus Kohistan, the lower reaches of the Kaghan Valley and Azad Kashmir and in the Murree hill range where it is very common. It continues east along the Himalayas through Kashmir and southern Tibet. In Kashmir it is irregularly distributed mainly at 1,800–2,600m, being commonest around 2,100m. Fifty years ago it was exceptionally common in valleys between Wular Lake and the Lolab. It was also very common in April at Domel and the lower reaches of the Kishenganga. It was considered likely to be a common permanent resident in both the Jhelum and lower Kishenganga valleys and on the Pir Panjal slopes (Bates & Lowther 1952). It was also found breeding on Sheopuri above 2,400m and on all inner ranges north of the Nepal Valley (Proud 1955). At the present time in Nepal it is a common and widespread resident being found along the entire Himalayan belt from 1,500–3,350m, generally above 1,800m. Breeding has been proved at Langtang National Park at 1,525–2,745m and it possibly breeds at similar altitudes throughout Nepal (H.S. Baral *in litt.* 2000).

In Bhutan it is a common and ubiquitous resident and altitudinal migrant from 610–3,350m (Inskipp & Inskipp 1993), although K.D. Bishop (*in litt.* 2001) considers it to be only moderately common throughout the kingdom in suitable habitat such as sparsely wooded areas and farmland.

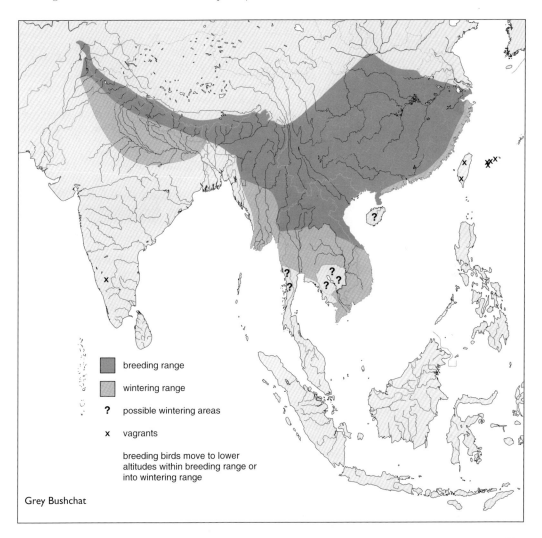

breeding range

wintering range

? possible wintering areas

x vagrants

breeding birds move to lower
altitudes within breeding range or
into wintering range

Grey Bushchat

It is found right across northern India from Himachal Pradesh in the north-west through Uttar Pradesh east to Assam (although at Kaziranga National Park, Assam, there are only a very few records of migrant birds: Barua and Sharma 1999) and Arunachal Pradesh in north-eastern India. It is a common breeding species from 1,500–3,300m, its range extending southwards through Nagaland, Meghalaya and Manipur as far south as Mizoram. A presumably vagrant individual was seen at Narasambudhi Lake, Mysore, in southern India on 9 December 2001 (Thejawsi *et al. in litt.* 2002). Its range continues eastwards to encompass northern and central parts of Myanmar as far south as the Arakan and Karen Hills. Birds were observed by Roseveare (1952) at Minbu in December 1935 and June 1936. They have also been seen in winter in the Kachin Hills and were said to breed in the eastern hills from 1,220m (Stanford & Ticehurst 1938). Two birding surveys of northern Myanmar near Putao in January–February 1998 and November 1999 found it present but uncommon at 440–1,100m (King *et al.* 2001).

In north-west Thailand it is a common winter visitor and local resident (Lekagul & Round 1991). Deignan (1945) found it to be a very common winter visitor to the provinces of Mae Hong Son, Chiang Mai and Chiang Rai, occurring up to 1,677m, and it was recorded on Doi Suthep between 10 October and 25 March. The first breeding record for Thailand was 4–5 April 1981 when two pairs were located in open areas at 1,650m on Doi Pha Hom Pok in Chiang Mai province – one pair carrying food and the other repeatedly calling in alarm. There were also others in the same year breeding commonly in open areas along the verge where the road passed through the forest to the summit of Doi Inthanon from 1,535m to the summit at 2,565m. A few of these pairs were carrying food on 18–19 April and most pairs appeared to have recently fledged young by the first half of May. This species has since been recorded breeding from Doi Ang Khang in Chiang Mai province where fledged young were being fed on 26–29 June 1999 (Ms Sopitcha Tantitadapitak per P.D. Round *in litt.* 2001) where it may only lately have colonised, as P.D. Round did not record it breeding there in July 1983. Apparently it does not breed on the only slightly lower (1,685m) mountain Doi Suthep-Pui but Round expected that it probably bred fairly widely on peaks above 1,800m throughout the north-west region (Round 1982).

Its range continues through northern, central and southern Laos, where it is said to be a winter visitor, occurring up to 1,650m (Duckworth *et al.* 1999). A survey from October 1994 to August 1995 found it was "occasional" around the Nam Leuk in Phou Khaokhoay NBCA and "abundant to locally common" on the Nakay Plateau in the Nam Theung drainage basin in central Laos (Duckworth *et al.* 1998). It has recently been found in south-east Cambodia: a female was seen during a brief survey near Senmonorom on 12 January 1997 (Duckworth & Hedges 1998). Its true status in this country is unknown and the 1997 survey was brief and only concentrated in and around human settlements. It is present and common in northern and central Vietnam (Delacour 1930). It inhabits the hills of south-east China as far north as Sichuan province in the west to Shanghai on the east coast.

The nominate race *S. f. ferrea* is generally judged to extend eastwards from Pakistan to around Sikkim on the borders of Nepal, Bhutan and Tibet. According to Vaurie (1959) specimens examined from Sikkim, Assam and Myanmar showed evidence of intergradation with the marginally darker race *S. f. haringtoni* which extends further eastwards as far as China. However, Cheng Tso-hsin (1987) lists the nominate race for China as far east as the southern and western parts of Yunnan province and in the southern parts of Nyalam, Yadong and Bomi in the Xizang Autonomous Region. It is then replaced by *S. f. haringtoni* south of 34°N in south-eastern Gansu province, southern Shaanxi province, Sichuan (eastern Wanxian, northern Maowen, central Baoxing and south-west Xichang), north-west to south-east Yunnan, Guizhou Zhuang Autonomous Region, Guangdong, Hubei, Henan, Anhui, Jiangxi and Fujian provinces and Shanghai municipality. In China and southern Tibet it is described as a fairly common resident in southern and central areas.

BREEDING

In Pakistan males commence singing from late March in the Murree hill ranges but nesting probably does not commence until late April or May (Roberts 1992). In India breeding is in February–May in Meghalaya, but does not commence until early April, continuing to early July, in the Himalayas (Ali & Ripley 1968–1998). In Kashmir breeding commences at the beginning of May and continues throughout June. In southern Tibet birds were probably breeding by early (6–10) April (Vaurie 1972). In Thailand birds were seen carrying food to young on 4–5 April so nesting must have started in late February or early March (Round 1982). Sites chosen for nests are often in exposed positions near human habitation, and predation of nests was high in the Murree hills area of Pakistan. Magrath (1908) commented: "Owing to the stupidly open situations often selected, the nests are much harried by jungle crows, mischievous boys and egg collectors". Out of 13 nests he observed at Thandiani from late May to 10 July, only one was successful. However, in India nests are usually well concealed.

Only the female builds the nest and incubates the eggs. The male is usually in close attendance but does not assist in either task. When the eggs hatch both parents bring food to the young but the male also sings in the early morning from a high vantage point. In Pakistan the nest is usually situated on the ground in a natural hollow under overhanging roots, or *Adiantum* ferns, in an eroded bank or sometimes under a bush (Roberts 1992). In India it is usually found in a little depression on sloping ground concealed by grasses. Other nests have been found in a hole under stones or clods of earth and rarely in holes in walls or stone revetments on hill roads. In Myanmar nests have been found in roadside banks (Stanford & Ticehurst 1938). Other nests that have occasionally been found above ground were 1.5m up in an old Yew tree *Taxus baccata* and 23cm above ground in a thicket of *Skimmia laureola* (Roberts 1992). The nest is fairly well constructed and usually consists of grasses, roots and occasionally leaves, with moss built into the outer walls. The nest cup is scantily lined with finer grasses, stems, rootlets, hairs, fur, *Adiantum* fern ribs in Pakistan and the occasional feather. Sometimes the lining will consist of only fur or hair. In Kashmir one nest was lined with pine needles (Bates & Lowther 1952). The normal clutch is 4–5, rarely 6 eggs.

The eggs can vary from pale blue to a deeper blue with little gloss and are slightly larger (and in the latter case darker) than those of Siberian Stonechat. Markings vary from an ill-defined ring or cap of reddish speckles at the larger end to some which are strongly defined. Eggs from Pakistan were freckled all over in varying intensity with pale reddish-brown markings. Some eggs with dense freckling appeared almost reddish in colour. In India the reddish freckles were mainly found at the larger end of the egg. Baker (1924) described the eggs of *S. f. haringtoni* as being very different to those of *S. f. ferrea*. In *S. f. haringtoni* the ground colour is a brighter, deeper blue with most eggs devoid of reddish markings (those with markings have so few that the eggs still appear bright blue). Occasionally one or two eggs in a clutch will be much bluer than the others (Magrath 1908).

The mean size of 100 *S. f. ferrea* eggs was 17.9 x 14.2mm (maxima 19.3 x 15.0 and 18.1 x 15.1mm, minima 16.1 x 13.2 and 18.0 x 13.1mm) (Baker 1924).

The mean size of 40 *S. f. haringtoni* eggs was 18.4 x 14.4mm (maxima 19.8 x 14.5 and 19.1 x 15.0mm, minima 17.1 x 14.2 and 18.2 x 14.0mm) (Baker 1924).

There is no information concerning the incubation period but it is likely to be 13–14 days. There is also no information concerning the time nestlings spend in the nest.

In Nepal many had newly fledged young by 24 May whilst others were still feeding nestlings (Proud 1955). In Kashmir young were found in the nest in the last week of May. Well-incubated eggs were also found in the first week of July. In Pakistan four fresh-laid eggs were found on 22 May at Dunga Gali and a nest with a less than five-day-old nestling on 3 June at Shahran in the Kaghan Valley. It is likely although not confirmed that this species normally attempts two broods. The period to fledging is unknown but is probably 13–15 days. Nestlings leave the nest before they can fly and seek cover in thick vegetation where they are fed by both parents until they are independent.

This species is often parasitised by Common Cuckoo *Cuculus canorus* in Pakistan (Magrath 1908) and Myanmar. In Kashmir Bates & Lowther (1952) state it is also parasitised by Oriental Cuckoo *C. saturatus*, although they had no direct evidence for the latter.

HABITAT

Throughout its range the Grey Bushchat appears to inhabit open areas in forests, scrub-covered hillsides and forest fringes, and seems able to tolerate more wooded country and denser, more extensive areas of bushes than Siberian Stonechat. In Pakistan it has been found breeding in clearings with scattered *Berberis* and on the fringes of Blue Pine *Pinus wallichiana* forest. At all elevations (1,980–2,900 m) it prefers open glades and grassy knolls on the edge of forest. In winter it frequents river valley bottoms, cultivated steep terraced hillsides and even gardens. In Kashmir it often occurs just within the outer fringes of mixed forests and was very common in little forest-encircled valleys (Bates & Lowther 1952).

In India it is found on open scrub-covered hillsides, especially along forest edges, and in glades and the vicinity of terraced cultivation. In winter it frequents cultivated areas, tea gardens and grassland especially *ekra* grass along rivers. A survey of the Dehra Dun valley and neighbouring hills in the lower Garhwal Himalayas found it to be a fairly common resident and altitudinal migrant in dry deciduous, moist deciduous, moist temperate, scrub and subtropical pine habitats (Singh 2000). In Madhya Pradesh wintering birds inhabited meadows, and a small meadow within a forest with *Flemingia* undergrowth, beside a track (Newton *et al.* 1986). In Bhutan in autumn (October–November) it was found in subalpine forest and shrubs (Inskipp & Inskipp 1993).

In central Nepal it inhabits secondary growth, forest clearings and edges, and barberry and juniper scrub on dry hillsides (H.S. Baral *in litt.* 2000). In Myanmar it is common in open country with scattered bushes and open forest and is often found in gardens in proximity to human habitation. It is also commonly found in bamboo jungle along mule roads (Stanford & Ticehurst 1938). In Thailand Deignan (1945) found it avoided cultivated areas and kept to tall grass on the open plains in Chiang Rai, frequenting the deciduous jungle on the lower mountain slopes and the brush and *lalang* grass *Imperata cylindrica* of the open hill-forest in Chiang Mai. On Doi Suthep it was one of the most conspicuous species during cold weather and, although not strictly gregarious, at favoured places it was present in numbers.

In Vietnam it is mainly a mountain species frequenting bushy areas and forest edges (Wildash 1968). In Laos it is the most numerous of the three *Saxicola* species (*S. ferrea, S. caprata* and *S. maura*) regularly found in *hai* (fallow ricefields) (J.W. Duckworth *in litt.* 2001). In China it is found in habitat similar to other countries, such as open hill forest and open scrub-covered hillsides in the vicinity of cultivation (Cheng Tso-hsin 1987, Carey *et al.* 2001). In Hong Kong birds observed in 1940 were in open pine wood on the lower slopes of hills (Herklots 1967).

VOICE

The song period in India is given as early April to the end of June with a resumption from early September to the end of October (Ali & Ripley 1968–1998).

The song of the male is brief, lasting around 1.5 seconds, and can be repeated continuously for up to ten minutes from a higher perch than is used for other activities, such as the top of a hedgerow or the highest bush around, sometimes high up in a Blue Pine. In Pakistan the male has never been seen to deliver its song in flight (Roberts 1992) but in India Ali & Ripley (1968–1998) report that as well as being delivered from a perch it is also delivered in a display-flight. The song has been described as canary-like in tone and sweetness or even robin-like, and commences with 2–3 emphatic notes and ends in a feeble trill, *tree-toooh tu treeeh-t-t-t-tuhr* (Roberts 1992). Ali & Ripley describe the song as *tiririririri* or *sisiri-swirrr*, the final *swirrr* being a rolling whistle with some variations. Smythies (1986) described the song as rather pretty but unsatisfactory and rendered it *titheratu-chak-tew-titatit* with variations (after Magrath 1908) and also pointed to its brevity and the fact that it was rarely varied. He also noted it was delivered with a rising inflection that ends suddenly.

When alarmed and also throughout the nesting season both sexes readily utter warning calls which are described as a very characteristic soft *zizzing* call. This alarm note has also been described as *geezing* reminiscent of a watch being wound (Magrath 1908). In Thailand its alarm call is described as a soft *churr* followed by a plaintive piping *hew* (Lekagul & Round 1991). Ali & Ripley (1968–1998) give the call note as a rising *prrei* and alarm notes as *zee-chunk* and *tak-tak-tak-tak*. They also mention a *tic-tic-brzeeee* call which may be an alarm call.

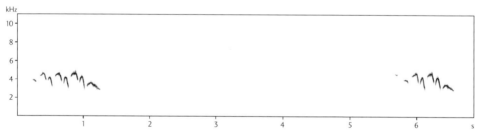

Grey Bushchat *Saxicola ferrea* **NSA 15077. Song. Bhutan 05 March 1967.** *B. Bertram.*

FOOD

Little information. Ali & Ripley (1968–1998) record it feeding on insects and some seeds. Roberts (1992) reports the diet as largely composed of insects supplemented by small molluscs, arthropods and spiders.

MOVEMENTS

The Grey Bushchat winters in the southern parts of its breeding range south to the plains of west and east Pakistan, the plains of northern India, central and southern parts of Myanmar, northern Thailand, southern Laos, northern and central Vietnam, possibly Cambodia and southern China.

Although resident in much of its range it makes altitudinal movements and even short migrations in some areas, moving to lower elevations in winter and returning to the higher parts of its breeding range in the spring. In Pakistan Roberts (1992) found it a rare straggler down to the foothills around Jhelum and the Margalla hills around Islamabad; it occupied gardens in Sialkot cantonment in December and throughout February in river valley bottoms of the Manshera division of Hazara tribal territories. It is numerous in winter around Balakot and Kawai in the Kaghan Valley and around Bhagnotar and Kala Pani on the north-west edge of the Murree Hills. It was recorded once (23 March 1995) in ten years (1988–1998) as a very rare migrant in the north-western plains of Dera Ismail Khan District, NWFP (Kylänpää

2000). In Kashmir it leaves the higher areas of its range in winter but rarely moves further south than the edge of the Himalayan foothills (Bates & Lowther 1952). In India it occurs on its breeding grounds from March to September and wintering areas from October to February. It winters from around 2,400m, but mainly below 1,200m, down to the foothills and into the Gangetic plain, south to the Yamuna River and throughout north-east India. It has been recorded in winter as far south as Meerut and Delhi in Uttar Pradesh (Mohan-Rai 1986) and single female birds have been seen further south at Keoladeo National Park in Bharatpur (27° 13′N, 77° 32′E), Rajasthan, in the last two weeks of January 1984 and at Karera (25° 30′N, 78° 05′E) in Shivpuri district, Madhya Pradesh, on 24 December 1985 (Kannan 1993).

It has also relatively recently been seen on seven occasions between 25 January and 8 March 1981 and on 2 January 1982 5km north of Kanha at 550m in Kanha Tiger Reserve (22° 17′N, 80° 38′E), Madhya Pradesh, close to the geographic centre of India (Newton *et al.* 1986) and also at Bandhavgarh National Park (23° 37′N, 80° 57′E), Madhya Pradesh.

At the time of going to press there is a record, backed by a reasonable description, of a male in an Acacia tree seen by a number of observers at 07:45hrs on 9 December 2001 at Narasambudhi Lake, Nanjanagud town (12° 5′N, 76° 43′E), 20km south of Mysore city, which is the furthest south it has ever been recorded if accepted[2] and the first record for southern India (Thejaswi & Shivaprakash *in litt.* 2001). The finder speculated that the intense cold spell in the north of India may have been the cause of this individual coming so far south.

Ali & Ripley (1968–1998) list it for Bangladesh, where according to Inskipp & Inskipp (1991) it is only a rare passage migrant. In Nepal it is a common altitudinal migrant moving down in October and returning in April, wintering between 915 and 2,135m, although it has been recorded as low as 75m and is a rare winter visitor to the terai (Inskipp & Inskipp 1991, H.S. Baral *in litt.* 2000). It is a regular winter visitor to Sukla Phanta in western Nepal (Baral 1998). It is a common resident in the higher hills of Myanmar excluding Tenessarim but is a migrant to central Myanmar. In northern Myanmar it does not descend to the plains to winter but is common in ones and twos in the Kachin Hills (Stanford &Ticehurst 1938). In the Mandalay district a specimen was obtained at c.250m in February and it has been observed in the plains of Minbu district in June and August (Smythies 1986).

It is a local resident in north-west Thailand, breeding from 1,500m upwards on mountains. In December and January when their numbers are probably increased by numerous winter visitors in both the north-west and north-east of Thailand, birds are found commonly on Doi Inthanon in deforested areas at 1,200–1,300m and along roadside verges as low as 825m. They also sporadically descend even lower, having been recorded from Khao Yai and Bang Phra. One was seen on the very early date of 11 September 1993 at Chonburi on the edge of the central plains roughly 100km east of Bangkok (P. Cureal per P.D. Round *in litt.* 2001) and the species was recorded in Kaeng Krachan National Park in May 2001 (T. Tarrant *in litt.* 2001). In April and May it is replaced in the lower zones (up to 1,600m) by Pied Bushchat *S. caprata* with some limited altitudinal overlap (Round 1982).

It makes short seasonal displacements in northern and central Vietnam, appearing in large groups in winter (Wildash 1968). Its exact status in Cambodia is unclear but the single female observed in regenerating scrub on agricultural land near Senmonorom may have been resident or only wintering (Duckworth & Hedges 1998). In Korea it is a rare vagrant (Lee *et al.* 2000). It has been recorded as a vagrant from Taiwan once, in October 1929. The individual was identified as belonging to the race *S. f. haringtoni* (Cheng Tso-hsin 1987).

In Hong Kong Herklots (1967) states that Swinhoe in 1861 described it as abundant in the hills around the valley for a few days in the first week of March but it then disappeared as it continued its migration. In the early nineteenth century it was a rare winter visitor with Herklots quoting that there were only three records in 20 years, two of which were on 10 and 29 January 1903 from Howlik and Kowloon respectively. It was next recorded by Herklots who saw a single bird on 14 January 1931 but did not find another until 1940 when several were in the Lam Tsun valley on 31 January and again on 17 February. More contemporary records since 1950 show it to be a scarce winter visitor and passage migrant occurring from the first week in October to the last week in February, with occasional records throughout March (extreme dates are 23 September and 20 April). Peak numbers have been recorded in December–February with January having the highest number of records. Carey *et al.* (2001) state a large number of recent records have been from the New Territories at sites such as Sha Lo Tung, Ho Chung, Ping Yeung and Tan Shan valley. It has also been recorded from various locations on Lantau during the winter. On migration in October it can be found in less typical habitat and has been recorded from Mount Austin, Mai Po, Kadoorie FBG and Shing Mun. Between 1958 and 1982 it was recorded in all winters in Hong Kong apart from 1960–1961. Peak numbers were in the winters of 1971–1972, 1972–1973 and 1976–1977. There was a dramatic decline in

---

[2] This record has recently been accepted by the relevant authorities in India.

records during the 1980s with none in 1983–1985 or in 1989 and only single records in 1987 and 1988. Records have increased again in the 1990s, possibly owing to increased observation. It has been recorded annually since 1990 and numbers in the winter 1992–1993 were the second highest on record, although generally records are still below the numbers recorded in the 1970s. It occurs singly or in small parties and favours areas such as Lam Tsuen valley, Tai Mong Tsai, Pak Tam Chung, Mong Tseng and the hills near Lok Ma Chau (Chalmers 1986).

It has also been recorded as an accidental visitor to Japan. There are four records between 16 March and 6 April from the Nansei Shoto in the extreme south-west of Japanese territorial waters, three of them involving four birds from the Yaeyama Islands. The first record was on 31 March–2 April 1979; a male was on Iriomote-shima on 4–6 April 1983, and two males were on Yonaguni-shima on 16 March 1984. There is also a more recent record of one bird again on Yonaguni-shima on 21–22 March 1988 (Brazil 1991). These were not assigned to race but presumably were *S. f. haringtoni*. These islands are located relatively close to mainland China and the individuals in question were probably displaced migrants moving north to breed.

BEHAVIOUR

The Grey Bushchat has been described in India as very parochial, frequenting the same spot day after day (Ali & Ripley 1968–1998). It is strongly territorial and in the breeding season it is intolerant of conspecifics and maintains well-spaced territories; it also establishes territories in winter (Roberts 1992). It is usually found in pairs or singly in the breeding season but often forms loose and sometimes large groups in winter, this behaviour being noted in both India and the eastern parts of the range such as Vietnam, although curiously not in Pakistan. Even when in considerable numbers the individuals in the groups forage separately.

In typical *Saxicola* fashion it perches on the tops of bushes, telephone wires or low branches of trees, using these exposed perches to survey the surrounding ground and air space. It catches its prey mainly by dropping to the ground or seizing it on the wing by sallies from its perch, immediately returning to the same or a similar perch. It usually perches quite low to the ground when hunting, but Roberts noted birds in Pakistan using telephone wires to hunt for prey, and males will perch at considerable heights on trees when singing. In Myanmar it often perches in trees. It was described as shy, disappearing from view if it was aware of being watched. When females were flushed from nests with eggs they disappeared rapidly down the hill and did not appear again anywhere near the nest (Stanford & Ticehurst 1938). In low anxiety they flirt their tails half-open, especially when the nest has young and is being approached by a potential predator (Magrath 1908).

MOULT

Little detailed information. There is a complete post-breeding moult of adult birds in August and September. Breeding plumage is acquired by wear to the winter plumage and not by a partial moult in spring.

Juvenile birds have a post-juvenile moult involving all body feathers and all coverts except the upperwing primary coverts and outer upperwing greater coverts. First-year birds, i.e. birds in their second calendar year, can be recognised by their retained juvenile upperwing primary and greater coverts together with the more worn unmoulted flight and tail feathers, which usually appear browner than the similar feathers of adults (these, being black and less worn, show less contrast).

CONSERVATION

The species does not appear to be threatened in any part of its range. The destruction of forest may actually benefit it by creating clearings and leaving open scrub for it to inhabit. Its willingness to occupy areas that are cultivated and in the vicinity of human habitation also assists it in maintaining its current status.

Oenanthe gutturalis Viellot, 1818, *Nouv. Dict. Hist. Nat.*, 21, p.421—New Holland [*errore* = Timor]

S.(axicola) luctuosa Bonaparte, 1851, *Consp. Av.*, 1 (1850), p.304—Semau

Etymology *gutturalis* derived from Latin meaning throated, of the throat
luctuosa derived from Latin *luctuosus* meaning mournful (*luctus*, mourning); referring to the bird's dark funereal plumage

Alternative names White-bellied Chat, Timor Bushchat, Sunda Bushchat

TAXONOMY

Polytypic. It is by no means certain that this species belongs in the genus *Saxicola*. Its morphology, behaviour and habitat are different to most other *Saxicola* species and suggest it is more like a flycatcher. The bill is substantial, viewed side on, with a pronounced downcurve to the culmen and hooked tip. Its habitat is not typical of the genus, being deciduous forest and woodland. It appears to nest relatively high off the ground, behaviour not found in any other *Saxicola*.

Coates & Bishop (1997) note it "Forages by gleaning and sallying in the canopy and sometimes in tall understorey shrubs. Males sing from the dense canopy of tall trees. Very similar in posture and movements to a *Myiagra* flycatcher, for which it can easily be mistaken". White & Bruce (1986) comment that "the species is one of the peculiar endimisms of Timor, with no close relative anywhere in Wallacea. Asian *S. ferrea* G.R. Gray 1846, and *S. jerdoni* (Blyth) 1867, may be its nearest allies but neither is sufficiently similar to indicate that it is derived from them. If the resemblance to *Saxicola* is not due to convergence and the species is actually a *Saxicola*, this is one of the most anomalous instances of distribution in Wallacea". The name *luctuosa* was given by Bonaparte to birds from Semau Island, west of Timor, but it was subsequently incorporated as a subspecies of *S. gutturalis* by Ripley *et al.* (1964). There are only small differences in plumage between the males of the nominate subspecies and *luctuosa*, the main one according to Hellmayr (1914) – who discusses this species under the name *Oreicola melanoleuca* – being the amount of white in the tail of the male: where nominate *gutturalis* has a variable but large amount of white at the base of the tail, *luctuosa* has the white greatly reduced. Mees (1975) commented that the specimens he examined, the two that Hellmayr examined in the BMNH and another bird studied by Salvadori (1890) all showed the reduction of white in the tail and demonstrated that this was a valid subspecific characteristic and not a matter of variation.

Differences relating to the white supercilium proved to reflect individual and not subspecific variation (Büttikofer 1891, Hellmayr 1914, Mees 1975), and females of the two subspecies are not separable (Mees 1975).

White & Bruce (1986) accept these subspecies, but both they and Coates & Bishop (1997) mention that there might be a third subspecies on the island of Roti, based on Mees' (1975) review of specimen material which yielded a single female specimen from the island. Mees intimated the possibility that this bird represented a third subspecies because its underparts were "a little whiter" than those of the other female specimens he had from Timor and Semau.

The facts surrounding this latter specimen point to some confusion and make the likelihood of a third subspecies appear dubious. Mees (1975) pointed out that there are three types of plumage for this species: adult males (black and white); immature males (brown with black uppertail-coverts and tails); and females (brown with rufous tails). Hellmayr (1914) had previously regarded all the brown specimens as females, and as the two brown specimens he had from Timor had black tails and the one from Semau a rufous-brown tail, he believed this difference to be of subspecific value rather than a sexual difference. However, prior to this Büttikofer in 1891 had suggested that a bird in brown plumage with a black tail was not a female but "a young male in the transitional stage of plumage". Mees examined the 13 male (10 from Timor, three from Semau) and four female (two from Timor, one from Semau and one from Roti) specimens at his disposal and found that Büttikofer's assumptions were correct. Mees also pointed out that Hellmayr appeared to have overlooked the fact that the brown bird with the black tail described by Büttikofer came from Semau. Thus, contrary to Hellmayr, there is little or no difference between the females of the two subspecies, so there is no way of identifying to which subspecies the female from Roti belongs or if it even represents a third subspecies. It might be pertinent to point out that Hellmayr's mistaken assumption that any brown specimen was a female is still being perpetuated. Specimens I examined in 2001 from both AMNH and UMNH labelled as female were in fact juvenile males. In addition, whilst studying skins of female Jerdon's Bushchat *S. jerdoni* in the BMNH, I discovered 12 specimens of *S. gutturalis*

267

mistakenly included as *S. jerdoni* including the female from Roti examined by Hellmayr and possibly Mees. The juvenile males in this collection were also designated by the original label as female.

Subspecies
Saxicola gutturalis gutturalis
Saxicola gutturalis luctuosa
Saxicola gutturalis ? [possible third subspecies]

IDENTIFICATION

Size15.0cm/5.9 inches. Sexually dimorphic. Appears less rounded and compact than a typical *Saxicola* with a heavier bill and slimmer, more attenuated profile due to longish tail. Males are a combination of black and white. They are entirely glossy black on the head (apart from the chin and throat) and upperparts. The tail is long and black with a large area of white at the base. The wings are black with a large white patch extending across all the inner upperwing-coverts and a smaller patch on the primary coverts. The underparts from chin to undertail-coverts are mainly white in all but fresh plumage, but with a creamy buff suffusion in fresh plumage strongest on the breast. Females are medium, slightly olive brown above and buff-white below. The upperparts are slightly streaked darker brown and there is a long buff supercilium extending from the bill to the rear of the ear-coverts. The rump and uppertail-coverts are a bright chestnut-brown contrasting with the darker brown mantle. The closed tail appears dark brown with bright rufous edges but mainly rufous when spread. There is no white in the tail. The wings are dark brown with no white wing-patch.

Immature males are superficially like females but the grey brown upperparts are slightly more olive in tone, often with a greyish caste on the head. The underparts are mainly white with pale buff on the breast and flanks. The uppertail-coverts and tail are black, the latter with white bases to the feathers as in the adult male.

Confusion species The only other *Saxicola* species to occur on Timor, Roti and Semau islands is the Pied Bushchat *S. caprata*. Males of both species are a combination of black and white, but can be told apart as follows: *gutturalis* is more attenuated in profile with a proportionately long tail, *caprata* is typically more rounded and stocky with a proportionately shorter tail; *gutturalis* has a heavier, thicker bill with a markedly downcurved culmen, *caprata* has a smaller, flatter, more delicate bill; *gutturalis* has all-white underparts, *caprata* is all black below apart from a white ventral area and undertail-coverts; *gutturalis* has a black rump, *caprata* a white rump; *gutturalis* has an extensive white base to the tail, *caprata* has an all-black tail; some *gutturalis* males have a variable-length white supercilium, *caprata* has an all-black head; *gutturalis* has white on the primary coverts and a long broad white shoulder-stripe, *caprata* has no white on the primary coverts and only a narrow shoulder-stripe which does not extend onto the innermost secondaries and tertials as in *gutturalis*.

Females differ in the same way structurally as the adult male; *S. gutturalis* is medium slightly rufous brown above, *S. caprata* is darker brownish-grey above; *gutturalis* is entirely pale buff-white below (contrasting with the upperparts), *caprata* is much darker greyish-brown below (hence less contrast), often with streaking and with rufous undertail-coverts; *gutturalis* uppertail-coverts are chestnut-brown showing little contrast with the similar-coloured long tail, *caprata* rump and uppertail-coverts are bright chestnut-buff contrasting with the short blackish-brown tail; *gutturalis* has a long buff supercilium extending to the rear of the ear-coverts, *caprata* shows at best a very faint supercilium that never extends beyond the eye.

Immature male *S. gutturalis* can be told from female *S. caprata* by structure and by its black uppertail-coverts and extensive (but slightly less than adult male) white base to the black tail.

DESCRIPTION (Based on nominate *S. g. gutturalis*)

Adult male in fresh plumage Forehead, crown, nape, neck, lores, malar region, cheeks, ear-coverts, mantle and scapulars are glossy black with a slight blue sheen. It has been stated that some birds also show a white supercilium but none of eight adult male specimens in BMNH show this character and it would appear that more males lack than possess this feature. The rump is black with some greyish-white fringes. Uppertail-coverts glossy black. Chin and throat pale buff-white. The upper breast is creamy-buff fading to silky white on the lower breast, flanks, belly, ventral area and undertail-coverts. The white of the throat extends slightly onto the foreneck but not enough to form a distinct neck-patch.

The remiges are glossy black on the outer webs and brownish-black on the inner webs. The six secondaries have white bases with the greatest amount of white being on the innermost secondary (06 = 50% of both webs of feather) then declining proportionately outwards on the others and only present on the outer webs of secondaries 05–01. The tertials are glossy black with the basal third of the outer webs white. The white bases of the tertials and innermost secondary form an extension to the white wing-patch of the coverts and are visible when the wing is spread. The outer upperwing lesser and median coverts are glossy black. The inner ones are pure white. The outer three upperwing greater coverts are glossy black with the remaining ones showing proportionately greater amounts of white up to the innermost, which is entirely white apart from a small black spot at the tip of the outer web. The white on the upperwing lesser, median and greater coverts forms an extensive and striking wing-patch. The alula is glossy black. The upperwing primary coverts are predominantly white with black tips, although the central ones are partially obscured by the largest alula creating a noticeable black gap in the centre of the white primary covert feather tract. The underwing-coverts are dark grey with extensive white fringes, and the axillaries are white.

The rectrices are glossy black with the bases showing extensive amounts of white, present only on the inner web of 06 but on both webs of 05–03 with the white extending slightly further down on the outer web. Tail feather 02 has a very small amount of white on the inner web and the central pair (01) have no white at all. The tail is long in proportion to the body, slightly graduated, with the outer tail feather (06) proportionately shorter than the others.

Listed below are typical measurements of the extent of white in the tail of *S. g. gutturalis*.

White on both webs of feathers apart from outermost pair where only on outer webs

Tail feather	Total length	Amount of white	Proportion
6	59.5	30.5	51.3%
5	63.0	34.0	54.0%
4	64.5	43.5	67.4%
3	64.5	37.3	57.8%
2	65.0	09.3	14.3%
1	66.0	0.0	0%

The bill is black, slightly glossy and appears slightly heavier and more substantial, having a greater depth than on typical *Saxicola* spp. The culmen has a marked downcurve on the distal half and is slightly hooked at the tip, and the base of the bill is laterally quite wide. The legs and feet are dark brown, the irides dark brown.

Males of the subspecies *S. g. luctuosa* are virtually identical. However, the white on the tail of males is considerably less. Of three male specimens in BMNH two show virtually no white in the tail (not visible in flight) and the third shows white bases but less in extent than for *S. g. gutturalis* and only on the inner webs of the feathers (see below). The primary coverts show less white than in typical *S. g. gutturalis* with the primary coverts mainly black apart from a white base (50% of feather) on the innermost primary covert. The amount of white on the inner upperwing-coverts also appeared slightly less. However, the sample is too small to say if these are consistent differences between the subspecies. Two of these specimens also showed no white supercilium but the third showed a discontinuous white line from just behind the eye to the rear of the ear-coverts.

Listed below are measurements of white in the tail of *S. g. luctuosa* demonstrating the variable extent of white in the tail but always less than *S. g. gutturalis*. Also only the outer four tail feathers on *luctuosa* as opposed to five in *S. g. gutturalis* show white at the base.

Specimen with some white in the tail
White present on inner webs only

Tail feather	Total length	Amount of white	Proportion
6	59.0	23.0	39.0%
5	64.5	28.0	43.0%
4	65.0	37.5	57.7%
3	69.0	38.0	55.1%

(No white on feathers 2 and 1)

Specimen with much reduced white in the tail
White present on inner webs only

Tail feather	Total length	Amount of white	Proportion
6	61.0	16.0	9.76%
5	64.5	17.5	11.29%
4	66.5	18.0	11.97%
3	70.0	22.0	15.4%

(No white on feathers 2 and 1)

First-year male Males in the adult-type black and white plumage and collected at the same time have shown marked differences in the colour and wear of the remiges and to a lesser extent the rectrices. It is reasonable to assume that individuals with brown and worn flight feathers contrasting with the black body plumage and the moulted and therefore blacker upperwing-coverts are probably first-year birds which have undergone a partial post-juvenile moult, while those with black flight feathers showing little contrast with the coverts and body feathers are adults which have undergone at least one full post-breeding moult. Presumed first-year males in adult-type plumage are not so glossy and deep a black as full adults, often showing the occasional duller feather of brownish-black on the head and mantle, and have a less extensive white wing-patch. The alula, upperwing primary coverts, most if not all of the upperwing median coverts and most of the outer upperwing greater coverts are unmoulted and therefore more worn and brown. The upperwing lesser coverts are moulted and therefore new and glossy black. The primary coverts do not show any white but the innermost have buff-white tips. The unmoulted outer upperwing greater coverts have rufous-brown tips whilst the inner upperwing white greater coverts are not as clean white as in the full adult and show variable amounts of black on the outer fringes and the occasional black tip. The tertials are also unmoulted with rufous-brown outer fringes and paler buff crescentic tips. The underparts are also less pure white with a greater degree of buff showing on the chin, throat, breast and belly. Individuals in this plumage have also shown thin brown fringes and spots on the breast feathers forming an indistinct necklace across the breast, similar to juvenile males.

Juvenile male Forehead, crown and nape are a mouse-like brown with a greyish caste. The feathers have indistinct darker centres creating a slightly streaked appearance. The lores, malar region and ear-coverts are brown with thin hair-like streaks of pale buff. There is a buff supercilium extending from the bill to the rear of the ear-coverts which becomes paler, wider and more distinct from the rear of the eye. The neck, mantle, scapulars and back are slightly warmer grey-brown than on the head, appearing fairly uniform with only very faint streaking, less so than on the head. The rump is chestnut-brown with long buff-white fringes and tips. The uppertail-coverts are black. The outer uppertail-coverts are noticeably long (extending one-third down the length of the exposed tail), glossy black with chestnut tips; the central ones are shorter and black with cinnamon-brown tips. The chin and throat are dull white with indistinct brown streaks and fringes to the feathers. The breast is greyish-buff with faint brown shaft-streaks and the flanks are buff with similar streaks. The belly is dull white, the ventral area buff-white and the undertail-coverts silky white. The tail is black with a slight brown caste and can show very faint dull white at the extreme tip. The rectrices show the same pattern of white at the base as in the adult male although proportionately each feather has slightly less white (but still extensive: 59% of 04). The outer pair of rectrices (06) also have very narrow buff fringes and tips; 05–02 have a narrow buff fringe to the outer webs only, and the central pair (01) have no buff fringes at all.

The remiges are dark brown with narrow rufous-brown fringes to the outer webs and paler buff to greyish-white tips. The rufous fringes to the inner secondaries are slightly broader than on the rest of the remiges combining with the tertial fringes to create a distinct panel on the closed wing. The upperwing lesser coverts are dark brown with paler rufous fringes and greyish-buff tips. The upperwing median coverts are similar but the inner ones have buff-white fringes and tips with a dark brown subterminal spot on the shaft. The extreme inner median coverts have white at the base of both shafts. The upperwing greater coverts are dark brown with rufous-brown fringes to the outer webs and tips. The inner four have a variable amount of white at the base of the outer webs and in some birds the tips can be greyish-white. The upperwing inner greater coverts can also show paler buff outer fringes which contrast with the darker rufous fringes of the outer greater coverts. The upperwing primary coverts are brown with buffish-white tips to the innermost. The alula is grey-brown. The tertials are dark brown with prominent rufous-brown fringes to the outer webs and slightly paler buff- to greyish-white crescentic tips. The underwing-coverts and axillaries are buff-white. Occasionally the tertials and inner secondaries show a minute amount of white on the rufous fringes and at the base of the longest tertial.

The bill is black, legs and feet are horn brown. The irides are dark brown.

Specimens labelled 'immature' and in this plumage but only examined in digital photographs have also shown buff spots to the tips of the feathers on the forehead, crown, nape, mantle and scapulars as well as thin brown fringes to the buff feathers on the throat and breast. Whether this is indicative of newly fledged individuals and these tips and fringes wear away is unknown.

It is not known for certain how long immature males remain in this plumage. Only two of six specimens examined in this plumage had the date of collection shown on the label, one each in January and August. Whether this is a juvenile plumage adopted for the first few months before a post-juvenile moult when these birds would moult into adult type plumage is also unknown. Certainly the disparity in dates for the two specimens is confusing but possibly indicates two separate breeding times.

270

Adult female Forehead, crown, nape, mantle and scapulars dull slightly rufous-brown but brighter than juvenile male with indistinct darker brown central streaks. There is a long, broad and continuous buff supercilium extending from the base of the bill over the eye to the rear of the ear-coverts. The malar region and ear-coverts are rufous-brown with thin pale buff shaft-streaks. The rump is concolorous with the mantle but contrasts with the brighter chestnut uppertail-coverts. The chin and throat are white. The breast and flanks are creamy-buff, the belly, ventral area and undertail-coverts are almost white with a slight buff suffusion. The tail is a similar bright chestnut to the uppertail-coverts. The central pair of rectrices are dark brown with narrow chestnut fringes to the outer web; rectrices 02–05 are entirely bright chestnut on both webs whilst the outermost pair 06 have the outer web dark brown. There is no white in the tail at all. When the tail is closed it appears dark brown with broad chestnut fringes merging with the uppertail-coverts. The remiges are dark brown. The primaries have narrow rufous-brown fringes to the outer webs. The secondaries are the same but with slightly broader fringes and faint buff to greyish-white tips. The upperwing lesser, median and greater coverts are dark brown prominently fringed with rufous-buff. The inner upperwing lesser coverts have pale creamy-buff fringes and tips with the innermost covert almost completely white. The innermost upperwing median covert has the whole of the outer web white and the next covert has a white central streak, and all the inner medians have pale creamy-white fringes and tips which together form a very insignificant white patch on the inner upperwing. The inner upperwing greater coverts are fringed with pale creamy-buff contrasting with the darker buff fringes of the outer greater coverts. The tertials also have broad rufous fringes to the outer webs and tips which combine with the inner secondaries to form a rufous panel on the closed wing. The underwing-coverts and axillaries are buff. The legs, feet and bill are black-brown. The lower mandible is pale horn-brown on the basal third. The irides are dark brown.

First-year female Virtually identical to the adult female although marginally duller on the upperparts and some upperpart feathers show pale buff spots and streaks. Underparts are also duller than in the adult female and the breast and foreflanks can show narrow brown fringes to the feathers giving a slightly mottled appearance.

Measurements

	Male *S. g. gutturalis* (adult) Timor	Male *S. g. gutturalis* (imm.) Timor
Wing	76.0/79.5	72.5
Tail	66.0/72.0	68.5
Bill	18.0/16.8	16.5

[Own measurements based on the three specimens from LMNH- two adult males and one immature male]

	Male *S. g. gutturalis* (juvenile) UMNH NMNH
Wing	72.0
Tail	64.5 worn
Bill	15.5 worn

	Male *S. g. gutturalis* (juvenile) AMNH	Male *S. g. gutturalis* (adult) AMNH
Wing	70.5/72.0	74.5/76.5
Tail	61.5/66.5	65.5/70.5
Bill	18.0/17.0	16.3/16.5

	Male *S. g. gutturalis* (juvenile) BMNH
Wing	74.0/–/75.5/70.0
Tail	67.0/66.0/68.0/65.5
Bill	16.9/–/17.0/17.0

	Male *S. g. gutturalis* (adult) BMNH	Male *S. g. luctuosa* (adult) BMNH
Wing	73.5/78.5/73.0/76.0/78.0/77.0/79.0	75.0/77.5/78.0
Tail	69.0/69.0/66.0/69.0 /68.5/68.5/67.8	66.5/67.0/69.0
Bill	17.0/17.5/–/17.0/17.0/17.5/18.0	17.3/17.0/17.5

	Female *S. g. gutturalis* (adult) Roti BMNH
Wing	69.5
Tail	68.5
Bill	16.5

[Own measurements 2001]

Male *S. g. gutturalis* (adult) Timor		Female *S. g. gutturalis* Timor
Wing	77.0/74.0/81.0/78.0/80.0/75.0/77.0	77.5/75.0
Tail	63.0/61.0/71.0/64.0/68.0/63.0/64.0	63.0/64.0
Bill	16.5/17.0/17.0/18.0/16.0/16.0/16.5	17.75/17.5

Male *S. g. luctuosa* (adult) Semau		Female *S. g. luctuosa* Samao [Semau]
Wing	76.0/76.0	73.0
Tail	65.0/66.0	63.0
Bill	17.0/17.0	17.0

Male *S. g. gutturalis* (juvenile) Timor		Female subspecies undetermined Roti
Wing	71.0/72.0/76.0	74.0
Tail	60.5/64.0/63.0	63.0
Bill	16.5/16.5/15.75	16.5

Male *S. g. luctuosa* (juvenile) Semau	
Wing	73.0
Tail	63.0
Bill	16.0

[Mees 1975]

Male *S. g. gutturalis* Besi Pae, W. Timor		Female *S. g. gutturalis* Besi Pae, W. Timor
Wing	78.0/81.0	79.0
Tail	68.0/70.0	67.0
Bill	18.0/18.3	18.7
Tarsus	27.5/28.1	28.5
Weight	21.8	21.5

[Live specimens measured by R. Noske 1993]

DISTRIBUTION AND STATUS

The White-bellied Bushchat is endemic to the eastern Lesser Sunda Islands where it is restricted to the Timor and Wetar Endemic Bird Area (E17) (Stattersfield *et al.* 1998). The two, possibly three subspecies inhabit the islands of Timor (*S. g. gutturalis*), Semau (*S. g. luctuosa*) and Roti (racially indeterminate). It has been described as locally common (Mayr 1944, Coates & Bishop 1997), but very little is known about its exact distribution. Museum specimens and comments in trip reports reveal the following:

East Timor

Four adult males collected from East Timor (no location given) by A.R. Wallace 1861 (specimens in BMNH).

Two juvenile males collected from East Timor (no location given) by A.R. Wallace 1861. Wrongly labelled by Wallace as female (specimens in BMNH).

One juvenile male collected from East Timor (no date or location given) by A.R. Wallace (specimen in BMNH).

One juvenile male collected from East Timor August 1829. Collector and location unknown. Label states ex Gould Collection and wrongly labelled as female (specimen in BMNH).

One adult male collected from East Timor (no location given) 1861 by A.R. Wallace although label states it is subspecies *S. g. luctuosa* which is from Semau (specimen in BMNH).

Thompson *et al.* (1974–1975) state "16 May 1974 – one collected from semi cleared area amongst secondary monsoon forest, hillside near Bocola".

West Timor

Noske & Saleh (1996) conducted surveys in West Timor from 13 May–6 July 1993 during the dry season in natural or semi-natural habitats and recorded this species at the following localities: Menipo, Bipolo, Aisio, Baumata, Camplong, Besi Pae, Naiola and Buat – see below:

Mees (1975) examined a series of seven adult male, three immature male and one female for which no specific location was available except they were collected on Timor.

Adult male:

One April 1829, one May 1829, three 1829 all collected by S. Muller.

One no date or details of collector.

One 1880 collected by v. Lansberge.

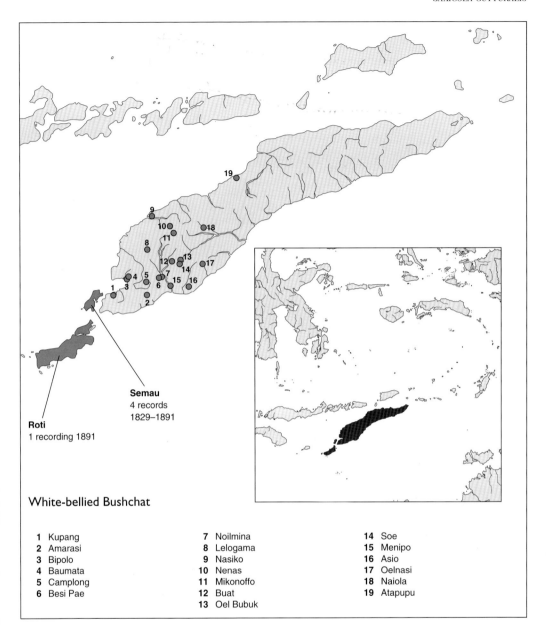

Semau
4 records
1829–1891

Roti
1 recording 1891

White-bellied Bushchat

1	Kupang	7	Noilmina	14	Soe
2	Amarasi	8	Lelogama	15	Menipo
3	Bipolo	9	Nasiko	16	Asio
4	Baumata	10	Nenas	17	Oelnasi
5	Camplong	11	Mikonoffo	18	Naiola
6	Besi Pae	12	Buat	19	Atapupu
		13	Oel Bubuk		

Immature male:
   One March 1829, one 1828/1829 collected by S. Muller.
   One 1880 collected by v. Lansberge.
Female:
   One 1828/1829 collected by S. Muller.
There is also a juvenile male wrongly labelled female in the USNM with no details of locality, collection date or collector USNM 98111 (J. Dean *in litt.* 2002).

First-year male collected Timor but no date or location. Label states Verreaux and that it is *S. g. luctuosa* although Timor is written on label.

Amarasi 10° 12´S, 123° 57´E
   Probably common in forest margins Holmes (1993).

Asio 10° 07´S, 124° 24´E
Described as abundant between 13 May–6 July 1993 (Noske & Saleh 1996).

Atapupu 9° 00´S, 124° 51´E
One male July 1896; one female July 1897(AMNH collection).
A male specimen in USNM was collected in July 1896 (J. Dean *in litt.* 2001).
Everett obtained a large series near Atapupu July–August 1897 (Hartert 1898, Bishop *in litt.* 2001).

Baumata 10° 13´S, 123° 41´E
June–July 1993 one male trapped and released (R. Noske *in litt.* 2001).

Besi Pae 9° 56´S, 124° 08´E
June-July 1993 one male, one juvenile male trapped and released (R. Noske *in litt.* 2001).

Bipolo 10° 01´S, 123° 45´E
It occurs but is uncommon at Bipolo (K.D. Bishop *in litt.* 2001)
Recorded between 13 May–6 July 1993 (Noske & Saleh 1996)
Recorded 5–8 October 1995 (Verbelen 1995)

Buat 9° 48´S, 124° 16´E
Recorded between 13 May–6 July 1993 (Noske & Saleh 1996).

Camplong 10° 02´S, 123° 55´E
Two males 160m a.s.l 7 January 1932; one male 9 January 1932; two males 16 January 1932; one female
 25 January 1932 (specimens in AMNH collection); plus two males and one female collected by Stein
 no date but presumably 1931/1932.
Two 19 July 1991, five 20 July 1991 and one 24 July 1991 (Nils Poul Dreyer unpublished report).
Derek Holmes (1993) states "It is probably rather common in forest margins at Camplong and Amarasi,
 but difficult to get good views".
Verbelen (1995) gives records from Camplong on 26–29 September 1995.
A male at Camplong on 18 November 2001 (J. Hornbuckle *in litt.* 2001).
Described as abundant on dry plain at Camplong during survey 13 May–6 July 1993 (Noske & Saleh 1996).

Gunung Mutis 9° 34´S, 124° 14´E
The inclusion of this species under Gunang Mutis in Noske & Saleh (1996) represents a typographical
 error (Noske *in litt.* 2001).

Kupang 10° 10´S, 123° 35´E
Two adult males and a juvenile male collected October 1840 (specimens in MCML).
One female July 1891 collected by H.F.C ten Kate (Mees 1975).
Two males collected 21 December 1931; one female collected 23 December 1931 (AMNH collection).
These were probably collected by Stein on his expedition to Timor & Sumba 1931/1932 as reported in
 Mayr (1944).

Lelogama 9° 44´S, 123° 57´E
A pair with two newly fledged young 11 November 1997 (R. Noske *in litt.* 2001).

Menipo
Recorded between 13 May–6 July 1993 (Noske & Saleh 1996).

Mikonoffo
Adult male collected S. Muller 1829 (Mees 1975).

Nasiko 9° 21´S, 123° 59´E
May 1829 adult male collected by S. Muller (Mees 1975).

Noilmina 9° 58´S, 124° 06´E
One female 300m a.s.l. 30 January 1932 (AMNH collection); one male also collected by Stein.

Nenas 9° 35´S, 124° 12´E
One male 1,200m a.s.l 2 March 1932; one male 5 March 1932; one male 7 March 1932 (AMNH
collection); plus one male and one female collected by Stein?

Oelnasi 9° 50´S, 124° 33´E
K.D. Bishop found it to be common at Oelnasi, 15km west of Soe in 1999 (J. Hornbuckle *in litt.* 2001).

Oel Bubuk

A female was seen in a remnant forest at Oel Bubuk at 1,000m, 13km north of Soe on 16 November 2001 (J. Hornbuckle *in litt.* 2001).

Soe 9° 52´S, 124° 17´E

Pair with young in nest 12 November 1997 1km north of Soe. (R. Noske *in litt.* 2001).

Naiola 9° 31´S, 124° 27´E

Recorded between 13 May and 6 July 1993 (Noske & Saleh 1996).

Semau Island

Immature male and adult male collected July 1891 by H.F.C. ten Kate (Mees 1975).

Adult male and female collected by S. Muller March 1829 (Mees 1975).

Two adult males. One of these collected 9 May 1857 (specimens in BMNH).

Adult female collected at Lamas 1854 by A.R. Wallace.

Roti Island

Female collected between 22 August–9 September 1891 by H.F.C. ten Kate (Mees 1975) (this is probably the specimen in BMNH).

BREEDING

There is very little information. R. Noske (in prep.) kindly supplied information on two important field observations. On 11 November 1997 near Lelogama a pair were feeding two recently fledged young. The fledglings were perched in low bushes in a sparsely vegetated gully among bare hills with outcrops of rocks c1,000m a.s.l. The following day, 12 November, 1km north of Soe at 950m a.s.l., a nest was found with young. It was located in a dead spout (0.7m long) approximately 5.5m above ground, arising at an angle of 20 degrees from the trunk of a White Gum *Eucalyptus alba*. Both sexes were observed to feed the young and were highly agitated by observers' presence. The tree was located by a dirt road and was surrounded by bare ground for a 50m radius, beyond which was recently burnt, open eucalypt savanna with no understorey. Noske's observations would indicate that breeding occurs in at least October and November. Three individuals he trapped in June–July showed no sign of brood-patches.

HABITAT

White-bellied Bushchat shows a preference for dry deciduous forest and woodland and is uncommon in semi-evergreen (i.e. moister) forest. Noske & Saleh (1996) state that all the endemic species occurring on Timor and its satellites, Roti and Semau, mainly inhabit lowland forest. They commented on this species that it was found in "tiny patches of forest and riparian vegetation surrounded by cleared pasture land (Naiola near Kefamananui), secondary growth (Baumata) and tamarind plantations with some regrowth of native species near Asio. It was the second most common species at Besi Pae, and was abundant at Camplong which still retains extensive forest areas, suggesting a preference for deciduous forest and woodland. Indeed it was scarce in evergreen forest and apparently avoids high altitudes". It has been recorded from sea level up to 1,200m, at which elevation Stein (in Mayr 1944) collected four males and an immature female at Nenas.

VOICE

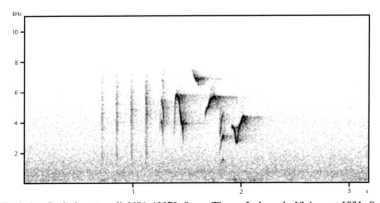

White-bellied Bushchat *Saxicola gutturalis* **NSA 43370. Song. Timor, Indonesia 13 August 1991.** *S. Smith.*

Based on tape recordings made by Bishop at Camplong, Coates & Bishop (1997) describe the song as "a clear, sweet unhurried series of four, occasionally five, moderately high-pitched, whistled notes; the first note long and upslurred followed by three deliberate notes alternating up and down (duration of 2.1 sec). This song, or variations of it, are repeated at 6–14 second intervals." The male delivers the song from the dense canopy of tall trees. At Camplong on West Timor it was described as singing *ad nauseam* from a high perch (Jepson & Ounsted 1997). However, a male was seen singing from perches only c.4m high (J. Hornbuckle *in litt.* 2001).

The female gives a subdued, easily overlooked, two-note *tchk tchk* (Coates & Bishop 1997). Taped calls of fledglings in November 1997 were described as incessant, insect-like, short, buzzing churrs (R. Noske in prep.).

FOOD

No information apart from insects and invertebrates.

MOVEMENTS

Little information. Probably sedentary.

BEHAVIOUR

Little information. Usually found in pairs foraging and sallying after insects in the forest canopy or in tall understorey shrubs. Very similar in posture to and can be mistaken for a *Myiagra* flycatcher (Coates & Bishop 1997).

MOULT

No information. Examination of specimens in BMNH suggests that juveniles possibly have a partial post-juvenile moult into first-adult plumage, while adults have a full post-breeding moult. There is no information on the timing of moult. Three individuals (two males and a female) trapped by R. Noske in June–July 1993 showed no sign of moult of the primaries. If as appears likely the breeding season is in October and November at the very least, then moult probably occurs after breeding ceases. As the extent of the breeding season is unknown it is only possible to make an educated guess that adult post-breeding moult may take place either in December and January or possibly more likely in January and February.

CONSERVATION

Timor is the driest island in Indonesia and because the island is mountainous in parts there is still some natural vegetation left in the regions of the mountains as it is less easy to clear. Eucalyptus trees grow on the mountains but most of the undergrowth has been grazed away. In the lowlands and foothills only scrub and deciduous trees such as fig trees survive (Poul Dreyer unpublished 1991).

Loss of forest on Timor has been extensive and is likely to prove of increasing concern. A large proportion of West Timor is deforested and tropical monsoon forest, which was formerly widespread, now consists of mainly small remnants. The largest remaining area is around 90km² and is isolated and unmanaged. Few of these patches remain untouched and are subject to grazing by cattle and pigs, which possibly restrict the natural regeneration of trees with a detrimental effect on lowland forest species (Noske & Saleh 1996). Noske & Saleh (1996) suggest that it is not threatened; their surveys on West Timor from 13 May to 6 July 1993 recorded it at three of the five major survey sites and four minor sites and it was found to be common at three sites, Besi Pae, Camplong and Asio. However, under IUCN criteria it is treated as Near-Threatened, and Collar *et al.* (2001), in pointing out how extensive has been the loss of forest on Timor, state that its total numbers may not be great (irrespective of how abundant it may be at the relatively few sites in which it survives).

Collar & Andrew (1988) suggest that it is largely excluded from savanna and open scrub in West Timor by the Pied Bushchat *Saxicola caprata* but there is no real evidence of this and it may well dislike certain types of savanna. Its preferred habitat and habits are different to Pied Bushchat so it is unlikely to come into conflict with that species.

The Lesser Sundas zoogeographic zone and Timor island in particular is arguably one of the most neglected areas in the world with regard to ornithological research and knowledge. Although a field guide exists to this region, fewer than 12 papers have been published on Timor birds in the last 100 years (Noske & Saleh 1996). R. Noske has collected data on the ecology of forest birds in Timor and when this is published information will be available on their abundance, habitat requirements and breeding ecology, which will assist at the very least in establishing a baseline for conservation priorities and action.

Saxicola bifasciata Temminck, 1829, in Temminck and Laugier, *Nouv. Rec. de Planch. Color. d'Ois.* (4) 79, 1829, pl.472, fig.2—Caffrerie [= King William's Town district, eastern Cape Province, South Africa]

Etymology *bifasciata* from Latin *bifasciatus* meaning double- or two-barred. *Bi* = twice or double; *fasciatus* = banded or striped

Alternative names Buff-streaked Wheatear, Buff-streaked Chat

TAXONOMY

Monotypic. This species has an interesting and still contentious taxonomic history which has been discussed at length by Tye (1989) and Clancey (1990) and on which much of the following is based. The species has troubled taxonomists for many years with the result that it has been placed in no fewer than five genera of chats. Hall & Moreau (1970) described it as of "uncertain affinities". Even now its classification is by no means certain with both Tye and Clancey coming to different conclusions but both questioning whether it should be classified in the genus *Oenanthe*.

When Temminck first named this species in 1829 he placed it in the genus *Saxicola*, which was then very much larger than it is today, encompassing a variety of chats including the majority of wheatears. Later it was placed under *Thamnolaea* Cabanis, 1850 (type: *Turdus cinnamomeiventris* Lafresnaye) and *Myrmecocichla* Cabanis, 1850 (type: *Motacilla formicivora* Wilkes). In 1881 Seebohm transferred it to a genus of ant chats incorporated under *Myrmecocichla*, leaving other similar wheatears in the genus *Saxicola*. [Seebohm considered *Myrmecocichla* to comprise of eight species in three separate groups. Two of these groups, consisting of six species, are now currently included in the genus *Cercomela*. The remainder were included with the wheatears in the genus *Saxicola*. This third of Seebohm's groups consisted of two species, Southern Anteater Chat *M. formicivora* and Buff-streaked Bushchat.] The genus *Myrmecocichla* as listed by Seebohm in 1881 was in time radically changed and most of its species transferred to the genus *Cercomela*. However, other species were added to *Myrmecocichla*, resulting in a genus greatly changed from its original composition and bearing little relation to that in which Seebohm had placed Buff-streaked Bushchat. In 1922 yet another genus, *Campicoloides*, was proposed to accommodate it by Roberts (type: *Saxicola bifasciata* Temminck). Roberts judged the species "far removed from *T. cinnamomeiventris* (the genotype of *Thamnolaea*) and is more closely allied to *Campicola* (= *Oenanthe pileata*), but as its affinity is obscure, I propose to place it in a new genus bearing the name *Campicoloides*". However, this was not adopted at the time and it remained in *Myrmecocichla*.

Ripley *et al.* (1964), based on its plumage and behaviour, removed it from *Myrmecocichla* and placed it in the genus *Oenanthe*, which by then also included wheatears and to which it seemed most suited. However, Wolters (1980) accorded it monotypic generic status under *Campicoloides* based on Roberts's classification. The classification in *Oenanthe* by Ripley *et al.* (1964) was generally accepted (Dean 1971, Maclean 1985), but Tye (1989) reviewed its taxonomic position and argued that it should be returned to its original genus thus becoming *Saxicola bifasciata*. This has now been generally accepted and most crucially by Keith *et al.* (1992) authors of the authoritative *Birds of Africa*, although Sinclair *et al.* (1993) and Harrison *et al.* (1997) apparently disagree as they still include it as *Oenanthe bifasciata*.

Tye (1989) reasoned that although its buff-white shoulder-patches give Buff-streaked Bushchat a superficial resemblance to some ant-chats, these are formed by the scapulars whereas in ant-chats they are formed by the wing-coverts. It also differs from ant-chats in plumage, egg colour and behaviour, and generally does not appear to be closely related to them. Using traditional (BSC) taxonomic criteria Tye argued that Buff-streaked Bushchat bears a far closer resemblance to the African Stonechat *Saxicola torquata* than to any species in the genus *Oenanthe*. He considered that details of plumage, structure and behaviour shared with *Saxicola* indicated an evolutionary relationship and that Buff-streaked Bushchat could be considered as a giant African Stonechat. It is one of the two largest species in its genus – only Hodgson's Bushchat *S. insignis* is similar in size. It would be interesting to see if mtDNA confirms Tye's assertion. Clancey (1986, 1990), however, took a different and more radical view, asserting that "the evolutionary background to the Buff-streaked Chat, *Oenanthe bifasciata*, is uncertain. Even its current treatment as a wheatear of the genus *Oenanthe* is questionable. It can safely be judged to be a relict species".

Tye compared in detail what is known of this species' plumage, morphology, behaviour and ecology with *Oenanthe* and *Saxicola*. He based his comparisons primarily on *S. torquata* but they can also be made favourably with the majority of other species in *Saxicola*. His comparisons were as follows.

Plumage The throat of the male is black and it has a cream supercilium similar to features found in both *Saxicola* and *Oenanthe*, but the underparts are otherwise deep cinnamon-buff similar to both African

Stonechat and Whinchat *S. rubetra* but different from any *Oenanthe* species except Desert Wheatear *O. deserti*. Crown to back are a patterned combination of black and brown, totally unlike any wheatear species but very similar to African Stonechat and Whinchat. In all three species in fresh plumage the feathers of the upperparts are black in the centre with wide brown fringes. Tye thought that the close similarity of this plumage character alone strongly suggests a relationship between the species. The rump is cinnamon or deep buff similar to African Stonechat in fresh plumage but also is similar to two wheatear species, Tristram's *O. moesta* and Red-tailed *O. xanthoprymna*.

Tye also stated that one of the most striking plumage characters of the male are the cinnamon-buff or creamy-white inner upperwing-coverts and scapulars, which form a sharp contrast to the dark wings and remaining upperparts. He goes on to state that this precise pattern, although not found in any *Oenanthe*, is most closely reflected in Mountain Wheatear *O. monticola* and Somali Wheatear *O. phillipsi*, in which most or all of the wing-coverts are white or pale grey, and in Desert Wheatear, in which the innermost wing-coverts are buff, concolorous with the back. He then states "However, cream or white inner wing coverts and outer scapulars are a prominent feature of several *Saxicola* spp., including the [African] Stonechat, in which the extent of white varies greatly between subspecies and individuals. The females of the [African] Stonechat and Buff-streaked Chat resemble one another closely, except that the wing flash is absent from the female Buff-streaked Chat".

Tye appears to have made a major error concerning the plumage comparison between *bifasciata* and *torquata*. Male *bifasciata* does not have buff or white inner upperwing coverts and no other *Saxicola* species male or female, including African Stonechat, has white outer scapulars.

In *Saxicola* species the tail is either wholly black or black and white. The Buff-streaked Bushchat has an all-black tail. All *Oenanthe* species, except one subspecies of Mountain Wheatear *O. monticola nigricauda*, have a patterned black and white tail. Although *O. m. nigricauda* shows that a wholly black tail can occur in *Oenanthe* this character actually allies Buff-streaked Bushchat more closely with *Saxicola*.

Morphology Tye pointed out that although *bifasciata* is larger than any other *Saxicola* spp., this may not be of much significance as similar differences exist between subspecies of other chat species. It may be pertinent to also point out that similar differences exist between species in the genus *Saxicola* i.e. Hodgson's Bushchat *S. insignis* is almost as large as *bifasciata* whereas *S. torquata* is much smaller.

Tye pointed to structural differences between *Saxicola* and *Oenanthe* such as the bill of *Saxicola* is shorter and flatter at the base than in *Oenanthe*; *Oenanthe* has shorter, finer and fewer rictal bristles than *Saxicola*; the wing and tail of *Saxicola* are shorter in comparison with body size than in *Oenanthe*.

Tye made a comparison between the genera *Saxicola* and *Oenanthe* based on lengths of wing, tail and bill in relation to body size (measured by body weight). He compared Buff-streaked Bushchat to African Stonechat and Whinchat, and to Mountain Wheatear and Desert Wheatear. The two *Saxicola* spp., were chosen as those with closest geographical distribution to *bifasciata* and the two *Oenanthe* spp. represent extremes of body size in that genus.

The results demonstrated two points. First that *Saxicola* and *Oenanthe* differ considerably, and there is no overlap in the three characters. Second, Buff-streaked Bushchat, despite being considerably larger than most *Saxicola*, falls within the range of the two *Saxicola* species measurements in all three features. Differences between Buff-streaked Bushchat and Mountain Wheatear, which are similar-sized, and similarities between the two *Oenanthe* species, which differ greatly in size, suggest that the results are not the product of allometry but are likely to be true generic characteristics.

		Body weight (g)	Wing length (mm)	Tail length (mm)	Bill length (mm)
Saxicola torquata	♂	15	66(26.7)	46(18.6)	15(6.1)
	♀	14	65(27.0)	45(18.7)	15(6.2)
S. rubetra	♂	19	77(28.8)	45(16.9)	15(5.6)
	♀	17	76(29.6)	43(16.7)	15(5.8)
bifasciata	♂	{35}	93(28.4)	61(18.7)	20(6.1)
	♀		87(26.6)	58(17.7)	19(5.8)
Oenanthe monticola	♂	{33}	113(35.2)	75(23.4)	22(6.9)
	♀		109(34.0)	73(22.7)	22(6.9)
O. deserti	♂	{20}	90(33.2)	61(22.5)	18(6.6)
	♀		87(32.1)	58(21.4)	18(6.6)

Structural characterisitics of the Buff-streaked Bushchat compared with *Saxicola* and *Oenanthe* spp. Figures in brackets are measurements divided by body weight. (After A. Tye, *Bull. B.O.C.* 1989.)

278

The bill of *bifasciata* is finer than most *Saxicola* but broader than *Oenanthe* and thus falls, taking into account bill length proportional to body size and shape, between the two genera being short as in *Saxicola* and fine as in *Oenanthe*.

Buff-streaked Bushchat also possesses long, prominent rictal bristles as in the *Saxicola* species.

Ecology and behaviour Buff-streaked Bushchat nests mainly in crevices, often siting its nest on the ground on the downslope side of a rock concealed by grasses. This resembles other *Saxicola* species. *Oenanthe* species nest mainly underground in holes. In habitat selection and feeding Buff-streaked Bushchat again demonstrates similar preferences and behaviour to *Saxicola*. It favours montane grasslands with tall grasses; this is also the normal habitat of many *Saxicola* species including African Stonechat with which it is found in the Drakensberg Mountains of South Africa. Feeding behaviour is similar, especially where the two species use similar habitat. In Tye's study area both species favoured aerial-sallying. African Stonechats use mainly vegetation as perches to locate prey whereas Buff-streaked Bushchat prefers rocks. However, where rocks are available African Stonechat will use them freely as hunting perches. In Tye's study area Buff-streaked Bushchat used rocks for 96% of their perches whilst African Stonechat used them for 53% of perches. It was suggested by Tye that the stronger preference for rocks shown by *S. bifasciata* was due to their heavier build.

Taken in isolation none of the morphological characters linking Buff-streaked Bushchat to *Saxicola* is particularly convincing, but Tye judged that as a group of shared characters, the overall similarity, especially with African Stonechat, seems unlikely to have arisen by convergence. In contrast, one or other isolated characters shared with different species in *Oenanthe*, such as general colour with Desert Wheatear and rump colour with Tristram's, are less likely to indicate a close relationship and more likely to represent convergence. Tye speculated that the three genera *Oenanthe*, *Myrmecocichla* and *Cercomela* (and possibly including *Thamnolea*, *Saxicola* and others) may stem from an early chat radiation, although the exact relationship between these genera and their individual species groups remains unclear. He suggested that although Buff-streaked Bushchat most closely resembles *Saxicola* it might represent an evolutionary line which has been independent since the suggested early chat radiation and that, if so, it should be assigned its own monotypic genus; but he concluded that, in the absence of clear evidence on this point, it should be placed with the genus to which it appears most closely related. He therefore returned it to its original, although now much changed genus, *Saxicola*.

	Buff-streaked Bushchat	Stonechat	*Oenanthe* spp.
Underparts	rich cinnamon-buff	+	– (+ *deserti*)
Tail	black	+	– (+ *m. nigricauda*)
Upperparts	mottled black and brown	+	–
Rump	cinnamon-buff	+	– (+ *moesta* & *xanthopryma*)
Shoulder-patch	contrasting buff-white	+	– (+ *monticola*)

Comparison of plumage characteristics of Buff-streaked Bushchat with Stonechat *Saxicola torquata* and wheatears. + signifies agreement with Buff-streaked Bushchat, - signifies disagreement. (After A. Tye, *Bull. B.O.C.* 1989.)

There is one particular aspect of Buff-streaked Bushchat that is dissimilar to both *Saxicola* and *Oenanthe*. The egg has a creamy-white or buff ground colour liberally speckled with lilac and reddish-brown spots and freckles. *Saxicola* and *Oenanthe* eggs usually have a blue ground colour with reddish-brown spots and freckles. The egg of *S. bifasciata* is closer in appearance to those of *Thamnolea* and *Monticola*. However, Tye suggested that the egg colour of Turdidae is quite variable and therefore "these resemblances may not bear any taxonomic significance" (Lack 1958).

Clancey (1990) disagreed with Tye, and provided the following evidence and background to corroborate his and Wolters' proposed acceptance of this species in its own monotypic genus *Campicoloides*.

Clancey outlined the fact that Ripley *et al.* (1964), in their treatment of Afrotropical chats, list in generic sequence *Cercomela*, then *Saxicola*, *Myrmecocichla*, *Thamnolaea* and *Oenanthe*; in this Roberts' (1922) proposed genus *Campicoloides* is shown as a synonym of *Oenanthe*. Buff-streaked Bushchat has at one time or the other featured in all these genera. Clancey was of the opinion that these genera were "in most instances based on relatively tenuous morphological characters, reflecting disparities in the length of the tail to that of the wing, tarsal length, bill mass, development of the rictal bristles, colour pattern and levels of difference between the sexes".

The area that Buff-streaked Bushchat inhabits in south-eastern Africa is remarkable in that it supports a number of diverse remnant forms at generic, specific and subspecific levels, "deriving from early evolutionary radiations within the Afrotropics and of still earlier colonizing invasions of ancestral extralimital elements, among which can be listed Southern Bald Ibis, *Geronticus calvus*, Ground Woodpecker, *Geocolaptes olivaceous*, Rudd's Lark, *Heteromirafra ruddi*, Bush Blackcap, *Lioptilus nigricapillus*, Orange-breasted Rockjumper, *Chaetops aurantius*, Saffron-breasted Prinia, *Prinia hypoxantha*, Mountain Pipit, *Anthus hoeschi*, Yellow-tufted Pipit, *Anthus crenatus* ..."

The restricted and tenuous breeding range of Buff-streaked Bushchat is very similar to some of the endemic bird species referred to above and substantiates the view that it is a relict species. Clancey also added that it appears to have no close affinities with any rock-dwelling genera of smaller turdines of the Palearctic.

He pointed to one of Tye's main assertions for classification in *Saxicola* – that males are similar in plumage to African Stonechat males – and stated that this may be no more than fortuitous or the result of convergence, as both birds are found in broadly similar habitats. He argued that it can be

"postulated that it is the sole remaining representative of an early and putatively successful chat radiation. Conversely, the widespread and highly polytypic [African] Stonechat... is in a relatively early expansionary phase of its evolutionary history. Apart from the Ethiopian population (*S. t. albofasciata*), the continental (Afrotropical) subspecies are only moderately well-differentiated, whereas to the east of them, in the insular forms occurring in the Malagasy subregion, speciation is more advanced, as in the case of the Reunion form (*S. t. tectes*) [now accorded full species status (Sibley & Monroe 1990)]. In biogeographical terms, the Buff-streaked Bushchat is to be seen as the last of an early and chronologically distant chat radiation, whereas in so far as continental Africa is concerned the much smaller Common [African] Stonechat is viewed as a more adaptive invasive species of recent Palearctic origin."

Clancey argued that the above merits a monotypic genus for Buff-streaked Bushchat and gave it the binomial name *Campicoloides bifasciatus* (Temminck 1829), characterising the genus as follows:

"Of much larger and robust proportions than all species included in the genus *Saxicola* by Ripley *et al.* (1964), as confirmed by its longer tail compared to the wing: *C. bifasciatus* with mean of wing in males 92.4/tail 60.7 versus 71.4/52.7mm in the immediately sympatric subspecies of the [African] Stonechat (*S. t. torquata*). [As already indicated, one species in *Saxicola*, Hodgson's Bushchat, is similar in size and proportions, so Clancey was mistaken here.]

Bill heavier, and rictal bristles stronger; legs and toes heavier, the tail >32, versus <25mm. Rump sharply demarcated from the mantle and scapulars in coloration, and feathers longer (to c.39 mm), tending to form a pronounced bustle. Wings and tail entirely black in the male.

Female comparably separable on structural grounds and in lacking white in the wings and tail (in the [African] Stonechat both sexes have white in the wings and some races have white in the tail of the male). Ventrally finely streaked and not plain.

Juvenile distinctive in exhibiting virtual loss of light scaling to the scapulars, which are light brown with dark shaft-streaks, and contrast with the mantle, which character probably reflects symplesiomorphy [a shared primitive character, i.e. this feature is ancestral and not recently derived].

The rump and uppertail-coverts are plain yellowish-buff as in adults."

Clancey came to the conclusion that Roberts' (1922) assignment of this species to *Campicoloides* was valid and gave it the following official designation:

Genus Campicoloides
Campicoloides Roberts, *Ann. Trans. Mus.* vol viii, 1922, p.22:
Type, by monotypy, *Saxicola bifasciata* Temminck.
With sole species
Campicoloides bifasciatus (Temminck 1829)
Saxicola bifasciata Temminck, *Planch. Color.*, vol. 4, livr. 79, 1829, pl.472, fig.2: Caffrerie = King William's Town district, eastern Cape Province.
Saxicola spectabilis Hartlaub, *Proc. Zool. Soc. London*, 1865 (9 May), p.428, pl. 23: Windvogelberg, Cathcart district, eastern Cape Province.

I would concur with both Tye (1989) and Clancey (1990) that this species probably does not belong in the genus *Oenanthe*. I am also dubious that it qualifies to be included in the genus *Saxicola* and that Tye's suggestions that it should be because it bears more similarity to *Saxicola* than *Oenanthe* or any other closely related genera is unsatisfactory. However, he is only the latest in a series of systematists who have struggled to assign this enigmatic species a satisfactory taxonomic classification.

The plumage similarities highlighted by Tye between *bifasciata* and other *Saxicola* spp. are weak and in one case wrong. The reference to the similarities in having cinnamon-buff underparts ignores the fact that *bifasciata* retains completely orange underparts all year round, whereas those *Saxicola* spp. which show this characteristic have the majority of the underparts orange-buff only in fresh plumage. For the rest of the year the underparts become progressively white apart from the breast. I also disagree with Tye when he says the upperparts from crown to back are a similar mottled brown and black and the exactitude of resemblance in this character alone would strongly suggest relationship. S*axicola* spp. males lose through abrasion the fringes to the head and back which then become predominantly black, whereas *bifasciata* never becomes predominantly black on the back but always retains brown-buff fringes, creating a mottled appearance. The rump comparison is also misleading in that male *bifasciata* retains an orange-buff rump and uppertail-coverts all year round whereas those *Saxicola* spp. where the male has an orange-buff rump and uppertail-coverts, usually lose the orange as the fringes wear away and the rump and uppertail coverts become pure white. The comparison between buff-white wing coverts and scapulars has been shown earlier to be wrong. The assertion that a wholly black tail allies *bifasciata* more closely to *Saxicola* spp., than *Oenanthe* which have mainly black and white tails is also weak. Tye himself points out that a subspecies of Mountain Wheatear, *Oenanthe monticola nigricauda* has a wholly black tail and it is a fact that a number of species and subspecies of *Saxicola* have white in the tail.

Tye states that taken individually each of his plumage resemblances is weak but taken as a whole they are convincing and the overall similarity between *bifasciata* and especially the African Stonechat seems unlikely to have arisen out of convergence. I do not think it is possible to come to such a conclusion based on his plumage comparisons, as they are far too unconvincing on detail.

Tye also admits to differences in the egg colour of *bifasciata* and other *Saxicola* spp. He comments that these species' eggs bear closest resemblance to *Thamnolea* and *Monticola* spp., although sometimes they resemble a few species of both *Saxicola* and *Oenanthe*.

The remark that egg colour is quite labile in the Turdidae and that these resemblances may not bear any taxonomic significance hardly convinces that this is justification for not considering this difference in greater depth.

Tye also states that most aspects of its behaviour and ecology do not ally it more closely to either *Saxicola* or *Oenanthe* partly because these two genera are quite similar to each other. There are also differences in the breeding biology of *bifasciata* and *Saxicola* spp. Tye asserts that *bifasciata* and *Saxicola* spp. share similarities in nest site in that both nest on the ground. However *bifasciata* usually place their nest below fairly large overhanging rocks at their base or even in a crevice. *Saxicola* spp., notably African Stonechat, also nest on the ground but not at the base of rocks or in crevices but in depressions in the ground often below bushes and grass clumps. The number of eggs laid in a clutch is slightly smaller than those laid by African Stonechat: *bifasciata* mean of 18 clutches 2.8 eggs, African Stonechat mean of 50 clutches 3.2 eggs (Maclean 1985).

Bifasciata also shows a marked difference in preference of perch to *Saxicola* spp. Tye (1988) showed that in areas where there are rocks *bifasciata* used them 96% of the time to hunt prey whereas African Stonechat used them only 53% of the time, reverting for the rest of the time to more typical elevated perches on vegetation. Tye suggested that *bifasciata* used rocks as perches because of its bulk but Hodgson's Bushchat *Saxicola insignis* from India, which is similar in size, and presumably weight, does not show such a preference.

A point not considered by Tye (1989) is that female *bifasciata* also sing, especially when breeding and to a lesser extent outside of the breeding season, whereas no female of any *Saxicola* spp. has been heard to sing. Male *bifasciata* also sing to defend non-breeding territories in winter whereas African Stonechats do not.

Tye (1989) states "the genus *Oenanthe* may not be monophyletic, even after excluding the Buff-streaked Chat from it. Certain *Oenanthe* spp., or superspecies seem closely linked with *Myrmecocichla* on the one hand (e.g. *O. monticola*) and *Cercomela* on the other (e.g. *O. pileata* superspecies). These three genera, perhaps together with *Thamnolea*, *Saxicola* and others, seem to stem from an early chat radiation, although the precise relationships between these genera and their constituent species-groups are obscure". Tye does concede that even though it most closely resembles *Saxicola* spp., it is possible that *bifasciata* represents an evolutionary line which has been independent since the time of the postulated early chat radiation and if true, *bifasciata* should be assigned its own monotypic genus. However, because Tye lacked any clear evidence as to what the chain of events was at the time of isolation of the present genera's ancestors, he took the less radical option of placing *bifasciata* with what appeared to be its nearest relatives – the genus *Saxicola*. Unfortunately, as shown above there is considerable evidence that placing it in the genus *Saxicola* may not be so appropriate, even though superficially it may appear to be closest to this genus. I would suggest that Clancey's reasoning might be more appropriate for this species. Both Tye and Clancey queried this species' taxonomic status and made their assertions before the real onset of DNA techniques. Hopefully mtDNA research might point to this species' true relationship to other allied taxa and settle its rather turbulent taxonomic history.

IDENTIFICATION

Size 17–18cm/6.5–7.0 inches. The largest species in the genus. Sexually dimorphic. The male is an unmistakable combination of black, buff and white. The head, upper breast, wings and tail are black. A long, broad, buff-white supercilium extends from the bill over the eye around the ear-coverts and merges with the pale sides of the neck. The mantle is brown, streaked with black, contrasting with the buff-white scapulars which form a distinct V-shape from the sides of the neck to the sides of the rump. The rump and entire underparts are orange-buff. The female has the head and upperparts generally brown with an orange-buff rump contrasting with the black tail. The supercilium is indistinct and pale buff. The chin and throat whitish-buff, the rest of the underparts orange-buff, narrowly streaked dark brown on the chin, throat and breast.

Confusion species Only one other member of the genus, African Stonechat *S. t. torquata*, occurs in the same habitat. Both sexes of *S. bifasciata* are unlikely to be confused with that species as they are much larger. Male *bifasciata* does not have a white rump and uppertail-coverts or white on the upperwing-coverts. The head is black with a long, broad buff-white supercilium. The scapulars are pale buff. Female *bifasciata* is less streaked brown and black on the upperparts and lacks the white rump, uppertail-coverts and wing-patch on the inner greater upperwing-coverts. The chin and throat are pale and lack dark feathers. Female *S. bifasciata* can be told from the superficially similar female *Cercomela* chats by its generally paler orange and brown plumage, pale buff supercilium and black tail; and from immature Capped Wheatear *Oenanthe pileata* by its buff not white rump. The species' habits are slightly different to African Stonechat in that it prefers to perch on boulders rather than vegetation.

DESCRIPTION

Adult male fresh plumage Crown, nape, lores, malar region, ear-coverts, chin, throat and the centre of the upper breast are glossy velvety black. The crown and nape, chin, throat and upper breast have dark ginger-brown fringes contrasting slightly with the narrower ginger-brown fringes and consequently blacker feathers on the sides of the head. The nape also has occasional pale buff fringes which create a mottled appearance. The forehead and supercilium are buff-white with stronger orange-buff fringes. The supercilium extends in a broad line from the base of the bill above the eye and around the ear-coverts where it merges with the side of the neck, breast and outer scapulars, which are also buff-white. The mantle and innermost scapulars are black with extensive dark ginger-brown tips which largely conceal the black. Some of the mantle feathers show very fine white tips and the occasional feather is entirely pale buff. Most scapulars are buff-white with orange-buff tips. The foremost scapulars tend to be paler, becoming a stronger orange-buff towards the rear. The odd dark brown feather also occurs within the pale feathering. The scapulars form a broad band extending down above the wings to the sides of the rump. The back, rump and uppertail-coverts are creamy orange-buff with the uppertail-coverts markedly paler. They form a striking contrast between the dark mantle and black rectrices. The lower breast, flanks, belly and undertail-coverts are a uniform rich, orange-buff stronger in tone than the whitish-buff areas on the upperparts.

The remiges are black with fine, pale buff crescentic tips. The upperwing lesser, median, greater and primary coverts are velvety-black. The tertials are black with prominent whitish-buff tips extending upwards in a thin fringe along the outer web of the feather. There are similar narrow pale fringes to the outer webs of the two innermost secondaries. The underwing-coverts and axillaries are black.

The bill, legs and feet are black. The irides are dark brown.

The plumage varies only slightly through the year. As it wears the crown and nape become entirely black. The mantle becomes blacker as more of the black centres to the feathers are exposed but still retains a large number of ginger-brown fringes. The uppertail-coverts become buff-white contrasting even more strongly with the black tail. The pale tips and fringes to the tertials and remiges wear away completely. The lower rear scapulars retain their strong orange-buff tone and if anything become slightly darker and almost as strongly coloured as the underparts. The remaining pale scapulars lose their orange-buff tips and become an even paler buff-white than in fresh plumage.

First-year male Very similar in pattern to the adult male but differs in showing much more extensive ginger-brown fringing to the black feathering. The whole of the crown, nape, chin, throat and upper breast have scattered narrow ginger-brown fringes. The pale buff on the scapulars is very much reduced and this area, together with the supercilium, back, rump, uppertail-coverts and entire underparts, is darker orange-buff than in the adult male. The remiges and rectrices are brown rather than black, becoming increasingly faded brown with wear. The tertials, inner secondaries and outer upperwing greater coverts have broad orange-brown tips and fringes. The inner upperwing greater coverts have smaller similar-coloured fringes. The upperwing primary coverts are fringed and tipped with paler orange-buff than the upperwing greater coverts. The underwing-coverts are black with buff tips.

Adult female The forehead and crown are predominantly dark brown/black with narrow pale orange-brown fringes. These contrast with the nape and mantle, which do not have dark bases to the feathers but are a uniform vinaceous-brown with a marked pink tone in fresh plumage. The scapulars are slightly paler vinaceous-brown, also with a pink tone in fresh plumage, and both the mantle and scapulars have slightly darker brown central shaft-streaks. In very fresh plumage the feathers of especially the lower mantle, scapulars and underparts show whitish-buff fringes, creating a slightly paler appearance and obscuring the darker central shaft-streaks on the mantle and scapulars. The back and rump are orange-buff, becoming slightly paler on the lower rump and uppertail-coverts. The lores and malar region are brown with very fine buff tips to the feathers, creating a grizzled appearance. The ear-coverts are brown. The supercilium is dark buff and meets on the forehead, extending from the base of the bill above the eye to the rear of the ear-coverts. It is much narrower and far less distinct than in the male, becoming more prominent from the eye to the rear of the ear-coverts. The chin and throat are greyish-white with an orange-buff tinge to the sides of the throat. The feathers have very fine, dark brown shaft-streaks which form narrow lines down the chin and throat. The sides of the neck, upper and lower breast, flanks and belly are a fairly uniform orange-buff with a pink tone in fresh plumage. The tone of the underparts becomes generally stronger as the pale whitish-buff fringes wear away. The colouring is strongest on the upper and lower breast. The breast and flank feathers have narrow, dark brown shaft-streaks running down the centre of each feather, creating a streaked effect. The undertail-coverts are orange-buff, slightly stronger in tone than on the belly and ventral area.

The rectrices are dark brown, almost black with a slight gloss. The remiges and tertials are dark brown but not as dark as the tail. The inner secondaries have very narrow orange-brown fringes to the outer webs and tips. The upperwing lesser coverts are black, virtually obscured by broad greyish-olive fringes. The upperwing median coverts are dark brown with triangular black centres almost obscured by broad orange-brown fringes. The upperwing greater coverts are dark brown broadly fringed and tipped greyish-orange. The upperwing primary coverts are black with grey-buff fringes to the outer webs. The underwing-coverts are black, almost totally obscured by buff fringes. The axillaries are cinnamon-buff. The bill is dark brown, almost black. The legs and feet are black. The irides are dark brown.

Juvenile Superficially similar to the female. The feathers of the forehead, crown, nape, lores, malar region and ear-coverts are dull dark brown with buff spots and streaks to the feather centres, giving a speckled appearance. The mantle and scapulars are pale yellowish-buff with narrow dark brown/black fringes to some of the feathers. The back is orange-buff and the rump and uppertail-coverts are a deeper buff-orange. The rectrices are black, the remiges brown, and secondaries and inner primaries have pale buff crescentic tips. The upperwing greater, median and lesser coverts are dark brown with orange-buff fringes and tips. The upperwing primary coverts are also dark brown with large pale buff fringes and tips. The tertials are dark brown with prominent orange-buff tips and fringes to the outer webs. The chin, throat and breast are cinnamon-buff with narrow brown fringes to each feather creating a mottled appearance. The flanks, belly and ventral area are also cinnamon-buff and some of the feathers have very faint brown shaft-streaks. The undertail-coverts are dull orange-buff.

Juvenile females are said to be identifiable by their tails being browner rather than black as in the male. Examination of male and female specimens did not appear to confirm this.

Clancey examined 52 male specimens and found a degree of regional variation. Six specimens from the uplands of Transvaal [Mpumalanga] and Swaziland ranging from Wakkerstroom in the extreme south of Transvaal [Mpumalanga] to the northern limits of its range at c.24°S differed from specimens in the Eastern Cape. They had either the frons or entire forehead white. In the 19 Transvaal [Mpumalanga] specimens 31.5% of the birds had the fore-pileum white.

Measurements

	Male	Female
Wing	87.0–97.0 (91.85)	85.5–91.0 (88.08)
Tail	68.0–76.0 (72.65)	67.0–70.5 (68.64)
Bill	17.5–19.5 (18.95)	17.0–19.0 (18.29)

[Own measurements BMNH 2000]

DISTRIBUTION AND STATUS

The Buff-streaked Bushchat is a common but localised endemic resident of South Africa, Swaziland and Lesotho, although in the latter it is apparently only marginal. Its distribution is closely allied to the distribution of sour grasslands (Harrison *et al.* 1997), only extending beyond the grassland biome in the westward extension of its range in the Northern Province [Limpopo Province] where it is restricted to a few mountains. There are isolated populations in mountains north of Potgietersrus and in central and western Waterberg [Limpopo Province]. It was formerly found in Magaliesberg but is now extinct there. It is notably absent from the sour grasslands of Witwatersrand and southern Mpumalanga. It is found from 26°E in Eastern Cape north and east of a line from Grahamstown to Graaf-Reinet. It then ranges north-east through the Drakensberg Mountain Range, avoiding the alpine summit but present along the whole of the seaward-facing slopes below the 2,000m contour. Also found inland in KwaZulu-Natal, eastern Lesotho and the eastern Free State, north through western Swaziland, eastern Mpumalanga and Northern Province [Limpopo Province] highveld to the Soutspanberg, extending to 24°S (Kemp *et al.* 1985). It usually frequents montane grassland plateaux above 1,000m and is rarely found below 900m, but occurs from sea level upwards on the coast of Eastern Cape, and KwaZulu-Natal.

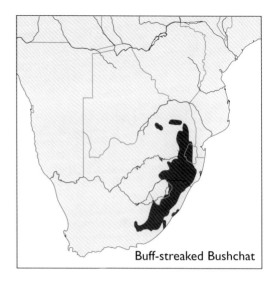

Buff-streaked Bushchat

BREEDING

Monogamous. It is strongly territorial in the breeding season, with males singing from prominent rocks and boulders; females also sing. Cooperative breeding may occasionally occur in which a second male will assist a pair in feeding the young (M. Muchane *in litt.* 2000). The breeding season extends from September to December in KwaZulu-Natal and from September to February in the Transvaal [Mpumalanga]. The peak laying period appears to be October–November (Dean 1971, Tarboton *et al.* 1987). The nest is usually sited on the ground, on the downslope side and at the base of a rock or under the overhang of a boulder, often concealed by grass. Less often nests are built in a crevice in rocks or a wall: of 13 nests found, 12 were under a rock and one was in the cleft of a rock. The rocks these nests were situated under were 0.5–2m high (W.R. Tarboton *in litt.* 2000). The nest is usually very well hidden but it can also occasionally be in an exposed position (Vincent 1947, W.R. Tarboton *in litt.* 2000) Although the male will follow the female and accompany her to the nest site when she is building, he does not take any part in collecting nest material or constructing the nest. Nests can face in virtually any direction and have been found facing SW/W/S/SE/E/NE. Pairs can make more than one breeding attempt per season but whether these are replacements for predated nests or second nests following a successful first breeding attempt is unconfirmed.

The foundation of the nest is bulky and untidy, constructed of coarse grasses and roots. The nest cup is large, relatively deep and also untidy, made from softer grasses and lined with animal hair and finer grasses. One nest had a lining of woolly material (W.R. Tarboton *in litt.* 2000). The diameter of the nest cup is 70–80mm with a depth of 40–50mm. Two nests found in early November consisted of a platform of tough grass roots on which was built a flimsy saucer of dry grass, with horsehair arranged in a ring round the inner rim (Vincent 1947). Incubation is mainly or possibly entirely done by the female with a full clutch being from 2–4 eggs but usually 3. Eleven Nest Record Cards showed eight (72.7%) with clutches of three eggs (Dean 1971). Another eleven nests revealed seven (63.6%) with clutches of three and four with two eggs (W.R. Tarboton *in litt.* 2000). The mean of 18 clutches was 2.8 eggs (Maclean 1985). The eggs are subelliptical and smooth with a slight gloss, the ground colour being creamy-white or buff although some can be bluish-white. They are profusely speckled and blotched with lilac or red-brown, normally with a cap or ring of denser, richer-coloured speckles and blotches, and a close spotting of slate-grey, at the larger end. Some eggs only have a few spots on a clear background apart from a heavy suffusion of markings in a cap or ring at the larger end (Vincent 1947). The mean of 20 eggs measured was 23.1 x 16.5mm with extremes of 21–25.2 x 15.1–17.3mm. Another sample of nine gave a mean of 23.1 x 16.4mm with maxima of 24.4 x 16.3 and 22.5 x 17.0 and minima of 22.0 x 16.0 and 22.2 x 15.5mm.

One egg is laid each day until the clutch is complete and incubation begins the same day as the last egg is laid (M. Muchane *in litt.* 2000). There is no detailed information concerning the incubation or nestling period but both are thought to be c.14 days (M. Muchane *in litt.* 2000). On hatching the young are covered with fine hair-like greyish-black feathers.

The young are fed by both parents whilst in the nest and when they fledge. In a period of 4.5 hours both birds of a pair were observed bringing food to their young in the nest at the rate of c.10 visits per hour, with the female making more visits than the male by a ratio of 3:2 (W.R. Tarboton *in litt.* 2000). Out of five nests under observation at Wakkerstroom in Mpumalanga Province only one was successful (M. Muchane *in litt.* 2000).

HABITAT

The Buff-streaked Bushchat generally inhabits the taller, lusher, submontane sour grasslands. Typical habitat is usually scattered boulders, rocky outcrops, often with aloes, small scattered bushes and trees on rocky, open, ungrazed mountainsides, hillsides, ridges and escarpments. Where it is found in or near mixed and sweet grasslands this is probably due to interdigitation with sour grasslands as its range does not significantly extend into the former two vegetation types. It is absent from the KwaZulu-Natal alpine belt and from similar habitat in Lesotho. It is most frequently found at intermediate altitudes between [500>] 1,500 and 1,700 [<2,000]m but on the KwaZulu-Natal/Eastern Cape border is found down to sea level (Harrison *et al.* 1997). It is generally sedentary in its preferred habitat but in the non-breeding season it often wanders to cattle kraals and farmyards, abandoned old houses, fallow uncultivated land and along roadside areas. Normally wary, it becomes relatively confiding around human settlements. It actively avoids woodlands and plantations. A breeding pair with a nest in unburnt grassland fed in the adjacent burnt grassland. A male was observed feeding a fully fledged juvenile on a bird table in a garden bordering montane grassland and protea scrub.

Habitat in the Drakensberg mountains in KwaZulu-Natal used by Tye (1988) to study the foraging behaviour, prey and perch selection of non-breeding birds consisted of montane grassland between 1,300–1,800m with rocky cliff outcrops at 1,700–1,800m and grassy slopes and boulder fields lying below. The species showed a preference for the boulder fields. Tye's study site was on north-facing slopes including three boulder fields each of around 1ha which supported 1–3 individuals each. The angle of slope averaged 35° with continuous grass cover except on rocky outcrops and boulders. The height of the grass was mainly c.50cm but was shorter, averaging 35cm, on the steeper slopes and with scattered patches of even shorter grass. Boulders ranged up to 15m across and protruded up to 10m above the surrounding grassland. Occasional trees up to 6m such as *Protea* spp, *Cussonia paniculata* and *Cyathea dregei* were scattered through the grassland but mainly on the lower, less steep slopes. In another study area at Wakkerstroom in Mpumalanga around seven individuals were found per 20ha (M. Muchane *in litt.* 2000).

VOICE

Uniquely in the genus both male and female sing, both inside and outside the breeding season. The song consists of melodious, short, quick phrases 2–6 seconds long, each interspersed by pauses of 2–10 seconds. A phrase will often commence with 1–4 *chack* notes followed by a series of penetrating whistling, trilled or harsh notes. Pauses between song phrases are often broken with *chack* notes. Maclean (1985) describes the song as *klitik tweeoo, trrrpeetoo* (pause), *klitik tritri tweeoo, tritritri*, etc. It mimics other species' calls and the song is frequently interspersed with phrases of songs of other species in the same area. It has been heard to mimic Diederik Cuckoo *Chrysococcyx caprius*, Orange-throated Longclaw *Macronyx capensis*, Greater Striped Swallow *Hirundo cucullata* and various *Cisticola* species (W.R. Tarboton in Ginn *et al.* 1989).

Birds sing throughout the breeding season and Tye (1988) found that males spend much time singing in the early part of the non-breeding season and that song forms part of the defence of its non-breeding territory. Keith *et al.* (1992) state that it will sing briefly during aggressive interactions with others of its species and in the non-breeding season frequently sings quietly whilst foraging for prey. Apparently Buff-streaked Bushchat will counter-sing with a whistling human being (K. Gamble in Keith *et al.* 1992).

The call notes used by both sexes are *chack* and a short squeaky whistled *wheet*. These are uttered as single notes or in a combination of both notes or a sequence of just one. The *chack* calls are the commoner of the two, and are mainly used in territorial defence and in alarm when an intruder is in their territory

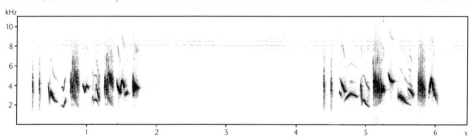

Buff-streaked Bushchat *Saxicola bifasciata* **Southern African Birdsounds. Song. South Africa, 1995.** *G. Gibbon.*

(Keith *et al.* 1992). Although no research has been done it is likely that the call notes used when breeding perform a similar function to those uttered by African Stonechat which is often found breeding in the same habitat.

FOOD

Based largely on a study by Tye (1988) in montane grassland in the KwaZulu-Natal Drakensberg Mountains. The Buff-streaked Bushchat is almost exclusively insectivorous. It was found from faecal analysis that ants (virtually all of which were alates), grasshoppers and beetles were numerically the most important prey, although grasshoppers were probably energetically the most important owing to their larger size. From visual observation it was found that the commonest prey was grasshoppers (75%) with other insects comprising the remaining 25%. Most prey seen had a body length greater than 6mm, although smaller prey were probably under-recorded. However, even if all capture attempts where prey could not be seen and/or where the outcome of the attempt was unknown are assumed to have provided a prey item less than 6mm long, the proportion of larger prey was still high (31% of 209 attempts).

PREY SIZE		NUMBER OF PREY CAUGHT IN EACH SIZE CLASS				
x bill	Approx. mm equiv.	Total prey	Unidentified	Grasshoppers Acrididae	Crickets Beetles Moths Alate ants	Alate Termites Isoptera
(a) When termites not available						
<0.5	<6	6	5	1		
0.5	6–9	14	10	1	3	
0.75	10–13	10	9	1		
1	14–17	19	14	5		
1.25	18–20	2	1	1		
1.5	21–24	3	1	1	1	
2	28–32	1	0	1		
Identified but not sized		5	–	4	1	
(b) When termites available						
<0.5	<6	216				216
1	14–17	1		1		
Identified but not sized		3	–	3		

Prey size and identity, determined during direct observation of prey capture. (After Tye, 1988.)

When termites swarmed after showers and were consequently available as prey, birds switched to hunting them almost exclusively. The mean body length of termites collected from individuals feeding areas was 4.0 ± 0.3mm, thus 98% of the diet then comprised prey less than 6mm long.

Comparison of the results of direct observation with faecal analysis confirmed that grasshoppers were the major prey item when termites were not swarming. Faecal analysis further confirmed that smaller prey not visually identified during capture may have consisted largely of beetles, winged ants, spiders and worker ants. Prey not well sampled by either faecal or visual method include small soft-bodied prey such as spiders. Termites were not found in faeces, though they are normally identifiable by jaws, head capsules and wing fragments. Their absence from collected faeces may just have reflected the fact that swarms were only available for a relatively short time and mostly did not contribute to the diet.

	Ants Formicidae	Spiders Araneae	Grasshopppers Acrididae	Beetles Coleoptera
Pellets containing prey taxon: number (%)	15 (83)	4 (22)	18 (100)	10 (56)
Mean minimum number of individuals: in pellets containing at least one in all 18 pellets	4,8±1,0 4,0±1,0	1±0 0,2±0,1	3,6±0,5 3,6±0,5	2,0±0,3 1,1±0,3
Body length of prey (mm): mean ±SE (n) range	5,9±0,2(34) 5–10		13,7±0,6(17) 10–20	7,4±1,2(7) 2–10

Composition of faecal pellets. (After Tye, 1988.)

Half-grown nestlings have been observed to be fed grasshoppers, caterpillars and unidentified insects (Tarboton in Keith *et al.* 1992). Adults also take moths, other larvae and pupae. Adult birds that visited bird tables took a fat and maize-meal mixture (Gamble in Keith *et al.* 1992).

Tye (1988) found that Buff-Streaked Bushchats employ four different foraging techniques to capture their prey in four types of location. 'Dash-and-jab' is used to obtain invertebrate prey from horizontal rock surfaces and occasionally from vegetated ground. On rocks it consists of running along the rock surface from a stationary position to peck at prey on the rock. Most prey were found when the bird was stationary. This hunting technique was occasionally employed in dense short grass no more than 20cm high with birds bounding over the grass to seize prey. 'Ground-sallying' consists of perching on a rock or very rarely a bush, then flying to the ground to seize prey located from the elevated perch. The bird then either swallows the prey and returns to the same perch or another, or occasionally returns to a perch and then swallows the prey. Occasionally, from perches less than 0.5m high, an action between dash-and-jab and ground-sallying was observed, when a bird would jump to the ground and then run a short distance to make a capture. It would then either run or fly back to its perch. Most sallies were made within a radius of 3m of the perch. There was no relationship between the height of a perch and the distance flown from it to seize prey on the ground. 'Aerial-sallying' also involved waiting on an elevated perch, usually a rock, then flying to catch airborne prey. Smaller prey was swallowed in mid-air but most sorties resulted in the bird (a) dropping to the ground with the prey before returning to a rock or (b) returning directly to a rock. This technique was also used if the previous two techniques failed and the prey evaded capture by taking wing. Many large grasshoppers, beetles and unidentified prey were dealt with in this way, often being beaten on the rock before being eaten. Two beetles and a large grasshopper took over 50 seconds to be dealt with between capture and swallowing. 'Sally-gleaning' was very occasionally used to seize prey from tall grass or tree trunks. The bird would fly up from its perch on a rock, seize the prey from the vegetation, and return to its perch in one movement.

All four techniques can be termed sit-and-wait techniques. Since they all involve a similar search phase it would appear that birds do not devote a discrete period of time to any given technique but that prey availability determines which technique is used on any given occasion (see Table above). The data are divided according to whether alate termites were available or not, as the frequencies of each technique changed dramatically during termite swarms. During a swarm birds ignored dash-and-jab and ground-sallying in grassland and concentrated on dash-and-jab on rocks as alates landed and aerial-sallying when they were on the wing. Most prey were swallowed immediately or after returning to a perch, whatever technique was used.

Birds perch mainly on rocks whether hunting or not, and only occasionally settle on vegetation. Plant perches include low sticks, which were occasionally used for hunting, and perches up to 8m above ground in the lower branches of trees which were also used for resting in the shade. The species has been noted on rare occasions to alight on the tops of high trees (Clancey 1964). In Tye's study there were potentially far more suitable plant perches than rock perches, suggesting that the predominant use of the latter (511 to 21 vegetative) represents a true preference. Birds often left plant perches without making a feeding attempt (52.4%), whilst a greater proportion of rock perches yielded a feeding attempt (70.6%).

When selecting perches Buff-streaked Bushchats show a preference for rocks 1.5–3m in height, avoiding lower or higher perches. When termites were swarming they prefer large flat rocks for hunting termites presumably because they were easier to see. Perches 1.5–3m high were more likely to result in an aerial sally, while those less than 1.5m were more likely to result in a ground sally or be left without a foraging attempt. Giving-up times were longer on perches 1.5–3m high, but pre-capture waiting times were similar for perches at all heights. Giving-up times were longer than pre-capture times on perches 1.5–3m high but of similar duration to pre-capture times on lower perches (Tye 1988). Birds are easily caught using ground traps baited with mealworms, although they quickly associate traps with danger after being captured a few times (M. Muchane *in litt.* 2000).

MOVEMENTS

Non-migratory. After the breeding season it makes local movements. There is some evidence of altitudinal movement, with higher numbers of sightings at lower altitudes in winter suggesting movement away from higher altitudes. It may be that migratory birds at higher altitudes actually leapfrog resident birds at mid-altitudes to winter lower down, although this has not been proven. In Swaziland it is entirely sedentary and there are no seasonal movements (Harrison *et al.* 1997).

BEHAVIOUR

Pairs are strongly territorial in the breeding season. Outside the breeding season they are more scattered in larger territories. In the Drakensberg mountains of KwaZulu-Natal they maintained broadly overlapping home ranges rather than strictly defended territories (Tye 1988) and showed little overt aggression towards neighbouring individuals, although foraging birds maintained a large individual distance. Birds are usually encountered singly, in pairs or in groups of 3–7 outside the breeding season. Larger groups probably consist of an adult pair with their fledged young in a family party. Non-breeding territories are defended by display and song, to which the male devotes much time, and by inter- and intraspecific encounters. Twice as much time was spent on interspecific encounters (2.0%) as on intraspecific (1.0%) and the former were significantly more frequent (18/6).

In the latter instances an individual would chase, display at or stand close to and watch a conspecific. In the former it would chase or displace other smaller insectivorous species such as *Cisticola* warblers including Neddicky *C. fulvicapilla*, Wailing Cisticola *C. lais* and Levaillant's Cisticola *C. tinniens*. Similar interactions have been observed also with African Stonechat, Familiar Chat *Cercomela familaris* and Long-billed Pipit *Anthus similis*. It was in turn chased or displaced by Fiscal Shrike *Lanius collaris*. All these species had home ranges which overlapped with those of Buff-streaked Bushchat. Displaced birds normally flew only a short distance and stayed within the aggressor's home range (Tye 1984, 1988).

During Tye's observations of non-breeding birds in the Drakensberg both males and females sang although most song came from males. Song was delivered without any apparent stimulation from another bird and was apparently not directed at any particular bird. Song was also heard briefly during inter- and intraspecific disputes. Feeding individuals were observed sometimes to sing quietly whilst perched on a rock between capture attempts, but feeding birds were silent more often (60.3%) than not (11.6%) when feeding.

Normally the species is wary but it can become comparatively tame around human dwellings if it is not persecuted, and Tye noted that it quickly became used to the presence of an observer in his study area, often feeding within 30m. When alarmed by an overflying Jackal Buzzard *Buteo rufofuscus* one individual stood looking up, bobbing its head, flicking its wings and hopping about.

The individuals in Tye's study area spent up to 71.9% of their time foraging. Little time is spent on other activities apart from resting, which occupied 19.1% of their time. It was not possible from the data available to determine whether resting was commoner around mid-day or on hotter days. Of the remainder of the time, 3.3% was spent on singing; 1.4% on entering holes in rocks (the reason for this was unknown but Tye speculated birds were either foraging or prospecting for future nest sites); 2.0% on interspecific interactions; 1.2% on preening; 1.0% on intraspecific interactions; and 0.3% on alarm.

Flight between perches on boulders is low and a bird may flick its wings and tail on alighting. On the ground it moves with a bounding gait, with leaps much longer than those used by similar *Oenanthe* species.

MOULT

Little information. A juvenile specimen in BMNH, collected on 17 March 1870 at Grahamstown in Cape Province [Eastern Cape], had started moulting into first-year female plumage showing new feathers on the mantle and scapulars. Another juvenile collected on 12 February 1885 at Stutterheim [Eastern Cape] had just started moulting into first-year male plumage. All feathers were juvenile apart from the lesser coverts, which had been moulted and were black.

A male specimen in BMNH in worn first breeding plumage collected at Stutterheim [Eastern Cape] on 12 February 1885 was in active wing and tail moult. Primaries 01–04 were new, primary 05 was being replaced and was two-thirds grown, and primaries 06–10 were old. The secondaries appeared not to have commenced moult. Tertials 07–08 appeared to be new but 09 was old. The upperwing lesser, median and greater coverts all appeared to be new. Tail feather pair (05) were in active moult being c.50% of their normal length. February is around two months after the breeding season ceases in the Eastern Cape. One other male specimen in BMNH in very worn plumage, collected on 12 December 1876 which is just within the breeding season, had not commenced moult.

CONSERVATION

Under IUCN criteria Buff-streaked Bushchat has been evaluated as Near Threatened (Collar *et al.* 1994).

It has suffered from commercial afforestation of moist grasslands. Local extinction of populations may already have occurred. Its disappearance from the Magaliesberg range in the southern Transvaal [Mpumalanga] would suggest that it may be sensitive to even relatively subtle habitat alterations. Its virtual absence from Lesotho may be due to extreme sensitivity to disturbance. Its conservation status should be closely monitored (Harrison *et al.* 1997), especially as commercial afforestation continues to be a threat to its habitat.

Whinchat *S. rubetra* male, June 1980, UK. Bold head pattern. Brown/black face mask framed by long, white supercilium curving round rear crown and white lower border. Supercilium shape gives distinctive flat-crowned impression. *James Walford.*

Whinchat *S. rubetra* migrant, second calendar-year male, May 1991, Saudi Arabia. Orange extends onto throat/chin. White base to p.c. and tail. Large dark spots on rump and upper t.c. White on p.c. > 50% and brownish outer g.c. indicate second-year. *Arnoud B. van den Berg.*

Whinchat *S. rubetra* male, September 2000, Turkey. Broad buff supercilium. Face pattern obscured by buff fringes. White spots at tips of mantle and scapulars. Extent of white on p.c. indicates male. White base to short tail. Large spots on rump/upper t.c. *Markus Römhild.*

Whinchat *S. rubetra* female, June 1980, UK. Head pattern much duller version of male. Face mask indistinct pale brown-buff. Supercilium buff not white. Breast buff-orange often spotted black, rest of underparts whitish buff. *James Walford.*

Whinchat *S. rubetra* first-year female, September 1985, Netherlands. Similar to autumn adult female and first-year male. Upperparts show white spots. Underparts uniform buff. Stronger tone on breast often spotted black. Prominent buff supercilium. White base to tail. *Arnoud B. van den Berg.*

White-tailed Stonechat *S. leucura* male, Feb. 2001, Punjab, India. Similar to Siberian. Pale grey-buff crown and mantle. Tail brown with broad pale buff fringes to outer webs and tips, white on inner webs. Base of outer webs of outer tail feathers white. Mainly white rump and orange tips to upper t.c. *Werner Suter.*

White-tailed Stonechat *S. leucura* male, March 1988, Assam, India. Orange restricted to small patch on central breast. Rest of underparts white. *Des Allen.*

White-tailed Stonechat *S. leucura* male, January 1993, Delhi, India. Despite photo being one month earlier than bird from Punjab above, this individual is in more advanced breeding plumage. Note all-black head including chin/throat, buff-orange on breast/flanks, white bases of outer rectrices just visible. *Tim Loseby.*

White-tailed Stonechat *S. leucura* male and juvenile, March 1988, Assam, India. Relatively large white wing patch on male. White sides to tail just visible. Unusually exposed situation for a fledgling to be fed. *Des Allen.*

White-tailed Stonechat *S. leucura* female, January 1993, Delhi, India. Uniform grey-brown head and upperparts with indistinct streaking. White chin and throat with grey feather bases just showing. Underparts tawny-buff contrasting with pale throat. *Tim Loseby.*

White-tailed Stonechat *S. leucura* female, March 1988, Assam, India. Overall plumage pale. Chin to under t.c. white with yellowish-buff suffusion on breast. Note supercilium and pale brown head and upperparts. *Des Allen.*

Stoliczka's Bushchat *S. macrorhyncha* male in partial summer plumage, Feb/March 2001, Sultanpur, India. Attenuated profile with longish tail and bill. Whinchat-like face mask. Prominent supercilium extending onto nape. White chin and throat. Rest of underparts buff. *N. Devasar.*

Stoliczka's Bushchat *S. macrorhyncha* male in partial summer plumage, Feb/March 2001, Sultanpur, India. Sides of head almost black. Upperwing coverts mainly black with buff-white fringes. White fringes to tail and white p.c. patch visible. *N. Devasar.*

Stoliczka's Bushchat *S. macrorhyncha* female, Feb/March 2001, Sultanpur, India. Uniform buff-streaked head and upperparts. Distinct buff supercilium. Buff wing-bar across tips of g.c. Pale buff edge to tail. Underparts uniform whitish buff. *N. Devasar.*

Stoliczka's Bushchat *S. macrorhyncha* male in partial summer plumage, Feb/March 2001, Sultanpur, India. Supercilia meet on forehead. White throat contrasts with yellow-buff breast. Contrast between white p.c./inner upperwing g.c. and remaining black upperwing coverts. Crown/mantle paler brown contrasting with black sides of head. *N. Devasar.*

Stoliczka's Bushchat *S. macrorhyncha* female, Feb/March 2001, Sultanpur, India. Open-faced appearance – no face mask. Uniform whitish underparts. Long buff fringes to crown/upperparts mainly hide dark brown feather centres. Long, broad supercilium. *N. Devasar.*

Stoliczka's Bushchat Probable hybrid Stoliczka's Bushchat x Siberian Stonechat race *S. m. indica*, December 1996, Goa, India. *James Walford.*

Hodgson's Bushchat *S. insignis* winter male, Dec 1998, Nepal. White chin/throat. Black spots on orange upper breast. White on upperwing over all coverts and majority of remiges, smaller patch on p.c. Unmarked white rump and upper t.c., some with orange tips. *Hem Sagar Baral.*

Hodgson's Bushchat *S. insignis* breeding female, June 1970, Altay, Russian Federation. Prominent supercilium. White chin and throat. Extensive white to wings, rump and upper t.c. *E.N. Panov.*

Hodgson's Bushchat *S. insignis* winter male, Dec 1998, Nepal. White neck patches almost meeting on hindneck, obscured by buff fringes. Scapulars with grey-buff fringes. Prominent buff-white tips to bunched tertials/secondaries and edge of outer rectrices and tips of other rectrices. *Hem Sagar Baral.*

Hodgson's Bushchat *S. insignis* spring male, April 1999, Bhutan. Large area of white on throat extends around neck almost encircling black head. Orange restricted to breast. Rest of underparts white. *Steve Chalmers.*

Hodgson's Bushchat *S. insignis* spring male, April 1999, Bhutan. Extensive white on hind neck and on wings. Note prominent white spots at tip of bunched tertials/inner secondaries. *Steve Chalmers.*

Réunion Stonechat *S. tectes* breeding male, Nov 1995, Réunion. Black head. Prominent narrow white supercilium extending beyond eye. Small bright orange breast-patch. White chin and throat. *Jan Vermeulen.*

Réunion Stonechat *S. tectes* breeding male, Nov 1995, Réunion. Note white chin and throat joins white neck patch. Prominent white wing-patch. *Jan Vermeulen.*

Réunion Stonechat *S. tectes* breeding female, Nov 2001, Réunion. No white on neck or wings. Indistinct buff-white supercilium. Very small, dull orange-buff breast-patch. *Roger Charlwood.*

Réunion Stonechat *S. tectes* breeding female, Nov 2001, Réunion. Relatively featureless plumage. Drab brownish upperparts with little dark streaking. Underparts from chin to undertail-coverts predominantly dull white. *Roger Charlwood.*

Réunion Stonechat *S. tectes* juvenile (right), Feb 1998, Réunion. Overall brown head and upperparts with buff streaks and fringes. Buff underparts. Dark brown streaks and fringes on breast and flanks creating mottled appearance. Buff not white chin and throat and short buff supercilium. *Jean-Michel Probst.*

Réunion Stonechat *S. tectes* breeding male, Oct. 1994, Réunion. This individual shows slightly broader supercilium behind the eye and more extensive orange breast-patch. *Jean-Michel Probst.*

Réunion Stonechat *S. tectes* breeding female, Oct 1994, Réunion. *Jean-Michel Probst.*

European Stonechat *S. r. rubicola* first-winter male, Oct 1993, Germany. Upperparts contrast more with underparts than *hibernans*. Upperpart feather fringes slightly more extensive than *hibernans*. Black sides to head contrasting with brown-fringed forehead, crown and throat previously considered feature of adult only. Wider, whiter neck-patch than *hibernans*. Secondary 08 is new. *Heiner Flinks.*

European Stonechat *S. r. rubicola* male, April 1999, Spain. White areas larger than *hibernans*, especially this early in year with much white on belly, flanks and under t.c. Extensive white neck patches, on sides of breast, inner upperwing, rump and upper t.c. *Olaf Lessow.*

European Stonechat *S. r. rubicola* male, April 1998, Spain. Orange confined to breast/upper flanks. Rest of underparts white marginally extending onto central lower breast. On *hibernans* these areas only fade to buff but not as early in the year. *Olaf Lessow.*

European Stonechat *S. r. rubicola* first-winter male, Sept. 1993. Extensive amount of white on rump, appearing unstreaked. Upper t.c. mainly orange with black spots although central ones almost white. Rump patch only extends to middle (08) tertial. *Heiner Flinks.*

European Stonechat *S. r. rubicola* juvenile female, August 1991, Germany. First-winter feathers on wing, back and flanks, rest juvenile. Head and mantle show typical juvenile white triangular tips. Upperwing g.c. moulted, 01–02 25% renewed. *Heiner Flinks.*

European Stonechat *S. r. rubicola* juvenile male, July 1990, Germany. Slightly darker base colour to feathers (see left). White inner g.c. diagnostic of male in juvenile plumage. Juvenile female has no white on g.c. until completion of post-juvenile moult. *Heiner Flinks.*

European Stonechat *S. r. rubicola* first-winter male, Sept. 1991, Netherlands. Pointed tips to rectrices indicate first-winter. Greyish-brown fringes to head and upperparts *Hibernans* fringes are slightly darker rufous. Spots on upper t.c., faint streaks on rump. Some white feather bases on rump and upper t.c. showing through. *Arnoud B.van den Berg*

European Stonechat *S. r. rubicola* first-winter male, July 1993, Germany. Broad brown fringes to upperpart feathers and dark-streaked rump/upper t.c. White tips to upperwing p.c. indicate this is first-year. *Heiner Flinks*

European Stonechat *S. r. hibernans* first-winter male, Oct 2001, England. Neck-patch reduced to thin buff line which also divides black throat from breast. Rump tawny brown streaked black. *Nigel Blake.*

European Stonechat *S. r. hibernans* breeding male, June 1992, Scotland. Entire underparts except under t. c. orange-buff. Contrast with p. 294 top right and middle left. Neck-patch slightly smaller and does not extend far down breast sides. *Gordon Langsbury.*

European Stonechat *S. r. hibernans* breeding female, June 1992, Scotland. Very dark on upperparts and underparts. No white on sides of neck. Almost black chin/throat. Diagnostic brown, streaked rump/upper t. c. *Gordon Langsbury.*

European Stonechat *S. r. hibernans* breeding male, June 1992, Scotland. Diagnostic streaked upper t.c. showing small amount of white. Mantle/scapulars still show paler brown fringes – contrast with p. 294 top right and middle left. *Gordon Langsbury.*

Siberian Stonechat *S. m. przewalskii* male, June 1996, China. Breast to vent orange, darker on breast. Black on chin marginally extends onto upper breast. Small white neck-patches. Pure white rump extending onto sides. *Ray Tipper.*

Siberian Stonechat *S. m. przewalskii* female, June 1996, China. Darker orange underparts than other Siberian races. Orange upper t.c., small area of white on upper rump. Mainly black chin/throat. *Ray Tipper.*

Siberian Stonechat *S. m. przewalskii* adult male, March 1998, India. Large white unmarked rump/upper t.c. patch – few orange tips to upper t.c. Solid black wing coverts and remiges with no contrast indicate adult. *Jon Hornbuckle.*

Siberian Stonechat *S. m. przewalskii* adult male, March 1998, India. Uniform black underwing coverts/axillaries is diagnostic of male. Note also underparts completely buff-orange. *Jon Hornbuckle.*

Siberian Stonechat *S. m. maura* summer male, June 1997, Finland. Orange only on breast and marginally on fore flanks, rest of underparts white. In short time orange confined to central breast. Note extensive white neck-patch. *Tomi Muukkonen.*

Siberian Stonechat *S. m. maura* spring male, Norway. Overall paler plumage than European Stonechat. Extensive neck-patches with buff fringes abrading to reveal white. Pale inner wing-panel. *Jan Kåre Ness.*

Siberian Stonechat *S. m. maura* first-year male/female, Oct. 2001, Netherlands. Very pale sandy-brown, longer fringes than European Stonechat. Pale inner wing-panel. Large white fringes/tips to p.c. contrast with black alula. *Marten van Dijl.*

Siberian Stonechat *S. m. maura* first-year male/female, Oct. 2001, Netherlands. Almost white tips and edges to tail. Dark lores' may indicate first-winter male. White chin and throat show no dark bases. *Marten van Dijl.*

Siberian Stonechat *S. m. maura* first-winter male, Oct 1988, Finland. Compare stronger plumage tone of this bird to Netherlands individual. Note distinct supercilia meeting on forehead. Pure white chin and throat contrast with rest of underparts. *Karno Mikkola.*

Siberian Stonechat *S. m. maura* first-winter male, Oct 1988, Finland. Unmarked large buff-orange rump and upper t.c. Almost black tertials with contrasting broad whitish fringes. No black on head except small area behind eye. *Karno Mikkola.*

Siberian Stonechat *S. m. maura* first-winter male, Oct 1988, Finland. Mainly black underwing-coverts indicate this is male. Some first-year males show this by early September *Karno Mikkola*

Siberian Stonechat *S. m. maura* first-winter male, Oct 1988, Finland. Orange rump becoming white on upper part. Rump patch level with innermost tertial 09. Extensive white inner wing-patch. Tips and outer edges to tail paler than European Stonechat. *Karno Mikkola.*

Siberian Stonechat *S. m. maura* female, July, Kuusamo, Finland. Paler overall plumage compared to European Stonechat. More obvious neck-patch. Pale chin and throat. Compare with p. 295 bottom left. *Tomi Muukkonen.*

Siberian Stonechat *S. m. indica* male, February, Goa, India. Underparts at this stage completely buff-orange, marginally darker on breast and flanks. Compare with p. 296 bottom left. *Alan Tate.*

Siberian Stonechat *S. m. armenica* male, May 2001. Note white base of tail just visible and underparts still mainly orange. *Klaus Drissner.*

Siberian Stonechat *S. m. armenica* female, May 2001. Pale buff-white chin/throat. Noticeable pale patches on neck. Prominent buff supercilium. *Klaus Drissner.*

Siberian Stonechat *S. m. variegata* first-winter male, Nov 1985, Eilat, Israel. Black on head mostly obscured by sandy fringes. Extensive neck-patches visible but white obscured by buff. White chin/throat. Pale orange rump, white already showing. (See also right.) *Per Alström.*

Siberian Stonechat *S. m. variegata* first-winter male, Nov 1985, Eilat, Israel. Extensive white on inner webs of rectrices except central pair. Long sandy-buff fringes to mantle/scapulars. Extensive white on innerwing-coverts. Neck-patches almost meet on hindneck. Pointed rectrices indicate first-winter. *Per Alström.*

African Stonechat *S. t. stonei* breeding male, Sept/Oct, Limpopo Prov., S. Africa. Entire underparts except under t.c. deep chestnut, darker than European or Siberian Stonechat. *Warwick Tarboton.*

African Stonechat *S. t. stonei* breeding male Sept/Oct, Limpopo Prov., S. Africa. White neck-patch does not extend onto breast-sides. Extensive white wing-patch and all-white rump/upper t.c. just visible. *Warwick Tarboton.*

African Stonechat *S. t. stonei* breeding female Sept/Oct, Limpopo Prov., S. Africa. Note the very dark head including chin and throat. Strong orange colouring on underparts. *Warwick Tarboton.*

African Stonechat *S. t. stonei* breeding female, Sept/Oct, Limpopo Prov., S. Africa. Small insignificant supercilium and no pale neck-patch. Dark head merging into similar coloured upperparts. *Warwick Tarboton.*

African Stonechat *S. t. oreobates* Nov 2000, Lesotho. Note the extensive white wing-patch and also the stronger and redder tone of the underparts. *Per Smitterberg.*

African Stonechat *S. t. albofasciata* adult male, Feb 1997, Ethiopia. Note basic black/white plumage, no chestnut on underparts. Black extends from chin to lower breast. Rest of underparts white. *Per Smitterberg.*

Pied Bushchat *S. caprata* adult male, Nov 1990, India. Variable white on underparts defines males of various races. This bird is likely intergrade *rossorum/bicolor* due to extensive white on belly and central lower breast. *George Reszeter.*

Pied Bushchat *S. c. bicolor* first-year male, Feb 1997, India. Dull black body plumage with brown fringes, brown upperwing p.c., remiges and rectrices indicate first-winter. White not on belly indicates *bicolor*. *Mark Yates.*

Pied Bushchat *S. caprata* adult male, Nov 1990, India. Note just visible white on upperwing-coverts and white extending into lower breast. Glossy black not so evident on other races. *George Reszeter.*

Pied Bushchat *S. c. bicolor* adult male, Jan 1993, Delhi, India. Black wing-coverts, remiges and rectrices indicate adult. Note black and buff fringes to some upper t.c. *Tim Loseby.*

Pied Bushchat *S. c. bicolor* first-year male, Jan 1993, Delhi, India. Note white wing-patch. White on belly indicates intergrade *bicolor/rossorum.* Scattered dark tips on rump and upper t.c. *Tim Loseby.*

Pied Bushchat *S. c. bicolor* winter female, Jan 1993, Delhi, India. Plain buff-brown face, paler grey on lores, chin and throat. Underparts brown with rufous tone becoming stronger on lower breast and belly. Underparts faintly streaked. *Tim Loseby.*

Pied Bushchat *S. c. atrata* female, Dec 1999, Sri Lanka. Note prominent dark streaking to underparts and buff tips to upperwing greater coverts. *Alan Hands.*

Pied Bushchat *S. c. bicolor* female, Jan 1993, India. Grey tone on head/upperparts. Pale rufous undertail-coverts, darker rufous upper t.c. Prominent buff tips to median and greater coverts. *Per Smitterberg.*

Pied Bushchat *S. c. bicolor* female, Feb 1999, India. Open-faced appearance. Buff tips to upperwing greater coverts form wingbar. Darker brown/black tail contrasts with paler upperparts. *Albert Steen-Hansen.*

301

Canary Island Stonechat *S. dacotiae* breeding male, April 1998, Fuerteventura. Narrow, irregular white supercilium. Pure white chin/throat joined to white neck-patches. Predominantly faded white underparts. *Steve Young/Windrush Photos.*

Canary Island Stonechat *S. dacotiae* breeding male, April 1998, Fuerteventura. Pinkish-chestnut breast contrast with otherwise white underparts. Note the almost black head and longish bill. *Steve Young/Windrush Photos.*

Canary Island Stonechat *S. dacotiae* breeding male, April 1999, Fuerteventura. Dark brown/black head contrasting with paler grey/brown, streaked mantle and scapulars. *Thomas Tams.*

Canary Island Stonechat *S. dacotiae* breeding female, April 1998, Fuerteventura. Short buff supercilium. Mainly buff-white underparts with pinkish-buff suffusion to restricted area on upper breast. Neck-patches less extensive than male. *Steve Young/Windrush Photos.*

Canary Island Stonechat *S. dacotiae* female in fresh plumage, July 1988, Fuerteventura. Indistinct, narrow, buff supercilium. Chin and throat buff-white. Pinkish-buff breast fading to paler buff on belly. *Magnus Ullman.*

Canary Island Stonechat *S. dacotiae* juvenile, April 1998, Fuerteventura. Similar to female. Pale unspotted buff rump and upper t.c. Mantle spotted buff/black. Scaly upper breast. Short pale supercilium and slightly darker grey ear-coverts. Note pale innerwing patch. *Steve Young/Windrush Photos.*

Grey Bushchat *S. ferrea* male, Feb 2002, India. Pure white chin/throat contrast with greyish-white underparts. Prominent white supercilium. White outer edges to tail. *Roger Charlwood.*

Grey Bushchat *S. ferrea* male, Feb 2002, India. *Roger Charlwood.*

Grey Bushchat *S. ferrea* male, Feb 2002, India. Black remiges and rectrices with prominent grey fringes. Long tail. Extensive supercilium reaching from bill to nape. *Roger Charlwood.*

Grey Bushchat *S. ferrea* male, Feb 2002, India. Black face mask contrasts with white supercilum and chin/throat. *Roger Charlwood.*

Grey Bushchat *S. ferrea* female, Feb 1992, India. Note rufous sides to tail, plus dark ear-coverts and long buff supercilium which separate it from female Jerdon's Bushchat. *Magnus Ullman.*

Jerdon's Bushchat *S. jerdoni* first-year male, March 1998, India. Brown p.c. and remiges contrasting with black mantle/scapulars and buff suffusion to white underparts indicate first-year. Note blue gloss to head and upperparts. *Jon Hornbuckle.*

303

White-bellied Bushchat *S. gutturalis* adult male, June 1993, Timor. Black upperparts, pure white underparts. Extensive white wing-patch. This bird shows no supercilium. Substantial bill with pronounced downcurve to culmen. *Richard Noske.*

White-bellied Bushchat *S. gutturalis* adult male, June 1993, Timor. Extensive white on all rectrices except central pair and on all inner upperwing-coverts. Note narrow white fringes to tertials. *Richard Noske*

White-bellied Bushchat *S. gutturalis* first-year male, June 1993, Timor. Note grey-brown upperparts. Rump, upper t.c. and tail black. Large amount of white on both webs of rectrices except central pair. *Richard Noske.*

White-bellied Bushchat *S. gutturalis* first-year male, June 1993, Timor. Grey-brown upperparts, pale buff underparts, chin/throat paler. Indistinct buff supercilium over eye. Dark centres to median coverts. *Richard Noske.*

Buff-streaked Bushchat *S. bifasciata* breeding male, Oct 1995, Mpumalanga Prov., S. Africa. Striking contrast of orange underparts and black head, remiges, rectrices. Broad buff supercilium extending down hind neck to join paler buff-white scapulars. *Warwick Tarboton.*

Buff-streaked Bushchat *S. bifasciata* breeding female Oct 1995, Mpumalanga Prov., S. Africa. Grey chin/throat. Indistinct grey-buff supercilum. Underparts orange-buff with pink tone on breast. Streaks on breast/flanks. Pink-brown mantle, unmarked buff rump/upper t.c. *Warwick Tarboton.*

GLOSSARY

Accidental A very unusual occurrence of a species well outside its normal range.

Afrotropical One of the major zoogeographical regions of Earth; consists largely of Africa south of the Sahara but excluding Madagascar and the Comoro Islands. Formerly known as the Ethiopian Region.

Albinism The complete loss of pigmentation in the feathers and body parts resulting in pure white feathering, red eyes and pale pink legs and bill.

Allopatric Mutually exclusive geographically (usually applied to taxonomically related populations, as in races/subspecies).

Alula Part of the upper wing feathers. Also referred to as bastard wing. Consists of a number of small quill feathers attached to the first digit.

Biome A significant biotic community existing in a large area defined by a number of general environmental features.

Boreal Climatic zone immediately south of the Arctic.

Cline A geographical gradient in a phenotypic character within the range of a species such as in European Stonechat *Saxicola rubicola* in Europe, with darker specimens in the north to lighter in the south. It may include recognised subspecies although where the gradation is continuous the validity of such subspecies is dubious.

Congeneric Two or more species placed in the same genus.

Conspecific Two or more races/subspecies belonging to the same species.

Culmen The dorsal ridge on the upper mandible running from where the mandible joins the forehead to the tip of the bill.

Dimorphic (sexual) The difference in appearance between the male and female of a species or subspecies.

Duar The eastern part of the band of alluvial soil running along the northern edge of the terai found in northern West Bengal, Bhutan and adjacent parts of Assam, extending up to 600m in the foothills of the Himalayas.

Endemic Restricted or confined to a specific country or geographical area.

Genus A taxonomic category representing a grouping of species of presumed common phylogenetic origin.

Hai Dryland rice-growing areas in Laos which are usually left fallow for a few years after a few years of successive cropping.

Jheel Shallow lake in India found in low-lying natural depression with floating and submerged vegetation, reedbeds and partly submerged trees.

Kaing Burmese word used to describe land in a riverbed, exposed and often cultivated when the waters recede in the dry season.

Lalang Colloquial (Malay) name for the grass *Imperata cylindrica* which often invades open deforested or burnt areas in uplands of Thailand. The Thai name is Yaa Kaa.

Leucistic Where there is a partial loss of pigmentation reducing all the colours of the plumage in intensity or there is a complete loss of feather pigment leaving the feathers white but the body parts normally coloured.

Malagasy Faunal region formed by Madgascar and its outlying islands extending east to the Mascarenes and north to the Seychelles.

Monogamous Where mating involves a single male and single female forming a pair for the duration of a breeding cycle although such pairs may change partners during the breeding season.

Monotypic A species with no recognised subspecies.

Nominate The first named subspecies of a species and which has therefore its trinomen the same as the specific binomen i.e. Siberian Stonechat *Saxicola maura maura*

Oriental One of the main zoogeographical divisions of Earth. Lies mainly in the Tropics between 68° and 135° East and between 10° South and 32° North. See Campbell & Lack (1985).

Palearctic Zoogeographical region comprising all of Europe, Africa north of the Sahara, and Arctic, boreal and temperate Asia north of the Himalayas. Southern boundaries with the Afrotropical and Oriental Regions are not clearly defined.

Phanta Open plains of short grasslands.

Polyandry Mating system where a female mates with two or more males at the same time during a single breeding season.

Polygyny Mating system where a male mates with two or more females at the same time during a single breeding season.

Polytypic Term to describe a species that has more than one recognised subspecies.

Race Synonymous with subspecies. Used to describe the various populations of one species that can be morphologically distinguished from other populations of the same species and have been assigned subspecific status.

Remiges The primary and secondary flight feathers of the wing.

Rectrices The tail feathers.

Rictal bristles The bristles around the gape where the bill joins the head.

Superspecies Term introduced by Mayr who defined it as "a monophyletic group of very closely related and largely or entirely allopatric species". The included species are geographical representatives of a common stock but have at least achieved true reproductive isolation and are not merely subspecies of a single polytypic species (Campbell & Lack 1985).

Sympatric Opposite of allopatric. Species occurring in the same geographical area.

Terai The undulating alluvial band, 25–45km wide, of often marshy land found north of the Gangetic Plain extending from Uttar Pradesh through Nepal, northern parts of west Bengal to Assam. Formerly naturally consisted of tall elephant grass and dense forest but now much of its area is drained and converted to agriculture.

Vagrant An individual of a species or subspecies that has strayed from its normal migratory range.

ABBREVIATIONS

AMNH   American Museum of Natural History, New York, USA
ASCN   Academia Sinica, Beijing, China
BMNH   Natural History Museum, Tring, England
BNHS   Bombay Natural History Society, Bombay, India
FMNH   Field Museum of Natural History, Chicago,USA
MCML   Merseyside County Museums, Liverpool, England
UMMZ   University of Michigan Museum of Zoology, Ann Arbor, USA
USNM   United States National Museum (Smithsonian Institution) Washington DC, USA
ZMMSU   Zoological Museum of Moscow State University, Russia
ZMUC   Zoological Museum of Cambridge University, Cambridge, England

In Photograhic Section only:
p.c.   primary coverts
t.c.   tail coverts
g.c.   greater coverts

BIBLIOGRAPHY

Adamian, M.S. & Klem Jr., D. (1999) *Handbook of the birds of Armenia*. Yerevan: American University of Armenia.

Agatho, Br. (1960-1961) De Roodborsttapuit, *Saxicola torquata rubicola* L., een onderzoek naar zijn leefwijze en broedbiologie. *Publ. Natuurhist. Genoot. Limburg* 12: 97-175.

Ali, S. & Ripley, S.D. (1968-1998) *Handbook of the birds of India and Pakistan*. Calcutta: Oxford University Press.

Allen, D. (1998) Report to the Indian Forestry Service concerning the Amarpur area of the Dibru-Saikhowa Biosphere Reserve. Unpublished report.

Allouse, B.E. (1953) The avifauna of Iraq. *Iraq nat. Hist. Mus. Publ.* 3.

Allsop, K. & Hume, R.A. (1981) Recent reports. *Brit. Birds* 74: 191-194.

Almond, W.E. (1956) Whinchat singing in winter-quarters. *Brit. Birds* 49: 183.

Alström, P. & Olsson, U. (1983) Notes on birds recorded in Nepal 1983. Unpublished.

Andrew, P. (1992) *The birds of Indonesia: a checklist (Peters sequence)*. Jakarta: Indonesia Ornithological Society (*Kukila* Checklist No 1).

Andrews, I.J. (1995) *The birds of the Hashemite Kingdom of Jordan*. Dundee: published by the author.

Andrews, P. (1981) Bittern-like posture of juvenile Whinchat. *Brit. Birds* 74: 266-267.

Ash, J.S. & Miskell, J.E. (1998) *Birds of Somalia*. Robertsbridge, Sussex: Pica Press.

Aspinwall, D.R., Beel, C. & Ellison, G. (1998) *A field guide to Zambian birds not found in southern Africa*. Lusaka: Zambian Ornithological Society.

Austin, O.L. (1948) The birds of Korea. *Bull. Mus. Comp. Zool.* 101: 1-301.

Austin, O.L. & Kuroda, N. (1953) The birds of Japan, their status and distribution. *Bull. Mus. Comp. Zool.* 109: 279–637.

Baker, E.C.S. (1894-1901) Birds of North Cachar, part 3. *J. Bombay Nat. Hist. Soc.* 9: 111-146.

Baker, E.C.S. (1907) Birds of the Khasia hills. *J. Bombay Nat. Hist. Soc.* 17: 783-795, 957-975.

Baker, E.C.S (1922-1930) *The fauna of British India, including Ceylon and Burma*. Second edition. London: Taylor and Francis.

Baker, E.C.S. (1923) *Saxicola caprata burmanica* subsp. nov. *Bull. Brit. Orn. Club* 43: 19.

Baker, E.C.S. (1924) *The fauna of British India (Birds)*, 2. London: Taylor & Francis.

Baker, E.C.S. (1933) *The nidification of birds of the Indian Empire*, 2. Second edition. London: Taylor & Francis.

Baker, E.C.S. (1942) *Cuckoo problems*. London: Witherby.

Bangs, O & van Tyne, J. (1931) Birds of the Kelley-Roosevelt expedition to French Indochina. *Publ. Field Mus. Nat. Hist.* (Zool. Ser.) 18: 33-119.

Banik, M. (2001) Distinctive behavioural traits of early stages of reproductive cycle in migratory populations of the Common Stonechat (*Saxicola torquata* (*L.*)) in Kharkiv region, Ukraine.P.26 in *Programme & Abstract Book, 3rd EOU Conference, 21-25 August 2001 Haren/Groningen Netherlands.*

Bannerman, D.A. (1912) Description of *Saxicola dacotiae murielae* and *Acanthis cannabina harterti* subspp. n. from Canary Islands. *Bull. Brit. Orn. Club* 33: 37-39.

Bannerman, D.A. (1914) An ornithological expedition to the eastern Canary Islands. *Ibis* (10)2: 38-90, 228-293.

Bannerman, D.A. (1919-1920) List of the birds of the Canary Islands, with detailed reference to the migratory species and the accidental visitors. *Ibis* (11)1: 84-131, 291-321, 457-495, 708-764; (11)2: 97-132, 323-360, 519-569.

Bannerman, D.A. (1922) *The Canary Islands: their history, natural history and scenery*. London & Edinburgh: Gurney and Jackson.

Bannerman, D.A. (1936) *Birds of tropical West Africa*, 4. London:

Crown Agents.

Bannerman, D.A. (1963) *Birds of the Atlantic Islands*, 1. Edinburgh: Oliver & Boyd.

Bannerman, D.A. & Lodge, G.E. (1954) *The birds of the British Isles*, 3. Edinburgh: Oliver & Boyd.

Bannerman, D.A. & Vella-Gaffiero, J.A. (1976) *Birds of the Maltese archipelago*. Valletta, Malta: Museums Department.

Baral, H.S. (1991) Bird notes from Sukila Phanta, March 1991. Unpublished.

Baral, H.S. (1995) Bird notes from Sukila Phanta, January 1995. Unpublished.

Baral, H.S. (1997) Birds recorded during grassland bird survey, Sukila Phanta, December 1996–January 1997. Unpublished.

Baral, H.S. (1998) Hodgson's Bushchat *Saxicola insignis* Gray and Gray 1846 in Nepal: a report submitted to the Dept. of National Parks and Wildlife Conservation (HMG Nepal), Biodiversity Support Program (USA) and Oriental Bird Club (UK). Amsterdam: Institute of Systematics and Population Biology, University of Amsterdam.

Baral, H.S. (1999) Hodgson's Bushchat in Nepal. *Oriental Bird Club Bull.* 30: 15-16.

Barré, N. (1983) Distribution et abondance des oiseaux terrestres de l'Ile de la Réunion. *Rev. Ecol. (Terre Vie)* 37: 37-85.

Barré, N. & Barau, A. (1982) *Oiseaux de la Réunion*. St Denis, Réunion: published by the authors.

Barré, N., Barau, A. & Jouanin, C. (1996) *Oiseaux de la Réunion*. Paris: Editions du Pacifique.

Barua, M. & Sharma, P. (1999) Birds of Kaziranga National Park, India. *Forktail* 15: 47-60.

Bastian, H.-V. (1989) Are corvids able to exterminate populations of Whinchats (*Saxicola rubetra*)? – a computer-simulation. *Vogelwelt* 110: 150-156.

Bastian, H.-V. (1992) Breeding and natal dispersal of Whinchats *Saxicola rubetra*. *Ringing & Migration* 13: 13-19.

Bastian, H.-V. & Bastian, A. (1993) Entwicklung der Körpermasse nestjunger Braunkehlchen (*Saxicola rubetra*).*J. Orn.* 134: 85-92.

Bastian, A. & Bastian, H.-V. (1994) Bestände und Bestandtrends des Braunkehlchens (*Saxicola rubetra*). *Limicola* 8: 242-270.

Bastian, A. & Bastian, H.-V. (1996) *Das Braunkehlchen: Opfer der ausgeräumten Kulturlandschaft*. Wiesbaden: Aula Verlag.

Bastian, A., Bastian, H.-V. & Sternberg, H.-E. (1994) Ist das Nahrungsangebot für die Brutrevierwahl von Braunkehlchen *Saxicola rubetra* entscheidend? *Vogelwelt* 115: 103-114.

Bastian, H.-V., Bastian, A., Bocca, M. & Suter, W. (1997) Whinchat *Saxicola rubetra*. Pp. 526 -527 in E.J.M. Hagemeijer & M.J. Blair, eds. *The EBCC Atlas of European breeding birds: their distribution and abundance*. London: T. & A.D. Poyser.

Bates, R.S.P. & Lowther, E.H.N. (1952) *The breeding birds of Kashmir*. Oxford: Oxford University Press.

Beaman, M. (ed.) (1978) *Orn. Soc. Turkey Bird Report 1974-1975*. Sandy, UK

Beaman, M. (1994) *Palearctic birds: a checklist of the birds of Europe, North Africa and Asia north of the foothills of the Himalayas*. Stonyhurst, England: Harrier Publications.

Beadle, D. & Whittaker, A. (1985) Sabah survey report. Pp. 79-118 & 155-162 in D. Parish & D.R. Wells, eds. *Interwader Annual Report 1984*. Kuala Lumpur: Interwader.

Beasley, A.J. (1995) The Birds of the Chimanimani Mountains. *Honeyguide* 41(1): 3-59.

Beavan, R.C. (1865-1868) Notes on various Indian birds. *Ibis* (2)1: 400-423; (2)3: 430-455; (2)4: 73-85, 165-181, 355-356, 370-406.

Bechstein, J.M. (1858) *Cage and chamber birds incorporating Sweet's British warblers*. London: H.G. Bohn.

307

Beehler, B.M., Pratt, T.K. & Zimmerman, D.A. (1986) *Birds of New Guinea*. Princeton: Princeton University Press.

Bell, H.L. & Swainson, G.W. (1985) The colonisation, ecology and breeding of the Pied Stonechat *Saxicola caprata* at Port Moresby, Papua New Guinea. *Ibis* 127: 74-83.

Benson, C.W., Brooke, R.K., Dowsett, R.J. & Irwin, M.P.S. (1971) *The birds of Zambia*. London: Collins.

van den Berg, A., Bosman, C.A.W. & Rozendaal, F.G. (1981) Records of Stoliczka's Whinchat in Rajasthan, India in August 1978. *Dutch Birding* 3: 20-21.

Berlioz, J. (1946) *Oiseaux de la Réunion*. Paris: Larose (Faune de l'Empire Français 4).

Bernis, F. (1958) Guion de la Avifauna Balear. *Ardeola* 4: 25-97.

Berthold, P. (1993) *Bird migration*. Oxford: Oxford University Press.

Bezzel, E. & Stiel, K. (1977) Zur Biologie des Braunkehlchens in den Bayerischen Alpen. *Anz. orn. Ges. Bayern* 16: 1-9.

Bibby, C.J. (1978) Passerines eating ladybirds. *Brit. Birds* 71: 310-311.

Bibby, C.J. & Hill, D.A. (1987[A]) The Fuerteventura Stonechat Project 1985. Cambridge: International Council for Bird Preservation (*Study Report* 8).

Bibby, C.J. & Hill, D.A. (1987[B]) Status of the Fuerteventura Stonechat *Saxicola dacotiae*. *Ibis* 129: 491-498.

Bijlsma, R. (1978) De reproduktie-kapaciteit van de Roodborsttapuit, *Saxicola torquata*. *Veldorn. Tijdschr.* 1: 126-135.

Bishop, K.D. (1999) Preliminary notes on some birds in Bhutan. *Forktail* 15: 87-91.

Blanchet, A. (1925) Description d'une sous-espèce nouvelle de *Saxicola torquata*. *Rev. Fr. Orn.* 9: 277-278.

Blanford, W.T. (1870) A list of birds obtained in the Irrawaddy valley around Ava, Thayet, Myo and Bassein. *Ibis* (2)6: 462-470.

Blasius, W. (1884) Vögel von Borneo, im Südosten der Insel gesammelt von Herrn F.J. Grabowsky. *Verhand.K.K. Zool.-Bot. Ges. Wien* 33: 1–90.

Bloch, D. & Sørensen, S. (1984) *Yvirlit yvir Føroya fuglar. Checklist of Faroese birds*. Tórshavn: Føroya Skúlabókagrunnur.

Bold, A. (1997) Birds. Pp.85-129 in *Mongolian Red Book*. Second edition. Ulaanbaatar, Mongolia.

Bose, A.K., Curson, J. & Jarman, N. (1989) Report on birds in some national parks and other areas of special interest in India and Nepal '88-89'. Unpublished report.

Boulton, R. & Rand, A.L. (1952) A collection of birds from Mount Cameroun. *Fieldiana Zool.* 34: 35-64.

Bräunlich, A. (1995) Report on the first WWF expedition to the Great Lakes Basin, western Mongolia, May-July 1995, and preliminary recommendations for the establishment of a new protected area. Ulaanbaatar: WWF Mongolia.

Brazil, M.A. (1991) *The birds of Japan*. London: Christopher Helm.

Brensing, D. (1977) Nahrungsökologische Untersuchungen an Zugvögeln in einem südwestdeutschen Durchzugsgebiet während des Wegzuges. *Vogelwarte* 29: 44-56.

Britton, P.L., ed. (1980) *Birds of East Africa: their habitat, status and distribution*. Nairobi: East Africa Natural History Society.

Brodkorb, P. (1978) Catalogue of fossil birds, part 5 (Passeriformes). *Bull. Florida State Mus.* 23: 139-228.

Brosset, A. & Erard, C. (1986) *Les oiseaux des régions forestières du nord-est du Gabon. 1. Ecologie et comportement des espèces*. Paris: Société Nationale de Protection de la Nature.

Brown, C.J. & Barnes, P.R. (1987) Birds of the Natal Alpine Belt. *Lammergeyer* 33: 1-13.

Bundy, G. (1976) *The birds of Libya*. London: British Ornithologists' Union (Check-list 1).

Bundy, G., Connor, R.J. & Harrison, C.J.O. (1989) *Birds of the Eastern Province of Aaudi Arabia*. London: Witherby.

Burkhardt, R.W. (1987) Lamarck and species. In: *Histoire du concept d'espece dans les sciences de la vie*. Paris: Fondation Singer-Polignac.

But'ev, V.T. (1983) [Hodgson's Bushchat *Saxicola insignis* Gray, 1846.] Pp. 294-295 in A.M. Kolosov, ed. [*Red Data Book of the R.S.F.S.R.*] Moscow: Rossel'khozizdat. [In Russian.]

Butler, E.A. (1875-1877) Notes on the avifauna of Mount Aboo and northern Guzerat. *Stray Feathers* 3: 437-500; 4: 1-41; 5: 207-235.

Büttikofer, J. (1891) On a collection of birds from Flores, Samao and Timor. *Notes Leyden Mus.* 13: 210-216.

Campbell, B. (1980) Robin-like feeding by Stonechat. *Brit. Birds* 73: 366.

Campbell, R. (1975) Observations (Waitape, Central District). *PNG Bird Soc. Newsletter* 113: 6-7.

Campbell, B. & Lack, E. (1985) *A dictionary of birds*. Calton, UK: T. & A.D. Poyser.

Carey, G.J., Chalmers, M.L., Diskin, D.A., Kennerley, P.R., Leader, P.J., Leven, M.R., Lewthwaite, M.S., Melville, M.S., Turnbull, M. & Young, L. (2001) *The Avifauna of Hong Kong*. Hong Kong, China: Hong Kong Birdwatching Society.

Carter, G.S. (1951). *Animal Evolution. A Study of Recent Views of its Causes.* London

Castelijns, H. & van Westrienen, R. (1994) De Roodborsttapuit *Saxicola torquata* in Zeeuws- Vlaanderen: status aparte? *Limosa* 67: 101-108

Chalmers, M.L. (1986) *Annotated checklist of the birds of Hong Kong*. Hong Kong: Hong Kong Birdwatching Society.

Chang, J. Wan-Fu (1980) *A field guide to the birds of Taiwan*. Taiwan: Tunghai University.

Cheesman, R.E. & Sclater, W.L. (1935) On a collection of birds from north western Abyssinia. *Ibis* (13)5: 605-606.

Cheke, A.S. (1987) Réunion Stonechat *Saxicola tectes*. Pp.124-126, 327-332, 407-410 in A.W. Diamond, ed. *Studies of Mascarene island birds*. Cambridge, UK: Cambridge University Press.

Cheng Tso-Hsin (1987) *Synopsis of the avifauna of China*. Beijing: Science Press.

Choudhury, A. (1995) Bird survey of Dibru-Saikhowa Wildlife Sanctuary. *Oriental Bird Club Bull.* 22: 15.

Choudhury, A. (1997) The status of the birds of Dibru–Saikhowa Sanctuary, Assam, India. *Oriental Bird Club Bull.* 25: 27-29.

Christison, A.F.P. (1941) Notes on the birds of Chagai. *Ibis* (14)5: 531-536.

Chunikhin, S.P. & Drozdov, N.N. (1968) [On the breeding ecology of *Saxicola caprata*.] *Ornitologiya* 9: 378. [In Russian.]

Clancey, P.A. (1956) Miscellaneous taxonomic notes on African birds. *Saxicola torquata oreobates*, subsp. nov. *Durban Mus. Novit.* 4(17): 281-282.

Clancey, P.A. (1961) Miscellaneous taxonomic notes on African birds. The South African races of the Stonechat *Saxicola torquata* (Linnaeus). *Durban Mus. Novit.* 6(6): 87-96.

Clancey, P.A. (1964) *The birds of Natal & Zululand*. Edinburgh: Oliver & Boyd.

Clancey, P.A. (1966) A catalogue of birds of the South African sub-region (Part III: Families Alaudidae-Turdidae). *Durban Mus. Novit.* 7 (11): 389-464.

Clancey, P.A., ed. (1980) *SAOS checklist of southern African birds*. Pretoria: SAOS.

Clancey, P.A. (1986) Miscellaneous taxonomic notes on African birds. *Durban Mus. Novit.* 14(2): 7–27.

Clancey, P.A. (1988) A previously undescribed African race of the Stonechat *Saxicola torquata*. *Bull. Brit. Orn. Club* 108: 62-64.

Clancey, P.A. (1990) The generic status of the Buff-streaked Chat of the southern Afrotropics. *Gerfaut* 80: 179-181.

Clancey, P.A., ed. (1980) *Checklist of southern African birds*. Johannesburg: S.A.O.S.

Clancey, P.A., Brooke, R.K., Crowe, T.M. & Mendelsohn, J.M. (1991) *S.A.O.S checklist of southern African birds*. Second Updating Report 1991. Johannesburg: South African Ornithological Society.

Clark, J., ed. (2001) A few recent interesting recoveries. *Ringers' Bulletin* 10 (6): 45.

Clark, J.M. & Eyre, J.A., eds. (1993) *Birds of Hampshire*. Over Wallop, UK: Hampshire Ornithological Society.

Clarke, W.E. (1912) *Studies in bird migration*, 1–2. London: Gurney & Jackson and Edinburgh: Oliver & Boyd.

Clements, J.F. (2000) *Birds of the world: a checklist*. Robertsbridge, UK: Pica Press.

Coates, B.J. (1990) *The birds of Papua New Guinea*, 2. Alderley, Queensland: Dove Publications.

Coates, B.J. & Bishop, K.D. (1997) *A guide to the birds of Wallacea: Sulawesi, The Moluccas and Lesser Sunda Islands, Indonesia*. Alderley, Queensland: Dove Publications.

Collar, N.J. & Stuart, S.N. (1985) *Threatened birds of Africa and related islands: the ICBP/IUCN Red Data Book*. Cambridge, UK: International Council for Bird Preservation.

Collar, N.J., Crosby, M.J. & Stattersfield, A.J. (1994) *Birds to watch 2: the world list of threatened birds*. Cambridge, UK: BirdLife International.

Collar, N.J., Andreev, A.V., Chan, S., Crosby, M.J., Subramanya, S. & Tobias, J.A., eds. (2001) *Threatened birds of Asia: the BirdLife International Red Data Book*. Cambridge, UK: BirdLife International.

Collins, D.R. (1984) Studies of West Palearctic Birds, 187. Canary Islands Stonechat. *Brit. Birds* 77: 467-474.

Collinson, M. (2001) Shifting sands: taxonomic changes in the world of the field ornithologist. *Brit. Birds* 94: 2-27.

Colston, P.R. & Gallagher, M.D. (1984) First record of the Pied Stonechat *Saxicola caprata* for Arabia. *Bull. Brit. Orn. Club* 104: 69-71.

Cornish, A.V. (1950) Stonechat catching lizard. *Brit. Birds*. 43: 164.

Corso, A. (2001) Plumages of Common Stonechats in Sicily and comparison with vagrant Siberian Stonechats. *Brit. Birds* 94: 315-318.

Cottridge, D. & Vinicombe, K. (1996) *Rare birds in Britain and Ireland*. London: Harper Collins.

Coverley, H.W. (1933) Nesting notes from Portugal. *Ibis* (13)3: 782-785.

Craik, R. (1998) Bird trade in Vietnam. *Oriental Bird Club Bull.* 28: 22-23.

Cramp, S., ed. (1988) *Handbook of the birds of Europe, the Middle East and North Africa (The birds of the Western Palearctic)*, 5. Oxford: Oxford University Press.

Crick, H. (2000) Editorial comment on Common Stonechat breeding in February in reedbed. *Brit. Birds* 93: 288.

Dahl, F. (1899) Das Leben der Vögel auf den Bismarckinseln. *Mitt. Zool. Samml. Naturkde. Berlin* 1: 107-222.

Dal [Dahl], S.K. (1946) [Data on the distribution of the Common Stonechat (*Saxicola torquata* L.) in the Armenian SSR.] *Dokl. Akad. Nauk. Arm. SSR* 4 (5): 51-54.

Dally, A. (2001) Stonechats in Essex. *Birding World* 14: 305-306.

Daulne, J.M. & Goblet, C. (1996) Nepal March 1996. Unpublished.

David-Beaulieu, A. (1944) *Les oiseaux du Tranninh*. Hanoi: Université Indochinoise.

Davidson, P. & Heywood, D. (1996) Bird records of interest, Nepal (March 10–April 22 1996). Unpublished.

Davis, P. (1972) Early, yes, but good.....? *BTO News* 53: 6

Davis, P. (1974) Observations on the nesting of some heathland birds. *Surrey Bird Report* 21: 56-65.

Dean, W.R.J. (1971) Breeding data for the birds of Natal and Zululand. *Durban Mus. Novit.* 9(6): 59-91.

Debussche, M. & Isenmann, P. (1986) L'ornithochorie dans les garrigues languedociennes. Les petits passereaux disseminateurs d'importance secondaire. *Oiseau et R.F.O.* 56: 71-76.

De Garnica, R. (1986) Young Stonechats *Saxicola torquata* returning to the nest after ringing. *Ringing and Migration* 7: 50.

Deignan, H.G. (1945) The birds of northern Thailand. *U.S. Natn. Mus. Bull.* 186.

Delacour, J. (1930) On the birds collected during the Fifth Expedition to French Indo-China. *Ibis* (12)6: 564-599.

Delacour, J. & Jabouille, P. (1927) *Recherches ornithologiques dans les Provinces du Tranninh (Laos), de Thua-Thien et de Kontoum (Annam) et quelques autres régions de l'Indochine Française*. Paris: Société Nationale d'Acclimatation de France.

Dement'ev, G.P. & Gladkov, N.A., eds. (1968) *Birds of the Soviet Union*, 6. Jerusalem: Israel Program for Scientific Translations.

Dennis, R.H. (1976) Scottish Bird Report 1975. *Scott. Birds* 9 (4): 173-235.

Dharmakumarsinhji, R.S. (1954) *Birds of Saurashtra*. Bombay: Times of India Press.

Dickinson, E.C., Kennedy, R.S. & Parkes, K.C. (1991) *The birds of the Philippines*. Tring, UK: British Ornithologists' Union (Check-list 12).

Dittami, J.P. & Gwinner, E. (1985) Annual cycles in the African stonechat *Saxicola torquata axillaris* and their relationship to environmental factors. *J. Zool. Lond. (A)* 207: 357-370.

Dolan, B. (1938) Zoological results of the second Dolan expedition to western China and eastern Tibet, 1934-1936. *Proc.Acad. Nat. Sci. Philadelphia* 90: 159-260.

Doughty, J. (1970) Breeding the Stonechat (*Saxicola torquata*). *Avic. Mag.* 76: 227-230.

Draulans, D. & van Vessem, J. (1982) Flock size and feeding behaviour of migrating Whinchats *Saxicola rubetra*. *Ibis* 124: 347-351.

Drijvers, R. (1995) Birds recorded in India and Nepal, Feb 1992, Dec 1993–May 1994, Jan 1995–May 1995. Unpublished.

Duckett, J.E. (1987) A second set of general bird notes from the Fourth Division of Sarawak. *Sarawak Mus.J.* 37(58): 123-137.

Duckworth, J.W. (1994) Habitat selection by migrant Redstarts *Phoenicurus phoenicurus* and Whinchats *Saxicola rubetra* in lowland English farmland. *Ringing and Migration* 15: 119-122.

Duckworth, J.W. (1997) Observations on a population of Jerdon's Bushchat *Saxicola jerdoni* in the Mekong channel, Laos. *Bull. Brit. Orn. Club* 117: 210-220.

Duckworth, J.W. & Hedges, S. (1998) Bird records from Cambodia in 1997, including records of sixteen species new for the country. *Forktail* 14: 29-36.

Duckworth, J.W., Tizard, R.J., Timmins, R.J., Thewlis, R.M., Robichaud, W.G. & Evans, T.D. (1998) Bird records from Laos, October 1994–August 1995. *Forktail* 13: 33-68.

Duckworth, J.W., Davidson, P. & Timmins, R.J. (1999) Birds. Pp.69-159 in J.W. Duckworth, R.E. Salter & K. Khounboline, compilers (1999) *Wildlife in Lao PDR: 1999 Status Report*. Vientiane: IUCN–The World Conservation Union, Wildlife Conservation Society, and Centre for Protected Areas and Watershed Management.

Duckworth, J.W., Davidson, P., Evans, T.D., Round, P.D. & Timmins, R.J. (2001) Bird records from Laos, principally the upper Lao Mekong and Xiangkhouang Province, in 1998–2000. Unpublished.

Dymond, N. (1993) Sighting of a Common Stonechat on Nias Island, Sumatra. *Kukila* 6: 134.

Eccles, L. (1955) Whinchats choosing nest-site. *Brit. Birds* 48: 421-422.

Eccles, L. (1967) Nest of Whinchat with twelve eggs. *Brit. Birds* 60: 169-170

Edwards, G., Hosking, E. & Smith, S. (1949) Reactions of some passerine birds to a stuffed Cuckoo. *Brit. Birds* 42: 13-19.

Elgood, J.H., Sharland R.E. & Ward, P. (1966) Palearctic migrants in Nigeria. *Ibis* 108: 84-116.

Elphick, C., Dunning, J.B., Jr. Sibley, D. eds (2001) *The Sibley guide to bird life and behaviour*. London. Christopher Helm

Erard, C. & Etchécopar, D. (1970) Contribution à l'étude des oiseaux d'Iran (Résultats de la Mission Etchécopar 1967). *Mém. Mus. natn. Hist. nat. (A)* 66.

Etchécopar, R.-D. & Hüe, F. (1957) Nouvelles données sur l'avifaune des îles Canaries recueillies au printemps 1956. *Oiseau et R.F.O.* 27: 309 –334.

Etchécopar, R.-D. & Hüe, F. (1967) *The birds of North Africa*. Edinburgh: Oliver & Boyd.

Evans, T.D. (2001) Ornithological records from Savannakhet Province, Lao PDR, January–July 1997. *Forktail* 17: 21-28.

Eve, R. & Guigue, A.M. (1996) *Birds of Thailand*. Singapore: Times Editions.

Feulner, J. (1995) Zur Populationsökologie des Braunkehlchens (*Saxicola rubetra*) in der Teuschnitzaue, Landkreis Kronach. Zulassungsarbeit Universität Bayreuth.

Finch, B.W. (1985) Noteworthy observations in Papua New Guinea and Solomons. *PNG Bird Soc. Newsletter* 215: 6-12.

Fisher, C. (1979) Stonechat hammering snail on wall. *Brit. Birds* 72: 38.

Fleming, R.L., Sr., Fleming, R.L., Jr. & Bangdel, L.S. (1984) *Birds of Nepal with reference to Kashmir and Sikkim*. Third edition. Kathmandu: Nature Himalayas.

Flinks, H. (1994) Die Altersbestimmung des Schwarzkehlchens *Saxicola torquata rubicola* an Gefiedermerkmalen. *Limicola* 8: 28-37.

Flinks, H. (1999) Muster, Intensität und zeitliche Aspekte der postjuvenilen Mauser beim Schwarzkehlchen (*Saxicola torquata*). *Vogelwarte* 40: 11-27.

Flinks, H. & Pfeifer, F. (1984) Zur Verbreitung und Populationsentwicklung des Schwarzkehlchens in Nordrhein-Westfalen. Brutpopulation. *Vogelwelt* 105: 41-51.

Flinks, H. & Pfeifer, F. (1987A) Nahrung adulter und nestjunger Schwarzkehlchen einer westfälischen Brutpopulation. *Vogelwelt* 108: 41-47.

Flinks, H. & Pfeifer, F. (1987B) Brutzeit, Gelegegrösse und Bruterfolg beim Schwarzkehlchen. *Charadrius* 23: 128–140.

Flinks, H. & Pfeifer, F. (1993) Vergleich der Habitatstrukturen ehemaliger und aktueller Schwarzkehlchen – (*Saxicola torquata*) – Brutplätze in einer agrarisch genutzen Landschaft. *Ökol. Vögel (Ecol. Birds)* 15: 85-97.

Flint, P.R. & Stewart, P.F. (1992) *The birds of Cyprus*. Revised edition. Tring, UK: British Ornithologists' Union (Check-list 6).

Flint, V.E., Boehme, R.L., Kostin, Y.V. & Kuznetsov, A.A. (1984) *A field guide to the birds of the USSR*. Princeton: Princeton University Press.

Fomin, V.E. & Bold, A. (1991) [*Catalogue of the birds of the Mongolian People's Republic*.] Moscow: Nauka. [In Russian.]

Frankevoort, W. & Hubatsch, H. (1966) *Unsere Wiesenschmätzer*. Wittenberg Lutherstadt: Ziemsen Verlag (Neue Brehm-Bücherei 370).

Freitag, F. (1943) Weitere Beobachtungen am Schwarzkehlchen. *Beitr. Fortpflanzungsbiol. Vögel* 19: 133-137.

Friedmann, H. (1937) Birds of Ethiopia and Kenya Colony, Part 2: Passeres.*U.S. Natn. Mus. Bull.* 153.

Fry, C.H. (1971) Migration, moult and weights of birds in northern Guinea savanna in Nigeria and Ghana. *Ostrich* supplement 8. 239–263.

Fujimaki, Y., Takamata, M. & Sato, F. (1994) Breeding biology of the Stonechat in southeastern Hokkaido, Japan. *Res. Bull. Obihiro Univ.*19: 37-46.

Fuller, R.J. & Glue, D.E. (1977) The breeding biology of the Stonechat and Whinchat. *Bird Study* 24: 215-228.

Gallagher, M. & Woodcock, M.W. (1980) *The birds of Oman*. London: Quartet Books.

Gantlett, S. (1997) 1996: the Western Palearctic year. *Birding World* 10: 19-35.

Gantlett, S. (1998) 1997: the Western Palearctic year. *Birding World* 11: 21-37.

Garland, T.P. & Melville, D. (1981) Notes on the Stonechat in Hong Kong. *Hong Kong Bird Report 1979*: 47-56. Hong Kong Birdwatching Society.

Garling, M. (1933) Zur Brutbiologie von *Saxicola rubetra rubetra* (L.). *Beitr. Fortpflanzungsbiol. Vögel* 9: 27.

Gatter, W. (1997) *Birds of Liberia*. Robertsbridge, UK: Pica Press.

Géroudet, P. (1957) Observations sur le Traquet tarier au val Ferret. *Nos Oiseaux* 24: 109-117.

Gilliard, E.T. & LeCroy, M. (1967) Annotated list of birds of the Adelbert Mountains, New Guinea. *Bull. Amer. Mus. Nat. Hist.* 138: 51-82.

Ginn, H.B. & Melville, D.S. (1983) *Moult in birds*. Tring, UK: British Trust for Ornithology (BTO Guide 19).

Ginn, P.J., McIlleron, W.G. and Milstein, P. le S. (1989) *The complete book of southern African birds*. Cape Town: Struik.

Giri, T. (1997) Naturetrek checklist: Nepal's Rara Lake, Bardia and Sukla Phanta Extension. Unpublished.

Gjershaug, J.O., Thingstad, P.G., Eldøy, S. & Byrkjeland, S. (1994) *Norsk fugleatlas*. Klæbu, Norway: Norsk Ornitologisk Forening.

Glutz von Blotzheim, U.N. & Sauter, W. (1962) *Die Brutvögel der Schweiz*. Aarau, Switzerland: Verlag Aargauer Tagblatt A.G.

Glutz von Blotzheim, U.N. & Bauer, K.M. (1988) *Handbuch der Vögel Mitteleuropas*, 11/1 Passeriformes (2. Teil) Turdidae. Wiesbaden: Aula Verlag.

Godwin-Austen, H.H. (1870) Second list of birds obtained in the Khasi and North Cachar hill ranges, including the Garo hills and country at their base in the Mymensingh and Sylhet districts.*J. Asiatic Soc. Bengal* 39: 264-275.

Goodman, S.M. & Meininger, P.L. (1989) *The birds of Egypt*. Oxford: Oxford University Press.

Gore, M.E.J. (1990) *Birds of The Gambia*. Revised edition. Tring, UK: British Ornithologists' Union (Check-list 3).

Gottschling, M., Kratzer, D., Huppop, O., Wittenberg, J. *et al.* (2000) Schwarzkehlchen *Saxicola torquata*.P.320 in Deutsche Seltenheitenkommission, Seltene Vogelarten in Deutschland 1997. *Limicola* 14: 273-340.

Gray, D.B. (1973) Whinchats on a disused railway. *Bird Study* 20: 80-82.

Gray, D.B. (1974) Breeding behaviour of Whinchats. *Bird Study* 21: 280–282.

Gregory, P. (1995) *The birds of the OK Tedi area*. Port Moresby: Independent Publishing.

Greig-Smith, P.W. (1979) The behavioural ecology of the Stonechat *Saxicola torquata*. Ph.D. thesis, University of Sussex.

Greig-Smith, P.W. (1980) Parental investment in nest defence by Stonechats (*Saxicola torquata*). *Anim. Behav.* 28: 604-619.

Greig-Smith, P.W. (1981) The role of alarm responses in the formation of mixed-species flocks of heathland birds. *Behav. Ecol. Sociobiol.* 8: 7–10.

Greig-Smith, P.W. (1982A) Song–rates and parental care by individual male Stonechats (*Saxicola torquata*). *Anim. Behav.* 30: 245-252.

Greig-Smith, P.W. (1982B) Interspecific aggression between chats. *Bird Study* 29: 162-164.

Greig-Smith, P.W. (1982C) Notes on the wing-flicking behaviour of the Stonechat *Saxicola torquata*. *Ibis* 124: 72-76.

Greig-Smith, P.W. (1983) Use of perches as vantage points during foraging by male and female Stonechats *Saxicola torquata*. *Behaviour* 86: 215-236.

Greig-Smith, P.W. (1984) Seasonal changes in the use of nesting cover by Stonechats *Saxicola torquata*. *Orn. Scand.* 15: 11-15.

Greig-Smith, P.W. (1985) Weight differences, brood reduction and sibling competition among nestling Stonechats *Saxicola torquata* (Aves: Turdidae).*J. Zool. Lond.* (A) 205: 453-465.

Greig-Smith, P.W. & Quicke, D.L.J. (1983) The diet of nestling Stonechats. *Bird Study* 30: 47-50.

Grell, M.B. (2000) Truede og sjældne ynglefugle i Danmark 1999. *Dansk Orn. Foren. Tidsskr.* 94: 55–72.

Grimes, L.G. (1972) The passerine list of birds of the Accra Plains, Ghana. Unpublished manuscript in Alexander Library, Oxford University.

Grimes, L.G. (1987) *The birds of Ghana*. London: British Ornithologists' Union (Check-list 9).

Grimmett, R., Inskipp, C. & Inskipp, T. (1998) *Birds of the Indian subcontinent*. London: Christopher Helm.

Groebbels, F. (1950) Ein Beitrag zur Brutökologie und Brutbiologie des Braunkehlchens und Schwarzkehlchens. *Orn. Abhand.* 5:1-16.

Grotenhuis, J.W. & van Os, B.L.J. (1986) Sterke achteruitgang van het Paapje als broedvogel in Drenthe. *Limosa* 59: 57-60.

Gubin, B.M. (1994) [New data for sightings and breeding records of the Pied Bushchat *Saxicola caprata* in southern Kazakhstan.] *Russian J. Orn.* 3: 277-278. [In Russian.]

Guérin, R. (1940-1953) *Faune ornithologique ancienne et actuelle des îles Mascareignes, Seychelles, Comores et des îles avoisinantes.* 3 vols. Port Louis, Mauritius: General Printing & Stationery Co.

Guldi, R. (1965) Zur Brutbiologie des Schwarzkehlchens (*Saxicola torquata*). *Orn. Mitt.* 17: 146-147.

Gwinner, E. (1991) Circannual rhythms in tropical and temperate zone stonechats: a comparison of properties under constant conditions. *Ökol. Vögel (Ecol. Birds)* 13: 5-14.

Gwinner, E. & Dittami, J. (1985) Photoperiodic responses in temperate zone and equatorial stonechats: a contribution to the problem of photoperiodism in tropical organisms. Pp. 279-294 in B.K. Follett, S. Ishii and A. Chandola, eds. *The endocrine system and the environment.* Tokyo and Berlin: Jap. Sci. Soc. Press and Springer-Verlag.

Gwinner, E., Dittami J. & Gwinner H. (1983) Postjuvenile molt in East African and Central European stonechats (*Saxicola torquata axillaris* and *S. t. rubicola*) and its modification by photoperiod. *Oecologia* 60: 66-70.

Gwinner, E., Neußer, V., Engl, D., Schmidl, D. & Bals, L. (1987) Haltung, Zucht und Eiaufzucht afrikanischer und europäischer Schwarzkehlchen (*Saxicola torquata*). *Gefiederte Welt* 111: 118-120, 145-147.

Gwinner, E., König, S. & Haley, C.S. (1995) Genetic and environmental factors influencing clutch size in equatorial and temperate zone Stonechats (*Saxicola torquata axillaris* and *S. t. rubicola*): an experimental study. *Auk* 112: 748-755.

Gwinner, E., Rodl, T. & Schawbl, H. (1994) Pair territoriality of wintering Stonechats: behaviour, function and hormones. *Behav. Ecol. Sociobiol.* 34: 321-327

von Haartmann, L. (1969) The nesting habits of Finnish birds, I: Passeriformes. *Comm. Biol. Soc. Sci. Fenn.* 32.

Hadden, D. (1975) Observations. *PNG Bird Soc. Newsletter* 115: 9.

Haffer, J. (1992) The history of species concepts and species limits in ornithology. *Bull. BOC Centenary Suppl.* 112A: 107-158.

Haftorn, S. (1971) *Norges fugler.* Oslo: Universitetsforlaget.

Hagemeijer, W.J.M. & Blair, M.J., eds. (1997) *The EBCC atlas of European breeding birds: their distribution and abundance.* London: T. & A.D. Poyser.

Hall, B.P. & Moreau, R.E. (1970) *An atlas of speciation in African passerine birds.* London: British Museum (Natural History).

Handrinos, G. & Akriotis, T. (1997) *The birds of Greece.* London: Christopher Helm.

Harber, D.D. (1948) Flocks of Whinchats on spring migration. *Brit. Birds.* 41: 348.

Harington, H.H. (1905) The nesting of some birds in Burma which have not been recorded before. *J. Bombay. Nat. Hist. Soc.* 16: 740-741.

Harington, H.H. (1909) A list of the birds of the Bhamo district, Upper Burma. *J. Bombay Nat. Hist. Soc.* 19: 299-313.

Harpum, J. (1978) Species-pair association of Stonechat and Black-lored Cisticola in southwest Tanzania. *Scopus* 2: 99-101.

Harrison, J.A., Allan, D.G., Underhill, L.G., Herremans, M., Tree, A.J. & Brown, C.J. (1997) *The atlas of southern African birds,* 2. Passerines. Johannesburg: BirdLife South Africa.

Harrisson, T. (1967) Borneo bird notes 1966–7, from various hands. *Sarawak Mus.J.* NS 15(30-31): 414-423.

Hartert, E. (1898) List of the birds collected in Timor by Mr Alfred Everett. *Novit. Zool.* 5: 455-476.

Hartert, E. (1910) Altes und Neues über die Gattung *Pratincola* Koch.J. *Orn.* 58: 171-182.

Hartert, E. (1922) *Saxicola torquata promiscua,* subsp. nov. *Bull. Brit. Orn. Club* 42: 51.

Hartert, E. & Steinbacher, F. (1932-1938) *Die Vögel der paläarktischen Fauna.* Ergänzungsband. Berlin.

Harvey, W. (2002) Stoliczka's Bushchat *Saxicola macrorhyncha* in Haryana, India. *Oriental Bird Club Bulletin* 35: 17-21.

Harvey, W.G. & Holmes, D.A. (1976) Additions to the avifaunas of Sumatra and Kalimantan, Indonesia. *Bull. Brit. Orn. Club* 96: 90-92.

Hazevoet, C.J. (1999) Fourth report on birds from the Cape Verde Islands including notes on conservation and records of 11 taxa new to the Archipelago. *Bull. Zool. Mus. Univ. Amsterdam* 17(3): 19- 32.

Heath, M., Borgreve, C. & Peet, N. (2000) *European bird populations: estimates and trends.* Cambridge, UK: BirdLife International (Conservation Series 10).

Heinen, J. (1988) Notes on birds recorded at Kosi Barrage and Kosi Tappu from January 1987 to March 1988. Unpublished.

Hellebrekers, W.P.J. & Hoogerwerf, A. (1967) A further contribution to our zoological knowledge of the island of Java (Indonesia). *Zool. Verh.* 88: 103.

Hellmayr, C.E. (1914) Die Avifauna von Timor. Pp.1-112 in C.B. Haniel, ed. *Zoologie von Timor.* Stuttgart: in Kommissionsverlag der E. Schweizerbartschen Verlags-buchhandlung, Nägele und Dr Sproesser in Stuttgart.

Helm, B. & Gwinner, E. (1999) Timing of postjuvenile moult in African (*Saxicola torquata axillaris*) and European (*Saxicola torquata rubicola*) Stonechats: effects of genetic and environmental factors. *Auk* 116: 589-603.

Helm, B. & Gwinner, E. (2001) Nestling growth and post-juvenile moult under a tight seasonal schedule in stonechats *Saxicola torquata maura* from Kazakhstan. *Avian Science* 1 (1):31-42.

Henning, H. (1967) Die Wirtsvögel des Kuckucks (*Cuculus canorus* L.) in der weiteren Umgebung Hamburgs. *Abh. Verh. Naturwiss. Ver. Hamburg* 11: 123-170.

Henry, G.M. (1998) *A guide to the birds of Sri Lanka.* Third edition. Calcutta: Oxford University Press.

Herklots, G.A.C. (1967) *Hong Kong birds.* Second edition. Hong Kong: South China Morning Post.

Herrera, C.M. (1984) Significance of ants in the diet of insectivorous birds in southern Spanish Mediterranean habitats. *Ardeola* 30: 77-81.

Herrman, K. (1987) Vorkommen des Schwarzkehlchens im Harz und Harzvorland. *Beitr. Vogelkde* 33: 114-118.

Hewitson, C.E. (1955) Observations on the Birdlife of Madhya Pradesh. *J. Bombay Nat. Hist. Soc.* 53: 595-645.

Hezekia, G. (1987) Fishing by Common Stonechat. *Honeyguide* 33(1): 18.

Hicks, R. (1985) Pelagic birding 14 December 1985. *PNG Bird Soc. Newsletter* 218: 7.

Hilden, O. & Saurola, P. (1982) Speed of autumn migration of birds ringed in Finland. *Orn. Fenn.* 59: 140-143.

Hirschfeld, E. (1995) *Birds in Bahrain – a study of their migration patterns 1990–1992.* Dubai: Hobby Publications.

Hodgson, C.J. (1978) Stonechat taking food from water. *Brit. Birds* 71: 313-314.

Holmes, D. & Nash, S. (1989) *The birds of Java and Bali.* Singapore: Oxford University Press.

Holmes, D.A. (1993) Birds on Timor: a synopsis of birds recorded on Timor. Unpublished

Holmes, D.A. & Wright, J.O. (1968-1969) The birds of Sind: a review. *J. Bombay Nat. Hist. Soc.* 65: 533-556; 66: 8-30.

Holt, P., Crossley, R. & Moores, C. (1986) Notes on birds recorded in Nepal, January–April 1986. Unpublished.

Hooker, T. (1958) Birds seen on the Eastern Canary Island of Fuerteventura. *Ibis* 100: 446-449.

Hope, P.M. & Pipe, G.E. (1961) Whinchat's nest surviving grass fire. *Brit Birds*. 44: 364.

Hornbuckle, J., Allen, D., Holt, P. & Kazmierczak, K. (1998) North East India: Arunchal Pradesh & Assam, 20 February 1998–13 March 1998. Unpublished.

Horstkotte E. (1962) Beiträge zum Brutverhalten des Braunkehlchens (*Saxicola rubetra* L.) *Ber. naturwiss. Ver. Bielefeld* 16: 107-165.

Hosking, E. & Lane, F.W. (1970) *An eye for a bird*. London: Hutchinson.

Hudson, R. (1973) *Early and late dates for summer migrants*. Tring, UK: British Trust for Ornithology (Guide 15).

Hudson, W.H. (1900) *Nature in Downland*. London: Longmans.

Hüe, F. & Etchécopar, R.-D. (1958) Un mois de recherches ornithologiques aux îles Canaries. *Terre et Vie* 105: 186–219.

Hume, A.O. (1877a) Notes about *Pratincola* species in India. *Stray Feathers* 5: 130-133.

Hume, A.O. (1877b) Notes on some of our Indian Stone Chats. *Stray Feathers* 5: 239-244.

Hume, A.O. (1877c) Notes. *Stray Feathers* 5: 117-140.

Hume, A.O. (1877d) Notes. *Stray Feathers* 5: 495-502.

Hume, A.O. (1878a) The birds of a drought. *Stray Feathers* 7: 52-68.

Hume, A.O. (1878b) Notes. *Stray Feathers* 7: 451-465.

Hume, A.O. (1878c) Notes. *Stray Feathers* 7: 516-523.

Hume, A.O. (1880a) Additional notes on some of our Indian stonechats. *Stray Feathers* 9: 133-137.

Hume, A.O. (1880b) Notes. *Stray Feathers* 9: 505-507.

Hume, A.O. (1888) Detailed list of species observed in Manipur, together with notices of all other species observed in Assam, Sylhet and Cachar. *Stray Feathers* 11: 1-353.

Husain, K.Z. (1979) *Birds of Bangladesh*. Dacca: Government of Bangladesh.

Hustler, K., Tree, A.J. & Irwin, M.P.S. (1992) Fourth report of the OAZ Rarities Committee: rare birds in Zimbabwe. *Honeyguide* 38: 113-118.

Iapichino, C. & Massa, B. (1989) *The birds of Sicily*. Tring, UK: British Ornithologists' Union (Check-list 11).

Inglis, C.M. (1901-1904) The birds of the Madhubani subdivision of the Darbhanga district, Tirhut, with notes on species noticed elsewhere in the district. *J. Bombay Nat. Hist. Soc.* 13: 621-631;14: 132-139, 362-371, 554-563, 764-771; 15: 70-77, 337-343; 16: 70-75.

Inglis, C.M. (1959-1969) Birds of the Duars,*J.Bengal Nat. Hist. Soc.* 24: 71-76; 25: 121-127, 164-169, 196-200; 26: 1-8, 47-56, 93-99, 149-156; 27: 9-12, 55-58, 83-95, 129-155; 28: 18-51, 102-115, 153-161; 29: 16-25, 88-94, 150-160; 30: 35-42, 81-97, 166-181; 31: 14-32, 49-60; 32: 1-9, 69-73; 33: 121-125, 181-184; 34: 1-4, 85-87; 35: 1-5, 49-63.

Inglis, C.M., Travers, W.L., O'Donel, H.V. & Shebeare, E.O. (1920) A tentative list of the vertebrates of the Jalpaiguri district, Bengal: birds. *J. Bombay Nat. Hist. Soc.* 26: 988-999; 27: 151-158.

Inskipp, C. & Inskipp, T. (1991) *A guide to the birds of Nepal*. Second edition. London: Christopher Helm.

Inskipp, C. & Inskipp, T. (1993) Birds recorded during a visit to Bhutan in autumn 1991. *Forktail* 8: 97-112.

Inskipp, C., Inskipp, T. & Sherub (2000) The ornithological importance of Thrumshingla National Park, Bhutan. *Forktail* 16: 147-162.

Irvin, R. (1994) Notes on birds from Nepal 1990–93. Unpublished.

Irwin, M.P.S. (1987) *The birds of Zimbabwe*. Second edition. Harare: Quest Publishing.

James, P., ed. (1996) *The birds of Sussex*. Over Wallop, Hampshire: Sussex Ornithological Society.

Jännes, H. (1990) Mustapäätaskun *Saxicola torquata* alalajien ja sukupuolen määrittämisestä sekä lajin esiintymisestä Suomessa. *Lintumies* 25: 162-175.

Jenni, L. & Winkler, R. (1994) *Moult and ageing of European passerines*. London: Academic Press.

Jennings, M.C. (1981A) *The birds of Saudi Arabia: a check list*. Whittlesford, Cambridge, England: M.C. Jennings.

Jennings, M.C. (1981B) *Birds of the Arabian Gulf*. London: Allen & Unwin.

Jensen, J.V. & Kirkeby, J. (1980) *The birds of the Gambia*. Århus: Aros Nature Guides.

Jepson, P. & Ounsted, R. eds. (1997) *Birding Indonesia*. Singapore: Periplus Editions and BirdLife International Indonesia Programme.

Jesse, W. (1902-1903) A list of the birds of Lucknow. *Ibis* (8)2: 470-490; (8)3: 531-566.

Jobling, J.A. (1991) *A dictionary of scientific bird names*. Oxford: Oxford University Press.

Johansen, H. (1954) Die Vogelfauna Westsibiriens. II Teil (Systematik und Verbreitung, Oekologie der Einzelarten) 3. Fortsetzung: *Turdus–Saxicola.J. Orn.* 95: 319-342.

Johnson, E.D.H. (1961) The pair relationship and polygyny in the Stonechat. *Bird Study* 54: 213-225.

Johnson, E.D.H. (1971A) Observations on a resident population of Stonechats in Jersey. *Bird Study* 64: 201-213

Johnson, E.D.H. (1971B) Observations on a resident population of Stonechats in Jersey. *Bird Study* 64: 267-279.

Johnson, E.D.H. (1971C) The Stonechat in Jersey. *Bull. Soc. Jersiaise* 20: 250-255.

Johnson, E.D.H. (1971D) Wintering of *Saxicola torquata* in the Algerian Sahara. *Bull. Brit. Orn. Club* 91: 103-107.

Jones, A.E. (1927) Further notes on the birds of the Ambala district. *J. Bombay Nat. Hist. Soc.* 31: 1000-1008.

Juliusberger, R. (1987) A birdwatching tour to India and Nepal, 30 November 1986–16 April 1987. Unpublished.

Kannan, R. (1993) Dark Grey Bush Chat *Saxicola ferrea* (Gray) in Rajasthan and Madhya Pradesh. *J. Bombay Nat. Hist. Soc.* 90(1): 98.

Kazmierczak, K. & Allen, D. (1997) A short ornithological survey of Dibru-Saikhowa Wildlife Sanctuary. *Newsletter for Birdwatchers* 37: 84-85.

Keith, S., Urban, E.K. & Fry, C.H. (1992) *The birds of Africa*, 4. London: Academic Press.

Kemp, M.I., Kemp, A.C. & Tarboton, W.R. (1985) A catalogue of the birds of the Transvaal Cyclostyled manuscript, 630 pages Pretoria: Transvaal Museum and Transvaal Nature Conservation Division.

Kempf, C. (1982) Approche écologique d'un peuplement d'oiseaux nicheurs des prairies de fauche d'Alsace. *Alauda* 50: 278-285.

Kennedy, R.S., Gonzales, P.C., Dickinson, E.C., Miranda Jr, H.C. & Fisher, T.C. (2000) *A guide to the birds of the Philippines*. Oxford: Oxford University Press.

Kierdorf-Traut, G. (1975) Zum Vorkommen von Braunkehlchen (*Saxicola rubetra*) im Gsieser Tal. *Monticola* 4: 1-4.

King, B. (1983) New bird distribution data from Burma. *Nat. Hist. Bull. Siam. Soc.* 31: 55-62.

King, B., Woodcock, M. & Dickinson, E.C. (1975) *A field guide to the birds of South-East Asia*. London: Collins.

King, B., Buck, H., Ferguson, R., Fisher, T., Goblet, C., Nickel, H. & Suter, W. (2001) Birds recorded during two expeditions to north Myanmar (Burma). *Forktail* 17: 29-40.

Kinnear, N.B. (1934) On the birds of the Adung Valley, north-east Burma. *J. Bombay Nat. Hist. Soc.* 37: 347-368.

Kinoshita, M. & Kato, C. (1995) Killing nestling Stonechat by the Common Cuckoo. *Japanese J. Orn.* 44: 99-100.

Kishchinskiy, A.A. (1980) [*Birds of the Koryak Highlands*]. Moscow: Nauka. [In Russian.]

Kishchinskiy, A.A., Fomin, V.E., Bold, A. & Tsevenmyadag, N. (1982) [Birds of the Monho-Hayrhan massif (Mongolian People's Republic).] Pp. 62-81 in V.E. Sokolov, ed. [*Zoological studies in the Mongolian People's Republic.*] Moscow: Nauka. [In Russian.]

Knox, A.G. 1994 Lumping and splitting. *Brit. Birds* 87: 149-159.

Knystautas, K. (1993) *Birds of Russia*. London: Harper Collins.

Kozlova, E. (1930a) Zur Biologie von *Pratincola insignis* Blyth. *Doklady Akad. Nauk SSSR [Comptes Rendus de l'Académie des Sciences de l'URSS]* 7: 175-178.

Kozlova, E. (1930b) [*The birds of south-western Transbaykalia, northern Mongolia and the central Gobi.*] Leningrad: Academy of Sciences of the USSR. [In Russian.]

Kozlova, E. (1932) [The birds of the alpine region of the Hangay, based on observations by the zoological section of the 1929 Mongolian expedition.] *Trudy Mongol'sk. Komiss.* 3 .[In Russian.]

Krechmar, A.V. (1963) [On seasonal phenomena in the bird life of the Norilskiye lakes area.] *Ornitologiya* 6: 37-48. [In Russian.]

Kumerloeve, H. (1969) Zur Avifauna des Van Gölü und Hakkâri-Gebietes (E/SE-Kleinasien). *Istanbul Üniv. Fen. Fakült. Mecmuasi* B34: 245-312.

Kunz, A. (1988) Verbreitung und Bestandssituation des Braunkehlchens in Rheinland-Pfalz. *Beih. Veröff. Naturschutz Landschaftspfl. Baden-Württemberg* 51: 69-78.

Kuroda, N. (1917) A collection of birds from Tonkin. *Annotates Zool. Jap.* 9: 217-254.

Kuzmenko, V. Ya. (1977) [Peculiarities of whinchat and stonechat ecology under conditions of drained areas in the Middle Dnieper territory.] *Vestnik Zool.* (4): 32–37. [In Russian.]

Kylänpää, J. (2000) Birds of Dera Ismail Khan District of North West Frontier Province in Pakistan. *Forktail* 16: 15-28.

Labhardt, A. (1984) Biometrie des Braunkehlchens: Variationen in den Flugelmaßen und im Körpergewicht zur Brutzeit. *Orn. Beob.* 81: 233-247.

Labhardt, A. (1988A) Siedlungsstruktur von Braunkehlchen-Populationen auf zwei Höhenstufen der Westschweizer Voralpen. *Beih. Veröff. Naturschutz Landschaftspfl. Baden-Württemberg* 51:139-158.

Labhardt, A. (1988B) Zum Bruterfolg des Braunkehlchens in Abhängigkeit von der Grünlandbewirtschaftung in den Westschweizer Voralpen. *Beih. Veröff. Naturschutz Landschaftspfl. Baden-Württemberg* 51:159-178.

Lack, D. (1933) Habitat selection in birds, with special reference to the effects of afforestation on the Breckland avifauna.*J. Anim. Ecol.* 2: 239-262.

Lack, D. (1943) The problem of partial migration. *Brit. Birds* 37: 122-130, 143-150.

Lack, D. (1963) Cuckoo hosts in England. *Bird Study* 10: 185-202.

Lack, D. (1976) *The life of the Robin.* London: Witherby.

Lack, P. (1986) *The atlas of wintering birds in Britain and Ireland.* Calton, UK: T. & A.D. Poyser.

Langrand, O. (1990) *Guide to the birds of Madagascar.* London: Yale University Press.

Lardelli, R. (1986) Verbreitung, Biotop und Populationsökologie des Schwarzkehlchens im Mendrisiotto, Südtessin. *Orn. Beob.* 83: 81-93.

Laubmann, A. (1927) Zur Ornithologie der Ionischen Inseln. *Verh. Orn. Ges. Bayern* 17: 291-376.

Leburdre, F. & Rapine, J. (1936) Ornithologie de la Basse-Bretagne. *Saxicola torquata hibernans. Oiseau* 6: 86-103.

Ledant, J.-P. (1986) L'habitat du Traquet tarier dans le centre de la Côte d'Ivoire. *Gerfaut* 76: 139-145.

Lee W.-S., Koo T.-H. & Park J.-Y. (2000) *A field guidé to the birds of Korea.* Seoul: LG Evergreen Foundation.

Lehikoinen, E. & Niemelä, P. (1977) Varpuslintujen sulkasadon tutkimus. *Lintumies* 12(2): 33–44.

Leibak, E., Lilleleht, V. & Veromann, H., eds. (1994) *Birds of Estonia: status, distribution and numbers.* Tallinn: Estonian Academy Publishers.

Lekagul, B. & Round, P.D. (1991) *A guide to the birds of Thailand.* Bangkok: Saha Kam Bhaet.

Lennerstedt, I. (1964) Some features of the breeding biology of the Willow Warbler, Whinchat, and Reed Bunting in Central Lapland. *Fauna och Flora* 59: 94-123.

Lennerstedt, I. (1973) Night rest during nestling period in four passerine species under subarctic summer conditions. *Orn. Scand.* 4: 17-23.

Linsenmair, K.E. (1960) Das Schwarzkehlchen. *Kosmos* 56: 190-194.

Lilleleht, V. (1999) Rarities in Estonia 1990–1997. Report of the Estonian Rarities Committee. *Hirundo* 12(2): 51-102.

Lippens, L. & Wille, H. (1972) *Atlas des oiseaux de Belgique et d'Europe occidentale.* Tielt, Belgium: Lannoo.

Little, R. (1984) An albino Stonechat. *Bokmakierie* 36(3): 71.

Löhrl, H. (1987) Observations on the Fuerteventura Stonechat *Saxicola dacotiae. Vogelwelt* 108: 105-109.

Lord, D. (1994) C.B.W.P.S. Stonechat Survey: June 1993. *Birds in Cornwall* (64th Annual Report), 161–165.

Loskot, V.M. (1986) [Evidence on birds of Tashanta environs (South-Eastern Altai).] *Trudy Zool. Inst. Akad. Nauk SSSR* 150: 44-56. [In Russian.]

Louette, M. (1981) *The birds of Cameroon. An annotated checklist.* Brussels: Verhandeling Wetenschappen 43 no. 163.

Lovegrove, R. (1971) BOU supported expedition to the northeast Canary Islands July–August 1970. *Ibis* 113: 269–272.

Mackinnon, J. & Phillips, K. (1993) *A field guide to the birds of Borneo, Sumatra, Java and Bali.* Oxford: Oxford University Press.

MacKinnon, J. & Phillipps, K. (2000) *A field guide to the birds of China.* Oxford: Oxford University Press.

Mackworth-Praed, C.W. & Grant, C.H.B. (1960) *Birds of Eastern and North Eastern Africa.* London: Longmans.

Maclean, G.L. (1985) *Roberts' birds of southern Africa.* Cape Town: John Voelcker Bird Book Fund.

Magrath, H.A.F. (1908) Notes on the birds of Thandiani. *J. Bombay Nat. Hist. Soc.* 18: 284-299.

Majnep, I.S. & Bulmer, R. (1977) *Birds of my Kalam country.* Auckland: Auckland University Press.

Malchevskiy, A.S. (1987) *Kukushka i ego vospitateli.* Leningrad: Leningrad State University Press. [In Russian.]

Mann, C.F. (1987) A checklist of the birds of Brunei Darussalam. *Brunei Mus.J.* 6: 170-212.

Marshall, C.H.T. & Marshall, G.F.L. (1875) [Letter about *Pratincola insignis, Caprimulgus mahrattensis* and *Meniceros bicornis.*] *Stray Feathers* 3: 330-331.

Martins, R.P. & Porter R.F. (1996) OSME Survey of southern Yemen and Socotra 1993. *Sandgrouse* 17: 60.

Martins, R.P., Parr, M.J., Robson, C.R., Speight, G.J. & Turton, J.M. (1983) Hodgson's Stonechats in Nepal in March and April 1982. *Dutch Birding* 5: 99-101.

Massey, P.R. (2000) Common Stonechat breeding in February in reedbed. *Brit. Birds* 93: 288.

Mayol, J. (1990) *Birds of the Balearic Islands.* Mallorca: Editorial Moll.

Mayr, E. (1941) *In* Stanford, J.K. The Varnay-Cutting Expedition to northern Burma (pt 3). *Ibis* (14) 5: 213-245.

Mayr, E. (1944) The birds of Timor and Sumba. *Bull. Amer. Mus. Nat. Hist.* 83: 123-194.

Mayr, E. & Gilliard, E.T. (1951) New species and subspecies of birds from the highlands of New Guinea. *Amer. Mus. Novit.* 1524.

Mayr, E. & Rand, A.L. (1937) Results of the Archbold expeditions. 14. Birds of the 1933–1934 Papuan expedition. *Bull. Amer. Mus. Nat. Hist.* 73: 1-248.

McCanch, N.A. (1985) *Lighthouse notebook.* London: M.Joseph.

McKitrick, M.C. & Zink, R.M. (1988) Species concepts in ornithology. *Condor* 90: 1-14.

Meade-Waldo, E.G. (1889a) Notes on some birds of the Canary Islands. *Ibis* (6)1: 1-13.

Meade-Waldo, E.G. (1889b) Further notes on the birds of the Canary Islands. *Ibis* (6)1: 503-520.

Meade-Waldo, E.G. (1893) List of birds observed in the Canary Islands. *Ibis* (6)5: 185-207.

Medway, Lord & Wells, D.R. (1976) *The birds of the Malay Peninsula,* 5. London: Witherby.

Mees, G.F. (1964) Notes on two small collections of birds from New Guinea. *Zool. Verh.* 66: 1-37.

Mees, G.F. (1975) A list of the birds known from Roti and adjacent islets (Lesser Sunda Islands). *Zool. Meded.* 49(12): 115 –140.

Meinertzhagen, R. (1920) Notes on the birds of Quetta. *Ibis* (11)2: 132-195.

Meinertzhagen, R. (1922) Notes on some birds from the Near East and from Tropical East Africa. *Ibis* (11)4: 1-74.

Meinertzhagen, R. (1924) Notes on a small collection of birds made in Iraq in the winter of 1922-23. *Ibis* (11)6: 601-624.

Meinertzhagen, R. (1934) The relation between plumage and environment, with special reference to the Outer Hebrides. *Ibis* (13)4: 52-61.

Meinertzhagen, R. (1953) On the validity of *Saxicola torquata hibernans* Hartert. *Bull. Brit.Orn.Club* 73: 14-15.

Meinertzhagen, R. (1954) *The birds of Arabia.* Edinburgh: Oliver & Boyd.

Melchior, E., Mentgen, E., Peltzer, R., Schmitt, R. & Weiss, J. eds. (1987) *Atlas der Brutvögel Luxemburgs.* Luxembourg: Lëtzebuerger Natur-a Vulleschutzliga.

Meyer de Schauensee, R. (1984) *The birds of China.* Oxford: Oxford University Press.

Meylan, O. (1937) Contribution à l'étude de l'avifaune des Alps, 4–La Haute-Maurienne. *Alauda* 9: 22-42.

Mildenberger, H. (1950) Beiträge zur Ökologie und Brutbiologie des Schwarkehlchens. *Bonn. zool. Beitr.* 1: 11-20.

Milon, P. (1951) Notes sur l'avifaune actuelle de la Réunion. *Terre et Vie* 98: 129-178.

Milon, P., Petter, J.J. & Randrianasolo, G. (1973) *Faune de Madagascar XXXV: Oiseaux.* Tananarive: ORSTOM.

Mohan-Rai, Y. (1986) The birds of Delhi and Meerut. *J. Bombay Nat. Hist. Soc.* 83: 212-214.

Moltoni, E. (1928) Risultati zoologici della Missione inviata dalla R. Società Geografica Italiana per l'esplorazione dell'oasi di Giarabub (1926-1927). Uccelli. *Ann. Mus. Civ. Stor. Nat. Genova* 52: 387-401.

Monk, J.F. (1953) The breeding biology of the Greenfinch. *Bird Study* 1: 2-14.

Monroe, B.L. & Sibley, C.G. (1993) *A world checklist of birds.* New Haven: Yale University Press.

Moore, N.W. (1962) The heaths of Dorset and their conservation. *J. Ecol.* 50: 369-391.

Moreau, R.E. (1961) Problems of Mediterranean–Saharan migration. *Ibis* 103A: 373-427, 580-623.

Moreau, R.E. (1972) *The Palearctic–African bird migration systems.* London: Academic Press.

Moreau, R. E & Moreau, W.M. (1953) Migrants on the north coast of Spain. *Ibis* 95: 375–376.

Moreno, J. (1984) Search strategies of Wheatears (*Oenanthe oenanthe*) and Stonechats (*Saxicola torquata*): adaptive variation in perch height, search time, sally distance and inter-perch move length. *Journ. Anim. Ecol.* 53: 147-159.

Morgan, R.A. & Davis, P.G. (1977) The number of broods reared by Stonechats in Surrey. *Bird Study* 24: 229-232.

Müller, H.E.J. (1999) Frühe Zweitbrut und verlängerte Jungenpflege beim Kanarenschmätzer *Saxicola dacotiae.* *Limicola* 13: 74-79.

Müller, M. (1985) Reviere, Reviernutzung und Nahrungssuchverhalten des Braunkehlchens (*Saxicola rubetra*) in zwei Populationen der Waadtländer Voralpen. Diplomarbeit der Universität Zürich. (Unpublished.)

Munkejord, A. (1981) The Stonechat *Saxicola torquata* in western Norway south of 62°N 1973–1980. *Fauna norv. Ser. C. Cinclus* 4: 69-75.

Narayan, G. & Rosalind, L. (1997) Wintering range and time extension of Hodgson's Bush Chat *Saxicola insignis* Gray in India. *J. Bombay Nat. Hist. Soc.* 94: 572-573.

Nepali, H.S. (1986) List of bird specimens collected in Nepal. Unpublished.

Neufeldt, I.A. (1986) [On some results of ornithological expedition to South-Eastern Altai.] *Trudy Zool. Inst. Akad. Nauk SSSR* 150: 7-43. [In Russian.]

Neufeldt, I.A. & Vietinghoff-Scheel, E.V. (1982) *Saxicola insignis* Gray. In H. Dathe and I.A. Neufeldt, eds. *Atlas der Verbreitung Palaearktischer Vögel,* 10. Berlin: Akademie Verlag.

Newby, J.E. (1979-1980) The birds of the Ouad Rime–Ouadi Achim Faunal Reserve: a contribution to the study of the Chadian avifauna. *Malimbus* 1: 90-109; 2: 29-50.

Newton, P.N., Breeden, S. & Norman, G.J. (1986) The birds of Kanha Tiger Reserve, Madhya Pradesh, India. *J. Bombay Nat. Hist. Soc.* 83(3): 477-498.

Nice, M.M. (1943) Studies in the life history of the Song Sparrow, 11. *Trans. Linn. Soc. New York* 6: 1-238.

van Niekerk, D.J. (1994) Interessante nes van Gewone Bontrokkie *Saxicola torquata. Mirafra* 11(1): 8.

Niethammer, G. (1937) *Handbuch der deutschen Vogelkunde, 1.* Leipzig: Akademische Verlagsgesellschaft.

Niethammer, G. (1938) Ornithologisches aus der Rheinprovinz. *Orn. Monatsber.* 46: 131-136.

Nightingale, T. & Hill, M. (1993) *Birds of Bahrain.* London: Immel Publishing.

Noske, R.A. & Saleh, N. (1996) The conservation status of forest birds in West Timor. Pp.65-74 in D.J. Kitchener and A. Suyanto, eds. *Proceedings of the first international conference on eastern Indonesian–Australian vertebrate fauna, Manado, Indonesia, November 22-26 1994.* Perth: Western Australian Museum.

Oates, E.W. (1883) *A handbook to the birds of British Burmah including those found in the adjoining state of Karanee.* London: Porter, Dulau and Co.

Oates, E.W. (1890) *Fauna of British India including Ceylon and Burma: Birds,* 2. London: Taylor and Francis.

Oggier, P.-A. (1979) Altitude et densité chez le Traquet tarier *Saxicola rubetra* en Valais. *Nos Oiseaux* 35: 85.

Oggier, P.-A. (1984) Une courtilière, *Gryllotalpa,* proie géante pour un Traquet tarier. *Nos Oiseaux* 37: 294.

Olsen, K.M. (1992) *Danmarks fugle – en oversigt.* Copenhagen: Dansk Ornitologisk Forening.

Olsson, V. (1947) Redogörelse för en fägelbonitering vid nedre Dalälven. *Vår Fågelvärld* 6: 93-125.

Oppermann, R. (1999) Nahrungsökologische Grundlagen und Habitatansprüche des Braunkehlchens *Saxicola rubetra. Vogelwelt* 120: 7-25.

Osborne, T.O. & Osborne, G.K. (1987) First specimen of Stonechat (*Saxicola torquata*) for North America. *Auk* 104: 542-543.

Ottow, J. & Verheijen, J.A.J. (1969) Zur Lebensweise der Kuckucke von Flores. *J. Orn.* 110: 27-29.

Paludan, K. (1959) On the birds of Afghanistan. *Vidensk Medd. Dansk. Naturh. For.* 122.

Panov, E.N. (1976) [New data on the biology and breeding of the Hodgson's Bushchat.] Pp. 204-211 in A.S. Rak, ed. [*Rare, threatened and inadequately-known birds of the U.S.S.R.*] Ryazan': Oka State Nature Reserve [*Trudy Oksk. gos. Zapoved.* 13]. [In Russian.]

Parker, J.E. (1990) Zur Biologie und Ökologie einer Braunkehlchen-Population (*Saxicola rubetra*) im Salzburger Voralpengebiet (Österreich). *Egretta* 33: 64-76.

Parker, V. (1994) *Swaziland Bird Atlas 1985–1991.* Mbabane, Swaziland: Websters.

Parkes, K.C. (1960) New subspecies of Philippine birds. *Saxicola caprata randi,* new subspecies. *Proc. Biol. Soc. Washington* 73: 59.

Parrack, J.D. (1973) *The naturalist in Majorca.* Newton Abbot, UK: David & Charles.

Parrinder, E.R. & Parrinder, D.E. (1945) Some observations on Stonechats in north Cornwall. *Brit. Birds* 38: 362-369.

Patton, S.J., ed. (1995) Whinchat. *The Sussex Bird Report* No. 48: 111.

Pérez Padrón, F. (1983) *Las aves de Canarias.* Third edition. Tenerife: ACT (Enciclopedia Canaria).

Perreau, G. (1910) Notes on the birds of Chitral. *J. Bombay Nat. Hist. Soc.* 19: 901-922.

Petrov, S. Yu. & Rudkovski, V.P. (1985) [Summer ornithofauna of Western Sayan range.] *Ornitologiya* 20: 76-83.

Pfeifer, G. (2000) Vorkommen und Ausbreitung des Schwarzkehlchens, *Saxicola torquata* Linnaeus 1766, in

Schleswig-Holstein unter Einbeziehung der Bestandsentwicklung in den Nachbarländern. *Corax* 18(2): 109-141.

Phillips, J.S. (1967) Winter territory in the Stonechat. *Bird Study* 14: 191-192.

Phillips, J.S. (1968) Stonechat breeding statistics. *Bird Study* 15: 104-105.

Phillips, J.S. (1970) Interspecific competition in Stonechat and Whinchat. *Bird Study* 17: 320-324.

Phillips, J.S. (1973) Stonechats in young forestry plantations. *Bird Study* 20: 82-84.

Phillips, J.S. & Greig-Smith, P.W. (1980) Breeding and wintering sites of Stonechats. *Bird Study* 27: 255-256.

Phillips, N.J. (1984) Migrant species new to Seychelles. *Bull. Brit. Orn. Club* 104: 9-10.

Pietiainen, H. (1983) Pensastasku *Saxicola rubetra.* pp 328-329 in K. Hyttia, J. Koistinen & E. Kellomaki, eds. *Suomen Lintuatlas.* Helsinki: Slyn: Lintutieto Oy.

Plucinski, A. (1956) Zur Brutbiologie des Schwarzkehlchens. *Orn. Mitt.* 8: 41-43.

Polatzek, J. (1908-1909) Die Vögel der Canaren. *Orn. Jahrb.* 19: 81-119, 161-197; 20: 1-24, 117-134, 202-210.

Pollen, F.P.L. (1868) Relation de Voyage. Volume 1 of *Recherches sur la faune de Madagascar et de ses dépendances, d'après les découvertes de François P.L. Pollen et D.C. van Dam.* Leiden: J.K. Steenhoff.

Ponomareva, T.S. & Vinokurov, A.A. (1984) [Hodgson's Bushchat *Saxicola insignis* Gray 1846] P.161 in A.M. Borodin, ed. [*Red Data Book of the U.S.S.R.*] 1. Second edition. Moscow: Lesnaya promyshlennost. [In Russian.]

Prager, E.M. & Wilson, A.C. (1975) Slow evolutionary loss of the potential for interspecific hybridisation in birds: a manifestation of slow regulatory evolution. *Proc. Nat. Acad. Sci.* 72: 200-204.

Prokofieva, I.V. (1980) [Food of meadow passerines during a nesting period.] *Ornitologiya* 15: 89-93. [In Russian.]

Proud, D. (1949) Some notes on the birds of the Nepal Valley. *J. Bombay Nat. Hist. Soc.* 48: 695-719.

Proud, D. (1955) More notes on the birds of the Nepal Valley. *J. Bombay Nat. Hist. Soc.* 53: 57-78.

Purroy, F.J. ed., (1997) *Atlas de las aves de España (1975–1995).* Barcelona: Lynx Edicions for Sociedad Española de Ornitologia and BirdLife.

Rahmani, A.R. (1988) Grassland birds of the Indian subcontinent: a review. Pp. 187-204 in P.D. Goriup, ed. *Ecology and conservation of grassland birds.* Cambridge, UK: International Council for Bird Preservation (Techn. Publ. 7).

Rahmani, A.R. (1993) Little-known Oriental bird: Whitebrowed Bushchat. *Oriental Bird Club Bull.* 17: 28-30.

Rahmani, A.R. (1994) Status and distribution of White-browed Bushchat *Saxicola macrorhyncha* in India. Oriental Bird Club: Unpublished report.

Rahmani, A.R. (1995) The little known life of the Whitebrowed Bushchat. *Sanctuary (Asia)* 15(6): 37-42.

Rahmani, A.R. (1996) Status and distribution of Stoliczka's Bushchat *Saxicola macrorhyncha* in India. *Forktail* 12: 61-67.

Rahmani, A.R. (1997) The effect of Indira Gandhi Nahar Project on the avifauna of the Thar Desert. *J. Bombay Nat. Hist. Soc.* 94: 233-260.

Rahmani, A.R. (1998) The uncertain future of the Desert National Park in Rajasthan, India. *Envir. Conserv.* 16: 237-244.

Rahmani, A.R. & Manakadan, R. (1988) *Bustard sanctuaries of India.* Bombay: Bombay Natural History Society (Tech. Rep. 13).

Ramos, E. (1996) *The birds of Menorca.* Majorca: Editorial Moll.

Ramsay, G. (1994) First record of Pied Stonechat *Saxicola caprata* in Saudi Arabia. *Sandgrouse* 16: 61-62.

Rand, A.L. (1936) The distribution and habitats of Madagascar birds. *Bull. Amer. Mus. Nat. Hist.* 72: 142-499.

Rand, A.L. (1940) Results of the Archbold Expeditions No 25. *Amer. Mus. Novit.* 1072.

Rand, A.L. & Gilliard, E.T. (1967) *Handbook of New Guinea birds.* London: Weidenfeld & Nicholson.

Rashid,H. (1967) *Systematic list of the birds of East Pakistan.* Asiatic Society of Pakistan (Publ.20).

Rebstock, H. & Maulbetsch, K.-E. (1988) Beobachtungen am Braunkehlchen in Balingen-Ostdorf. *Beih. Veröff. Naturschutz Landschaftspfl. Baden-Württemberg* 51: 91-118.

Rebstock, H. & Maulbetsch, K.-E. (1993) Bemerkungen zur Jugendentwicklung des Braunkehlchens (*Saxicola rubetra*). *Ökol. Vögel (Ecol. Birds)* 15: 137-153.

Redman, N.J., Lambert, F. & Grimmett, R.F. (1984) Some observations of scarce birds in Nepal. *J. Bombay Nat. Hist. Soc.* 81: 49-53.

Ree, V. (1977) Underartene av svartstrupe i Norge. *Fauna* 30: 41-47.

Regnaud, C. (1878) Tec-tec. [MS letter to Sir Edward Newton dated 14 February 1878]. In the Newton Library, Cambridge University, Zoology Dept. Published 1984 *Info-Nature, Ile Réunion* 21: 79-81.

Rensch, B. (1931) Ueber einige Vogelsammlungen des Buitenzorger Museums von den Kleinen Sunda-Inseln. *Treubia* 13(3-4): 371-400.

Richardson, C. (1990) *The birds of the United Arab Emirates.* Dubai: Hobby Publications.

Riddiford, N. (1981) Cautionary notes on ageing Redwings and Stonechats. *Ringers' Bulletin* 5(9): 120.

Riddiford, N. & Findley, P. (1981) *Seasonal movements of summer migrants.* Tring, UK: British Trust for Ornithology (BTO Guide 18).

Ripley, S.D. (1962) Brief comments on the thrushes. *Postilla* 63.

Ripley, S.D. (1964) Turdinae. Pp. 13–227 in E. Mayr & R.A. Paynter Jr., eds. *Check-list of birds of the world,* 10. Cambridge, Mass.: Museum of Comparative Zoology.

Risberg, E.L. (1972) Fågelobservationer i Varanger-området 1966–1971. *Sterna* 11(2): 81–95.

Ristow, D., Wink, C. & Wink, M. (1984) Assessment of Mediterranean autumn migration by prey analysis of Eleonora's Falcon. *Ric. Biol. Selvaggina Suppl.*10: 285-295.

Roberts, A. (1922) Review of the nomenclature of South African birds. *Ann. Transv. Mus.* 8 (4):187–272.

Roberts, T.J. (1992) *The birds of Pakistan,* 2. Karachi: Oxford University Press.

Roberson, D. (1980) *Rare birds of the West Coast of North America.* Pacific Grove, California: Woodcock Publications.

Robertson, I.S. (1975) Stonechats in Shetland – a change in status? *Shetland Bird Report:* 52-55.

Robertson, I.S. (1977) Identification and European status of eastern Stonechats. *Brit. Birds* 70: 237-245.

Rödl, T. (1994). Schwarzkehlchen *Saxicola torquata* frißt Skorpion. *Orn. Anzeiger* 33: 72.

Rödl, T. (1995) The wintering of territorial Stonechat pairs *Saxicola torquata* in Israel.*J. Orn.* 136: 423-433.

Rödl, T. (1999) Environmental factors determine numbers of overwintering European Stonechats *Saxicola rubicola* – a long-term study. *Ardea* 87: 247-259.

Rödl, T. & Flinks, H. (1996) Nutrition of Stonechats (*Saxicola torquata*) and Mourning Wheatears (*Oenanthe lugens*) wintering sympatrically in Israel. *Ökol. Vögel (Ecol. Birds)* 18: 107-126.

Rogacheva, E.V. (1992) *The birds of central Siberia.* Husum, Germany: Husum Druck- u. Verlagsgesellschaft.

Rogacheva, E.V., Ravkin, E.S., Syroechkovski, E.E. & Kuznetsov, E.A. (1983) [Fauna and population of birds of the Yenisey forest-tundra.] Pp.14-47 in [*Fauna of the Yenisey taiga and forest-tundra and natural zonation.*] Moscow: Nauka. [In Russian.]

Rogers, M.J. and the Rarities Committee (2001) Report on rare birds in Great Britain in 2000. *Brit. Birds* 94: 452-504.

Roseveare, W.L. (1949) Notes on birds of the irrigated area of Shwebo District, Burma. *J. Bombay Nat. Hist. Soc.* 48: 515-534.

Roseveare, W.L. (1952) Notes on birds of the irrigated area of Minbu District, Burma. *J. Bombay Nat. Hist. Soc.* 49: 244-287.

Rothschild, Lord (1926) On the avifauna of Yunnan, with critical notes. *Novit. Zool.* 33: 189–400.

Round, P.D. (1982) Notes on breeding birds in North West Thailand. *Nat. Hist. Bull. Siam Soc.* 30: 1-14.

Round, P.D. (1988) *Resident forest birds in Thailand.* Cambridge, UK: International Council for Bird Preservation (Monograph 2).

Rowan, M.K. (1983) *The doves, parrots, louries and cuckoos of southern Africa.* Cape Town: David Philip.

Rusila, N.Y. (1992) First sighting of Pied Bushchat in Sumatra. *Kukila* 6: 41.

Ruttledge, R.F. (1961) Voice of the Whinchat. *Brit Birds.* 54: 327–328.

Sacher, G. (1993) Zu Vorkommen und Brutbiologie des Braunkehlchens *Saxicola rubetra* im Thüringer Schiefergebirge. *Anz. Ver. Thüring. Orn.* 2: 29-45.

Sage, B.L. (1960) Field notes on some birds of eastern Iraq. *Ardea* 48: 160-178.

Sage, B.L. (1962) Albinism and melanism in birds. *Brit. Birds.* 55: 210–225.

Saha, S.S. & Datta, B.B. (1979) Taxonomic status of the eastern Grey Bush Chat, *Saxicola ferrea harringtoni* (Hartert). *Bull. Zool. Surv. India* 2: 113-114.

Salomonsen, F. (1953) Miscellaneous notes on Phillipine birds. *Vidensk. Medd. Dansk Naturhist. Foren.* 115: 205-281.

Salvadori, T. (1890) Viaggio di Lamberto Loria nella Papuasia orientale I. Collezioni ornitologiche. Nota prima. Uccelli di Pulo Penang, di Timor Cupang, di Pulo Semau e di Port Darwin. *Ann. Mus. Genova* 29: 476-505.

Sangster, G., Hazevoet, C.J., van den Berg, A.B. & Roselaar, C.S. (1998) Dutch avifaunal list: species concepts, taxonomic instability and taxonomic changes in 1998. *Dutch Birding* 20: 22-32.

Sarmento, A.A. (1936) *As aves do Arquipélago da Madeira.* Funchal, published by the author.

Schäfer, E. (1938) Ornithologische Ergebnisse zweier Forschungsreisen nach Tibet.*J. Orn.* 86: 1-79.

Schäfer, E. & Meyer de Schauensee, R. (1939) Zoological records of the second Dolan expedition to western China and western Tibet 1934–1936. Part 11: Birds. *Proc. Acad. Nat. Sci. Philadelphia* 90: 185-260.

Scheuerlein, A. (2000) Control of reproduction in a tropical bird, the Stonechat (*Saxicola torquata axillaris*). Munich: Dissertation der Fakultät für Biologie der Ludwig-Maximilians-Universität.

Schlegel, H. & Pollen, F.P.L. (1868) Mammifères et Oiseaux. Volume 2 of *Recherches sur la Faune de Madagascar et de ses dépendances, d'après les découvertes de François P.L. Pollen et D.C. van Dam.* Leiden: J.K. Steenhoff.

Schmidt, K. & Hantge, E. (1954) Studien an einer farbig beringten Population des Braunkehlchens (*Saxicola rubetra*).*J. Orn.* 95: 130-173.

Schmitz, E. (1909) Letzte Tagebuch-Notizen aus Madeira. *Orn. Jahrb.* 19: 58-63.

Schönwetter, M. (1979) *Handbuch der Oologie,* 2. Berlin: Akademie-Verlag.

Schwager, G. & Güttinger, H.R. (1984) Der Gesangsaufbau von Braunkehlchen (*Saxicola rubetra*) und Schwarzkehlchen (*S. torquata*) im Vergleich.*J. Orn.* 125: 261-278.

Scott, R.E. (1962) Passerines feeding on blackberries. *Brit. Birds* 55: 87–88.

Scully, J. (1881) A contribution to the ornithology of Gilgit. *Stray Feathers* 10: 88-146.

Seebohm, H. (1881) *Catalogue of the birds in the British Museum,* 5. London: British Museum (Natural History).

Serle, W. (1949) Birds of Sierra Leone (Part III). *Ostrich* 20: 70-85.

Sharma, P., Barua, M. & Menon, V. (1997) Orangebilled Jungle Mynah and Hodgson's Bush Chat in Kaziranga National Park. *J. Bombay Nat. Hist. Soc.* 94: 156-157.

Shepherd, K. (2001) Continental Stonechats. *Birding World* 14: 305.

Shirihai, H. (1995) *The birds of Israel.* London: Academic Press.

Shirt, D.B. (1983) The avifauna of Fuerteventura and Lanzarote. *Bustard Studies* 1: 57-68.

Sibley, C.G. & Ahlquist, J.E. (1990) *Phylogeny and classification of birds. A study in molecular evolution.* New Haven: Yale University Press.

Sibley, C.G., Ahlquist, J.E. & Monroe Jr, B.L. (1988) A classification of the living birds of the world based on DNA–DNA hybridization studies. *Auk* 105: 409-423.

Sibley, C.G. & Monroe Jr, B.L. (1990) *The distribution and taxonomy of the birds of the world.* New Haven: Yale University Press.

Sibley, C.G. & Monroe Jr, B.L. (1993) *A supplement to the distribution and taxonomy of the birds of the world.* New Haven: Yale University Press.

Simpson, D.M. (1984) Autumn migration of landbirds in Bombay offshore waters in 1983. *Sea Swallow* 33: 53-58.

Sinclair, I., Hockey, P. & Tarboton W. (1993) *Illustrated guide to the birds of Southern Africa.* London: New Holland.

Singh, A.P. (2000) Birds of lower Garwhal Himalayas: Dehra Dun valley and neighbouring hills. *Forktail* 16: 101-123.

Smith, B.D., Bhandari, B. & Sapkota, K. (1996) *Aquatic biodiversity in the Karnali and Narayani river basins, Nepal.* Kathmandu: IUCN Nepal.

Smith, K.D. (1957) An annotated check list of the birds of Eritrea. *Ibis* 99: 307-337.

Smith, S. (1990) Whinchats on Garn-Clochdy, Gwent. *BTO News* 168: 13.

Smith, V.W. & Cox, F.E.G. (1972) Blood parasites and the weights of Palaearctic migrants in central Nigeria. *Ibis* 114: 105-106.

Smythies, B.E. (1986) *The birds of Burma.* Liss, UK: Nimrod Press.

Smythies, B.E. (1999) *The birds of Borneo.* Fourth edition, revised by G.W.H. Davison. Kota Kinabalu: Natural History Publications (Borneo) in association with The Sabah Society.

Snow, D.W. & Perrins, C.M. (1998) *The birds of the Western Palearctic. Concise edition,* 2. Oxford: Oxford University Press.

Sokolov, G.A., Petrov, S. Yu., Balagura, N.P., Stakheev, V.A. & Zavatski, B.P. (1983) [Faunistic competition and ecology of some numerous species of mammals and birds.] Pp. 30–54 in [*The Sayano-Shushenski State Reserve*]. Krasnoyarsk: Institute of Forests of the USSR Academy of Sciences, Siberian section. [In Russian.]

van Someren, V.G.L. (1939) Birds of the Chyulu Hills.*J. East African Nat. Hist. Soc.* 14: 15-129.

Stanford, J.K. & Ticehurst, C.B. (1935) Notes on the birds of the Sittang, Irrawaddy plain, lower Burma. *J. Bombay Nat. Hist. Soc.* 37: 859–889.

Stanford, J.K. & Ticehurst, C.B. (1938) On the birds of northern Burma, Part II. *Ibis* (14)2: 197-229.

Stattersfield, A.J. & Capper, D.R., eds. (2000) *Threatened birds of the world.* Cambridge, UK: BirdLife International.

Stattersfield, A.J., Crosby, M.J., Long, A.J. & Wege, D.C. (1998) Endemic bird areas of the world: priorities for biodiversity conservation. Birdlife International Cambridge UK

Steinfatt, O. (1937) Nestbeobachtungen beim Rotkehlchen, Braunkehlchen, Buchfink und Hänfling. *Verh. orn. Ges. Bayern* 21: 139-154.

Stenhouse, J.H. (1921) Bird notes from southern Spain. *Ibis* (11)3: 573-594.

Stepanyan, L.S. (1990) Genus *Saxicola.* Pp. 501-505 in [*Conspectus of the ornithological fauna of the USSR*]. Moscow: Nauka. [In Russian.]

Stepanyan, L.S. (1995) [*Birds of Vietnam, based on the investigations of 1978-1990.*] Moscow: Nauka Press. [In Russian.]

Stevens, H. (1914-1915) Notes on the birds of Upper Assam. *J. Bombay. Nat. Hist. Soc.* 23: 234-268, 547-570, 721-736.

Stoddart, A. (1992) Identification of Siberian Stonechat. *Birding World* 5: 348-356.

Stoliczka, F. (1872) Notice of the mammals and birds inhabiting Kachh.J. *Asiatic Soc. Bengal* 41: 211-258.

Stresemann, E. (1912) Ornithologische Miszellen aus dem Indo-Australischen Gebiet. *Novit. Zool.* 19: 311-351.

Stresemann, E. (1920) *Avifauna Macedonica.* Munich: Dultz & Co.

Stresemann, E. & Heinrich, G. (1940) Die Vögel des Mount Victoria. *Mitt. Zool. Mus. Berlin* 24: 151-264.

Stöbener, W. (1977) Haltung und Zucht von Braunkehlchen. *Gefiederte Welt* 101: 202.

Sultana, A. & Khan, J.A. (2000) Birds of oak forests in the Kumaon Himalaya, Uttar Pradesh, India. *Forktail* 16: 131-146.

Summers-Smith, D. (1952) Breeding biology of the Spotted Flycatcher *Brit. Birds* 45:153-167.

Sushkin, P.P. (1938) [*Birds of Soviet Altai and adjacent parts of north-western Mongolia*], 2. Moscow & Leningrad: Academy of Sciences of USSR Press. [In Russian.]

Suter, W. (1988) *Saxicola rubetra* (pp. 392-446) and *Saxicola torquata rubicola* (pp. 449-499) in U.N. Glutz von Blotzheim & K.M. Bauer, eds. *Handbuch der Vögel Mitteleuropas,* 11. Wiesbaden: Aula Verlag.

Svensson, L. (1992) *Identification guide to European passerines.* Fourth edition. Stockholm: published by the author.

Swinhoe, C. (1882) On the birds of southern Afghanistan. *Ibis* (4)6: 95-126.

Tait, W.C. (1924) *The birds of Portugal.* London: H.F. & G. Witherby.

Talposh, V.S. (1996) [The Stonechat is a host species of the Cuckoo in the West of Ukraine.] *Berkut* 5: 87–88. [In Russian.]

Tarboton, W.R., Allan, D.G., Vernon, C.J. & Jenkins, A.R. *et al.* (1993) Baseline biological survey: fauna and flora: Lesotho Highlands Water Project, Phase 1A. Birds. Unpublished report. Cape Town: Avian Demography Unit, University of Cape Town.

Tarboton, W.R., Kemp, M.I. & Kemp, A.C. (1987) *Birds of the Transvaal.* Pretoria: Transvaal Museum.

Terry, M.M. (1980) Robin-like feeding by Stonechat. *Brit. Birds* 73: 354.

Thalmann, E. (1981) Braunkehlchen als Gesangsvirtuose. *Vögel der Heimat* 52 (1): 18-19.

von Thanner, R. (1905) Ein Sammelausflug nach Fuerteventura. *Orn. Jahrb.* 16: 50-66.

von Thanner, R. (1908) Ein Sammelausflug nach La Palma, Hierro und Fuerteventura. *Orn. Jahrb.* 19: 198–215.

von Thanner, R. (1910) Ornithologische Notizen, Fuerteventura betreffend. *Orn. Jahrb.* 21: 226-229.

von Thanner, R. (1914) Bemerkungen und Berichtigungen über die Verbreitung einzelner Vogelarten auf den Kanaren. *Orn. Jahrb.* 25: 86-94.

Thewlis, R.M., Timmins, R.J., Evans, T.D. & Duckworth, J.W. (1998) The conservation status of birds in Laos: a review of key species. *Bird Conserv. Internatn.* 8 (suppl.): 1-159.

Thibault, J.-C. (1983) *Les oiseaux de la Corse.* Ajaccio: Parc Naturel Regional de la Corse.

Thibault, J.-C. & Bonaccorsi, G. (1999) *The birds of Corsica.* Tring: British Ornithologists' Union (Check-list 17).

Thiollay, J.-M. (1967) Notes sur l'avifaune corse. *Oiseau & R.F.O.* 37: 104-113.

Thom, V.M. (1986) *Birds in Scotland.* Calton, UK: T. & A.D. Poyser.

Thompson, H., McKean, J. & Mason, I. (1974-1975) Observations of birds in Timor. Unpublished.

Thomsen, P. & Jacobsen, P. (1979) *The birds of Tunisia.* Copenhagen: privately published.

Thompson, P.M., Harvey, W.G., Johnson, D.L., Millin, D.J., Rashid, S.M.A., Scott, D.A., Stanford, C. & Woolner, J.D. (1993) Recent notable bird records from Bangladesh. *Forktail* 9: 12-44.

Thorpe, A. (1999) Stonechat colour-ringing in Aberdeenshire 1990-6: a summary. *Grampian R.G. Report* 1992-94 : 32-34.

Tiainen, J. & Ylimaunu, J. (1984) Suomen peltolinnuston muutokset ja tila. *Lintumies* 19: 26-29.

Ticehurst, C.B. (1922-1924) The birds of Sind. *Ibis* (11)4: 526-572, 605-662; (11)5: 1-43, 235-275, 438-474, 645-666; (11)6: 110-146, 495-518.

Ticehurst, C.B. (1926-1927) The birds of British Baluchistan. *J. Bombay Nat. Hist. Soc.* 31: 687-711, 862-881; 32: 64-97.

Ticehurst,C.B. (1933) Notes on some birds from southern Arakan.J.*Bombay Nat. Hist. Soc.* 36: 920-937.

Ticehurst, C.B. (1938) On *Saxicola maura* and *Saxicola indica. Ibis* (14)2: 338-341.

Toms, M.P. & Clark, J.A. (1998) Bird Ringing in Britain and Ireland in 1996. *Ringing and Migration* 19: 95-168. BTO Thetford.

Tristram, H.B. (1890) Notes on the island of Palma in the Canary group. *Ibis* (6)2: 67-76.

Tryjanowski, P. (1995) Is the Polish population of the Whinchat, *Saxicola rubetra,* stable? A view from the situation in a farmland area. *Bird Census News* 8(2): 72-74.

Tucker, G.M. & Heath, M.F. (1994) *Birds in Europe: their conservation status.* Cambridge, UK: BirdLife International (Conservation Series 3).

Tucker, J.J. (1972) Whinchats wintering in Zambia. *Bull. Zambian Orn. Soc.* 4: 29-30.

Tyabji, H.N. (1990) Record of some birds from Bandhavgarh National Park previously unrecorded in this area. *Newsletter for Birdwatchers.* 30 (5-6): 12

Tye, A. (1984) Attacks by shrikes *Lanius* spp. on wheatears *Oenanthe* spp.: competition, kleptoparasitism or predation? *Ibis* 126: 95-102.

Tye, A. (1988) Foraging behaviour and selection of prey and perches by the Buff-streaked Chat *Oenanthe bifasciata. Ostrich* 59: 105-115.

Tye, A. (1989) The systematic position of the Buff-streaked Chat (*Oenanthe/Saxicola bifasciata.*) *Bull. Brit. Orn. Club* 109: 53-58.

Uhl, H. (1998) Eine vermutliche Mischbrut von Braun-(*Saxicola rubetra*) und Schwarzkehlchen (*S. torquata*) in den oberösterreichischen Kremsauen 1994. *Egretta* 41: 27-34.

Ullman, M. (1986) Svarthakade buskskvättor och vita övergumpar. *Vår Fågelvärld* 45: 227-229.

Underhill, L.G. (1999) Avian demography: statistics and ornithology. *Ostrich* 70: 61-70.

Urban, E.K. & Brown, L.H. (1971) *A checklist of the birds of Ethiopia.* Addis Ababa: Haile Selassie I University Press.

Van Hecke, P. (1965) The migration of the West European Stonechat *Saxicola torquata* according to ringing data. *Gerfaut* 55: 146-194.

Vaurie, C. (1959) *The birds of the Palearctic fauna: order Passeriformes.* London: Witherby.

Vaurie, C. (1964) A survey of the birds of Mongolia. *Bull. Amer. Mus. Nat. Hist.* 127: 1-143.

Vaurie, C. (1972) *Tibet and its birds.* London: Witherby.

Verbeek, N.A.M. (1988) Development of a stable body temperature and growth rates in nestlings of three ground nesting passerines in alpine tundra.J. *Orn.* 129: 449-456.

Verbelen, F. (1995) Birding in Sumba and Timor Lesser Sundas, Indonesia. Unpublished.

Vere Benson, S. (1970) *Birds of Lebanon and the Jordan area.* London: International Council for Bird Preservation.

Verhoeye, J. & Holmes, D.A. (1999) The birds of the islands of Flores – a review. *Kukila* 10 (1998): 3-59.

Vincent, A.W. (1947) On the breeding habits of some African birds. *Ibis* 89: 196-198.

Volsøe, H. (1951) The breeding birds of the Canary Islands 1. Introduction and synopsis of the species. *Vidensk. Medd. fra Dansk naturh. Foren.* 113: 1-153.

Voous, K.H. (1960) *Atlas of European birds.* London: Nelson.

Voous, K.H. (1977) *List of recent Holarctic bird species.* London: Academic Press for The British Ornithologists' Union.

Vorob'ev, K.A. (1955) [On the bird fauna of Badkhyz (south eastern Turkmenistan).] *Zool. Zhurn.* 34: 898-901. [In Russian.]

Vowles, R.S. & Vowles, G.A. (1985) Some notes on the birds of Borneo. *Bull. Brit. Orn. Club* 105 (2): 71-73.

Vowles, G.A. & Vowles, R.S. (1997) *An annotated checklist of the birds of Brunei*. Newent, UK: Centro de Estudos Ornitológicos no Algarve.

Vyas, S. (1996) Checklist of the birds of the Delhi region: an update. *J. Bombay Nat. Hist. Soc.* 93: 219-237.

Walker, D. (2001) Apparent continental Stonechats in England. *Birding World* 14(4): 156-158.

Walpole-Bond, J. (1938) *A history of Sussex birds*, 2. London: Witherby.

Wardill, J.C., Fox, P.S., Hoare, D.J., Marthy, W. & Anggraini, K. (1992) Birds of the Rawa Aopa Watumohai National Park, South-East Sulawesi. *Kukila* 10: 91-114.

Watling, D. (1983) Ornithological notes from Sulawesi. *Emu* 83: 247-261.

Watson, J.D., Wheeler, W.R. & Whitbourn, E. (1961-1962) With the RAOU in Papua New Guinea. *Emu* 62: 31-50, 67-98.

Wells, D.R. (1976) Some bird communities in western Sabah, with distributional records, March 1975. *Sarawak Mus.J.* 24(45): 277-286.

Whistler, H. (1915) Some birds in Hissar district, Punjab. *J. Bombay Nat. Hist. Soc.* 24:190-191.

Whistler, H. (1922) Birds of the Jhang district. *Ibis* (11)4: 259-309.

Whistler, H. (1938) The ornithological survey of Jodhpur state. *J. Bombay Nat. Hist. Soc.* 40: 213–235.

Whistler, H. (1940) A new race of bush-chat from India. *Bull. Brit. Orn. Club* 60: 90.

Whistler, H. (1941) *Popular handbook of Indian birds*. London: Gurney & Jackson.

White, C.M.N. & Bruce, M.D. (1986) *The birds of Wallacea*. London: British Ornithologists' Union (Check-list 7).

Whitehead, C.H.T. (1911) On the birds of Kohat and the Kurram Valley, northern India. *J. Bombay Nat. Hist. Soc.* 20: 776–799.

Wickham, P.F. (1929-1930) Notes on the birds of the upper Burma hills. *J. Bombay Nat. Hist. Soc.* 33: 799-827: 34: 46-63, 337-349.

Wilcock, J. (1921) Male Whinchat mated to two females. *Brit. Birds* 14: 186-187.

Wildash, P. (1968) *Birds of South Vietnam*. Rutland, Vermont: Tuttle.

Willi, P. (1985) Langfristige Bestandestaxierungen im Rheindelta. *Egretta* 28: 1-62.

Williamson, K. (1965) *Fair Isle and its birds*. Edinburgh: Oliver & Boyd.

Wilson, J.G. (1986) Stonechat (*Saxicola torquata*) in New Brunswick – first record for North America. *Amer. Birds* 40 (1): 16-17.

Wink, M., Sauer-Gürth, H., Heidrich, P., Witt, H.-H. & Gwinner, E. (2001) A molecular phylogeny of stonechats and related turdids. Inst. Pharm. Biol. Univ. Heidelberg, Germany. Unpublished.

Wink, M., Sauer-Gürth, H. & Gwinner, E. 2002. Evolutionary relationships of stonechats and related species inferred from mitochondrial-DNA sequences and genomic fingerprinting. *British Birds* 95: 349-355.

Witherby, H.F., Jourdain, F.C.R., Ticehurst, N.F. & Tucker, B.W. (1948) *The handbook of British birds*, 2. London: Witherby.

Witt, H.-H. (1971) Ornithologische Beobachtungen auf den Kanaren. *Orn. Mitt.* 23: 145-148.

Wittmann, U., Heidrich, P., Wink, M. & Gwinner, E. (1995) Speciation in the Stonechat (*Saxicola torquata*) inferred from nucleotoide sequences of the cytochrome b-gene.J. *Zoo. Syst. Evol. Res.* 33: 116-122.

Woldhek, S. ed. (1980) *Bird killing in the Mediterranean*. London: International Council for Bird Preservation.

Wolters, H.E. (1980) *Die Vogelarten der Erde*, 6. Hamburg & Berlin: Paul Parey.

Xian Yaohua, Guan Guan-xun & Cheng Tso-hsin (1964) [An avifaunal survey of Qinghai province.] *Acta Zool. Sinica* 16: 690-709. [In Chinese.]

Zamora, R., Hodar, J.A. & Gomez, J.M. (1992) Dartford Warblers follow Stonechats while foraging. *Orn. Scand.* 23: 167-174.

Ziegler, G. (1966) Beobachtungen an Schwarzkehlchen, *Saxicola torquata rubicola*, im nördlichen Teil des Kreises Minden/Westf.J. *Orn.* 107: 187-200.

Zimmerman, D.A., Turner, D.A. & Pearson, D.J. (1996) *Birds of Kenya and northern Tanzania*. London: Christopher Helm.

Zino, F., Biscoito, M.J. & Zino, P.A. (1995) Birds of the Archipelago of Madeira and the Selvagens: new records and checklist. *Bol. Mus. Mun. Funchal* 47(262): 63-100.

Zink, G. (1973) *Der Zug europäischer Singvögel. Ein Atlas der Wiederfunde beringter Vögel*, 1. Möggingen: Vogelzug-Verlag.

Zinner, D. (2001) Ornithological notes from a primate survey in Eritrea. *Bull. African Bird Club* 8: 95-106.

INDEX

Species are listed by their vernacular name (e.g. Pied Bushchat) and by their scientific name. Specific scientific names are followed by their generic names as used in the book (e.g. *caprata, Saxicola*) and their subspecific names are followed by both the specific and generic names (e.g. *fruticola, Saxicola caprata*). Numbers in *italic* refer to the first page of the relevant systematic entry. Numbers in **bold** type refer to the colour plate numbers, numbers in ***bold italic*** to the photographic page.